IPT's METAL TRADES & WELDING TRAINING MANUAL

by

Ronald G. Garby
Bruce J. Ashton

Published by

IPT PUBLISHING AND TRAINING LTD.
Box 9590, Edmonton, Alberta, Canada, T6E 5X2
www.iptbooks.com
E-mail: info@iptbooks.com
Phone (780) 962-4548 Fax (780) 962-4819
Toll Free (888) 808-6763

Printed in Canada by
Elite Lithographers, Edmonton, Alberta

IPT's Metal Trades Training Manual
First Printing - October 1989, Ninth Printing - February 1992
Copyright ©1989, ISBN 0-920855-08-3

IPT's Metal Trades Training Manual (Revised Edition – 1993)
First Printing – December 1993, Third Printing – December 2000
Copyright ©1993, ISBN 0-920855-32-6

IPT's Metal Trades & Welding Training Manual
First Printing – August 2007
Second Printing – August 2009
Third Printing – August 2012
Fourth Printing – April 2015
Fifth Printing – October 2021

ISBN 10: 0-920855-46-6
ISBN 13: 978-0-920855-46-1

Acknowledgements

The authors and publisher express their sincere appreciation to the following for their assistance in developing this publication:

Welding Section Revisions:

Kem Frederiksen – Red Seal Boilermaker, Journeyman Welder, Welding Instructor

Illustrations and Book Layout:

Ian Holmes (Holmes Consulting), and Cindy Joly (Finelines Marketing & Communications Inc.). A well earned thank you to Ian and Cindy for their illustrations, text changes, and laying out this book with its revised sections.

Proofreading:

James Beauchamp – Bachelor of Science, Red Seal Boilermaker 1984, Red Seal Steel Fabricator, 1989, Boilermaker Instructor – Red River College, Winnipeg, Manitoba

Don and Karen Bennison – Retired School Teachers

Darren Trembecky - Trembecky Welding Training, (Pressure Welder, Welding Instructor, Senior International Trainer)

SECTION ONE – MOBILE CRANES

SECTION TWO – RIGGING

SECTION THREE – FIBER ROPE

SECTION FOUR – LAYOUT

SECTION FIVE – TANKS

SECTION SIX – TOWERS

SECTION SEVEN – HEAT EXCHANGERS

SECTION TEN – STRUCTURAL STEEL

SECTION ELEVEN – CONCRETE REINFORCING

SECTION THIRTEEN – WELD METALLURGY

SECTION FOURTEEN – NDT

SECTION FIFTEEN – CHARTS & DATA

SECTION ONE

MOBILE CRANES

Lift Plan Requirement

A lift plan of some type is necessary, including lifts that are classed as non-critical, prior to any crane lift. An ill-prepared one ton lift of a sign on a building can be more hazardous than a 400 ton lift of a pressure vessel in an operating refinery, if something is left unaccounted for and a mishap occurs. The plan can be as simple as the supervisor, the crane operator, and the rigger(s) discussing the lift prior to it being made. Or it can be extremely complex, involving detailed site and lift drawings, and a team composed of experienced riggers, crane operators, and engineers with a rigging background.

The lift plan identifies the requirements needed for the primary areas of every lift, including:

- Identifies the size, shape, and weight of the load that is to be lifted, where it will be lifted from, where it will be placed, and where the lifting crane(s) will be located.
- Describe the systematic assessment of important load and site factors. These factors are used to determine the size of crane needed, where it will be located and what site preparations will be required.
- The size, type and set-up, of the crane(s) (or other type of lifting device) as well as an up-to-date inspection report.
- The load lifting points, attachment methods, and rigging hardware to be used.
- The step by step movements of the crane(s) required to ensure a safe lift and work-site.
- Any environmental lifting conditions.
- The name of those preparing the plan.
- The lift supervisor, crane operator(s), rigger(s), and state their qualifications.
- A copy of the plan should go to any designated authority.

Crane Signals

Company owners, contractors, unions, and regulatory bodies are deeming it necessary that the person performing hand signals or voice communication understands exactly what he/she is doing during all aspects of a lift. Most jurisdictions require signal training and/or testing

The revised ANSI B30.5 standard, effective in 2005, requires the signal person to be tested prior to crane signaling. Merely attending a training session will not suffice, as testing will be required.

The person must demonstrate a basic understanding of crane operation, movements and limitations, and an understanding of the standard hand signals, and/or the standard voice signals with their elements.

- The person performing the signals must be positioned where the load can be plainly seen, and is in clear sight of the crane operator.
- Some organizations require audio communication anytime the load is out of sight of the operator, or the signalperson is over 100 feet from the operator.
- The crane operator must only respond to the signals from the designated person, other than a stop signal from any crew member.
- The operator and the person performing the signals must agree prior to the lift on any necessary signals that are not included among the standard hand signals (shown in illustrations #1, #2 & #3).

CONTROL OF PLATFORMS OR SKIPS

One bell or light........to STOP
Two bells or lights......to RAISE
Three bells or lights....to LOWER
Four bells or lights......ALL CLEAR

HORN SIGNALS FOR TRAVELLING AND MOBILE CRANES
(and as a warning for travel direction for Crawler Machines)

One blast............STOP
Two blasts.........FORWARD
Three blasts........... REVERSE

Illustration #1 - Bell, Light and Horn Signals

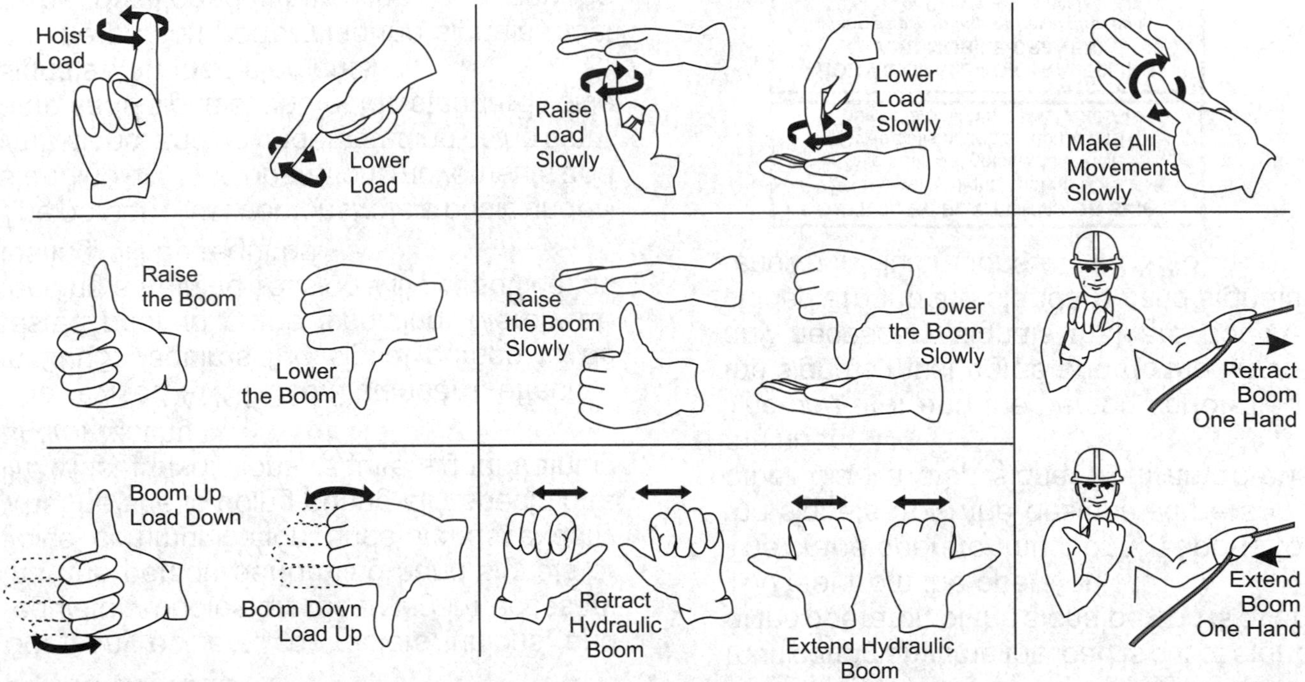
Hoist
Load
Lower
Load
Raise
Load
Slowly
Lower
Load
Slowly
Make Alll
Movements
Slowly
Raise
the Boom
Lower
the Boom
Raise
the Boom
Slowly
Lower
the Boom
Slowly
Retract
Boom
One Hand
Boom Up
Load Down
Boom Down
Load Up
Retract
Hydraulic
Boom
Extend Hydraulic
Boom
Extend
Boom
One Hand

Illustration #2 - Typical Hand Signals

Crawler or Track Signals

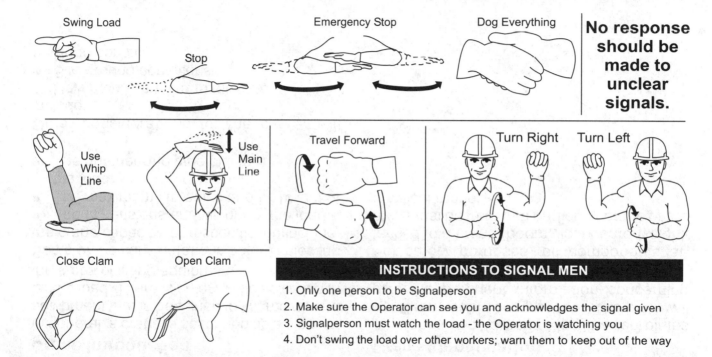

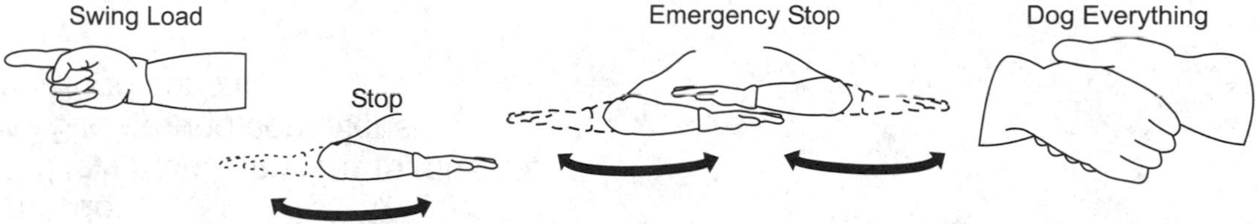
Swing Load
Stop
Emergency Stop
Dog Everything

No response should be made to unclear signals.

Use Whip Line
Use Main Line

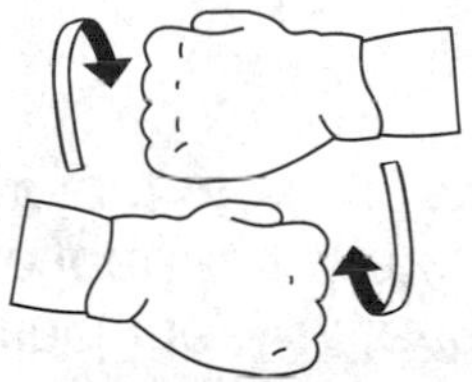
Travel Forward

Turn Right
Turn Left

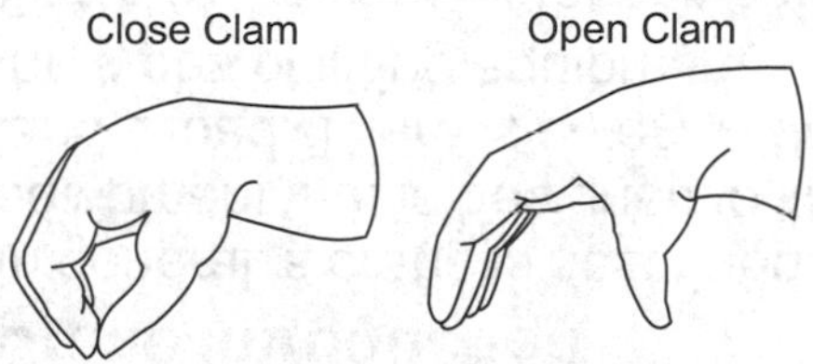
Close Clam
Open Clam

INSTRUCTIONS TO SIGNAL MEN

1. Only one person to be Signalperson
2. Make sure the Operator can see you and acknowledges the signal given
3. Signalperson must watch the load - the Operator is watching you
4. Don't swing the load over other workers; warn them to keep out of the way

Illustration #3 - Typical Hand Signals

Crane Introduction

In general, a crane is described as a piece of equipment that is designed to lift, move, and land a load. There is a very wide selection in the types of lifting equipment.

Some of the considerations before selecting the crane capacity for a specific job include:

- The dimensions and weight of the load.
- The maximum lift radius and lift height of the load.
- The number and type of lifts.

Other considerations for the carrier will include:

- How mobile the crane must be.
- Site ground conditions.
- Road conditions.

Crane Identification

All cranes should have identification plates on all removable components. The plate will give the pertinent information concerning that particular crane.

For safety purposes, all components attached to a crane (boom, jib, counterweight, etc.) must be from that particular crane or the identical model.

Crane Types

There are numerous types of cranes that range from smaller capacity mobile units for light industry, up through higher capacity mobile and crawler cranes. Cranes are grouped into several general categories. For each category there are a number of manufacturers with varying types, lift capacities, and boom attachments. Different types of hydraulic gantry lifting devices are also becoming common.

The general crane categories are:

- Telescoping boom rough terrain cranes with a fixed or swing cab
- Telescoping boom carrydeck cranes with a fixed or rotating boom
- Telescoping fixed boom pick and carry crane
- Telescoping boom all terrain crane
- Telescoping boom carrier mounted
- Telescoping boom crawler mounted
- Telescoping boom truck mounted
- Lattice boom carrier mounted
- Lattice boom crawler mounted
- Lattice boom truck mounted tower attachment
- Lattice boom carrier, tower attachment
- Lattice boom carrier mounted with long reach attachment
- Lattice boom crawler mounted with heavy lift attachment

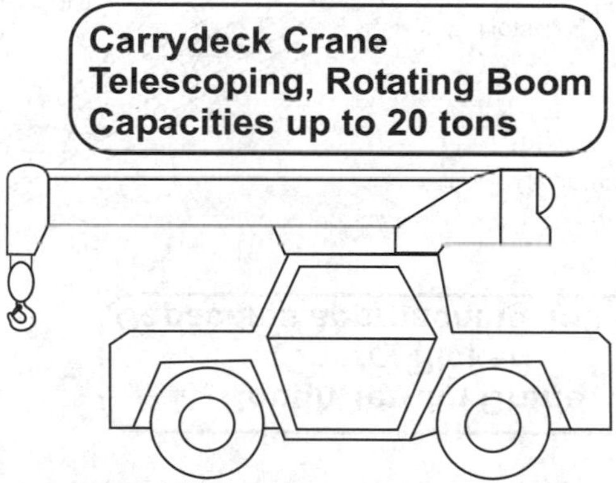
Carrydeck Crane
Telescoping, Rotating Boom
Capacities up to 20 tons

Illustration #4 - Crane Types

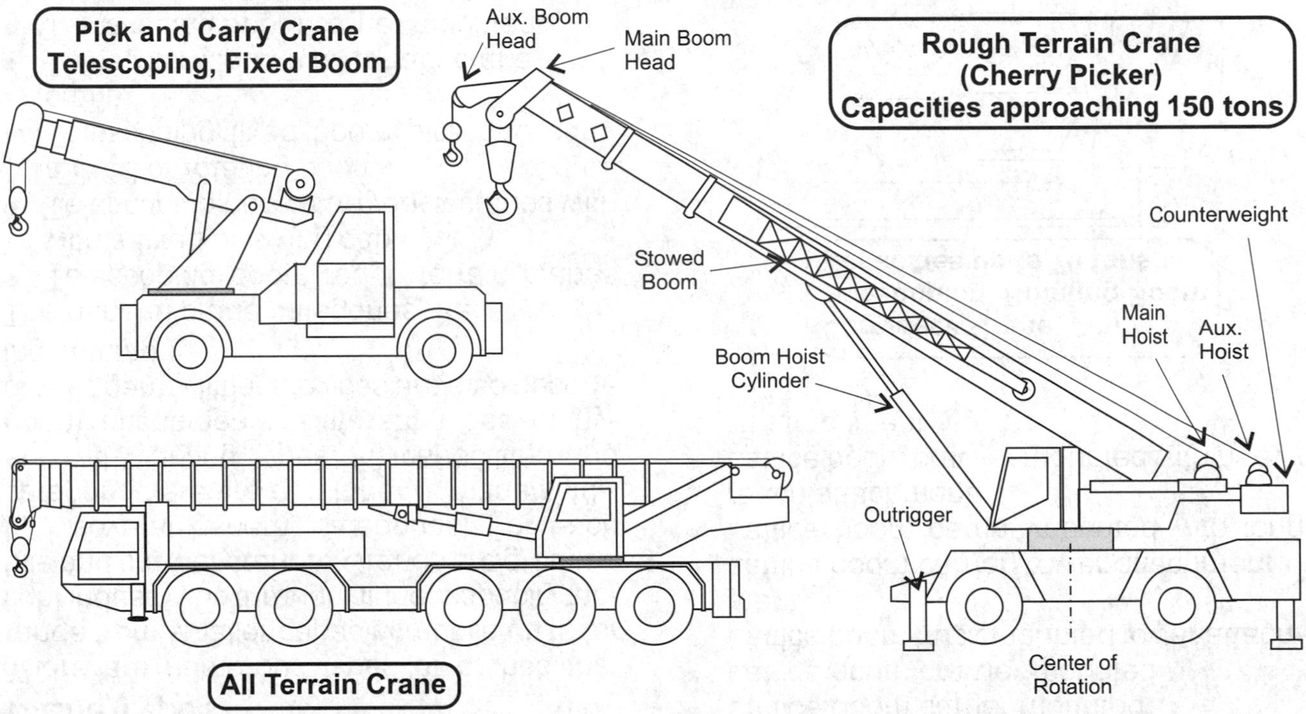
Pick and Carry Crane
Telescoping, Fixed Boom
Aux. Boom Head
Main Boom Head
Rough Terrain Crane
(Cherry Picker)
Capacities approaching 150 tons
Counterweight
Stowed Boom
Main Hoist
Aux. Hoist
Boom Hoist Cylinder
Outrigger
Center of Rotation
All Terrain Crane

Illustration #5 - Crane Types

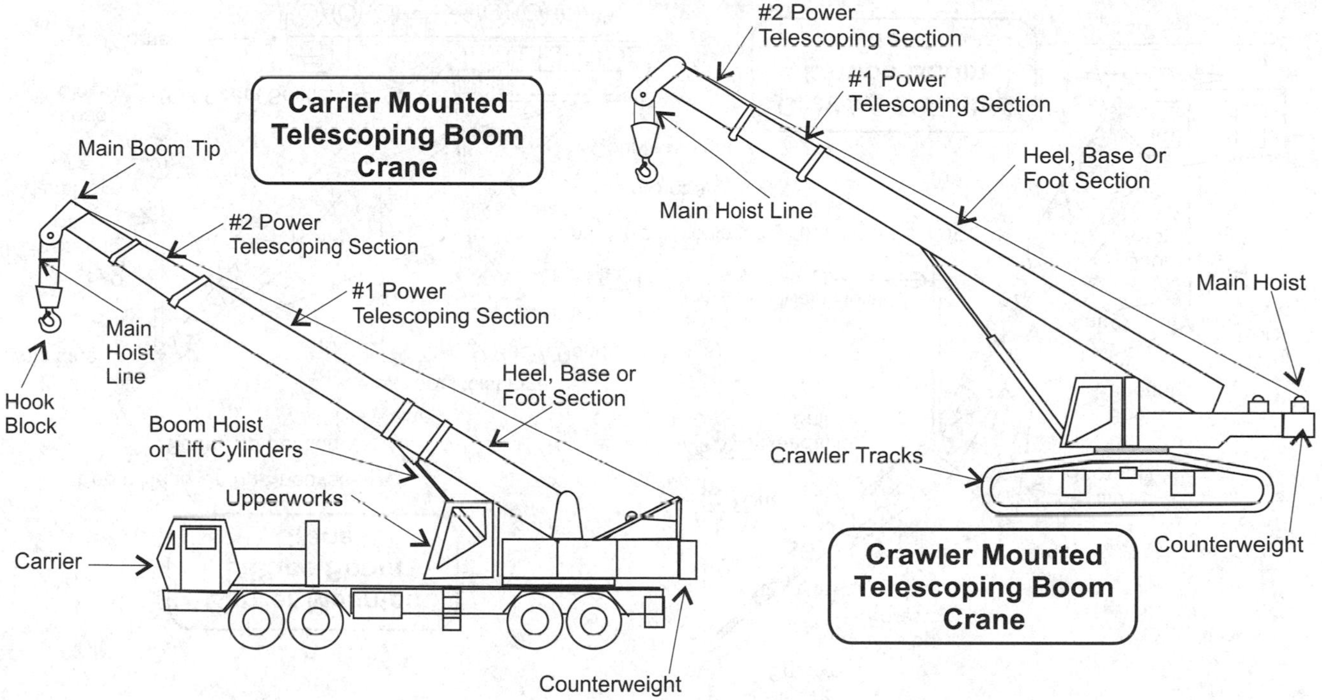
Carrier Mounted Telescoping Boom Crane
Main Boom Tip
#2 Power Telescoping Section
#1 Power Telescoping Section
Main Hoist Line
Hook Block
Heel, Base or Foot Section
Boom Hoist or Lift Cylinders
Upperworks
Carrier
Counterweight
#2 Power Telescoping Section
#1 Power Telescoping Section
Heel, Base Or Foot Section
Main Hoist Line
Main Hoist
Crawler Tracks
Counterweight
Crawler Mounted Telescoping Boom Crane

Illustration #6 - Crane Types

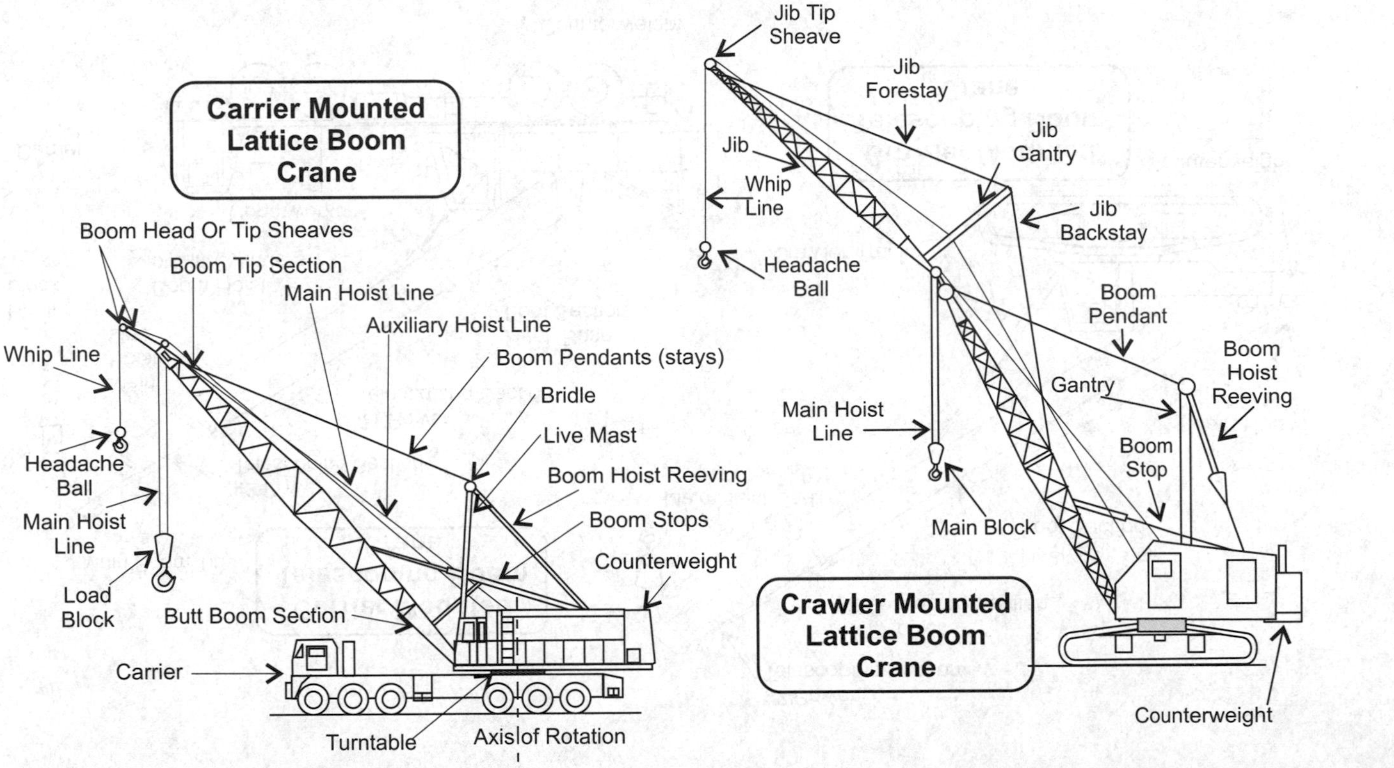
Carrier Mounted Lattice Boom Crane
Boom Head Or Tip Sheaves
Boom Tip Section
Main Hoist Line
Auxiliary Hoist Line
Boom Pendants (stays)
Whip Line
Bridle
Live Mast
Headache Ball
Boom Hoist Reeving
Main Hoist Line
Boom Stops
Counterweight
Load Block
Butt Boom Section
Carrier
Turntable
Axis of Rotation
Jib Tip Sheave
Jib Forestay
Jib
Jib Gantry
Whip Line
Jib Backstay
Headache Ball
Boom Pendant
Boom Hoist Reeving
Gantry
Main Hoist Line
Boom Stop
Main Block
Crawler Mounted Lattice Boom Crane
Counterweight

Illustration #7 - Crane Types

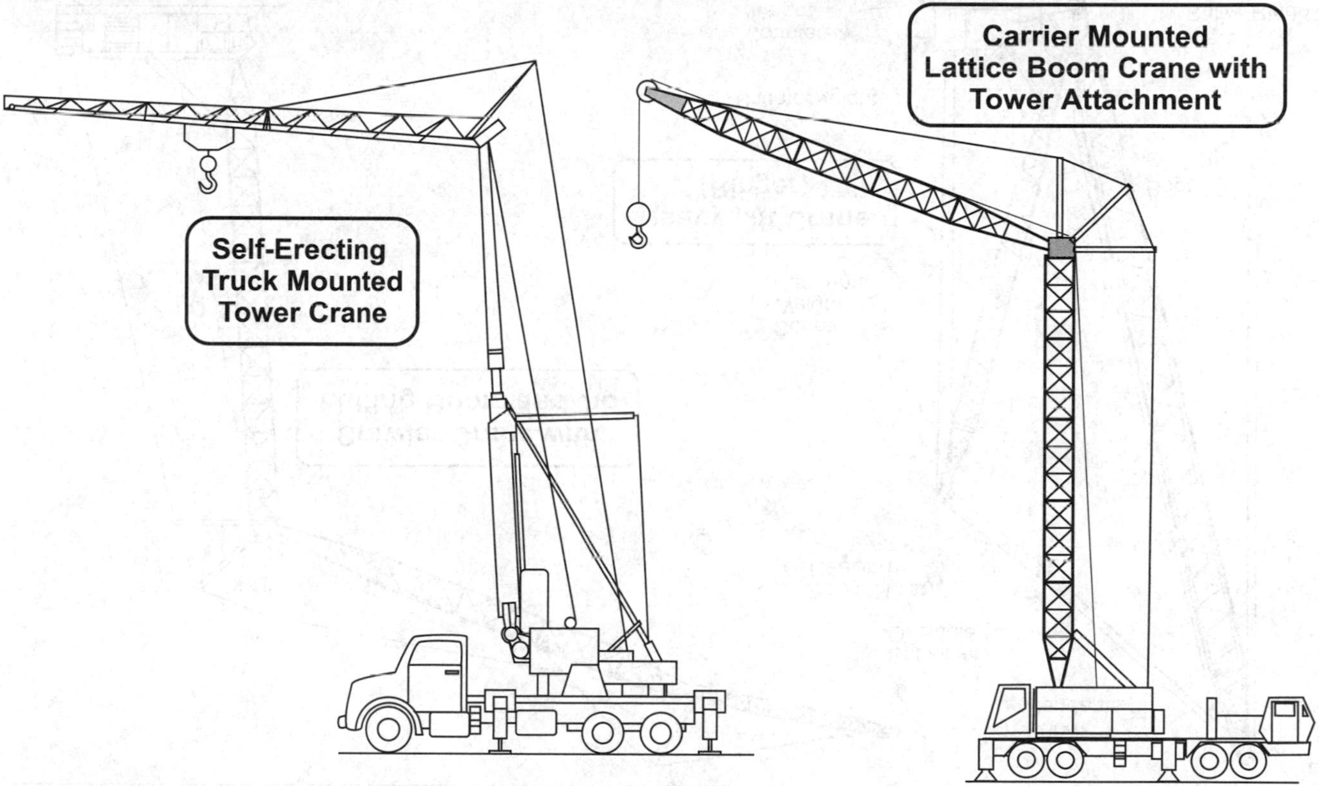
Self-Erecting
Truck Mounted
Tower Crane
Carrier Mounted
Lattice Boom Crane with
Tower Attachment

Illustration #8 - Crane Types

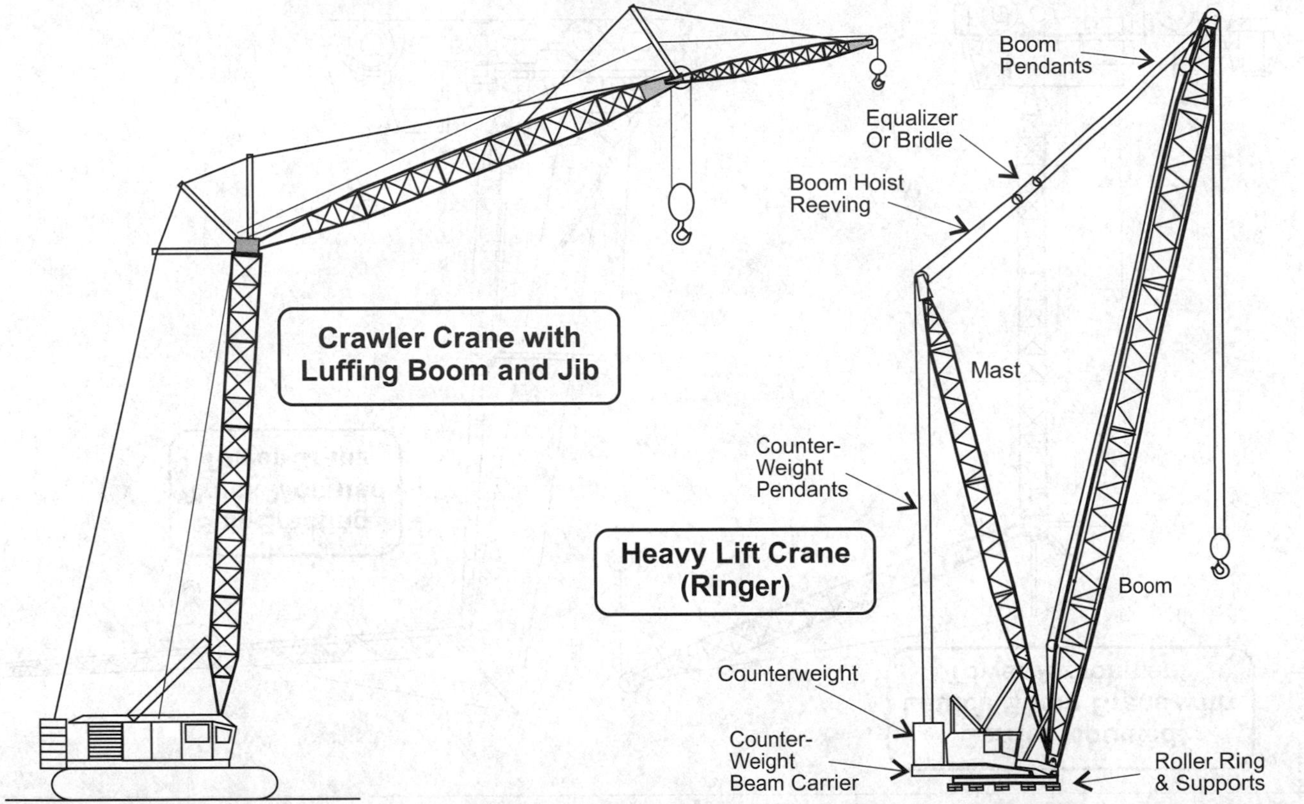
Crawler Crane with Luffing Boom and Jib
Heavy Lift Crane (Ringer)
Boom Pendants
Equalizer Or Bridle
Boom Hoist Reeving
Mast
Counter-Weight Pendants
Boom
Counterweight
Counter-Weight Beam Carrier
Roller Ring & Supports

Illustration #9 - Crane Types

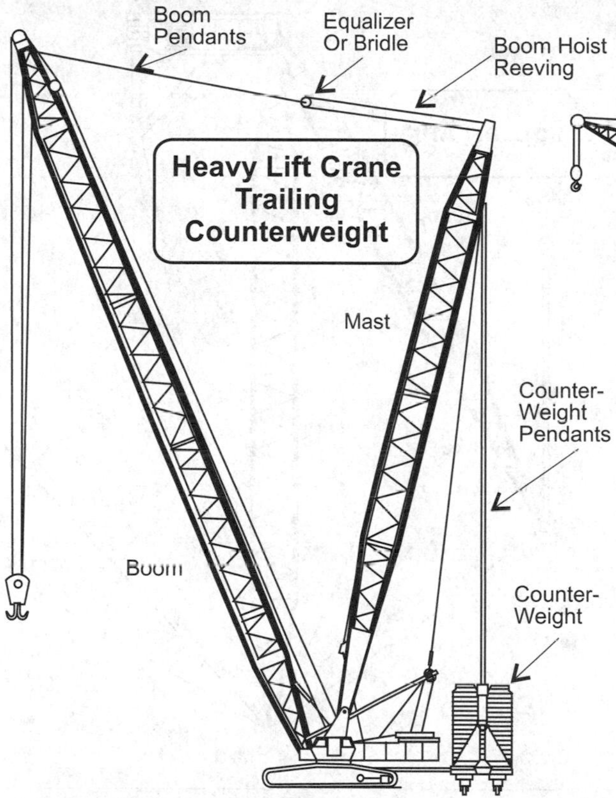
Boom
Pendants
Equalizer
Or Bridle
Boom Hoist
Reeving
Heavy Lift Crane
Trailing
Counterweight
Mast
Counter-
Weight
Pendants
Boom
Counter-
Weight

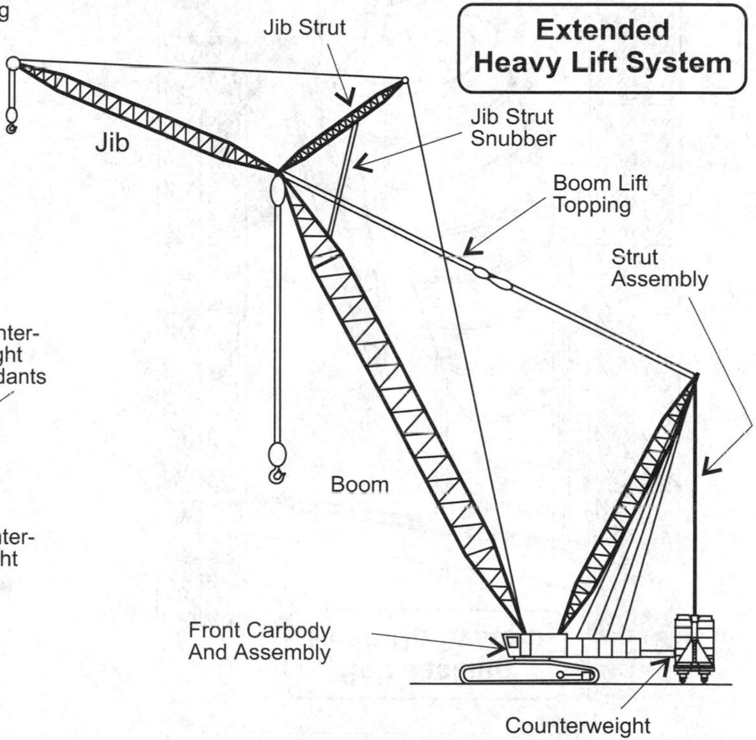
Extended
Heavy Lift System
Jib Strut
Jib
Jib Strut
Snubber
Boom Lift
Topping
Strut
Assembly
Boom
Front Carbody
And Assembly
Counterweight

Illustration #10 - Crane Types

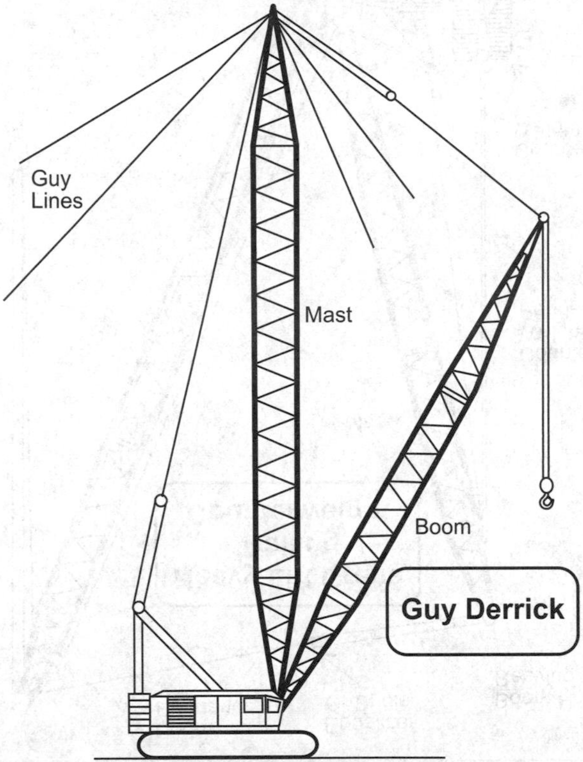
Guy Lines
Mast
Boom
Guy Derrick

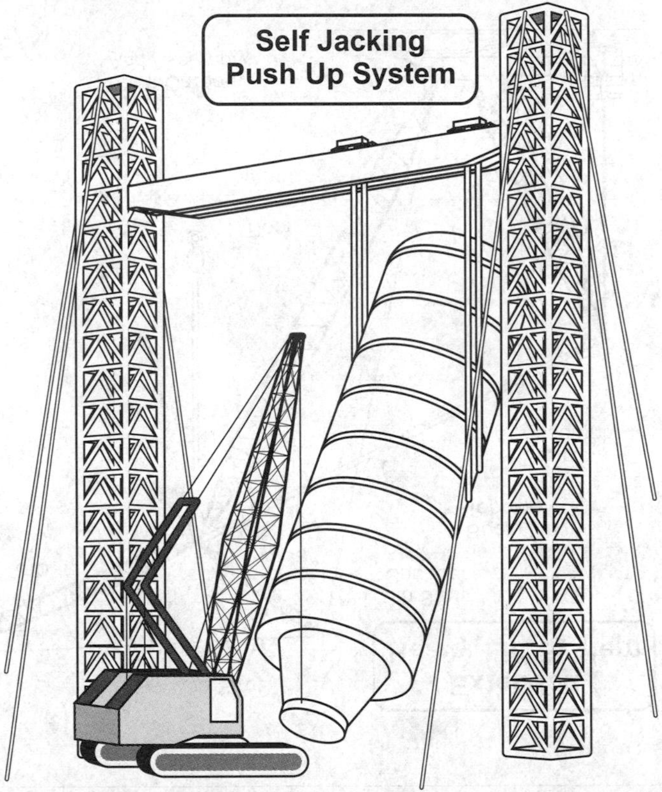
Self Jacking Push Up System

Illustration #11 - Crane Types

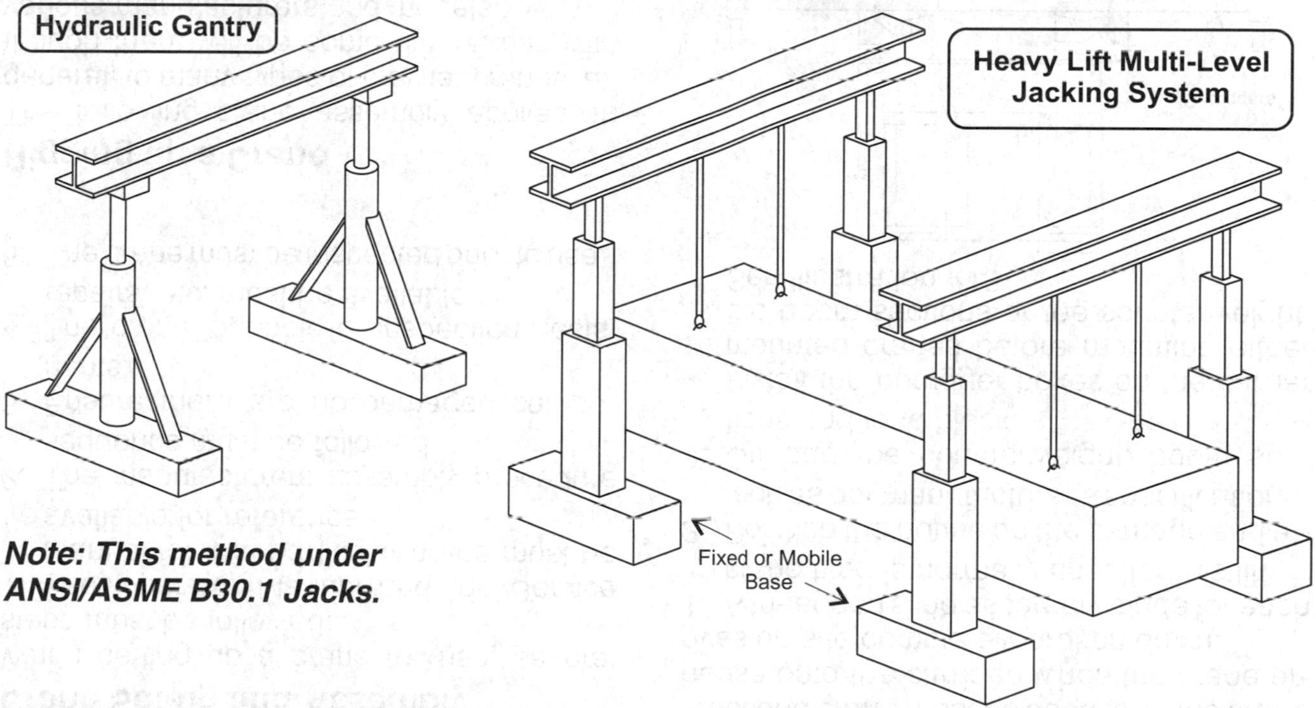
Hydraulic Gantry
Heavy Lift Multi-Level Jacking System
Fixed or Mobile Base

Note: This method under ANSI/ASME B30.1 Jacks.

Illustration #12 - Hydraulic Gantry Jacking System

Crane Set-up and Assembly

When setting up a crane for use, several steps must be followed:

1. The Operator Manual and the Service Manual for that particular crane must be available for reference.
2. The manufacturers assembly procedure sequence must be followed.
3. Ensure there are no damaged components.
4. The crane logbook for inspection, tests, repairs, etc. must be available.
5. The crane must be inspected prior to use.

Rigging up a Crane

The following crane assembly applies, in general, to many types of crawler cranes, although there will be some differences with various manufacturers and models.

A second crane must be used to lift the crane house onto the carriage when the crane arrives on site completely broken down.

1. A tri-legged sling assembly made for each crane type is normally used for this lift.
2. Position the house on the carriage and attach as per manufacturer's specifications.
3. Off-load the counterweight, boom sections and load block.
4. Install the outrigger boxes on the carrier mounted cranes before mounting either the boom sections or the counterweight. See illustration #13.

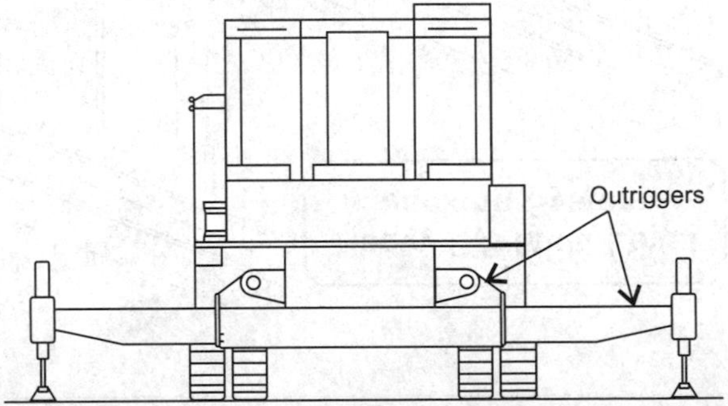
Outriggers

Illustration #13 - Always Use Crane Outriggers

Boom Installation

The same boom installation procedure should be used for both crawler and truck cranes, with the exception that truck cranes must erect booms with all outriggers extended and set.

Lifting Boom Sections

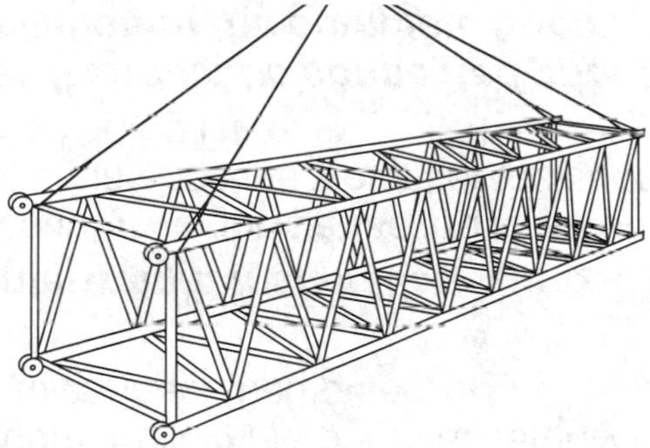

Illustration #14 - Lifting a Boom Section

To avoid boom damage, do not use chain hooks or choked wire rope slings to lift boom sections. Check the manufacturer's manual for the proper boom rigging procedure.

If possible, use synthetic web slings.

Basic Boom Installation

Pin the boom tail section to the machine. Reeve the bridle between the inner and outer ball, and pin the bail to the tail section ears, see illustration #15.

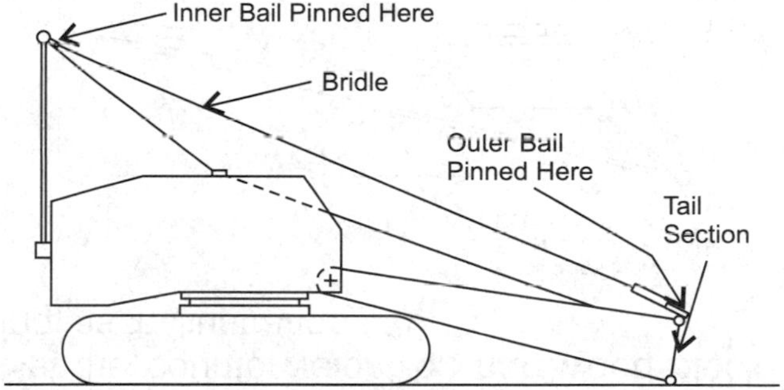
Inner Bail Pinned Here
Bridle
Outer Bail
Pinned Here
Tail
Section

Illustration #15 - Boom Tail Installation

If the counterweight is not on the crane prior to boom installation, connect the boom tip section to the tail section to complete the basic boom. Follow the boom assembly procedure to connect the tip section.

Counterweight Installation

The counterweight is attached to the crane to offset or balance the weight of the boom and the load being lifted.

Note: It should be connected prior to the installation of the complete boom.

A counterweight may be off-loaded from, or loaded onto a railroad car or flatbed truck by its own crane. Cranes can lift their own counterweight (following manufacturers recommendations) if the following requirements are met :

- Firm level ground.
- Gantry must be fully extended.
- Four parts of load line must be reeved on a basic boom.

Set the counterweight on hardwood blocking, as in illustration #16.

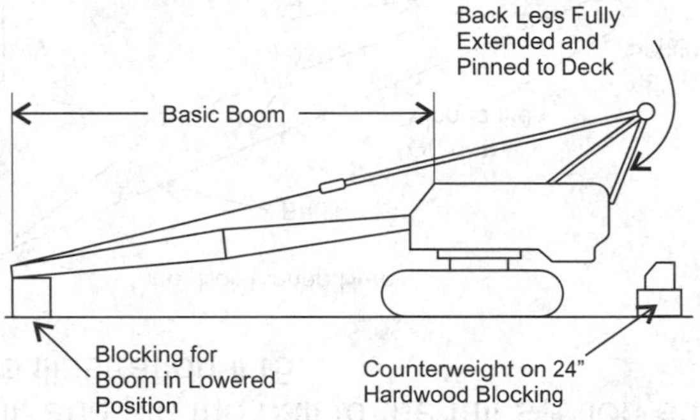
Back Legs Fully Extended and Pinned to Deck
Basic Boom
Blocking for Boom in Lowered Position
Counterweight on 24" Hardwood Blocking

Illustration #16 - Counterweight Blocking

Take the slack out of the boom suspension and backhinges. Slowly lower the boom gantry, (boom down) until the backlegs are in position to attach to the counterweight, then pin, see illustration #17.

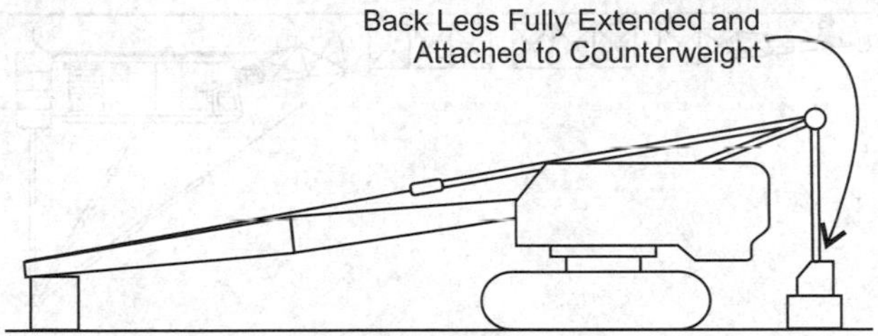
Back Legs Fully Extended and
Attached to Counterweight

Illustration #17 - Counterweight Connecting

Boom up until the boom is at approximately 30°, then hook onto the minimum required weight, as indicated in the manufacturer's instructions, #18.

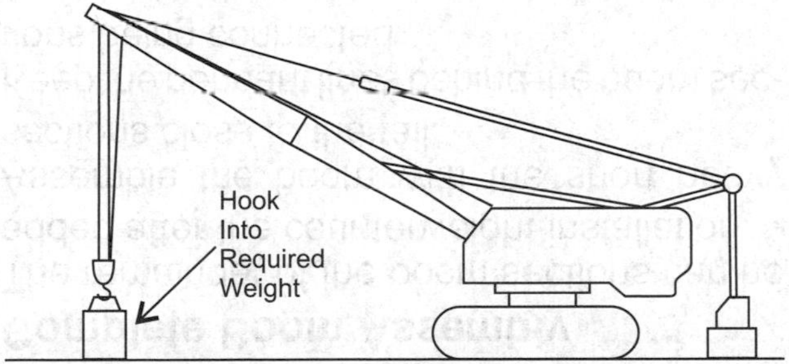
Hook
Into
Required
Weight

Illustration #18 - Counterweight Lifting

Slowly boom up until the counterweight is in position to be connected to the crane, see illustration #19.

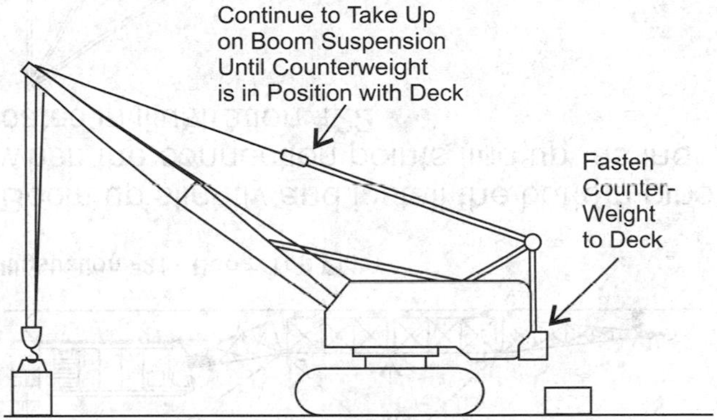
Continue to Take Up
on Boom Suspension
Until Counterweight
is in Position with Deck
Fasten
Counter-
Weight
to Deck

Illustration #19 - Counterweight Connected to Deck

Counterweight Removal

To remove the counterweight, the installation procedure should be followed in reverse order.

Complete Boom Assembly

The remainder of the boom sections can be added after the counterweight installation.

Assemble the boom with the short heavy sections close to the tail.

Keep the pendant lines behind the boom sections being connected.

Assemble the rest of the boom on the ground. Be sure to block up the boom tip to protect the sheave guards.

Lay out the boom sections on blocking, in the order specified by the crane manual, as indicated in illustration #20.

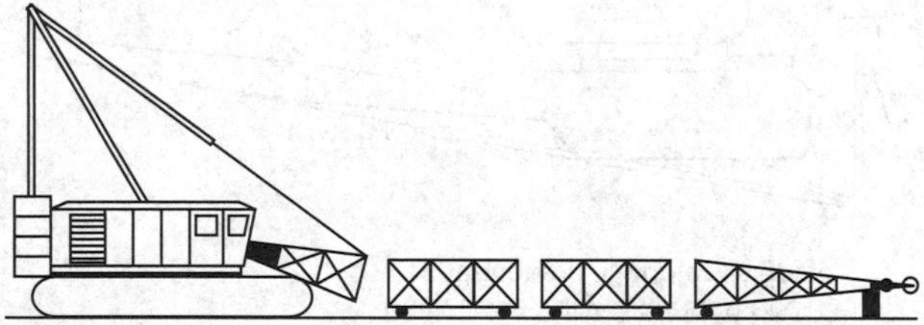

Illustration #20 - Boom Layout

Pull the sections together and line up the upper pin holes. Insert the top pins, using cotter pins as retainers, as in illustration #21.

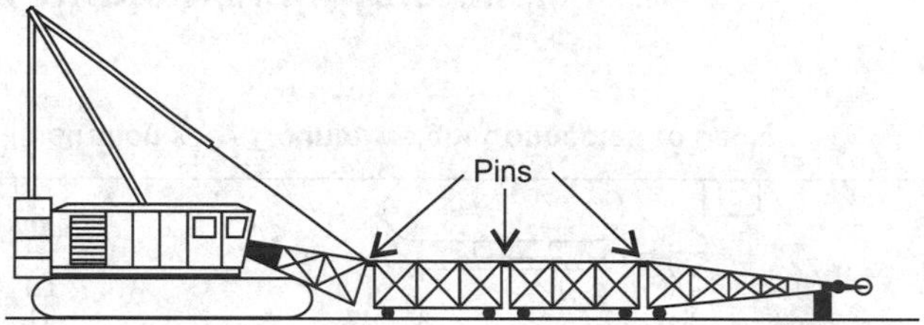
Pins

Illustration #21 - Boom Top Pins

Boom up slightly and install the bottom pins when the connection points line up, as indicated in illustration #22.

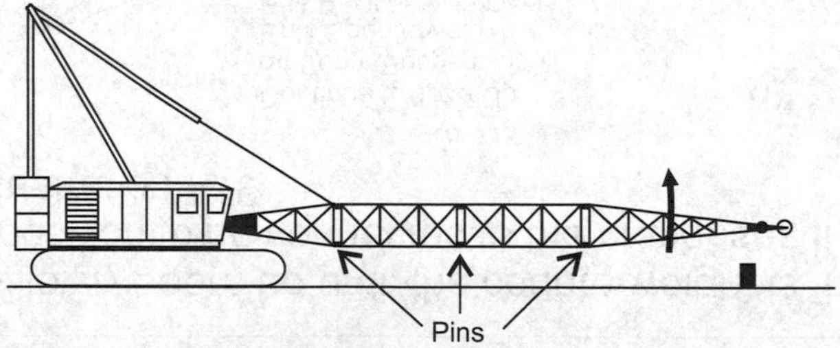
Pins

Illustration #22 - Boom Bottom Pins

Boom down onto blocking until the pendants are slack, as indicated in illustration #23.

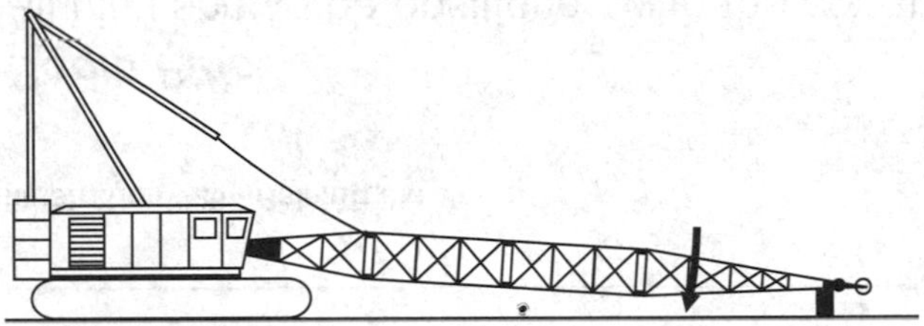

Illustration #23 - Move Pendant Lines

Move the pendants out to the end of the boom, see illustration #24.

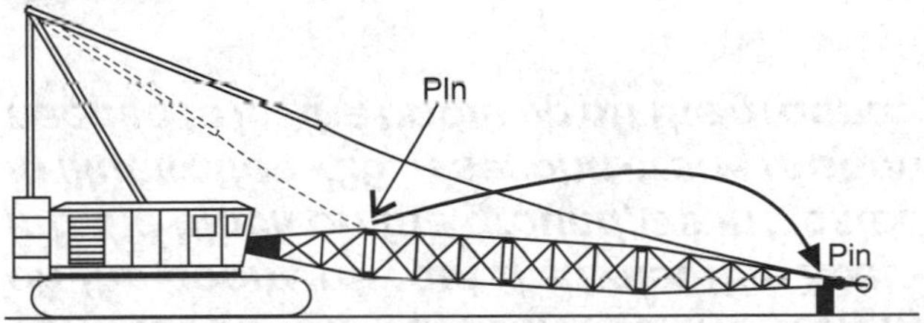
Pin
Pin

Illustration #24 - Pendant Lines Repositioned

Connect the pendants to the boom tip.

Note: Pin the pendants from the gantry to the boom section pendants together. The boom pendants must be a matched set to prevent boom twisting, and they should be lashed to the boom sections when dismantling.

Reeve the load blocks after booming up slightly. See illustration #25.

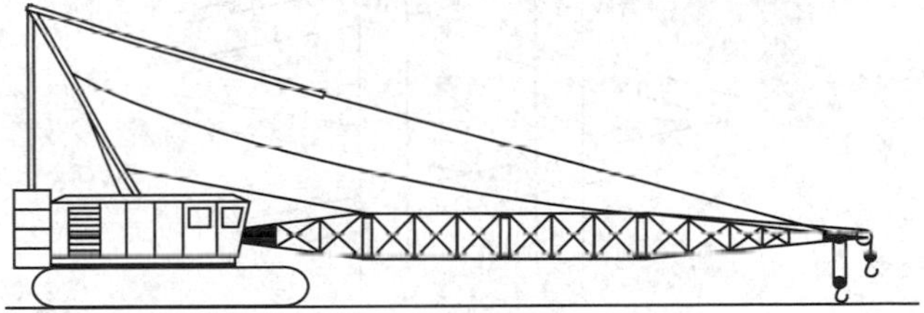

Illustration #25 - Block Reeving

Slowly raise the boom smoothly in one continuous lift. To decrease the weight on the boom, run out the hoist line keeping the block on the ground, as indicated in illustration #26. A second crane is often needed to lift the boom up off the ground.

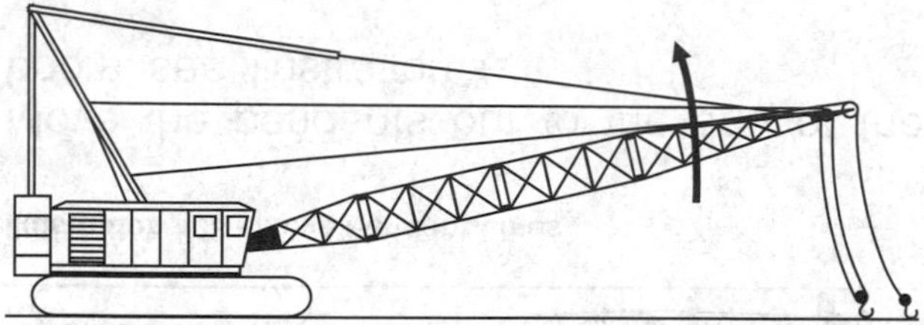

Illustration #26 - Raising the Boom

Boom Pins

All pins should be positioned with the cotter pins on the outside of the boom. The boom sections should go together reasonably easily.

The pins should be installed so they can be removed from the outside. The rigger should never have to climb under the boom to remove any pins, see illustration #27.

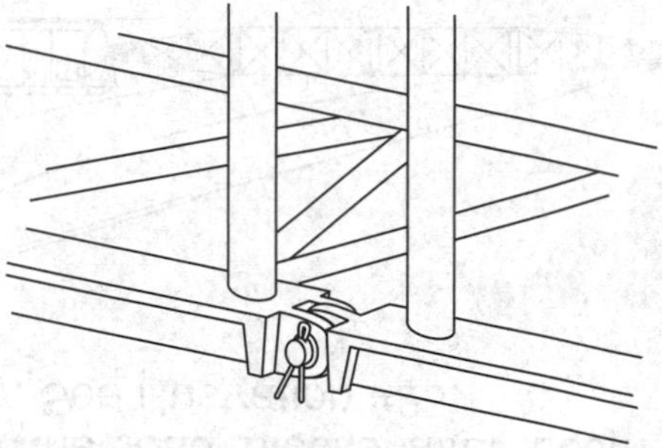

Illustration #27 - Boom Pins On Outside

Note: Some boom types are designed so that the pins are installed from the outside. Avoid pendant line snag. Use extreme caution when dismantling this type of boom.

Dismantling Boom Sections

Lower the boom until it is horizontal with the ground, unreeve and remove the load blocks, see illustration #28.

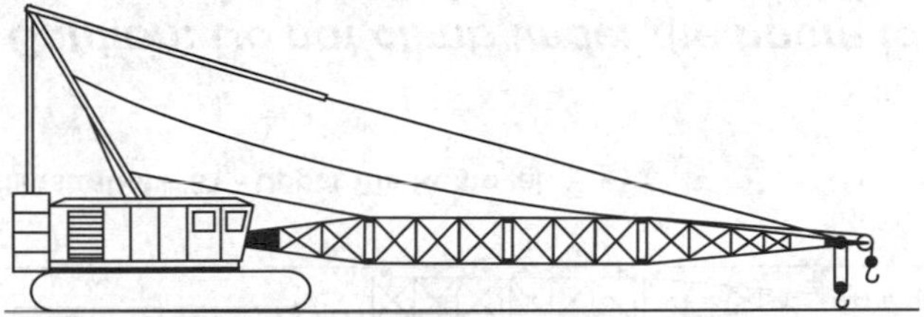

Illustration #28 - Removing the Blocks

Note: An important point to remember in dismantling crane boom sections is to remove the bottom pins first after relocating the pendant lines.

Rest the boom tip on blocking until the pendants are slack. Then move the pendants back no farther than the cantilever length allowed in the crane manual, see illustration #29.

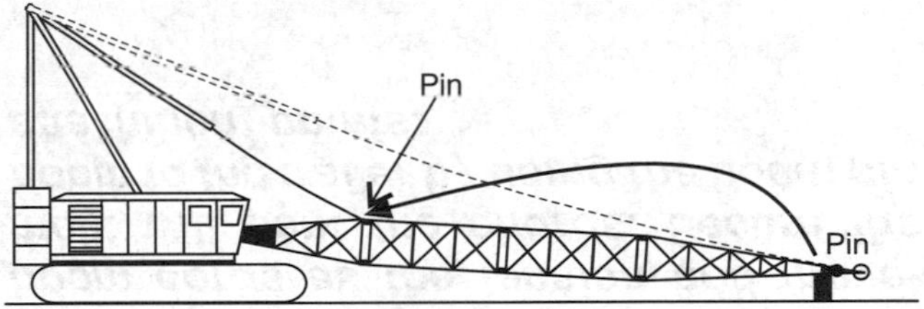
Pin
Pin

Illustration #29 - Reconnecting Pendant Lines

Boom up slightly and remove all lower pins on the sections ahead of the pendants, see illustration #30.

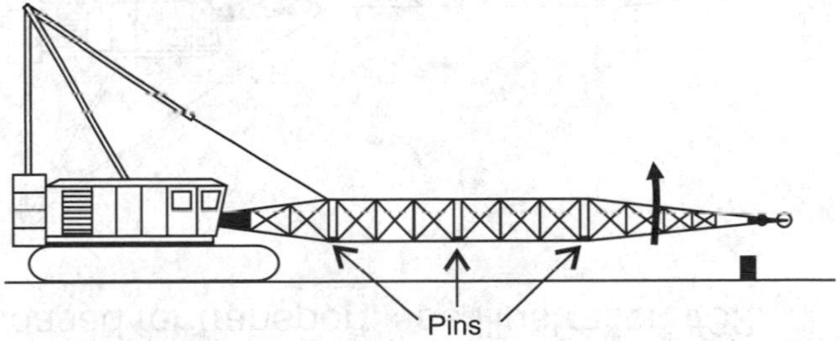
Pins

Illustration #30 - Remove Lower Pins

Make sure that every section is supported, then lower onto blocking. Remove the upper pins on the sections ahead of the pendants, as in illustration #31.

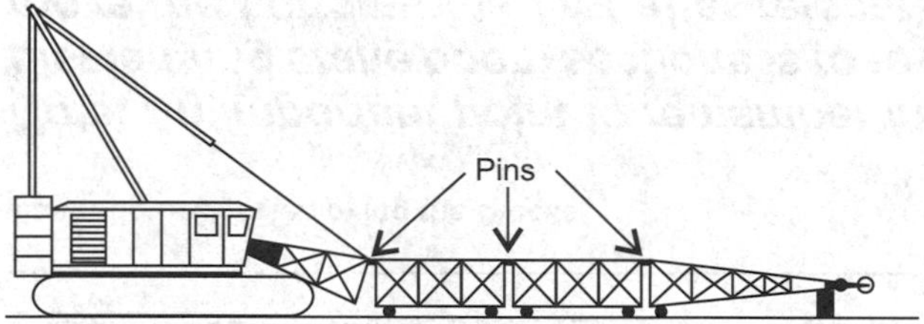
Pins

Illustration #31 - Upper Pin Removal

Caution: Do not climb under the boom to remove pins. Use a long bar to knock the pins out if installed with the cotter pins on the inside.

The sections can then be removed and loaded for transport, see illustration #32.

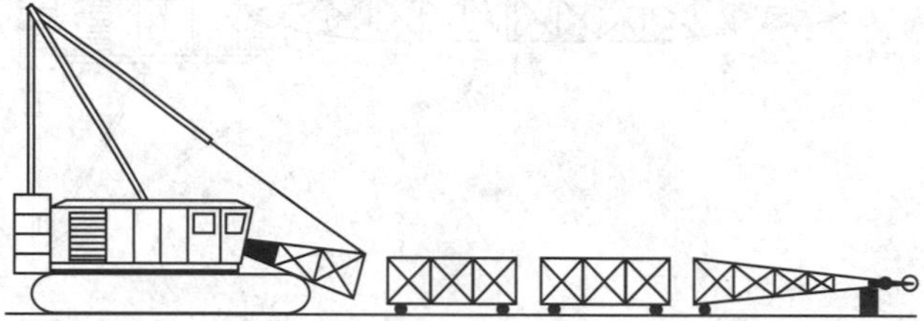

Illustration #32 - Section Separation

Note: If crane booms are transported on a trailer, use extreme caution when tying down. Do not pull a tight chain across the boom cords as the tension and movement will dent the chords. Secure the boom to the trailer by using the boom pin attachment points.

Gantry

The stress is lower on hoisting equipment when the gantry is used in its highest position. This gives longer life and added safety factors for equipment. When the crane is lifting a load the gantry must always be in the highest position, see illustration #33.

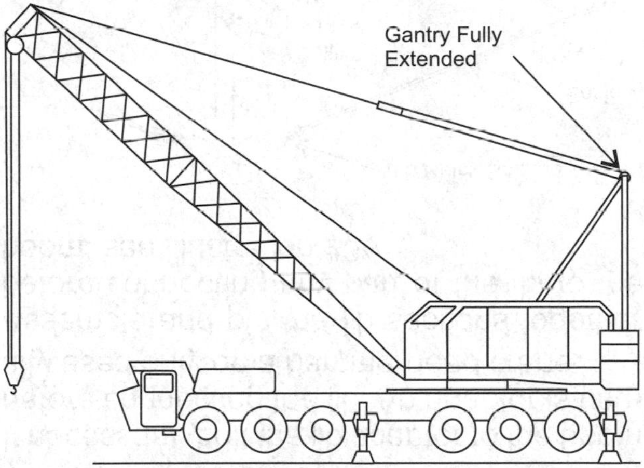
Gantry Fully
Extended

Illustration #33 - Crane Gantry

Jibs

A jib is an auxiliary boom. It may vary in length according to the capacity of the crane and the intended use. The jib can be used as a straight extension to the main boom, or at an angle (offset) to the main boom. A table of maximum safe working loads for the jib at the appropriate offset is always supplied with the crane.

The jib produces a greater clearance between the forward edge of the boom and the jib hook. This is useful in construction for placing loads beyond the outer perimeter of building structures.

The jib or whip line is usually a single line of wire rope, with a maximum capacity up to the cranes rating for a single line.

Jibs/Assembly

If necessary, bolt the jib adaptor to the boom before connecting the jib. An adaptor is usually used only on a hammerhead crane.

Assemble and pin the jib sections together before connecting any part of the jib to the boom, see illustration #34.

Assemble a wrap-around pendant by running it through the jib block sheave and connecting it on each side of the jib pendant adapter. Pin the jib to the boom tip. Attach the backstay lines to the jib mast and raise the mast. The backstay lines may be attached to various positions on the boom.

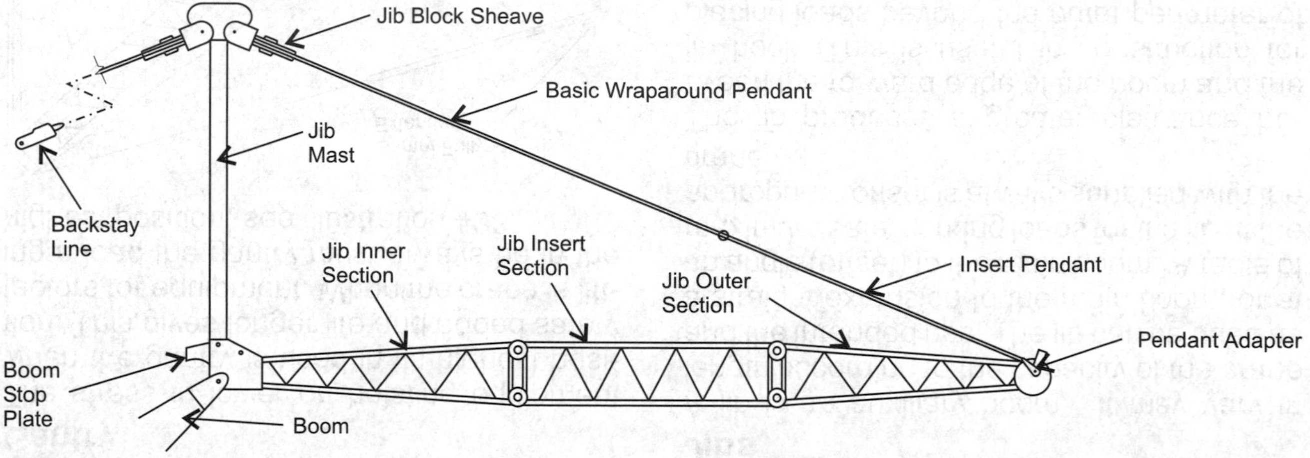
Jib Block Sheave
Basic Wraparound Pendant
Jib
Mast
Backstay
Line
Jib Inner
Section
Jib Insert
Section
Insert Pendant
Jib Outer
Section
Pendant Adapter
Boom
Stop
Plate
Boom

Illustration #34 - Jib Assembly

The distance to the jib backstay line connection from the boom point must be equal to or greater than the length of the jib.

Set the jib offset as allowed by the crane rating sheet. Coil the extra rope and lash it to the boom.

Jib offset is usually allowable to 25° from the centerline of the boom (however, check the crane set-up procedure for the particular crane model), see illustration #35. Run the load line up the boom through the jib mast sheave and jib tip sheave.

For optimum jib pendant loads, the jib backstay pendants and the jib forestay pendants should be of equal lengths, or the jib backstay pendants should be longer.

When a jib is attached on the boom, but is not in use, the working load for the boom must be reduced in accordance with the crane manufacturer's instructions to allow for the weight of the jib and hook.

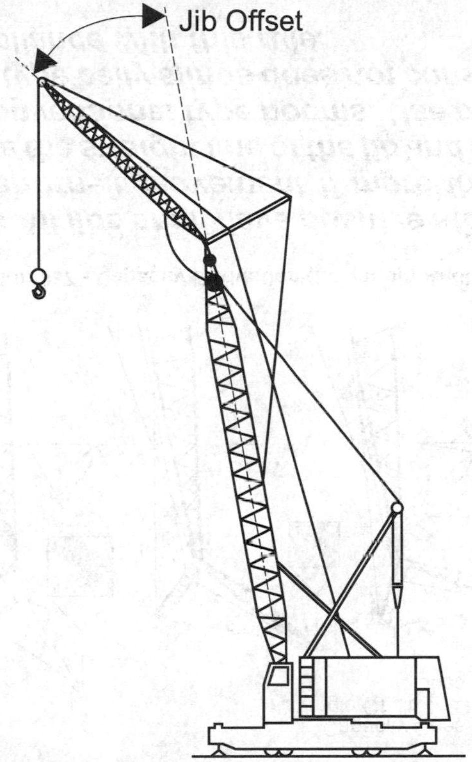
Jib Offset

Illustration #35 - Jib Offset

Jib Capacity

Do not use the boom hoist and jib simultaneously unless the crane has been designed for this operation.

Jib capacity decreases as the horizontal angle lowers. This can be due to a changing boom angle (illustration #36), or a changing jib offset angle (illustration #37).

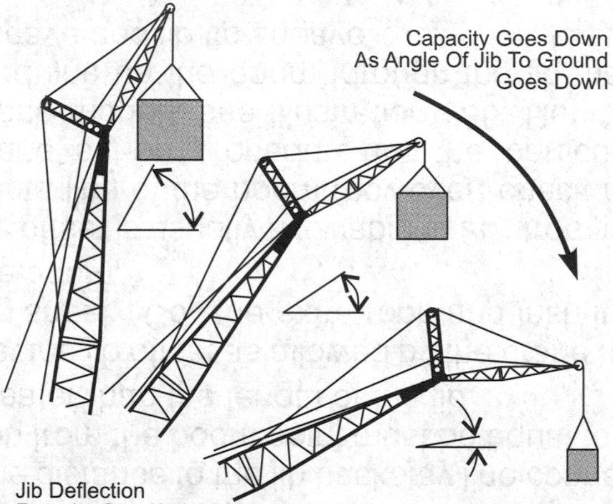
Capacity Goes Down
As Angle Of Jib To Ground
Goes Down
Jib Deflection
From Its Own Weight Also Increases

Illustration #36 - Capacity Reduction (Lower Boom Angle)

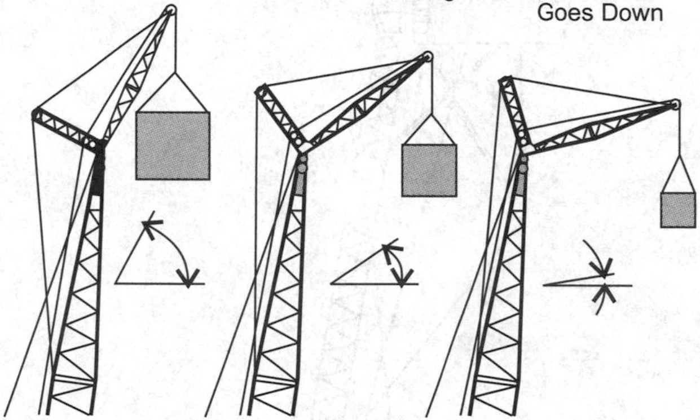
Capacity Goes Down
As Angle Of Jib To Ground
Goes Down

Illustration #37 - Capacity Reduction (Lower Jib Angle)

Note: All jibs shall have positive stops to prevent their movement if more than 5° above the straight line of the jib and boom on conventional type booms. Use of wire rope type belly slings does not constitute compliance with this rule.

Reeving Load Blocks

The boom tip sheaves should be symmetrically reeved to avoid torsional loading. This occurs whenever the main hoist line is reeved to one side of the boom tip.

Eccentric Reeving

Examples of eccentric reeving causing boom twisting are shown in illustrations #39 and #40.

NOTE: The blocks must be reeved as per the crane setup manual.

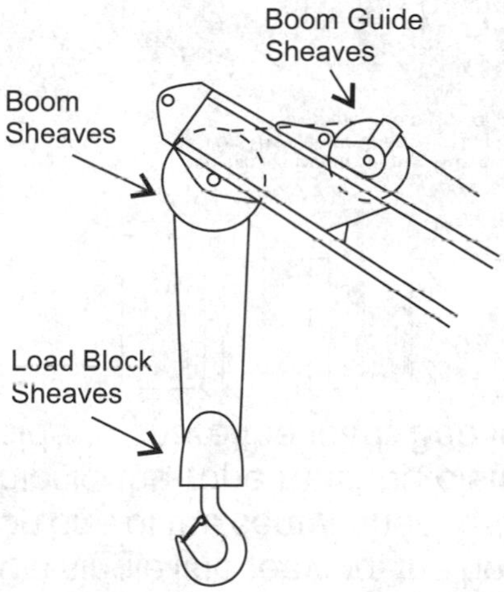
Boom Guide Sheaves
Boom Sheaves
Load Block Sheaves

Illustration #38 - Boom Tip Reeving

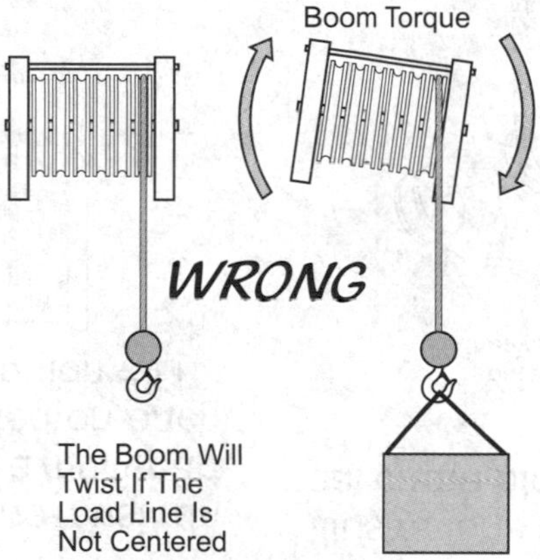
Boom Torque
WRONG
The Boom Will Twist If The Load Line Is Not Centered

Illustration #39 - Boom Twist

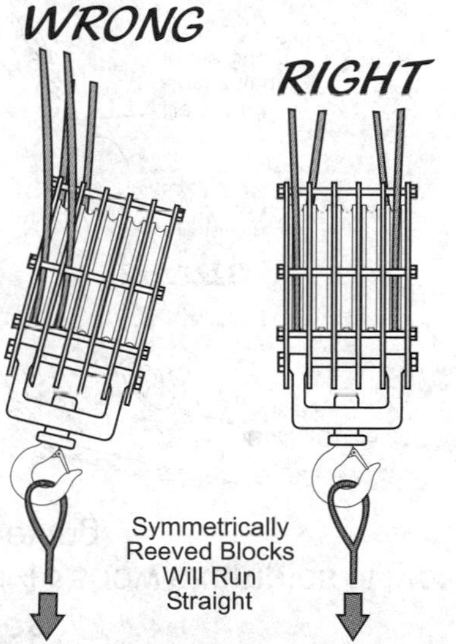
WRONG
RIGHT
Symmetrically Reeved Blocks Will Run Straight

Illustration #40- Balanced and Unbalanced Block Comparison

Symmetrical Reeving

On single line reeving, the hoist line must run on one of the center sheaves. On a multi-part block, the rope must be distributed on each side to share the load. See illustration #41.

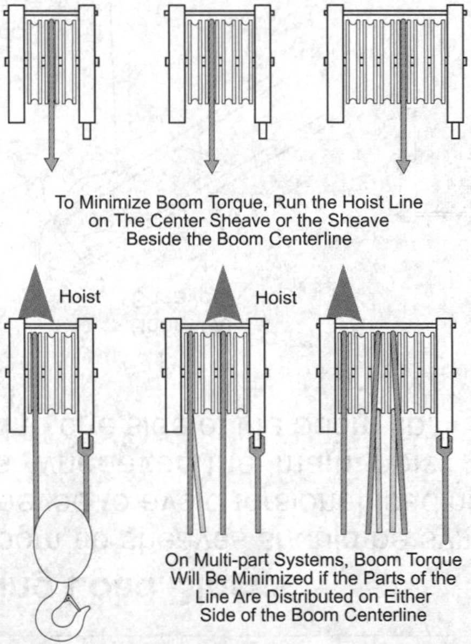

To Minimize Boom Torque, Run the Hoist Line on The Center Sheave or the Sheave Beside the Boom Centerline
Hoist
Hoist
On Multi-part Systems, Boom Torque Will Be Minimized if the Parts of the Line Are Distributed on Either Side of the Boom Centerline

Illustration #41 - Symmetrical Reeving

Reeving Examples

Illustrations #42 - #45 show examples of typical crane block reeving.

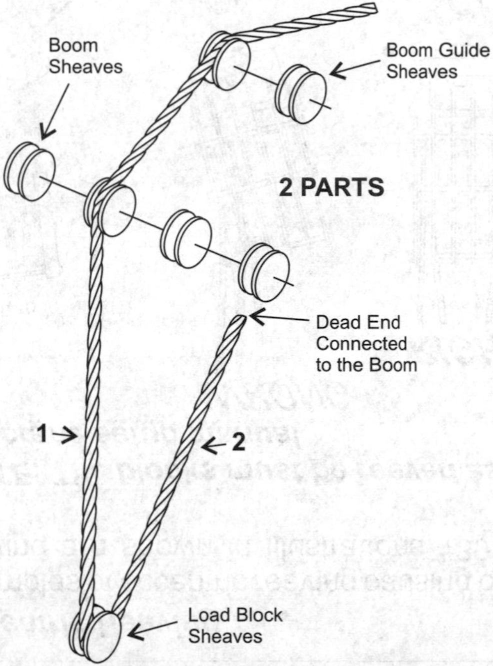

Boom Sheaves
Boom Guide Sheaves
2 PARTS
Dead End Connected to the Boom
1
2
Load Block Sheaves

Illustration #42 - Two Part Reeving

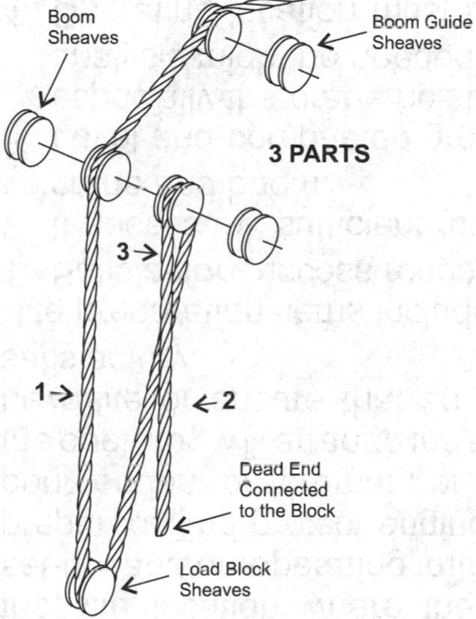
Boom
Sheaves
Boom Guide
Sheaves
3 PARTS
3
1
2
Dead End
Connected
to the Block
Load Block
Sheaves

Illustration #43 - Three Part Reeving

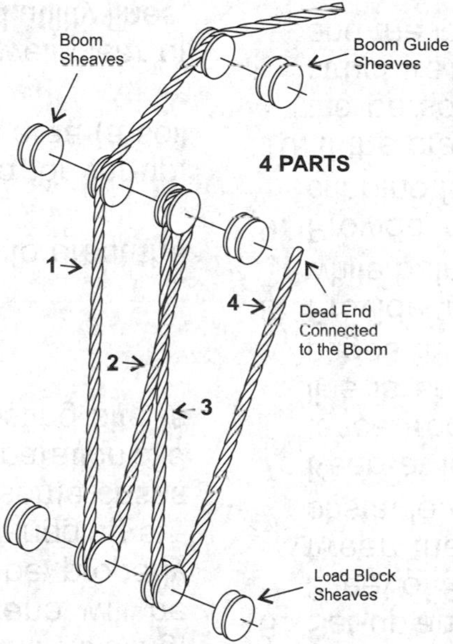
Boom
Sheaves
Boom Guide
Sheaves
4 PARTS
1
4
Dead End
Connected
to the Boom
2
3
Load Block
Sheaves

Illustration #44 - Four Part Reeving

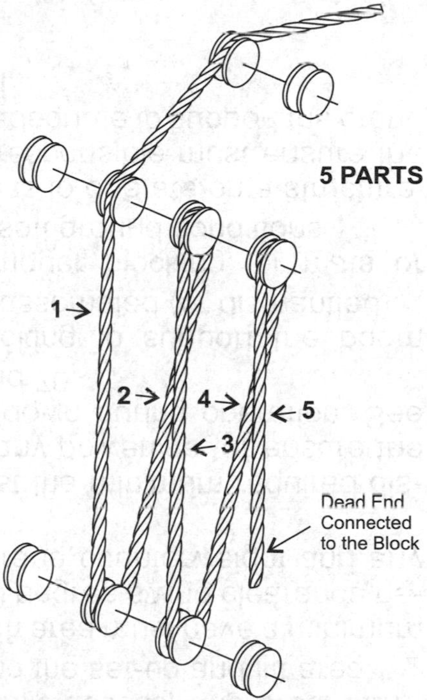
5 PARTS
1
2
4
5
3
Dead End
Connected
to the Block

Illustration #45 - Five Part Reeving

Site Preparation

Prior to any crane set-up or crane hoisting, the site location where the crane will be set-up and/or operating must be properly prepared. The project engineer, rigging superintendent or foreman, or in some cases the operator, will arrange the preparation of a new site or ensure that an existing site is satisfactory.

Site preparation items include:

1. Satisfactory access roads.
2. If necessary, sufficient room to erect the crane and boom.
3. Level and compacted ground for set-up, especially the crane hoisting area (a soil analysis might be needed).
4. Operating location must be well clear of any trenches, shoring, buried utility lines, etc. to avoid ground collapse from excessive machine and load weight.
5. Block off public access, and erect barricades around the set-up and lift area.
6. Set-up and lift area must have a minimum 2 feet of 360 degree swing clearance between the crane counterweight and any obstacle.
7. Keep at least the minimum required distance from any powerline, or ensure the line is shut down during operation. See pages 69 and 70.
8. Provide blocking to support the boom while being assembled (or dismantled).
9. Provide outrigger blocking, or mats or cribbing for soft ground conditions.
10. If the crane is to operate on a structure, the person responsible must ensure the structure is adequate to support the crane and the load.

Ground Conditions

The ground conditions must be suitable to operate a crane safely. The surface must have enough stability and bearing capacity to support all loads transferred to it by the crane. This includes the dead weight of the machine, the load, the rigging, plus any shock or impact loads and dynamic conditions such as swinging, hoisting, lowering and traveling.

Use extreme caution when hoisting beside buildings (particularly newly constructed) with uncompacted backfill, along trenches which could collapse, or in areas where water mains, sewer pipes, or steam lines may possibly undermine the soil. See illustrations #46, #47 and #48.

Note: Compacted soil is not as solid as undisturbed soil.

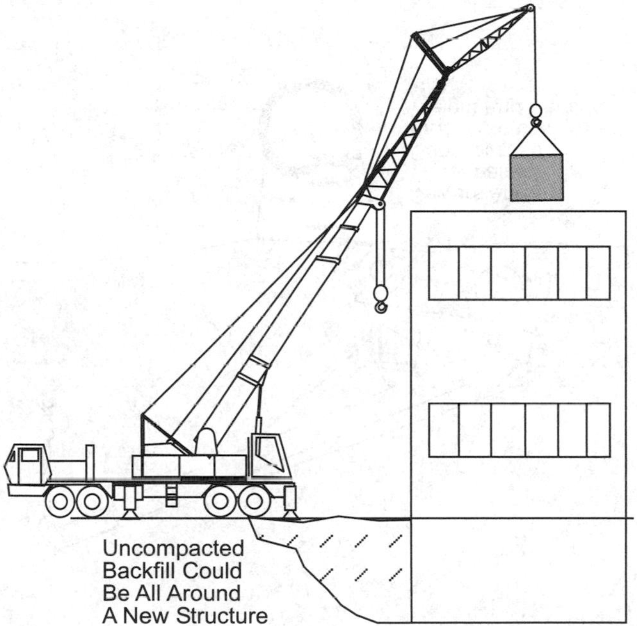
Uncompacted
Backfill Could
Be All Around
A New Structure

Illustration #46 - Uncompacted Soil

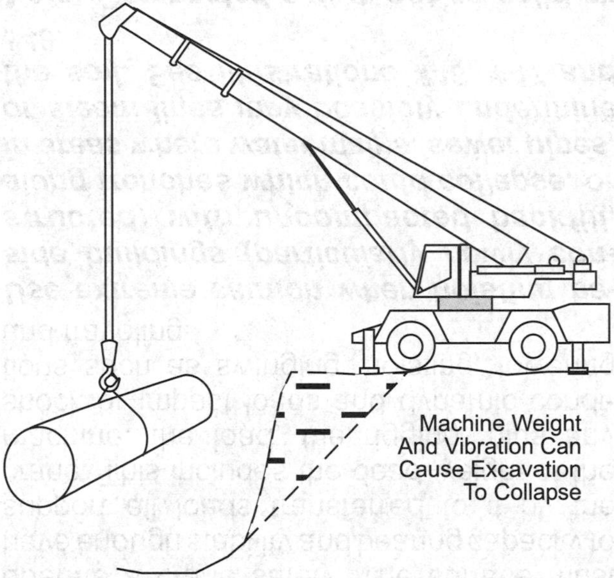
Machine Weight
And Vibration Can
Cause Excavation
To Collapse

Illustration #47 - Stay Away from Trenches

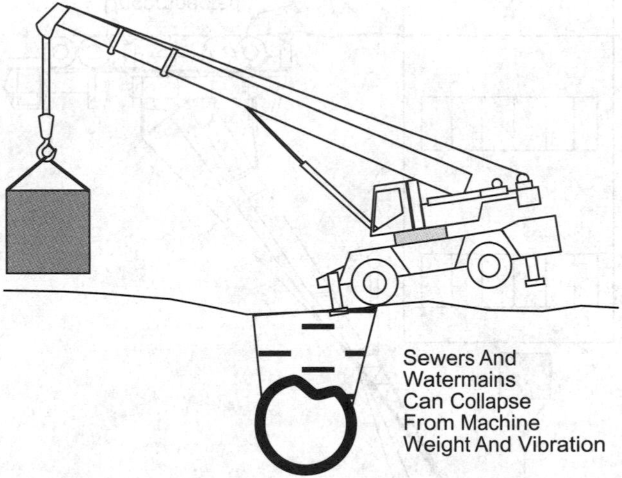
Sewers And
Watermains
Can Collapse
From Machine
Weight And Vibration

Illustration #48 - Try to Avoid Sewers and Watermains

Bearing Surface

When a crane sits on its bearing surface it exerts varying pressures depending on the operating conditions and area of operation (quadrant).

The lowest pressure on the ground is simply the total weight of the machine distributed over the entire area of both tracks or all outrigger pads.

Illustration #49 indicates the distribution of ground pressure when a crawler crane is used in different quadrants. The greater the density of dots, the greater the pressure. Illustration #50 shows a mobile crane and the weight distribution under its outriggers.

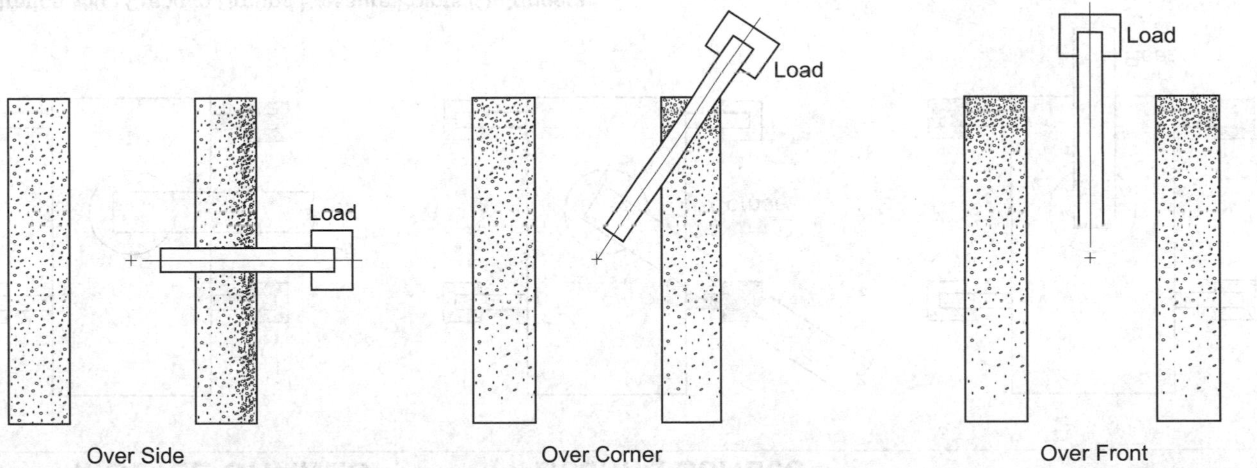
Load
Load
Load
Over Side
Over Corner
Over Front

Illustration #49 - Crane to Ground Pressure Points (Crawlers)

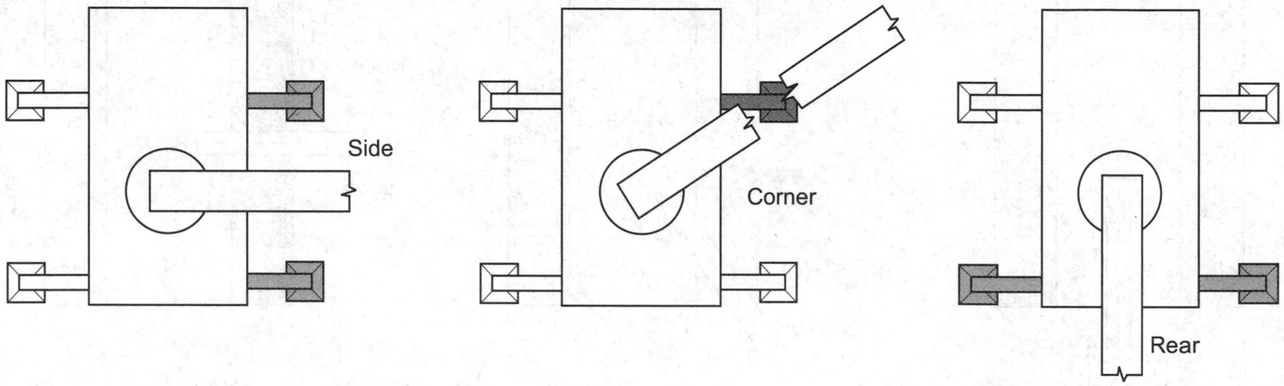
Side
Corner
Rear

illustration #50 - Crane to Ground Pressure Points (Outriggers)

Lifting a load over the corner produces the maximum ground bearing pressure. This is the most dangerous position to make a lift. Take into account any dynamic or impact loads. Rapid swinging of the machine or suddenly stopping the load will greatly increase the ground pressure.

The ground pressure on a truck crane can be higher than a crawler crane due to the smaller total bearing surface area of the pads. For this reason always make sure the ground under the outrigger is firm enough to support the machine in a fully loaded condition.

Outrigger Blocking

Any blocking under the outrigger float should be at least three times larger in area than the float. It should be rigid and completely support the total area. See illustration #51.

See illustrations #52 for an example of incorrect blocking.

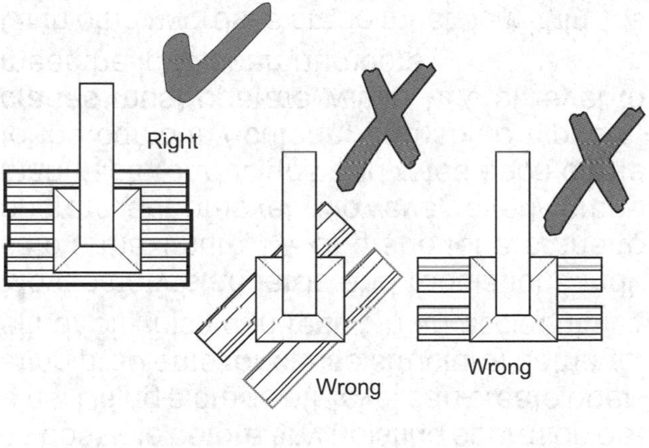
Right
Wrong
Wrong

Illustration #51 - Right and Wrong Outrigger Blocking

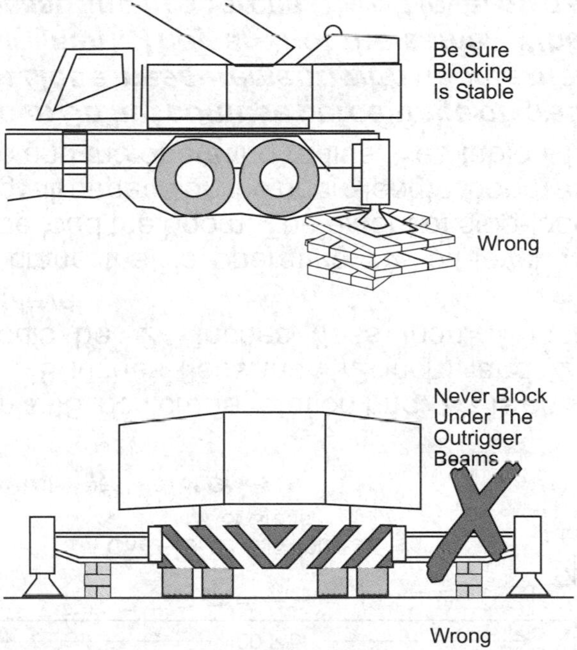
Be Sure Blocking Is Stable
Wrong
Never Block Under The Outrigger Beams
Wrong

Illustration #52 - Incorrect Blocking

Out-of-Level Cranes

Every crane must be set-up as perfectly level as possible before any hoisting operation begins. Using a crane off-level can create operating problems, or cause structural damage, either of which can result in an accident.

Most safety standards and regulations indicate a maximum 1% of grade for a crane to operate out-of-level. However every crane manufacturer designs and rates each crane to the company criteria, and some types of cranes must operate within ½% of level to meet the load chart numbers.

Or in other words, a crane must be within 1% of level, unless stated otherwise by the particular crane manufacturer.

ANSI/ASME states the degree of level as a percentage of grade. This means that in a horizontal length of 100 feet (1200 inches), a drop of 1 foot (12 inches) is equal to 1% (see illustration #53).

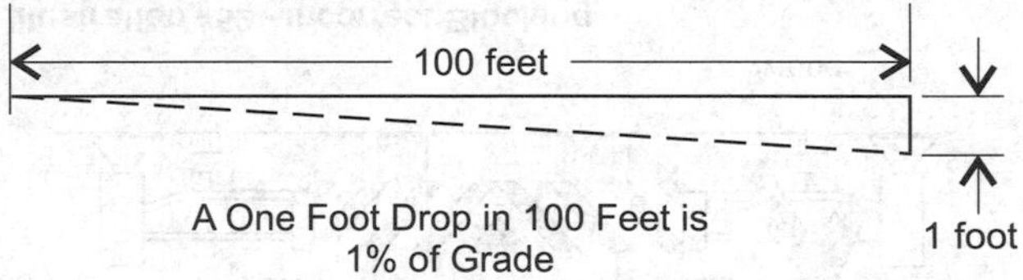
100 feet
1 foot
A One Foot Drop in 100 Feet is
1% of Grade

Illustration #53 - 1% of Grade

On a 48 inch crane rotation ring, 1% is equal to .48 inches (less than1/2 inch), and ½% would be .24 inches (less than ¼ inch) off-level.

A crane that is operating 1% off-level will side-load the boom. The extent of side-loading will depend on the boom length, boom angle and the operating radius. See table #1.

Note: Do not confuse percentage of grade (or slope measurement) with degree measurement. They are not the same. When measuring in degrees, 1% off level on a 48 inch ring would be .573 degrees (slightly over ½ degree).

Boom Length and Radius	Capacity Lost When Crane Out of Level By		
	1°	2°	3°
Short Boom, Minimum Radius	10%	20%	30%
Short Boom, Maximum Radius	8%	15%	20%
Long Boom, Minimum Radius	30%	41%	50%
Long Boom, Maximum Radius	5%	10%	15%

Table #1 - Off-level Lost Capacity

Crane Leveling

It is impossible to accurately level a crane by eye. Always use a level, preferably a longer carpenters level, or the birds-eye level(s) mounted in the cab or on the deck. See illustration #54 and #55.

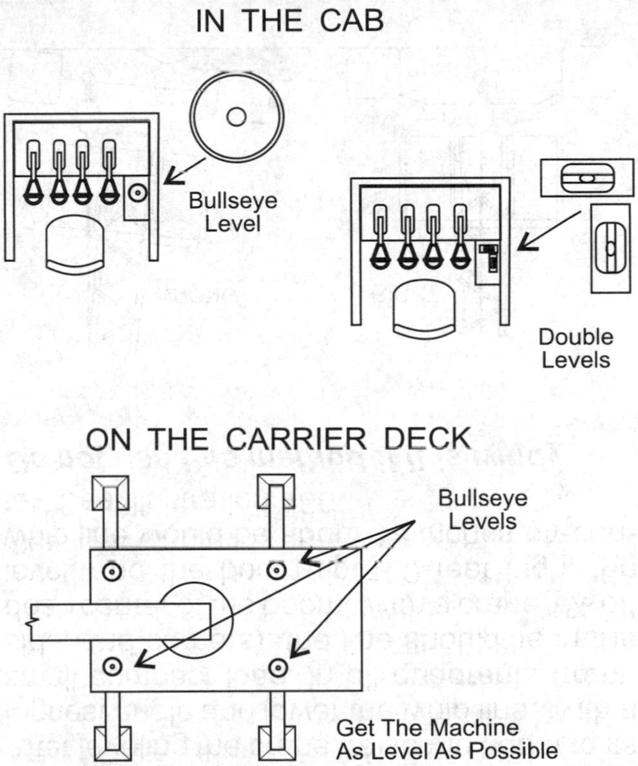
IN THE CAB
Bullseye Level
Double Levels
ON THE CARRIER DECK
Bullseye Levels
Get The Machine As Level As Possible

Illustration #54 - Crane Leveling Positions

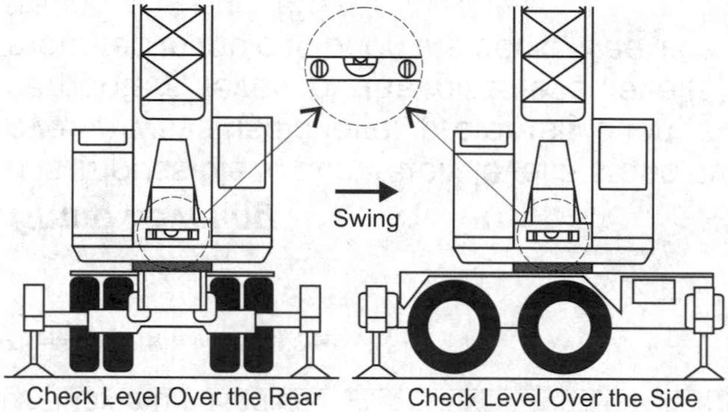
Swing
Check Level Over the Rear
Check Level Over the Side

Illustration #55 - Crane Leveling with a Level

When leveling, check the level front-to-back and side-to-side, then rotate the boom 90 degrees and check again. If making a series of lifts, recheck the level of the crane periodically.

After leveling the crane, raise the boom to its highest angle and lower the whip line. With a small compact load, in all quadrants (front, side, and corners), the line should lie in the dead center of the boom. With a crane 1% off level, and the boom tip 100 feet high, the whip line would be about 12 inches off-center. See illustration #56.

Do not use this method if it is windy.

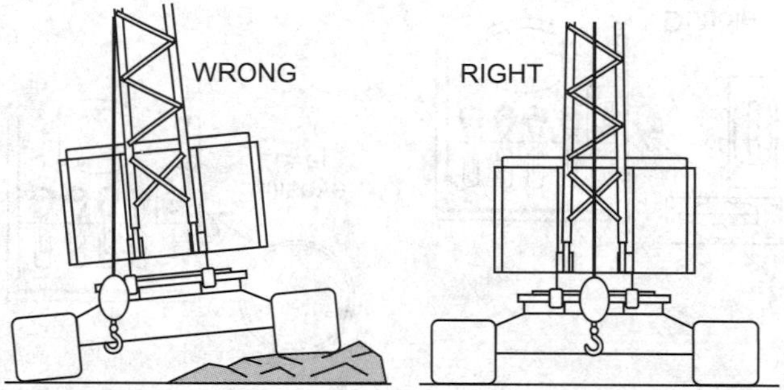
WRONG
RIGHT

Illustration #56 - Crane Leveling with the Whip Line

Intermediate Position Outriggers

Up until the introduction of cranes designed to work with outriggers in the intermediate position, it was a violation of safety standards to use a crane in the intermediate position. The two allowable positions were at 100% and 0% extension. Any crane that operated with the outriggers partially extended was still rated at the 0% extension.

Modern cranes so designed can now use 0%, 50%, and 100% extensions. Most cranes with this design are pinned at the 50% extension to guarantee that it actually is 50%. Also, it is normally specified that all outriggers be extended the same.

The majority of cranes are rated 85% of tipping with fully extended outriggers. However the rating varies with different manufacturers for the 50% and 0% position.

Computerized Load Indicators

Note: A Load Indicator, Rated Capacity Indicator, or Rated Capacity Limiter must be installed on any crane with a maximum rated capacity of 3 tons or more to warn the operator both visually and audibly when the crane is lifting beyond a preset capacity. The system senses an overload and can lock out the hoist control.

Note: These devices are an aid only. Verified load chart weight ratings and measured radii take precedence over the indicator readings.

A variety of different types of indicators are available as an after market item for older model cranes, and they are usually a standard feature on new cranes. In general terms the device can perform the following functions:

- Display boom angle
- Display boom length
- Display load radius
- Display boom tip height
- Display maximum permissible load
- Display actual lifted weight
- Display approaching two-block condition

Note: Load Indicator Safety Hazard

The proper use of these devices is a major step forward in job lifting safety. However, their use has also created an unexpected safety problem. That problem is the use of a load indicator as a method of test weighing a load. This use of the computerized system is in direct conflict with the crane manufacturers' instructions. Indicators must only be used to check the weight of a previously calculated load weight. The electronic equipment is intended strictly as an operator aid, and is not meant to replace crane load charts and operating instructions. The use of these devices to test weigh unknown loads is a violation of ANSI B30.5-3.2.1.1 (a)(b)(c).

Crane Stability Factor

Cranes operate on a safety factor to avoid tipping. The maximum rated capacity of a crane is a percentage of the load that would tip the crane.

Table #2 and illustration #57 show the rating percentages required by ANSI B30.5.

CAPACITY CHART RATING BASED ON PERCENTAGE OF TIPPING	
TYPE OF CRANE	**PERCENTAGE**
LOCOMOTIVE	85%
CRAWLERS	75%
MOBILES ON ROUGH TERRAIN	
on outriggers	85%
on tires	75%
COMMERCIAL BOOM TRUCKS	
on stabilizers	85%
Check your crane - above percentages not used by all manufacturers	
ANSI B 30.5 & CSA Z150	

Table #2 – Tipping Percentages

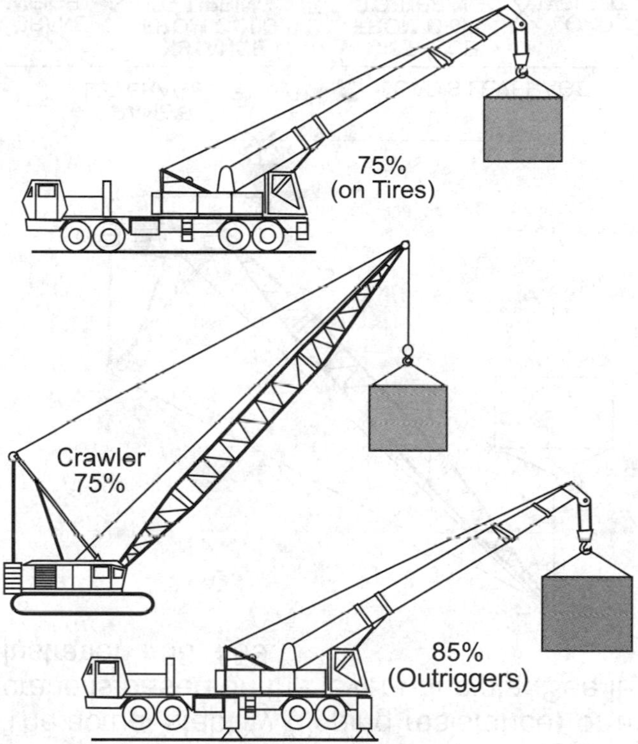
75%
(on Tires)
Crawler
75%
85%
(Outriggers)

Illustration #57 - Crane Stability Factors

Crane Stability

A crane uses the power of its hoisting apparatus to lift a load. This includes the motor, drum, wire rope, and block sheaves.

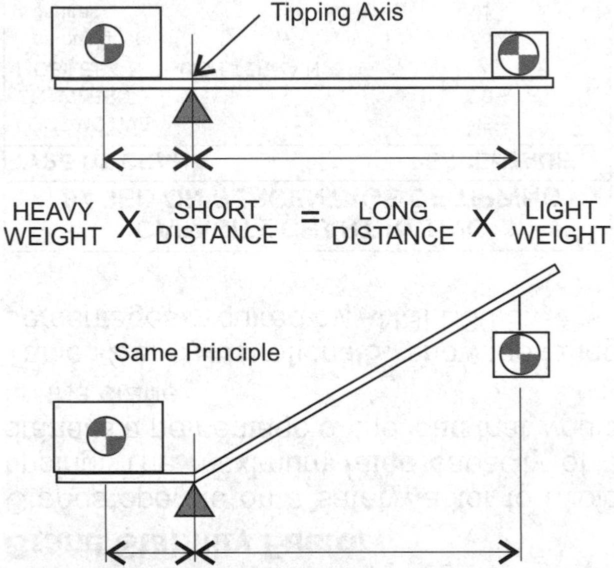
Tipping Axis
HEAVY WEIGHT X SHORT DISTANCE = LONG DISTANCE X LIGHT WEIGHT
Same Principle

Illustration #58 - Crane Leverage

The actual stability (tipping resistance) of a crane is based on the lever principle. See illustration #58, #59.

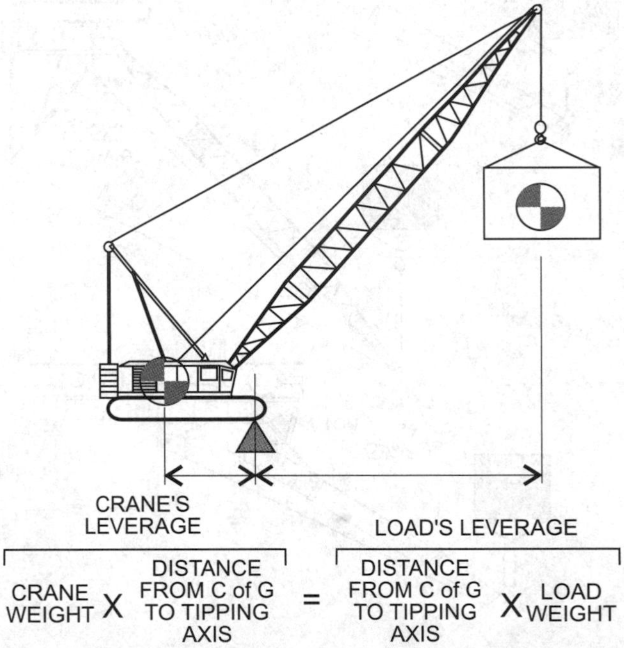
CRANE'S LEVERAGE
LOAD'S LEVERAGE
CRANE WEIGHT X DISTANCE FROM C of G TO TIPPING AXIS = DISTANCE FROM C of G TO TIPPING AXIS X LOAD WEIGHT

Illustration #59 - Crane vs Load Leverage

Crane Stability (Crawler)

Due to the configuration of a crawler crane with its center of gravity (C of G) almost at the center pin, the C of G changes very little as the crane rotates.

The tipping axis of a crawler crane is at the center of its track on a side lift (illustration #60). The leverage can be increased on some cranes by extending the tracks. The tipping axis is through the diameter of the drive or idler sprocket when lifting over the front or rear (illustration #61).

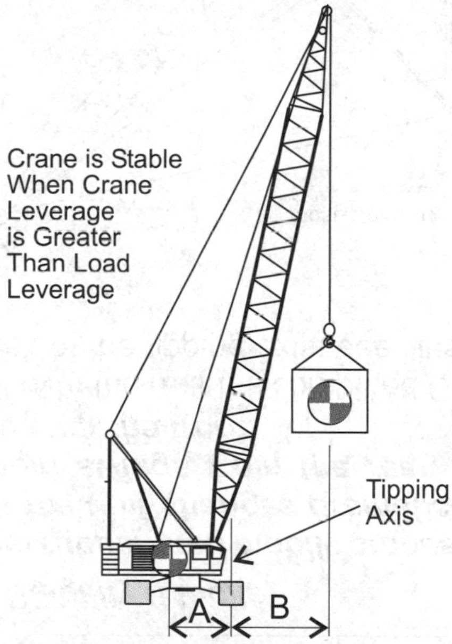

Crane is Stable When Crane Leverage is Greater Than Load Leverage
Tipping Axis
A
B

Illustration #60 - Tipping Axis Over the Side

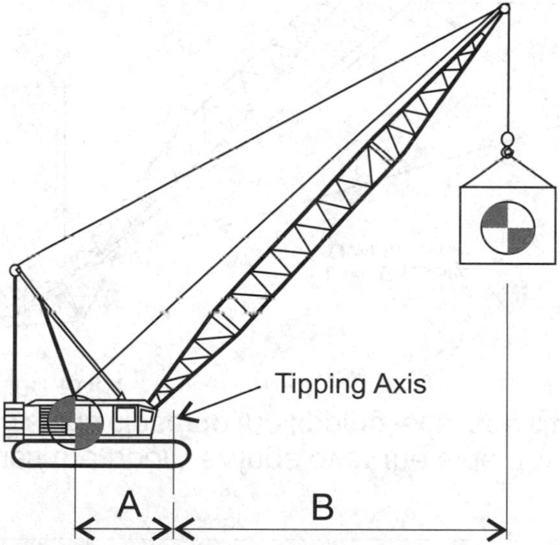

Tipping Axis
A
B

Illustration #61 - Tipping Axis Over the Front

Crane Stability (Mobile)

On most rubber tired mobile cranes, the C of G of the unit changes dramatically as the boom swings from the rear, to the side, to over the front.

On a lift over the rear the combined C of G is well back of the tipping axis, see illustration #62.

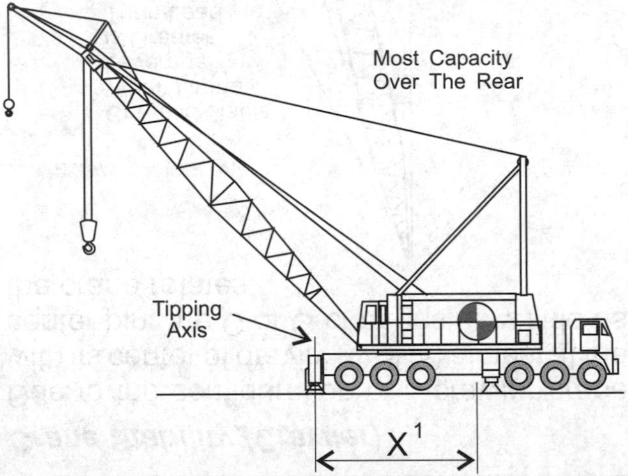
Most Capacity
Over The Rear
Tipping
Axis
X 1

Illustration #62 - Tipping Axis Over the Rear

When the boom swings over the side, the C of G shifts closer to the tipping axis, see illustration #63.

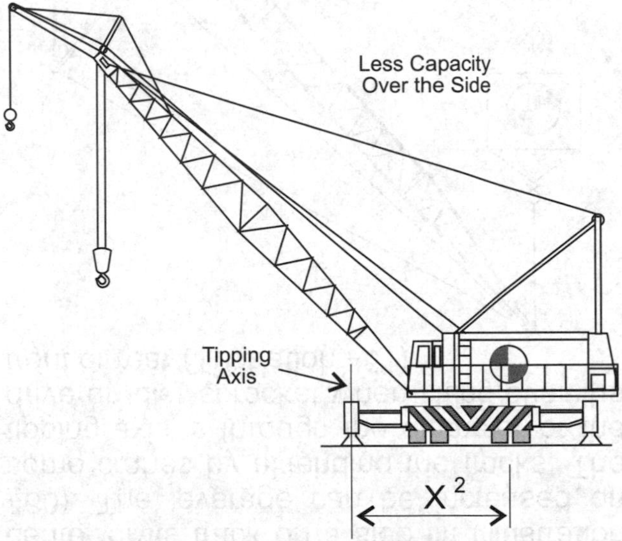
Less Capacity
Over the Side
Tipping
Axis
X 2

Illustration #63 - Tipping Axis Over the Side

Quadrants of Operation

Every crane has a Quadrant of Operation (or Area of Operation) diagram included with the load rating chart for that particular crane. The diagram shows the safe approved working areas of the crane.

Maximum lifting capacity is approved only in the areas shown in the diagram and listed in the load chart. Depending on the crane model, lifting outside the approved quadrant is either not permitted or there is a reduced capacity. Every crane model will have a quadrant of operation suitable for that crane model only. The quadrant of operation is based on the manufacturer, and on the ANSI B30.5 standard.

- The quadrants are over the rear, over the front, and over the sides. However the scope or shape of these quadrants varies.
- Check each crane for the permitted working quadrant, as there will be variations with every type, make, and model. For example some cranes may have a full 360 degree operation, while others may safely lift more over the rear than over the front or sides.
- Do not lift over the front unless so stated in the chart. Some carrier models may have a front mounted stabilizer or jack.
- Capacity ratings may change when swinging from one quadrant to another (for example, rear to side). If so, use the lower rating.
- Always extend the outriggers fully. The only exception is when the crane has an intermediate outrigger position rating specified in the rating chart.

Several examples of various quadrant areas are shown in illustrations #64 to #66.

Carrier mounted lattice boom

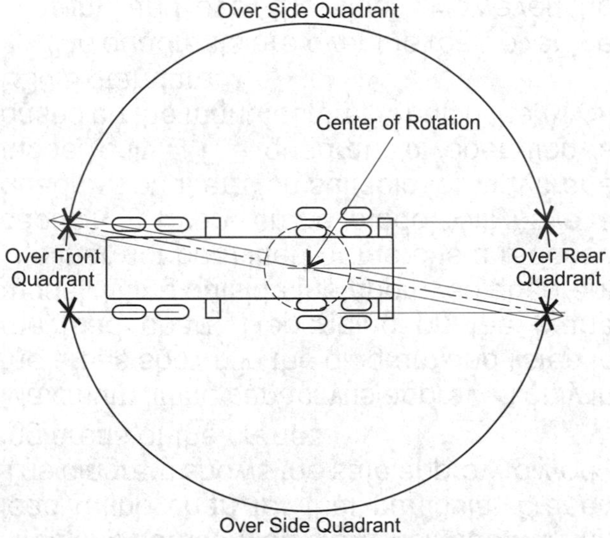
Over Side Quadrant
Center of Rotation
Over Front Quadrant
Over Rear Quadrant
Over Side Quadrant

Illustration #64 - Free Over Side and Free Over Rear (Outrigger Not Extended)

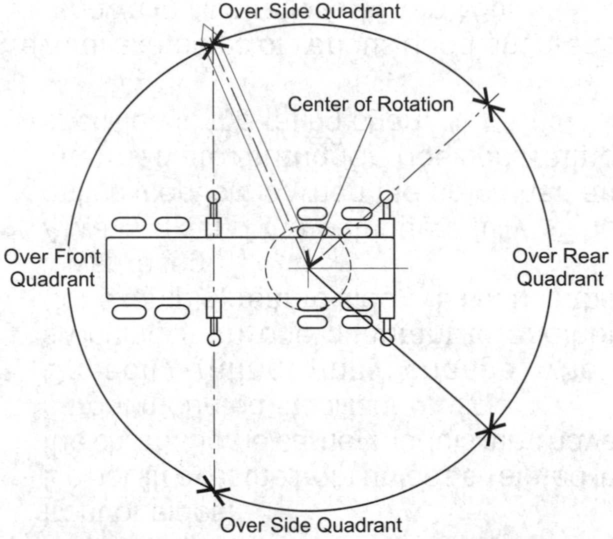
Over Side Quadrant
Center of Rotation
Over Front Quadrant
Over Rear Quadrant
Over Side Quadrant

Illustration #65 - Outrigger Extended and Set Over Side or Rear

Crawler Cranes

Crawlers Over the Side

Two methods are used to indicate the quadrants of a crawler crane.

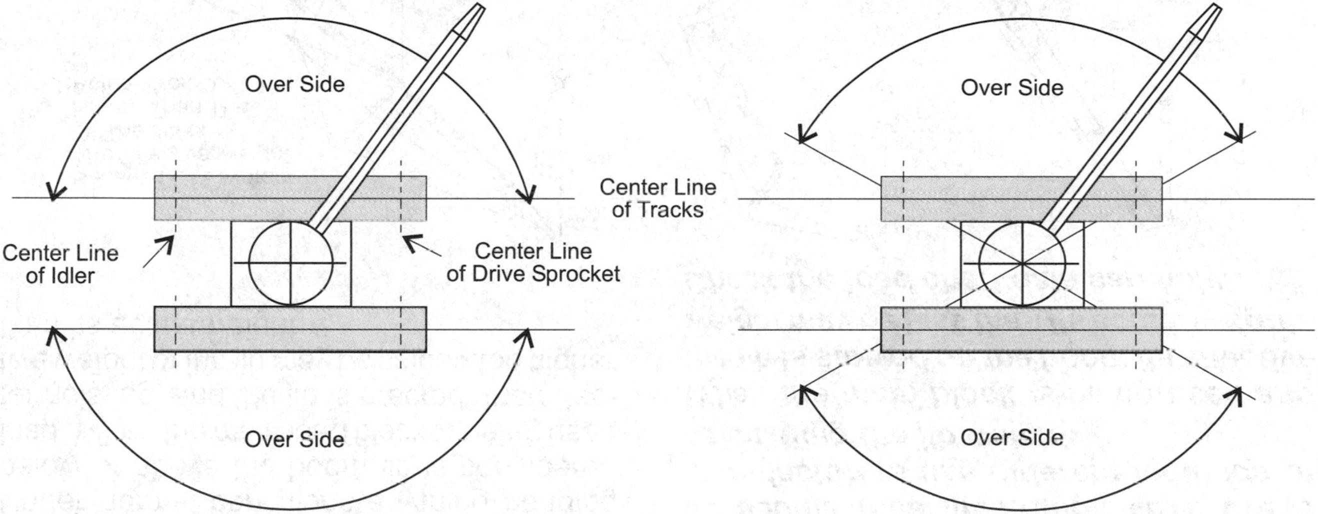
Over Side
Center Line of Idler
Center Line of Drive Sprocket
Over Side
Over Side
Center Line of Tracks
Over Side

Illustration #66 - Crawler Crane Quadrants

Actual vs Effective Load Weight

Under normal conditions anything hanging below or above the boom tip is considered load. When the main load block is being used for hoisting, and the jib is erected, the effective weight of the jib may be calculated higher than its actual weight.

This can apply to either lattice or hydraulic booms (see illustration #67). Crane manufacturers use different methods of calculating the jib weight.

When the main block is being used and the jib is stowed on the boom its effective weight may be less than its actual weight.

Check the load chart data carefully.

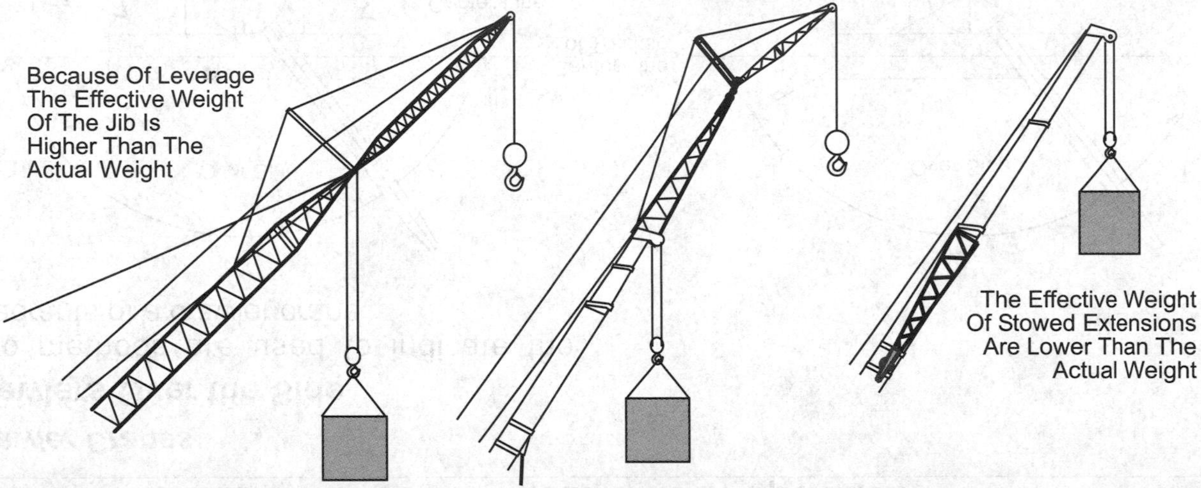
Because Of Leverage
The Effective Weight
Of The Jib Is
Higher Than The
Actual Weight
The Effective Weight
Of Stowed Extensions
Are Lower Than The
Actual Weight

Illustration #67 - Effective vs Actual Jib Weights

Load on Boom

Every crane has specific rules for its boom and jib makeup, however it can be safely assumed that everything under the boom tip is load.

This will include the object being lifted, slings and any rigging components, the hook and hoist block, and the hoist wire rope below the boom tip (on most cranes).

If the jib is erected, it is considered part of the load, as well as the jib gantry and jib pendants. The headache ball and hook are also included, as well as the jib line (on most cranes). See illustration #68. The crane manual and load charts must be followed closely as some types of cranes will double the jib weight as part of the load. For example a 2200 lb. (1000 kg.) jib could be a 4400 lb. (2000 kg.) capacity deduction.

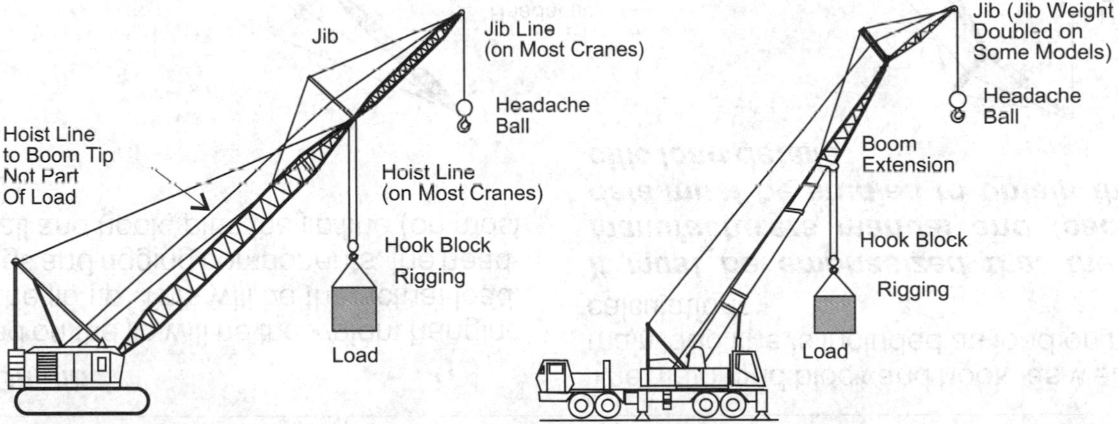
Jib
Jib Line
(on Most Cranes)
Headache
Ball
Hoist Line
to Boom Tip
Not Part
Of Load
Hoist Line
(on Most Cranes)
Hook Block
Rigging
Load
Jib (Jib Weight
Doubled on
Some Models)
Headache
Ball
Boom
Extension
Hook Block
Rigging
Load

Illustration #68 - Load on Boom With Jib

Load On Jib

The load on the jib will be the weight hanging below the jib tip. This will be the actual load, the slings and rigging components, the headache ball and hook, plus the jib line (on most cranes).

The main load block and hook, as well as the main load line is included as load on most jib calculations.

It must be emphasized that the crane manufacturers manual and load chart data must be studied to obtain the specific load details.

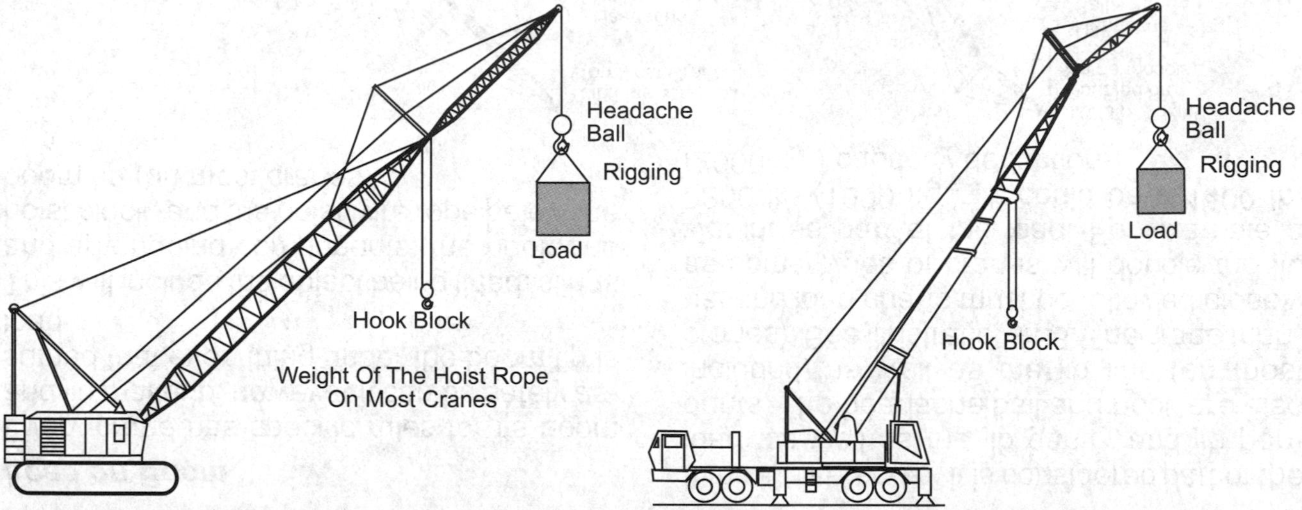
Headache
Ball
Rigging
Load
Hook Block
Weight Of The Hoist Rope
On Most Cranes
Headache
Ball
Rigging
Load
Hook Block

Illustration #69 - Load on Jib

Necessity of Load Charts

The load chart shows the maximum capacity of that specific crane under every permissible configuration. The ability to interpret this chart correctly is critical for those planning a lift, and to the safe operation of the crane.

Crane manufacturers place the capacity charts in readily accessible locations in the crane cab. They should be attached and not removed.

Load Charts vs Load Indicators

Modern technology, specifically Load Moment Indicators, and Capacity Limiters have taken away some of the old trial and error practices. However, accidents happen, almost always for reasons that should have been avoided. Any operator relying on guesswork and a sign of the crane going light (beginning to tip slightly) to warn of overload is playing a dangerous game.

Many modern cranes will be overloaded before there is any indication of tipping. The electronic operator aids must be tested every day to ensure their accuracy. If there is any doubt, the crane manufacturers load chart information will prevail.

Note: It is a conflict with the manufacturers guidelines and a violation of the ANSI standards to use a load indicator as a method to weigh a load.

- Do not use signs of tipping to indicate capacity limits.
- Some cranes are overloaded before any sign of tipping.
- Cranes at maximum lift configuration will probably fail structurally before there is any sign of tipping.
- An operator may not notice the point when a crane goes from stable to unstable.

- When a crane begins to tip it may be too late to recover, even by a quick release of the load.
- A crane is rated at its maximum capacity load ONLY with its shortest boom section, and lifting at the minimum radius.

Load Chart Information

All crane manufacturers have different capacity charts for each of their cranes, but they all include similar information:

- Type of crane base.
- Type of crane configuration.
- Quadrant of operation.
- Length of boom.
- Angle of boom.
- Load radius.

Subtract from gross capacity for additional equipment (jib, rigging, etc).

Two sample load charts are shown in tables #3 and #4.

Boom Lgth.: Feet	Rad. in Feet	Boom Ang.: Deg.	FREE		Outriggers Set	
			Over Side	Over Rear	Over Side	Over Rear
160 ft	27	83	77,590*	88,050	218,360*	218,360*
	30	82	69,620*	77,170	192,320*	192,320*
	35	80	59,030*	63,510	150,230	159,850*
	40	78	50,820*	53,490	122,360	136,210*
	50	75	38,920*	39,790	88,040	104,100*
	60	71	30,220	30,840	67,710	83,290*
	70	67	23,850	24,540	54,260	68,710*
	80	63	19,150	19,860	44,700	57,920*
	90	59	15,530	16,240	37,550	49,030
	100	55	12,670	13,350	31,990	42,090
	110	50	10,340	10,990	27,550	36,550
	120	45	8,400	9,030	23,920	32,040
	130	40	6,760	7,370	20,880	28,280
	140	34	5,350	5,930	18,310	25,100
	150	27	4,130	4,680	16,090	22,370
	160	17	3,040	3,570	14,150	19,990

Ratings with a * are based on strength, not stability.

Table #3 - Carrier Mounted Lattice Boom Example

Boom Lgth.: Feet	Oper. Rad.: Feet	Boom Ang.: Deg.	Boom Point: Elev.	Capacity: Crawlers Retracted	Capacity: Crawlers Extended
70 ft	16	80.1	76.0	392,000	400,000*
	17	79.3	75.8	349,600	383,300*
	18	78.5	75.6	315,400	365,300*
	19	77.6	75.4	287,100	348,900*
	20	76.8	75.1	263,400	319,800
	22	75.1	74.6	225,900	270,100
	24	73.4	74.1	197,500	235,600
	26	71.7	73.5	175,300	205,500
	28	69.9	72.8	157,500	183,400
	30	68.2	72.0	142,800	165,400
	32	66.4	71.2	130,500	150,500
	34	64.6	70.2	120,100	138,000
	36	62.8	69.3	111,100	127,300
	38	60.9	68.2	103,400	118,100
	40	59.1	67.0	96,600	110,000
	45	54.1	63.7	82,700	93,900
	50	48.9	59.8	72,100	81,600
	55	43.2	54.9	63,800	72,000
	60	36.9	49.0	57,000	64,300
	65	29.4	41.3	51,500	57,900
	70	19.5	30.3	46,800	52,600

Ratings with a * are based on strength, not stability.

Table #4 - Crawler Mounted Lattice Boom Example

Typical capacity chart nomenclature includes the following:

Boom length: The measurement from center of boom hinge pin to center of sheave pin.

Operating radius: The horizontal distance from rotation axis to center of load block with the load suspended.

Boom angle: The angle between horizontal and centerline of the boom when the load has been lifted off the ground and the boom has gone through deflection. This indicates operating radius. Operating radius governs capacity.

Maximum capacity: Free over side and rear (outriggers not extended).

Maximum capacity: Outriggers extended and set over side and rear.

Boom point elevation: The distance from ground to center of boom point shaft.

Chart Configurations

The three basic crane chart configurations are:

1. Boom extension and/or jib not installed.
2. Lifting from main load line but with boom extension and/or jib installed.
3. Load lifted from boom extension or jib.

Some cranes can have different styles of boom tops, such as open throat, hammerhead, or light tapered top. Each style of top has its own capacity chart. Some crane models use different numbered booms. The boom number listed on the capacity chart must correspond to the boom number on the crane. The amount of counterweight on the crane must match the specifications in the load chart.

Load Chart Strength vs Stability

The load numbers in the lower section of most capacity charts (indicating the lesser lifting capacities), are based on crane stability or tipping. The load numbers in the upper section of the chart indicate capacities based on structural strength. To indicate the difference, the upper numbers may be shaded, divided by a dark line, or shown with asterisks. These upper chart numbers mean a crane component will break before there is any sign of the crane tipping. See illustration #70 for examples.

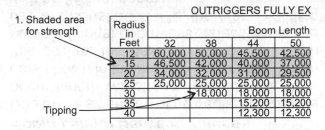

1. Shaded area for strength

OUTRIGGERS FULLY EX

Radius in Feet	Boom Length 32	38	44	50
12	60,000	50,000	45,500	42,500
15	46,500	42,000	40,000	37,000
20	34,000	32,000	31,000	29,500
25	25,000	25,000	25,000	25,000
30		18,000	18,000	18,000
35			15,200	15,200
40			12,300	12,300

Tipping

2. Solid line divides the two areas

Radius in Feet	Boom Length 36	49	62	75
12	160,000	103,000		
15	120,000	100,000	81,000	76,500
20	93,000	90,000	79,000	68,000
25	70,000	70,000	70,000	64,000
30	55,000	55,000	55,000	50,000
35		40,000	40,200	40,000
40		32,000	32,000	32,000
45		26,000	26,000	26,000
50			22,320	22,320

Strength

Tipping

3. Asterisks for strength

WITHOUT OUTRIGGERS

Radius in Feet	Max. Boom Extension Feet	16.00 x 24 (16 p.r.) Tires Over Front	Over Side
10	30	26,000*	19,300
12	36	23,700*	15,700
15	42	15,700*	11,050
20	48	9,900*	5,800
25	54	7,000	3,650
30	60	4850	2,100

Tipping

Illustration #70 - Strength vs Stability on Chart

Interpreting the Load Chart

Load radius, boom length and boom angle are three critical load chart factors. When calculating capacity from the chart, and any of these three do not match the actual crane set up, then the capacity numbers for a longer radius, a longer boom length, or a lower boom angle on the load chart must be used. It is not permitted to guess or mathematically calculate in-between (interpolate) chart values. The following text and illustration #71 on radius, #72 on boom length, and #73 on boom angle explains this more clearly.

Radius Between Chart Values

Frequently the measured load radius will fall between two numbers shown on the load chart. When this occurs, the chart radius number used must be the higher number (longer radius-less capacity). In illustration #71, the crane has an 80-foot boom, and is lifting at an off-the-ground radius of 38 feet. The chart (page 60) indicates a load rating of 67,000 pounds at a 35-foot radius, and a load rating of 54,300 at a 40-foot radius. With a measured distance of 38 feet, the 40-foot rating of 54,300 must be used.

Boom Length Between Values

Due to the extension of hydraulic booms, the boom length will often not match the numbers shown in the boom length chart. When this occurs, the next highest boom length number (longer boom-less capacity) must be used. In illustration #72, the crane is lifting with an 85-foot boom.

The chart indicates that an 80-foot boom, at a 50 foot radius, has a rating of 38,900 pounds. A 90-foot boom at a 50-foot radius is rated at 38,600. The 90-foot rating of 38,600 must be used.

Boom Angle Between Values

If the boom angle indicator shows an angle not matching the load chart, the angle value used (lower angle-less capacity) must be the next lowest number. In illustration #73, the crane has an 80 foot boom and the angle indicator shows 59 degrees.

The chart (illustration #73) shows a rating of 38,900 pounds at 55 degrees, and 54,300 at 63 degrees. The lower angle of 55 degrees with the 38,900 rating must be used.

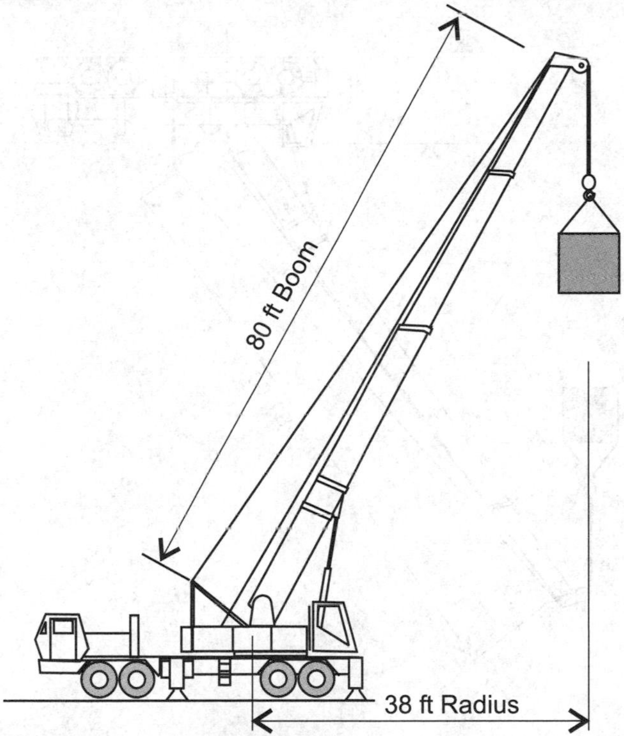
80 ft Boom
38 ft Radius

Illustration #71 - Radius Between Chart Values

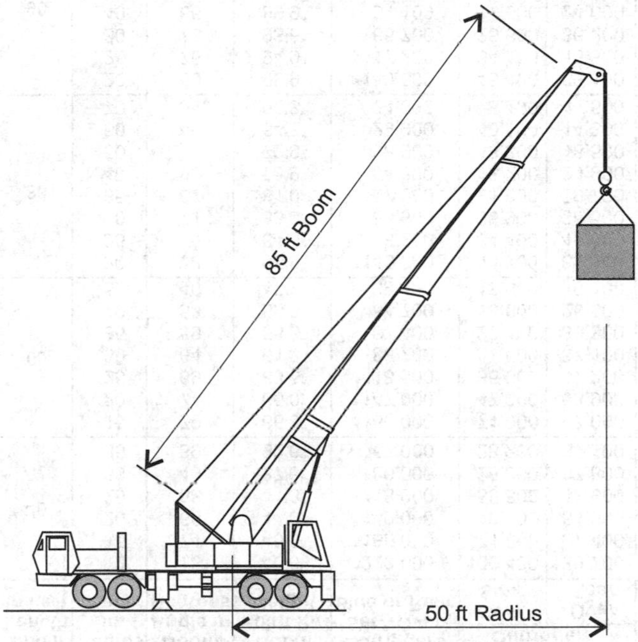
85 ft Boom
50 ft Radius

Illustration #72 - Boom Length Between Chart Values

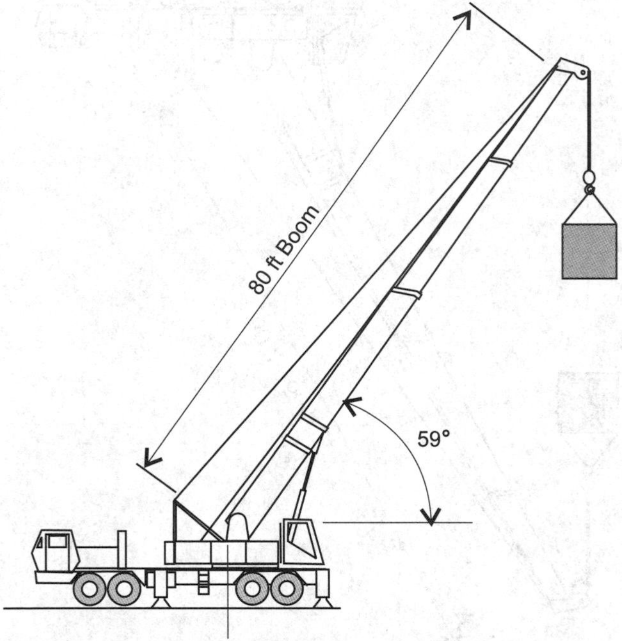
80 ft Boom
59°

Illustration #73 - Boom Angle Between Chart Values

MAXIMUM ALLOWABLE LOADS IN POUNDS						
Boom Length in Feet	Radius in Feet	Boom Angle in Degrees	Boom Point Pin Height	Outriggers Set * Over Side or Rear	Without Outriggers	
					Over Side	Over Rear
40	12	78	46'6"	*220,000	100,400	139,700
	15	74	45'9"	*185,000	71,800	97,400
	20	66	44'0"	*149,000	48,100	54,600
	25	58	41'3"	118,000	35,800	47,900
	30	49	37'6"	86,000	28,300	37,800
	35	39	32'6"	67,000	23,200	31,100
60	15	79	66'3"	*180,000	71,000	97,000
	20	74	65'0"	*147,000	47,300	63,900
	25	69	63'6"	*118,500	35,000	47,200
	30	64	61'3"	86,200	27,500	37,100
	35	59	58'6"	67,400	22,400	30,300
	40	53	55'3"	54,700	18,800	25,500
	50	40	45'9"	39,400	13,900	19,100
80	20	78	95'9"	*145,000	46,700	63,300
	25	75	84'6"	118,200	34,400	46,600
	30	71	83'0"	85,900	26,900	36,500
	35	67	81'0"	67,000	21,800	29,700
	40	63	78'9"	54,300	18,200	24,900
	50	55	72'9"	38,900	13,300	18,500
	60	45	64'3"	29,900	10,100	14,300
	70	34	52'3"	24,000	8,400	11,500
90	20	80	95'9"	*143,000	46,400	63,100
	25	76	94'9"	117,200	34,100	46,300
	30	73	93'6"	85,700	26,600	36,200
	40	66	89'9"	54,100	17,900	24,600
	50	59	84'6"	38,600	13,000	18,200
	60	51	77'9"	29,600	9,900	14,100
	70	43	68'3"	23,800	7,700	11,200
	80	32	55'3"	19,600	6,100	9,150

Do not make up in-between values.

Range Diagram

The range diagram included on all mobile cranes is a side view of the crane with its full range of configurations. It shows the crane placement, boom length, boom angle, load radius, jib and jib offset, and load heights, needed to lift and place the load.

Each chart is marked off with horizontal lines indicating boom tip height, vertical lines indicating load radius lines, radial boom angle lines and boom tip arcs that trace the position of the boom for each boom length as the radius and boom angle change.

If different jibs are used they would also be indicated on the diagram. See illustration #74 for an example of a range diagram.

Note: Boom angle and boom length determine load radius. Refer to load chart for lifting capacity at required boom length and radius.

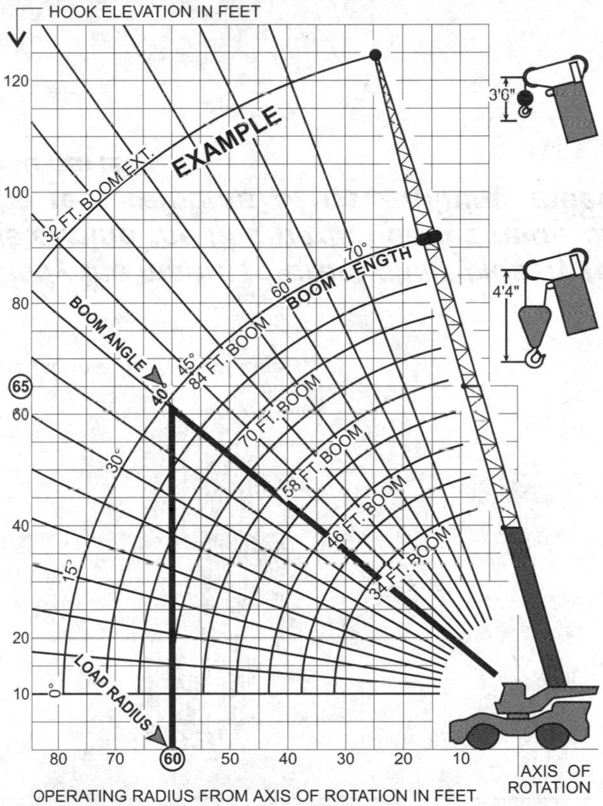
HOOK ELEVATION IN FEET
EXAMPLE
32 FT. BOOM EXT.
BOOM LENGTH
BOOM ANGLE
84 FT. BOOM
70 FT. BOOM
58 FT. BOOM
46 FT. BOOM
34 FT. BOOM
LOAD RADIUS
3'6"
4'4"
70°
60°
45°
40°
30°
15°
0°
120
100
80
65
60
40
20
10
80
70
60
50
40
30
20
10
AXIS OF ROTATION
OPERATING RADIUS FROM AXIS OF ROTATION IN FEET

Illustration #74 - Range Diagram Example

Number of Hoist Lines

A crane will often have to be equipped with more than a single hoist line. If the load lifted weighs more than the safe working load of the wire rope the crane will have to be reeved with more line parts.

The total weight of the load will be the lift plus the hook block, slings, and all components.

Example: The load weighs 60,000 pounds and the block and rigging weighs 1125 pounds. The crane wire rope has a WLL (SWL) of 18,000 pounds.

Line parts = 61,125 ÷ 18,000 = 3.39

The crane will need 4 parts of hoist line, assuming the block is equipped with roller bearing sheaves. See illustration #75.

Note: Some load charts may include the weight of the minimum parts of line required to lift a load. Excessive parts of line or an extra fall must be calculated.

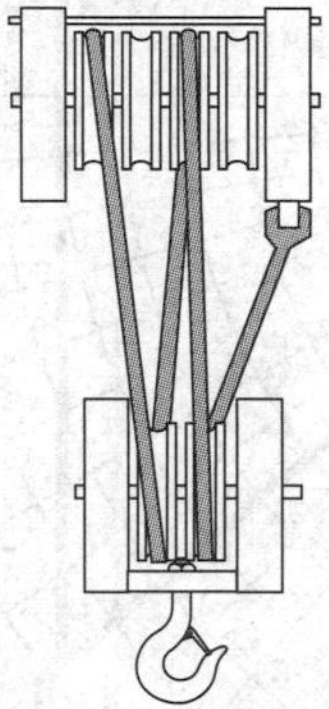
4 Parts

Illustration #75 - Parts of Line

Study the manufacturers chart closely to determine the line parts needed and / or the requirements of determining these line parts.

Calculating Jib Capacity

Jib capacity can be checked by a chart from either the tipping factor in the boom chart, or the strength factor in the jib rating chart.

The following basic requirements are used to calculate jib capacity for either lattice or hydraulic boom cranes:

- Use the jib chart, the boom chart, and the chart notes to find the proper jib offset, boom angle, or jib to ground angle.
- Use the jib chart (and/or the boom chart) to determine the capacity.
- Use the chart to determine which headache ball and hook to use.
- Use the chart notes and tables to determine the load deductions. Generally these will be anything below the jib tip, including the jib hoist wire rope, the ball and hook, the rigging components, and the load. In addition the wire rope, and the block and hook hanging from the main boom tip will be deducted, plus any boom extension stowed on the boom.

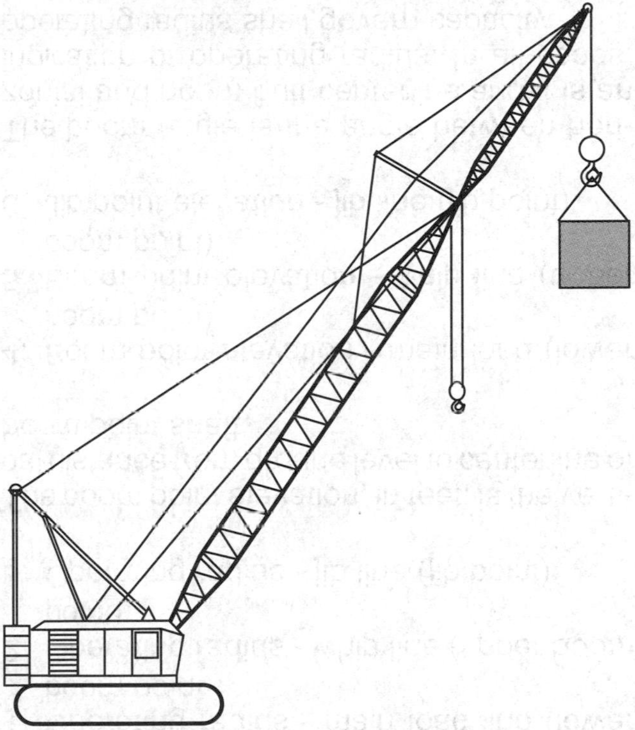

Illustration #76 - Jib Capacity

Capacity Chart Points

The example used is a Manitowoc Crane:

Operating Radius: operating radius is the horizontal distance from the axis of rotation to the center of vertical hoist line or load block with the load freely suspended. Add 14 inches to boom point radius for radius of sheave when using single part hoist line, see illustration #77.

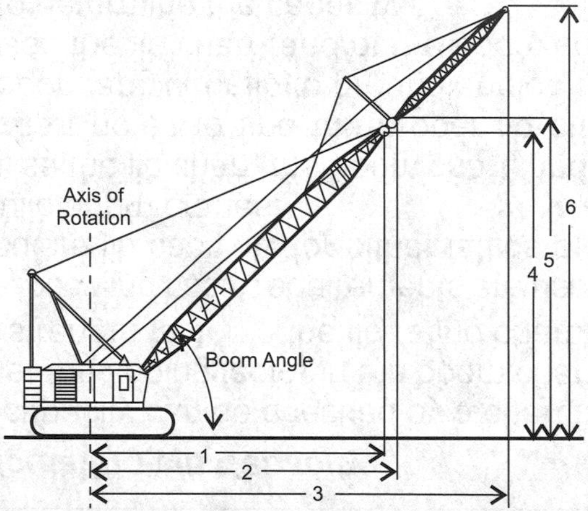
Axis of
Rotation
Boom Angle
1
2
3
4
5
6

Illustration #77 - Operating Radius and Boom Extension

1. Operating radius - main load line (lower boom point).
2. Operating radius - whip line (upper boom point).
3. Operating radius - jib line (jib point).

The boom point elevation, in feet, is the vertical distance from ground level to centerline of boom point shaft.

4. Boom point elevation - main load (lower boom point).
5. Boom point elevation - whip line (upper boom point).
6. Jib point elevation - jib line (jib point).

The boom angle is the angle between horizontal and boom butt centerline and it is an indication of operating radius. In all cases, operating radius shall govern capacity.

Load Calculation (Example One)

The following is a step method of calculating the crane limit when lifting with the main load line. The two charts used are samples only. With this example, all hoist lines below the boom and jib must be included for weight.

Step 1. The load block weighs 4,550 lbs. and the rigging weighs 760 lbs.

Step 2. Determine the parts of line for the main load block:

1. Load Block = 4,550 lbs.
2. Slings = 760 lbs.
3. Weight of Load = 49,600 lbs.
4. Total = 54,910 lbs.

Hoist reeving for main load block must have equal or greater capacity than the weight to be lifted. From table #5, use 65,000 lbs., which corresponds to a two part line.

Step 3. Determine the total weight of the jib, headache ball, hook and line (table #12, page 96), which is included in the overall weight. Assume 20 feet of line hanging from jib.

1. Jib Weight = 3,500 lbs.
2. Jib Line (20 ft of 1 1/8" @ 2.34) = 47 lbs.
3. Headache Ball and Hook = 950 lbs.
4. Total Jib Components = 4497 lbs.

Step 4. Determine the approximate weight to be lifted:

1. Weight of load = 49,600 lbs.
2. Rigging attachments = 760 lbs.
3. Jib components = 4497 lbs.
4. Load Block = 4,550 lbs.
5. Load block line weight (approximate) = (boom is 240 ft.) x (2 parts line) x (2.34 lbs. per ft.) = 1123 lbs.
6. Total Approx. Lifted Weight = 60,530 lbs.

Table #5 - Hoist Reeving Example for Main Load Block

No. Parts of Line	1	2	3	4	5	6	7	8	9	10	11	12
Max Load - Lbs	32,500	65,000	97,500	130,000	162,500	195,000	227,500	260,000	292,500	325,000	357,500	400,000

Step 5. The approximate weight is 60,530 lbs. From the load chart (table #6), with crawlers extended, the crane capacity is 64,600 at a 55 foot radius and with a boom point elevation of 241.5 feet.

As the boom tip elevation is 241.5 feet, the actual line weight will be: 241.5 x 2 x 2.34 lbs. = 1130.2 lbs. The actual total lifted weight will be 60, 497 lbs.

Note: Some load charts do not show the actual boom height to get this exact line length. Ensure the load chart being used belongs to the right crane.

Crawlers Extended: The total lifted weight is 60,497. With crawlers extended and operating at a 55 foot radius, the load is within the safe range of the crane capacity of 64,600.

Crawlers Retracted: If the crawlers were retracted, the crane capacity is reduced to 56,100 at a 55 foot radius.

Boom Lgth.: Feet	Oper. Rad.: Feet	Boom Ang.: Deg.	Boom Point: Elev.	Capacity: Crawlers Retracted	Capacity: Crawlers Extended
240 ft	40	81.4	244.3	89,200	103,100
	45	80.2	243.5	75,200	86,700
	50	78.9	242.6	64,500	74,300
	55	77.7	241.5	56,100	64,600
	60	76.5	240.4	49,300	56,800
	65	75.3	239.1	43,700	50,400
	70	74.0	237.7	38,900	45,000
	75	72.8	236.3	34,900	40,400
	80	71.5	234.6	31,400	36,500
	85	70.3	232.9	28,400	33,100
	90	69.0	231.1	25,700	30,100
	95	67.7	229.1	23,400	27,500
	100	66.4	227.0	21,300	25,100
	105	65.1	224.7	19,400	23,000
	110	63.8	222.3	17,700	21,100
	115	62.5	219.8	16,200	19,400
	120	61.1	217.1	14,800	17,800
	125	59.7	214.3	13,500	16,400
	130	58.3	211.3	12,300	15,100
	135	56.9	208.1	11,200	13,900
	140	55.5	204.7	10,200	12,800
	145	54.0	201.2	9,200	11,700
	150	52.5	197.5	8,300	10,800
	155	51.0	193.5	7,400	9,900
	160	49.5	189.4	6,600	9,900

Table #6 - Capacity Chart Example

Example Two Information

1. 50 ton carrier hydraulic boom crane
2. 50 ton, 4 - sheave block, hanging 15 feet below boom tip, with 3 / 4 inch wire rope @ 1.04 lbs. per foot.
3. 32 foot boom extension, 24 foot jib @ 17 degree offset
4. 7 1 / 2 ton headache ball, with 3 / 4 inch wire rope @ 1.04 lbs. per foot
5. Rigging components = 75 lbs.

In example two, the wire rope is considered only when more than the minimum required hoist reeving is in place on the unused block.

ON OUTRIGGERS FULLY EXTENDED								
Radius in Feet	Boom Length in Feet							84 ft. + 32 ft. Ext.
	34	40	44	54	64	74	84	**116
10	100,000 (70)	74,000 (73)	72,000 (76)					
12	90,000 (66.5)	70,000 (70)	67,500 (73.5)	64,000 (76.5)				
15	72,000 (61)	63,700 (65.5)	61,000 (69)	55,000 (73)	44,700 (76)			
20	53,000 (50.5)	52,200 (57.5)	49,800 (62)	44,000 (67.5)	37,900 (71)	35,000 (74)	31,000 (76.5)	
25	39,800 (38.5)	39,800 (48)	39,800 (54)	36,300 (66)	31,900 (61.5)	29,200 (70)	27,500 (73.5)	17,500 (76.5)
30	27,030 (21.5)	27,030 (37.5)	27,030 (45)	27,030 (55.5)	27,000 (60.5)	25,000 (65.5)	23,900 (69.5)	16,600 (75)
35		20,280 (23)	20,280 (34.5)	20,280 (48.5)	20,280 (55)	20,280 (61)	20,280 (66)	14,500 (72.5)
40			15,950 (19)	15,950 (41)	15,950 (49)	15,950 (56.5)	15,950 (62)	12,800 (70)
45				12,840 (31.5)	12,840 (42)	12,840 (51.5)	12,840 (58)	11,400 (67)
50				10,640 (17.5)	10,640 (35)	10,640 (46)	10,640 (53.5)	10,200 (64.5)
55					8,000 (26)	8,000 (40.5)	8,000 (49)	9,190 (61.5)
60					7,480 (12.5)	7,480 (34)	7,480 (44)	8,440 (59)
65						6,320 (25.5)	6,320 (38.5)	7,670 (56)
70						5,290 (14)	5,290 (32.5)	6,570 (53)
75							4,310 (25)	5,650 (49.5)
80							3,440 (13.5)	4,810 (46)

EXAMPLE

Table #7 – Capacity Chart - Example Two

JIB CAPACITIES IN POUNDS 24 ft. JIB and 32 ft. EXT. Combination			
Main Boom Angle	Min. 5 Offset	17 Offset	Max. 30 Offset
76	6,000	5,200	4,600
70	4,300	3,940	3,650
65	3,430	3,200	3,010
60	2,760	2,600	2,470
55	2,220	2,110	2,020

EXAMPLE

Jib Capacity Example Two

WEIGHT REDUCTION FOR LOAD HANDLING DEVICES
32 ft. BOOM EXTENSION
† STOWED ‡ ERECTED
24 ft. JIB & 32 ft. EXT. COMB.
‡ ERECTED ‡ ERECTED
† Reduction of main boom capacities. ‡ Reduction of 32 ft. Ext. capacities.

EXAMPLE

Weight Capacities Example Two

HOOK BLOCK	
50 Ton, 4 Sheave	700 lbs.
Auxiliary Boom Head	220 lbs.
5 Ton, Headache Ball	150 lbs.
7 1/2 Ton, Headache Ball	300 lbs.

Block Weight Example Two

Example Two Question

What is the net jib capacity when the boom is fully extended and is set at an angle of 59 degrees?

Answer – The jib capacity is based on the main boom angle (jib capacity - example two). There is no rating for 59 degrees.

The next lower rating is 55 degrees, and with a 17 degree offset, the capacity is 2,110 lbs.

Deduct: 50 ton block = 700 lbs.
Rigging = 75 lbs.
7 1/2 ton headache ball = 300 lbs.
4 parts of rope x 15 ft x 1.04 lbs/ft = 62.4 lbs
TOTAL = 1,137 lbs

The net jib capacity would be 973 lbs (2110 lbs - 1137 lbs).

Electrical Clearances

Accidental electrocutions are among the-most frequently repeated crane accidents. Most of these are caused when the boom contacts or approaches too close to overhead power lines. The fatality rate is high, particularly among riggers guiding the load. Inexperienced boom truck operators are another cause of high fatalities.

While the danger is greater from high voltage transmission lines, where flash over can occur without actual contact, fatal accidents have resulted from contact with 440 volts and 220 volt service lines and strut lighting systems.

The safest procedure is to request the local electrical authority to cut off the power.

If, for any reason this is not possible or practicable, and it is necessary for cranes to be under or near hot power lines lines follow the 20 foot (6.1 M) rule or see Table #8.

Electrical Hazards Clearance Guide

OPERATING NEAR HIGH VOLTAGE POWER LINES	
Normal Voltage (Phase to Phase)	**Minimum Required Clearance**
to 50 kV	10 ft. (3,05m)
Over 50 to 200 kV	15 ft. (4.60m)
Over 200 to 350 kV	20 ft. (6.10m)
Over 350 to 500 kV	25 ft. (7.62m)
Over 500 to 750 kV	30 ft. (10.67m)
Over 750 to 1,000 kV	45 ft. (13.72m)
IN TRANSIT WITH NO LOAD AND BOOM LOWERED	
Normal Voltage (Phase to Phase)	**Minimum Required Clearance**
to 0.75 kV	4 ft. (1.22m)
Over 0.75 to 50 kV	6 ft. (1.83m)
Over 50 to 345 kV	10 ft. (3.05m)
Over 345 to 750 kV	16 ft. (4.87m)
Over 750 to 1,000 kV	20 ft. (6.10m)

Table #8-Operating Near Powerlines

Absolute Limit of Approach

Every live powerline has an area around it called the limit of approach. A crane boom, loadline, or load cannot operate in this area without the power being cut off. This is an absolute, no exception rule.

The absolute limit of approach may vary somewhat with provincial, state, federal or other regulating bodies; however the guidelines shown in table #8 and illustration #78 should apply.

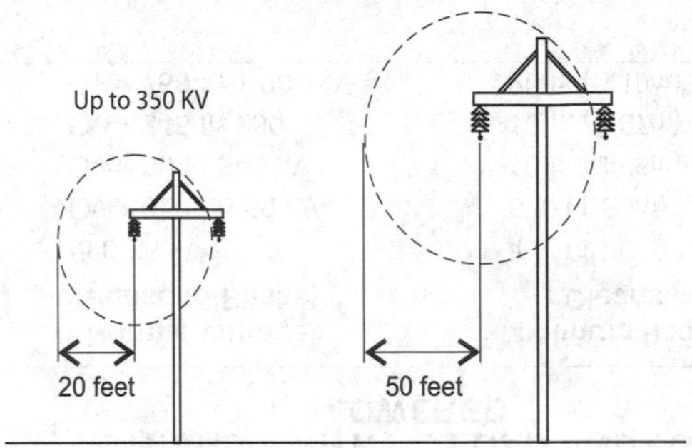
Over 350 KV
Up to 350 KV
20 feet
50 feet

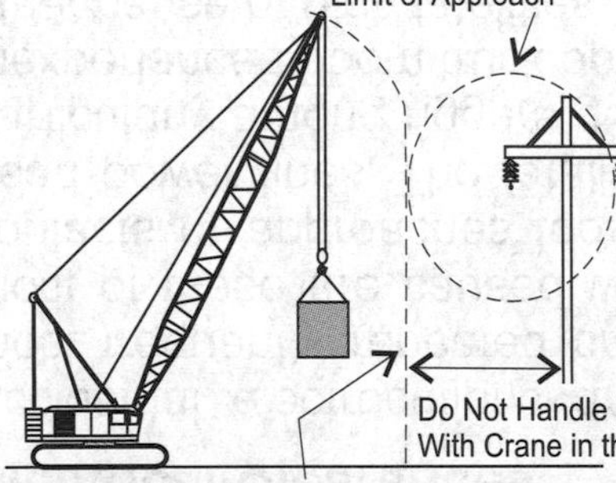
Limit of Approach
If a Crane Component or the Load Can Swing Within the Limits of Approach, a Signalman is Required
Do Not Handle Materials With Crane in this Area
Boom Shall Not Be Positioned Beyond this Line

Illustration #78 - Powerline Limit of Approach

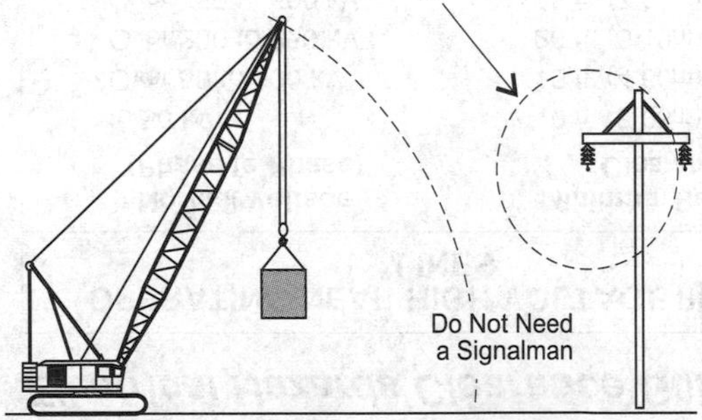
Limit of Approach
Do Not Need a Signalman

Illustration #79 - Use of Signalman Near Powerline

20 FOOT (6.1 M) RULE

Most safety jurisdictions and specifically OSHA 1926.1408, subpart CC, have the 20 foot (6.1 M) rule. This basically means that any part of a crane or load must maintain a 20 foot or more clearance for powerlines up to 350KV, and 50 feet (15.3M) if over 350 KV.

The exceptions are: (A) The powerline is de-energized and grounded. (B) If the utility company verifies the voltage, the distances in table #8 can be used along with other safety measures including a pre-job safety meeting with all the involved personnel and at least one of the following: (1) Dedicated spotter, (2) A proximity alarm for the operator, (3) An automatic stop movement or range control warning device, (4) An automatic crane motion limit device, (5) An insulating link between the load line and the load.

Powerline Approach Guidelines

1. All powerlines must be considered live until proven otherwise by the line owner.
2. Always notify the utility company when operating near a powerline.
3. All personnel (except the operator) must stay away from the crane when it is near the limit of approach. Do not touch the crane or the load.
4. Only use taglines to control the load or keep it from spinning. All ropes conduct electricity, although dry polypropylene is better than the other types.
5. Warning devices and various types of insulators are not fail safe. They all have limitations.
6. Use synthetic web slings.

Note: ANSI/ASME B30.5 code conditions apply to cranes working near powerlines. It may be necessary for a pre-lift meeting be tween the crane company and the util ity company. Check the B30.5 code, then contact the utility company.

Powerline Contact

The operator should remain in the cab after powerline contact until the power has been disconnected. If this is not practical, the operator must not step from the crane. The operator must jump clear with both feet together, being careful not to touch the crane. See illustration #80.

Illustration #80 - Jumping Clear of Crane After Contact

After jumping clear, the operator must hop or shuffle to a safe area. The area around the crane will be energized, and a normal step may cause the operator to be the conductor between a high and low voltage area. See illustration #81.

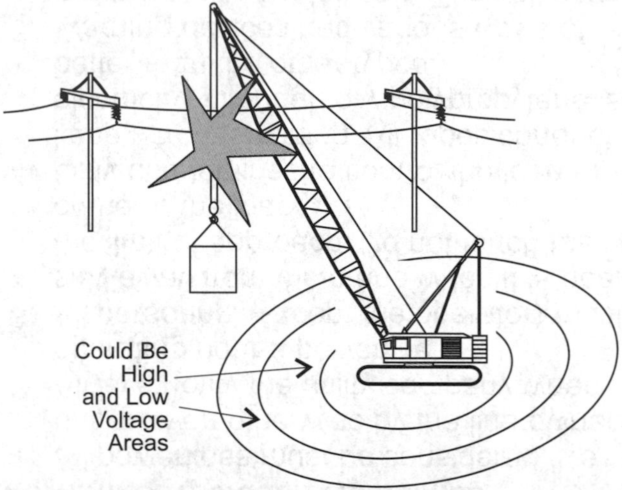
Could Be
High
and Low
Voltage
Areas

Illustration #81 - Energized Zone Around Crane

SECTION ONE QUESTIONS
Mobile Cranes

1. *Determine if this statement is true or false. All lifts require some type of lift plan.*
   ❒ true ❒ false

2. *Determine if this statement is true or false. All lift plans require an engineering staff and site drawing.*
   ❒ true ❒ false

3. *Which of the following would be included in a detailed lift plan:*
   ❒ size, shape, weight of the load
   ❒ size, type, set-up of crane(s)
   ❒ step-by-step movements of crane(s)
   ❒ all of above

4. *Determine if this statement is true or false. A documented pre-lift plan will state the names of the engineers and supervisors who have worked to prepare the plan.*
   ❒ true ❒ false

5. *Determine if this statement is true or false. A documented pre-lift plan will state the names of the operator(s) and the riggers who will rig the load and perform the lift.*
   ❒ true ❒ false

6. *Determine if this statement is true or false. As crane signaling is only a basic function and the signal-person knows where the loads will be positioned, training or testing of the signal-person should not be required.*
   ❒ true ❒ false

7. *When using hand signals to direct a crane operator, an extended arm with the thumb vertical and the fingers opening and closing into a fist indicates:*
   ❒ lower load
   ❒ raise boom and lower load
   ❒ raise the load line
   ❒ extend boom

8. *Two closed fists with both thumbs pointing toward each other is the signal for:*
   - ❒ retract hydraulic boom
   - ❒ lower jib
   - ❒ lower load slowly
   - ❒ secure load in position

9. *Determine if this statement is true or false. A crane component made by a crane company can be used on any other crane made by that company.*
   - ❒ true ❒ false

10. *Which type of crane would be best to use where a tight turning radius is required?*
    - ❒ all-terrain
    - ❒ crawler crane
    - ❒ carrier-mounted
    - ❒ ringer crane

11. *To prevent damage, what type of sling should be used to lift a lattice boom?*
    - ❒ wire rope slings
    - ❒ chain slings
    - ❒ metal mesh slings
    - ❒ synthetic web slings

12. *When is the proper time to attach the counterweight to the crane?*
    - ❒ before load is lifted
    - ❒ prior to installation of the complete boom
    - ❒ after installation of boom
    - ❒ only if load weight exceeds crane weight

13. *In order for a crane to lift its own counterweight for loading or off-loading, which of the following criteria should be met to ensure maximum safety?*
    - ❒ must be on firm level ground
    - ❒ gantry must be fully extended
    - ❒ four part load line must be used
    - ❒ all of the above

14. *When assembling lattice boom sections, which set of pins are installed first?*
    - ❒ left side
    - ❒ right side
    - ❒ both lower
    - ❒ both upper

15. *When installing the boom pins, the pin should be pointing:*
   - ❒ out away from boom center
   - ❒ in toward boom center

16. *When dismantling a lattice boom, which boom pins should be removed first?*
   - ❒ left side
   - ❒ right side
   - ❒ both lower
   - ❒ both upper

17. *Determine if this statement is true or false. It is safe to climb under a boom to knock out the boom pins if the crane has tension on the pendant lines.*
   - ❒ true ❒ false

18. *Which position should the gantry of a crane be in when lifting a load?*
   - ❒ highest position
   - ❒ third position
   - ❒ mid position
   - ❒ lowest position

19. *Jib forestay and backstay pendant lines should be:*
   - ❒ of equal length, or the forestay pendant lines should be longer
   - ❒ of equal length, or the backstay pendant lines should be longer

20. *Determine if this statement is true or false. Jib capacity "increases" as the angle to the ground decreases.*
   - ❒ true ❒ false

21. *To avoid torsional loading, the boom tip sheaves should be reeved:*
   - ❒ non-symmetrical
   - ❒ symmetrical
   - ❒ with an even number of line parts
   - ❒ with an uneven number of line parts

22. *Which of these conditions could be dangerous when operating a crane around a newly constructed building?*
   - ❒ height of structure
   - ❒ uncompacted soil
   - ❒ protected pedways
   - ❒ compacted soil

23. When hoisting on outriggers with a permitted 360 degree swing, which position is the most hazardous in most conditions?

- ❒ over front
- ❒ over rear
- ❒ over side
- ❒ over corner

24. Determine if this statement is true or false. The ground pressure under outriggers is higher than it is under a crawler track because of a smaller bearing surface.

- ❒ true
- ❒ false

25. Outrigger blocking should be approximately how much larger than the outrigger floats?

- ❒ same
- ❒ 1.5 times
- ❒ 2 times
- ❒ 3 times

26. Determine if this statement is true or false. When determining whether a crane is level, percentage of grade and degree measurement is the same.

- ❒ true
- ❒ false

27. On a 48 inch crane rotation ring, a crane 1% off-level would be how much in inches?

- ❒ almost 5 inches
- ❒ almost one-half inch
- ❒ almost one-eighth inch
- ❒ too small to measure

28. Determine if this statement is true or false. A crane sitting 3 degrees off-level with a long boom at minimum radius, can have an increase in boom stress of approximately 50%.

- ❒ true
- ❒ false

29. The load line is hanging in the dead center of the boom when positioned over the rear. With the boom over the side, the load line is observed to be off center. This means it is:

- ❒ safe to lift over the rear
- ❒ safe to lift over the corner
- ❒ safe to lift over the side
- ❒ not safe to lift until level in all positions

30. *Determine if this statement is true or false. Unless a crane has been so designed with a pinned intermediate location and a matching chart rating, a crane should be operated with all outriggers retracted or fully extended and set.*
- ❒ true
- ❒ false

31. *Determine if this statement is true or false. Computerized Load Moment Indicators warn the operator of an overload condition.*
- ❒ true
- ❒ false

32. *Determine if this statement is true or false. Use of Computerized Load Moment Indicators is a quick, easy method of checking a load weight that is approved by crane manufacturers and safety regulations.*
- ❒ true
- ❒ false

33. *Crane stability is based on:*
- ❒ lever principle
- ❒ ability of crane hoist to lift load
- ❒ load measurements
- ❒ height of lift

34. *The crane center of gravity will vary the most while swinging from rear to side to front with which type of machine?*
- ❒ crawler cranes
- ❒ truck cranes
- ❒ cherry pickers
- ❒ same with all types

35. *Determine if this statement is true or false. The approved swing working areas of a crane are referred to as quadrants of operation.*
- ❒ true
- ❒ false

36. *The effective weight of a jib is:*
- ❒ higher than the actual weight
- ❒ lower than the actual weight
- ❒ same as actual weight
- ❒ depends on crane, could be any of the above

37. *When using the main load line with the jib attached, the working load for the boom must be reduced by:*
- ❒ weight of jib attachments
- ❒ weight of jib pendants
- ❒ weight of jib
- ❒ manufacturer's specifications for jib and hook weight reduction

38. *Determine if this statement is true or false. A common practice and safe method of determining when a crane is overloaded is to watch for and back off at the first indication of tipping.*
❒ true ❒ false

39. *Determine if this statement is true or false. A crane that "goes light" is not yet overloaded, and can be safely returned to normal by rapid load lowering.*
❒ true ❒ false

40. *Boom angle is the measured angle between what and the centerline of the boom.*
❒ vertical ❒ horizontal

41. *On load charts with the upper and lower numbers divided, the upper numbers are in the range that mean the crane will do what if it is overloaded?*
- ❒ tip
- ❒ structurally fail
- ❒ cannot lift the load
- ❒ none of above

42. *Determine if this statement is true or false. When using crane load charts, it is not permitted to guess or calculate in between values.*
❒ true ❒ false

43. *If the measured radius between crane rotation point and load center is 57 feet, and the load chart only shows values at 55 feet and 60 feet, which value would be used?*
- ❒ 55 feet
- ❒ 60 feet
- ❒ must consider boom length
- ❒ depends on load weight

44. *Using the range diagram on page 61, determine the approximate load radius with a boom length of 84 feet at an angle of 30 degrees.*
- ❒ 80 feet
- ❒ 70 feet
- ❒ 67 feet
- ❒ 55 feet

45. *Determine if this statement is true or false. The crane is always set up to specification, therefore the load chart does not have to be used to determine the required number of parts of line in the main load block to lift a load.*
❒ true ❒ false

46. *Determine if this statement is true or false. In general terms, everything below the boom tip, or jib tip is considered load.*
❒ true ❒ false

47. *Using load calculation example one, on pages 65, 66, but with a load weight of 53,400 pounds, what would be the maximum operating radius allowed with the crawlers extended?*
- ❒ 50 feet
- ❒ 55 feet
- ❒ 60 feet
- ❒ 65 feet

48. *Determine if this statement is true or false. Even with high voltage power lines, it is not possible to have an electrical accident unless the crane or load actually hits the line.*
❒ true ❒ false

49. *Determine if this statement is true or false. A signal-person must be used if a crane can swing within the limit of approach of a power transmission line.*
❒ true ❒ false

50. *Determine if this statement is true or false. The operator should always jump out of the cab as quickly as possible if the crane makes contact with a power line.*
❒ true ❒ false

SECTION TWO

RIGGING

Wire Rope Parts

Wire rope is typically made of steel wires laid together to form a strand, as shown in illustration #82. These strands are formed into a rope, usually around a central core of either fiber or wire.

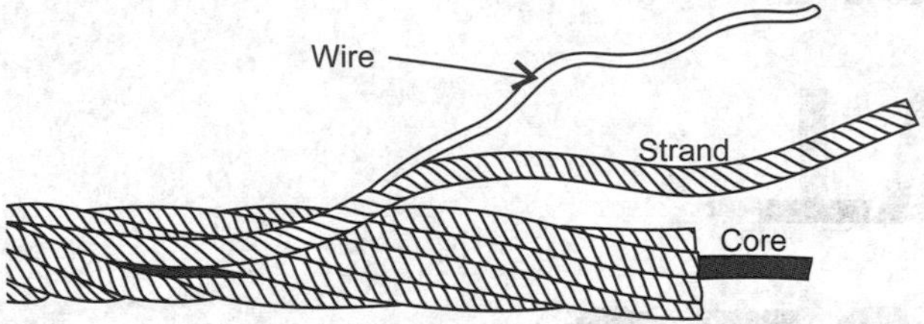
Wire
Strand
Core

Illustration #82 - Wire Rope Parts

Fiber core and wire core strands are shown in illustrations #83A and #83B.

Compacted strands are shown in illustration #83C and flattened strands in illustration #83D.

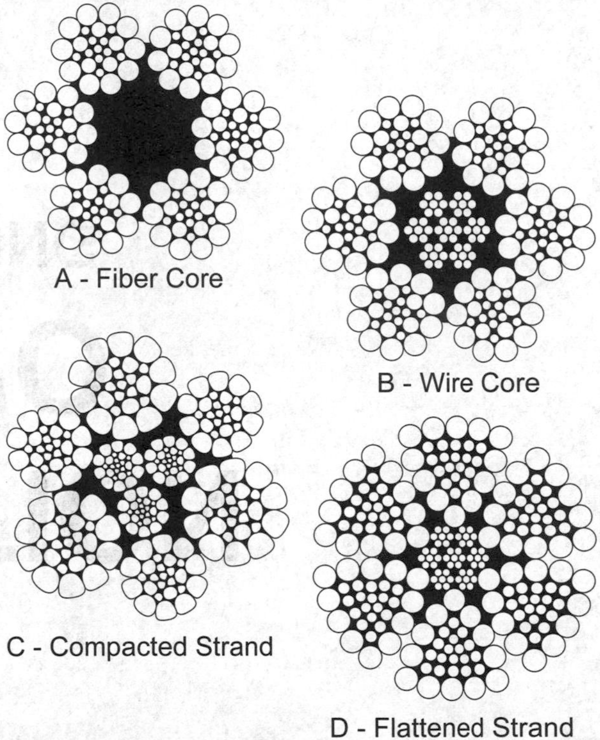
A - Fiber Core
B - Wire Core
C - Compacted Strand
D - Flattened Strand

Illustration #83 - Strand Types

Fiber Core

A fiber core is composed of vegetable fiber (manila, sisal, or jute), or a synthetic fiber such as polypropylene. The synthetic fibers offer better resistance to deterioration.

During manufacture the fiber core is impregnated with lubricant, which is released during rope use and helps keep the wires lubricated. A fiber core also helps to cushion the strands during operation.

Wire Core

IWRC is the abbreviation for independent wire rope core. This core, which is actually another strand (and can be called a mini-rope with its own strands and core), has several advantages over the fiber core. It adds about 7½% in strength, and helps resist rope crushing. In an extremely hot working environment a wire core is a requirement as a fiber core might burn or char.

Wire Rope Construction

Wire rope is made up of pre-formed strands. This pre-forming gives the rope strands an equal load distribution, and it helps prevent unraveling when the rope is cut.

The number of strands, number of wires per strand, type or quality of the wire material, and nature of the core will depend on the end use of the wire rope.

A wire rope, with many smaller wires and strands, is more flexible than rope with large diameter wires and fewer strands. Wire rope that is used with sheaves and drums should have a sufficient number of strands to be flexible enough to bend around the sheaves and drums.

The main consideration in the design and construction of wire rope is to impede the conditions that contribute to corrosion, over-tension, wear, crushing, and rotation. The result is many types and sizes of wire rope, with new rope designs continually coming on the market.

Wire Rope Grades

Wire rope manufacturers have many different grades to meet the varying demands for strength and toughness.

Grade 120/130 and 130/140
Extra Extra Improved Plow (EEIPS)

This rope is used when special installations require maximum rope strength, such as mine shaft hoisting. (About 10% stronger than Extra Improved Plow).

Grade 115/125
Extra Improved Plow (EIPS)

This rope is used when the need for higher breaking strength is required. The bending quality of this rope is not as good as Improved Plow (about 15% stronger than Improved Plow).

Grade 110/120 Improved Plow (IPS)

This is the most commonly used wire rope. It has good wear resistance, a high fatigue factor and high tensile strength.

Grade 100/110 Plow

Has lower tensile strength but can be used when strength is secondary to wear resistance.

Grade 90/100 Mild Plow

This rope has high fatigue resistance but is lower in tensile strength. Applications for this rope are limited.

Note: Check the applicable local authority for wire rope standards pertaining to elevators for construction, repair, and/or rope replacement.

Wire Rope Lays

The term lay refers to the direction of winding of both the wires in the strands and to the actual rope strands. The term also applies to the actual design, of which there are two basic types. These are Regular Lay and Lang Lay, as indicated in illustrations #84 to #87. These in turn can be either right lay, left lay, or a combination. Right or left lay is determined by the rotation of the strands as they recede from the observer. Most wire rope is manufactured right lay.

Regular Lay

The wires in the strands are laid in one direction, while the strands in the rope are laid in the opposite direction. Therefore the wires are able to withstand considerable crushing and distortion due to the short length of exposed wires. See illustrations #84 and #85.

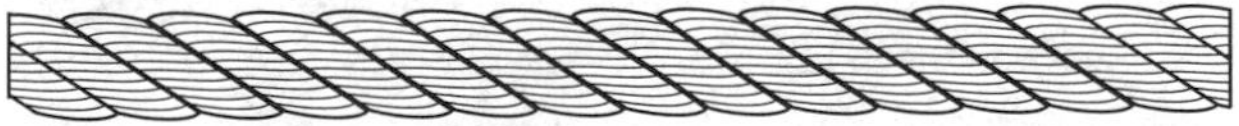

Illustration #84 - Right Regular Lay

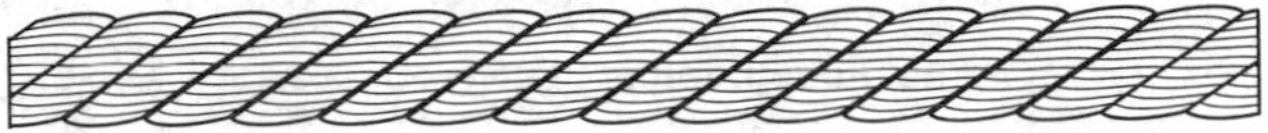

Illustration #85 - Left Regular Lay

Lang Lay

The wires in the strands, and the strands in the rope, are laid in the same direction. Lang Lay rope should not be used for single part hoisting due to its tendency to unwind or unravel. Its biggest advantage is its resistance to abrasion. See illustrations #86 and #87.

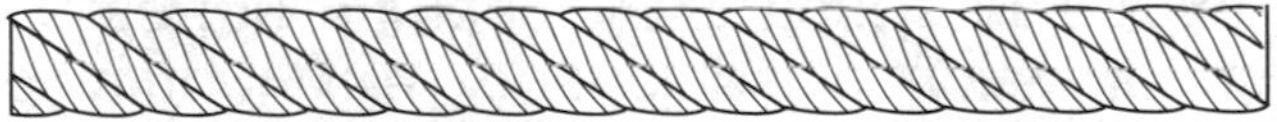

Illustration #86 - Right Lang Lay

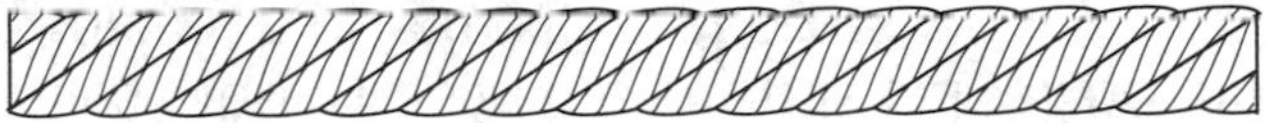

Illustration #87 - Left Lang Lay

Illustration #88 shows a right lay rope made of alternating strands of right regular lay and right lang lay.

Illustration #88 - Right Alternate Lay

Rotation-Resistant

There are several categories of this type of rope, but basically the outer layer and the inner layer of strands are laid in the opposite direction. The opposing torque from the right hand lay and the left hand lay helps to prevent rope rotation under load. See illustration #89.

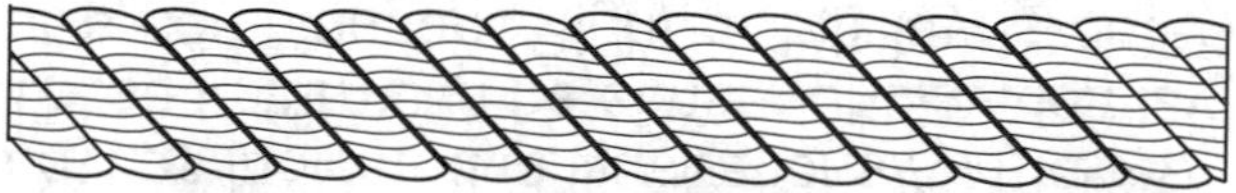

A - Outer Strands

B- Inner Strands

Illustration #89 - Rotation-Resistance

Strand Classification

Strands are grouped according to the number of wires per strand. The number of wires and the pattern defines the rope's characteristics. The wires in the strands can all be the same size or a mixture of sizes.

There are many different strand pattern design classifications. Table #9 shows four common wire rope classifications. In all cases the number of strands is given, followed by the number of wires in each strand.

Classification	No. of Strands	Wires Per Strand
6 x 7	6	3 to 14
6 x 19	6	16 to 26
6 x 37	6	27 to 49
8 x 19	8	16 to 26

Table #9 – Wire Rope Classification Examples

The wires per strand indicate that a rope may be chosen in one particular classification, 6 x 19, for example, but in that classification the individual strand could have from 16 to 26 wires, depending on the use.

Table #10 shows several wire rope classifications and their common uses.

Classification	Common Use
6 x 7	Regular lay — guy lines
6 x 19	Seale, regular lay — mines, including hoists
6 x 19	Filler wire, regular lay — misc. hoists, derricks, cranes, tackle blocks, mine hoists, elevators
6 x 37	Regular lay — hoists, traction elevators
8 x 19	Spin resistant — hoists having single line suspension

Table #10 — Common Wire Rope Uses

Strand Classification Examples

- 6 x 7 - This rope has large wires and is not very flexible but has good abrasion resistant qualities. It should be used on large diameter sheaves and/or drums. It is used for permanent guy-lines, ski tows and tramways.
- 6 x 19 - This rope has the most diverse use. The wide range of wire arrangements give it excellent combinations for both flexibility and abrasive wear. There can be from 8 to 12 outer wires in each strand, and up to 26 total wires in each strand. The more wires in a strand, the more flexible the wire rope.
- 6 x 37 - This rope will have 31 to 49 wires per strand. It is the most flexible, and therefore is commonly used on high-speed cranes, multiple reeving hoists, and also power shovels and draglines. It is not commonly used where multiple drum layers are required because of the tendency for wire crushing.

- 8 x 19 - This rope is more flexible than the 6 strand rope, but has poor abrasion resistance, and it crushes and distorts easily. It is used on high-speed cranes with multiple reeving.
- 8 x 19 is available in spin-resistant designs for applications such as tower cranes where reverse bends and small sheaves exclude the use of non-rotating rope and usually require a higher design (safety) factor.

Rotation Resistant Wire Rope

There are a wide variety of designs available for this type of rope, and each has its benefits and drawbacks.

Several of the general classifications are: 3 strand - torque balanced, 8 strand - spin resistant, 19 strand - rotation resistant, 35 strand - non-rotating. For each classification, there are a number of strand combinations.

The principle is that rope rotation is lessened, or prevented, as the inner and outer strand layers are laid in opposite directions (left lay - right lay). See illustration #90.

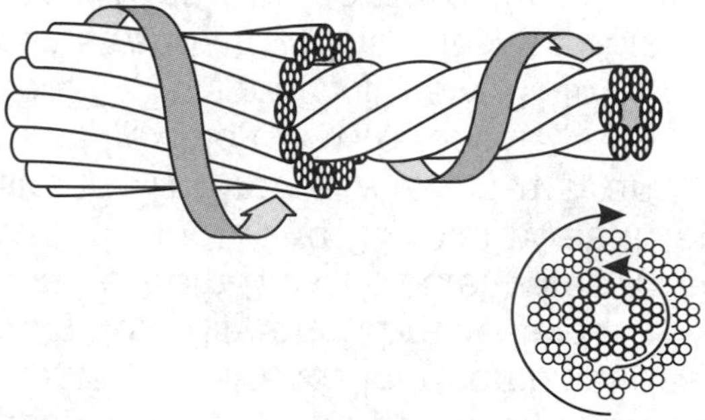

Illustration #90 - Rotation-Resistant Characteristics

The advantages of rotation resistant rope may be offset by some common disadvantages:

- More frequent inspection due to a tendency of inner wire breakage.
- Probably a lower listed strength.

- Strength affected by rotation. Rotation under load can cause rope core slippage where one layer of strands tighten (become shorter) while the other loosens (gets longer). Therefore one strand layer carries more load. See illustration #91.

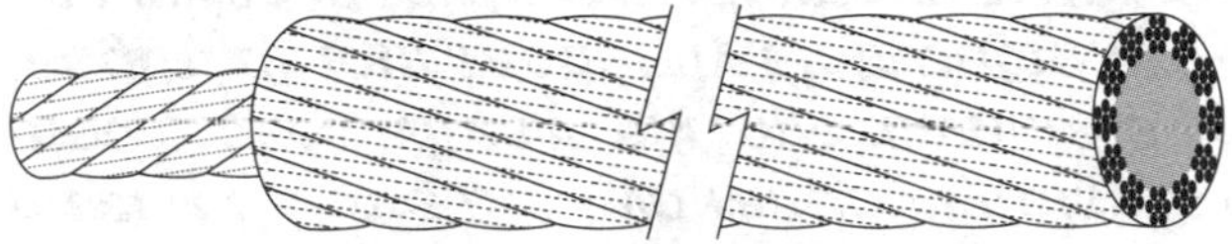

Illustration #91 - Rotation-Resistant Core Slippage

- A higher design (safety) factor needed.
- More crushing from multi-layer drum spooling.
- Check with the rope manufacturer concerning brazing or tightly seizing ends to prevent strand or core disturbance.
- Wedge sockets can cause rope core slippage due to their short bend radius.

The following precautions are also needed:

- Avoid disturbing the lay length.
- Avoid inducing twist into rope during handling and installation. Rope twist can be caused by improper fleet angle, sheave misalignment, poor spooling or improper reeving.
- Avoid high loads with small diameter sheaves.
- Maintain a tight rope on the drum by keeping tension on payoff reel when spooling.
- Break in a new rope by running it through several cycles with a light load.

Design (Safety) Factor

Note: For cranes equipped with rotation resistant wire rope, ANSI and most other safety standards and regulations require a minimum design (safety) factor of 5:1. This doubles to 10:1 when hoisting personnel. By comparison, when using IPS or EIPS (extra improved plow), the factor is 3.5:1, and 7:1 for hoisting personnel.

Some jurisdictions or companies may have a higher design factor requirement.

Many types of rotation resistant rope are rated at approximately 85% tensile strength of an equivalent size 6 x 19 improved plow rope. To be sure, check the rope being used with the manufacturers data.

The combination of a higher design factor and a lower tensile strength, reduces the working load limit (SWL).

Note: Rotation resistant rope must be replaced if there are two randomly distributed broken wires in six rope diameters of length; or four randomly distributed broken wires in thirty rope diameters; or one outer wire broken at the interior contact point with the core and is protruding from the rope.

Plastic-Enhanced Wire Rope

Wire rope deterioration from broken wires has been reduced considerably in recent years by placing a layer of plastic between the outer and inner layers of strands. This eliminates or reduces the metal to metal contact produced from the rope being repeatedly bent around sheaves. Earlier types of plastic deteriorated quite quickly. However, research into new types of plastic has resulted in some rope manufacturers using a plastic that could double the number of rope usage cycles.

This enhanced plastic protects the inner strand wires while supporting and protecting the outer strand wires. See illustration #92.

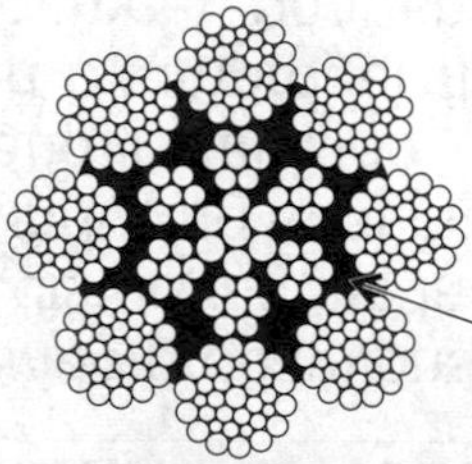
Plastic Fill

Illustration #92 - Plastic-Enhanced Wire Rope Cross Section

Drum Crushing Resistant Wire Rope

Continuous winding of wire rope on and off a drum results in excessive rope wear due to crushing from multiple layers, cross winding, and improper tensioning.

Some wire rope manufacturers have new ropes using individual specifically shaped wires and triangular shaped strands. They are designed to considerably reduce rope wear from drums and sheaves. See illustration #93.

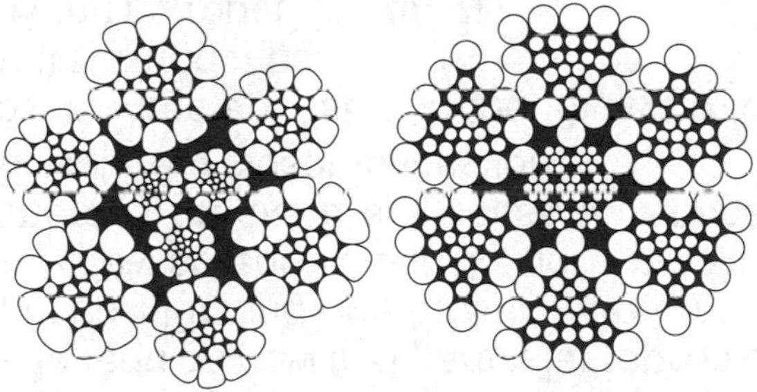

Illustration #93 - Drum Crushing Resistant Wire Rope Cross Sections

Wire Rope Sizing

A wire rope is measured across the diameter at its widest point. This is called measuring across the "crowns". Do not measure across the "flats". It is advisable to make three such measurements on a 6 strand rope and four on an 8 strand rope. The correct and incorrect methods are indicated in illustration #94.

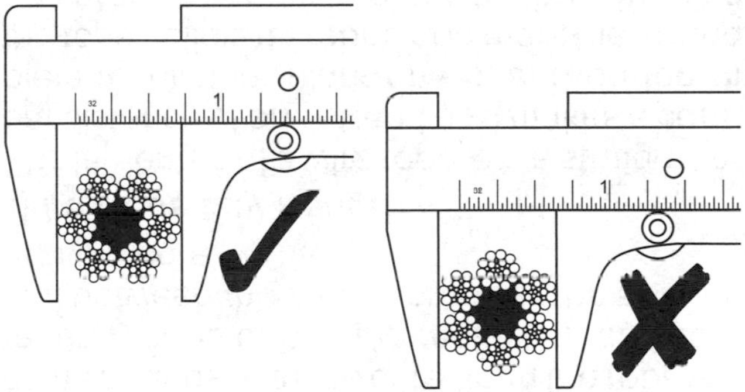

Illustration #94 - Wire Rope Diameter Measuring

Broken Wires - The required removal of a rope from service because of broken wires will depend on how that particular rope is being used. Finding one broken wire (or several widely spread) is usually not a problem. Numerous breaks are a cause for concern and require a closer inspection.

Broken wires are listed in the following four general categories:

- Running ropes (exterior)
- Standing ropes (pendants, guylines).
- Standing ropes (near fittings)
- Running ropes (valley breaks). Any sign of breakage in the valley indicates an abnormal problem and the rope must be replaced.

3/6 Rule: A commonly followed practice for rope replacement is the 3/6 rule, which is: three broken wires in one strand, or six broken wires randomly distributed among all strands, all within one lay length.

The problem with this rule is that a rope, subjected to repeated bending cycles, could have far more broken wires in the interior part of the strands or in the core, than the rope exterior. This is due to the metal to metal contact between the inner portion of the strands and the core.

Wire Rope Lay Length

The lay length of a wire rope is the straight linear distance of one strand as it makes a complete revolution. Mark one strand on top of the rope, follow it around and mark the strand again as it comes around to the top. The straight point to point distance is the lay length. See illustration #95. Determining lay length is one method used to check a rope for stretching.

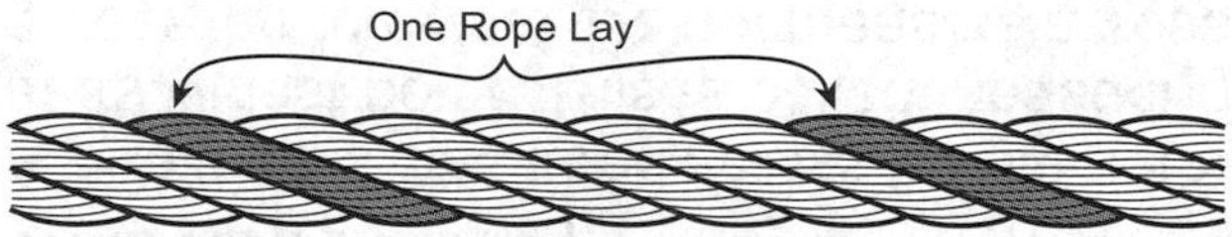
One Rope Lay

Illustration #95 - One Lay Length

Lay length is also used when the bending arc of a wire rope around an object is measured in a certain number of lay lengths.

Abrasion **–** Wire rope winding over drums or through sheaves will wear. The rope must be replaced if the wear reduces the diameter to specified limits. Watch for localized wear, shown in illustration #96.

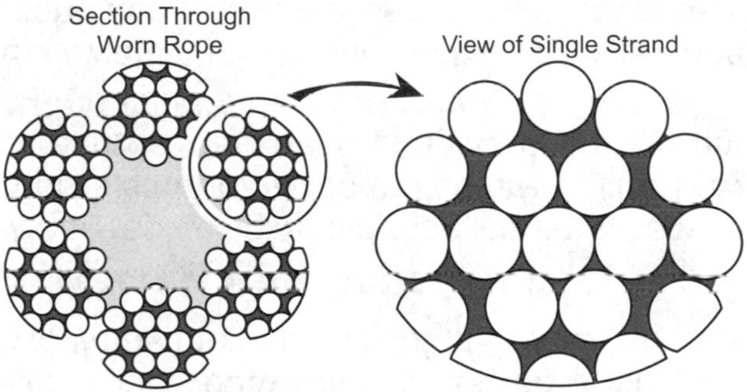
Section Through
Worn Rope
View of Single Strand

Illustration #96 - Wire Rope Localized Wear

Note: Replace rope if wire diameter wear is 1/3 or more.

Wire Rope Seizing

Seizing is a method of binding the end of a wire rope to prevent the wires and strands from unraveling. See illustration #97.

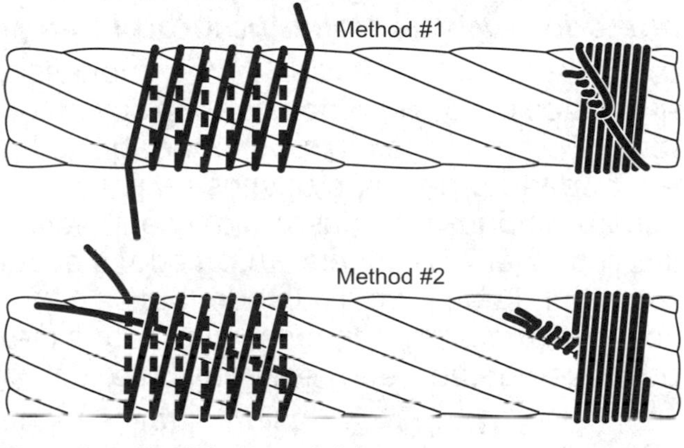
Method #1
Method #2

Illustration #97 - Wire Rope Seizing

Number of Seizings

The number of seizings to be applied equals approximately three times the diameter of the rope in inches to the next whole number.

Seizing Size/Spacing

The length of each seizing should be between 1 and 1½ times the rope diameter.

The space between the seizing should be two times the diameter of the rope.

Replacing Wire Rope

When replacing an old rope, contact the wire rope distributor or manufacturer. The new wire rope can be damaged if the proper method and procedure is not followed.

Be aware that recent studies by wire rope manufacturers have shown that several of the previously accepted replacement methods may result in the old rope faults, such as rope twisting and jumped sheaves, being transferred to the new rope. New methods of joining the old and new rope for replacement purposes are being developed to eliminate this problem.

Wire Rope Unreeling

Unreeling and Uncoiling

The best way to lift a reel of wire rope is to place an approved lifting device through the center hole of the reel and connect it to slings and a suitable hoist.

When removing wire rope from the shipping reel or coil, it is essential that the reel or coil rotate as the rope unwinds. Attempting to remove a rope from a stationary reel or coil will almost inevitably result in a tangled mess. This easily results in a kinked rope, and the rope will be ruined beyond repair at that point. The correct methods are indicated in illustration #98.

Note : For information on wire rope and drum spooling see following pages.

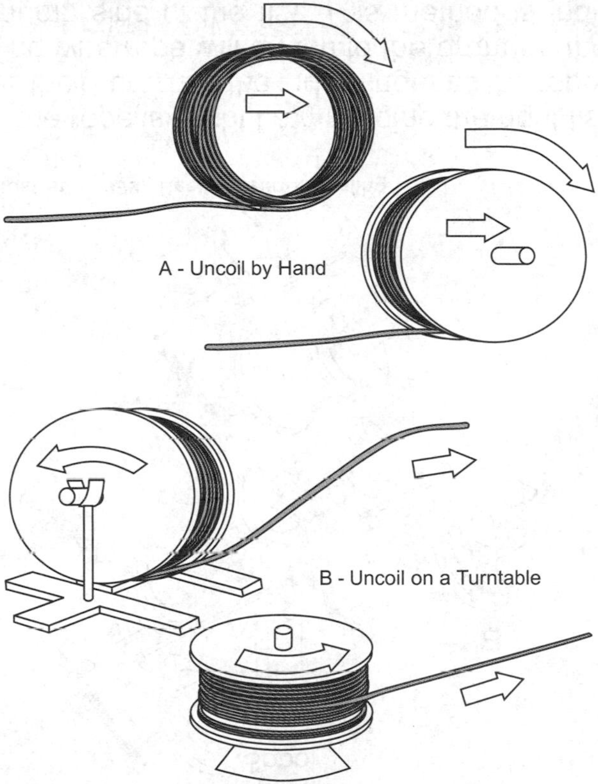
A - Uncoil by Hand
B - Uncoil on a Turntable
Illustration #98 - Uncoiling Wire Rope

Wire Rope Drums

When winding wire rope from a storage reel onto another reel or drum, the rope must be reeled correctly to avoid fighting the rope's natural looping and also prevent future winding problems.

The rope must wind from the top of one reel or drum to the top of the other; or, from the bottom of one reel or drum to the bottom of the other, as indicated in illustration #99.

Note: Do not cross wind the wire rope from top to bottom, see illustration #99C.

Winding Wire Rope on a Drum

To properly install a rope on a drum or winch stand behind the drum and face it. The right hand represents Right Lay Rope and the left hand represents Left Lay Rope. Make a fist and extend the index finger.

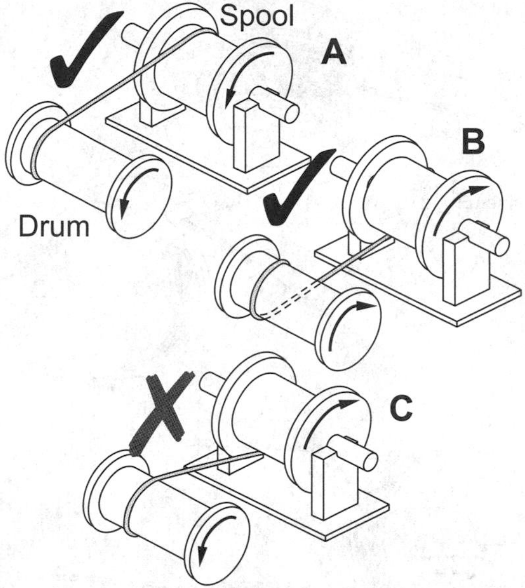
Spool
A
Drum
B
C

Illustration #99 - Reel to Drum Spooling

If the rope is Right Lay, imagine the right fist as the drum, and the index finger as the rope. The wire rope will attach to the drum on the thumb side of the fist. This method is indicated in illustration #100.

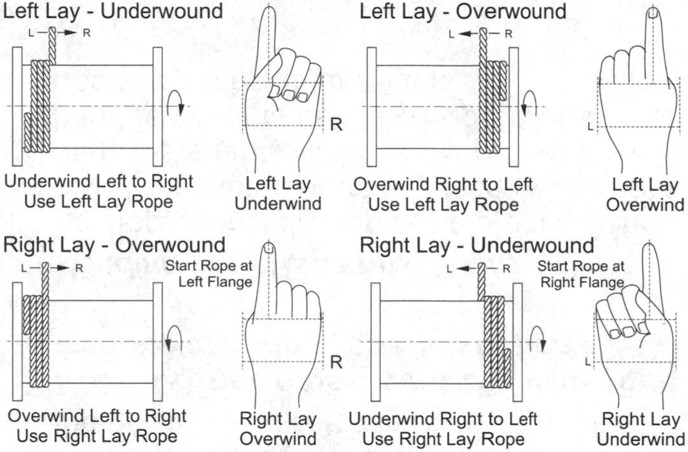
Left Lay - Underwound
L R
Underwind Left to Right
Use Left Lay Rope
R
Left Lay
Underwind
Left Lay - Overwound
L R
Overwind Right to Left
Use Left Lay Rope
L
Left Lay
Overwind
Right Lay - Overwound
L R
Start Rope at
Left Flange
Overwind Left to Right
Use Right Lay Rope
R
Right Lay
Overwind
Right Lay - Underwound
L R
Start Rope at
Right Flange
Underwind Right to Left
Use Right Lay Rope
L
Right Lay
Underwind

Illustration #100 - Winding Wire Rope on a Drum

Drum Grooves and Wire Rope Lay

In a multi-layer winding, rope lay direction usually does not affect the rope performance. However in a single layer application the general rule is for the drum grooves to be opposite that of the rope lay. That would be left hand drum grooving for a right lay rope. Rope winding is adversely affected with a wide fleet angle.

Fleet Angle and Sheave Alignment

The fleet angle is the off-center angle from the outside wire rope wrap on a drum to the working sheave. As indicated in illustration #101, one line is drawn from the center of the drum to the sheave, and the other line extends from the sheave to the outside wrap on the drum nearest the flange of the drum.

- On a grooved drum the fleet angle should not exceed 2° (30:1 ratio).
- On a smooth drum the fleet angle should not exceed 1½° (40:1 ratio).
- The ratio is based on half the drum width and the distance from the drum out to the sheave.

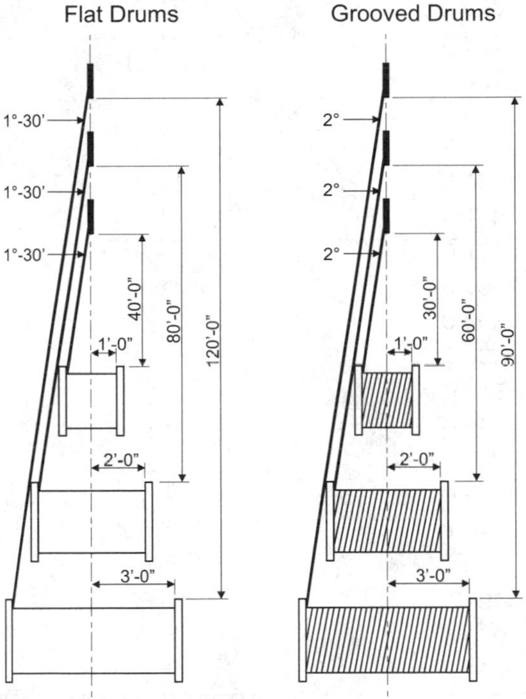
Flat Drums
Grooved Drums
1°-30'
1°-30'
1°-30'
2°
2°
2°
40'-0"
80'-0"
120'-0"
30'-0"
60'-0"
90'-0"
1'-0"
2'-0"
3'-0"
1'-0"
2'-0"
3'-0"

Illustration #101 - Fleet Angles

Wire Rope Drum Capacities

Illustration #102 and table #11 are used to calculate the approximate wire rope capacity of a drum or reel.

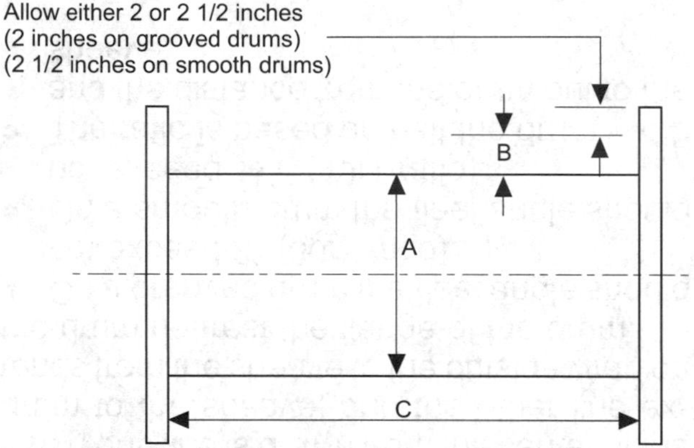
Allow either 2 or 2 1/2 inches
(2 inches on grooved drums)
(2 1/2 inches on smooth drums)
B
A
C

Illustration #102 - Drum Reference Capacities

Nominal Rope Diameter (inches)	Factor
1/4	4.160
5/16	2.670
3/8	1.860
7/16	1.370
1/2	1.050
9/16	0.828
5/8	0.672
3/4	0.465
7/8	0.342
1	0.262
1 1/8	0.207
1 1/4	0.167
1 3/8	0.138
1 1/2	0.116
1 5/8	0.099
1 3/4	0.085
1 7/8	0.074
2	0.066
2 1/8	0.058
2 1/4	0.052
2 3/8	0.046

Table #11 – Drum and Reel Factors

Formula to find the drum capacity (feet of rope) = (A + B) x B x C x F

Add the diameter of the drum (A) to the depth of the flange (B). Multiply this sum by the depth of the flange (B). Multiply the result by the distance between the drum flanges (C). Multiply this result by the factor of (F) listed in table #11 opposite the diameter of rope to be used.

Drum Capacity Example:

The diameter of the drum is 16 inches
The depth of the flange is 2 inches
The distance between flanges is 24 inches
The drum capacity for one inch is:
(A + B) x B x C x F =
(16 + 2) x 2 x 24 x .262 = 226 feet

(The dimensions are given in inches and the answer is in feet.)

Basic Drum Data

There are a number of different types of wire rope drums, ranging from crane and dragline hoists to a variety of different industrial tuggers

Check manufacturers' specifications where possible, although in general, at least two full wraps must remain on a drum in all service conditions. Check this number with the local ANSI/OSHA/OH&S regulations as the number of wraps required can be three, or up to five in some areas.

Observe the following conditions:

- The drum end of the rope should be anchored to the drum with a clamp supplied by the manufacturer.
- The flange on a grooved drum should project 2 rope diameters or 2 inches (whichever is larger) beyond the last layer of rope.

- The flange on a flat drum should project 2 rope diameters or 2½ inches (whichever is larger) beyond the last layer of rope.
- Whenever possible, not more than three layers of rope should be on the drum at one time. This will help prevent rope crushing.
- The maximum pull of the hoist occurs on the first layer, and decreases with every following wrap of the wire rope.

Drum Hoists (Tuggers)

Base mounted drum hoists (referred to as tuggers) are regulated by ANSI B30.7. This type of hoist can be powered by several methods including; gas or diesel engines, electric motors, compressed air, or hydraulics.

Smaller tuggers are used for hoisting or lowering loads, or pulling smaller loads laterally across a floor.

Electric or air powered units are often used on construction sites for hoisting small components up through the building steel (see illustration #103).

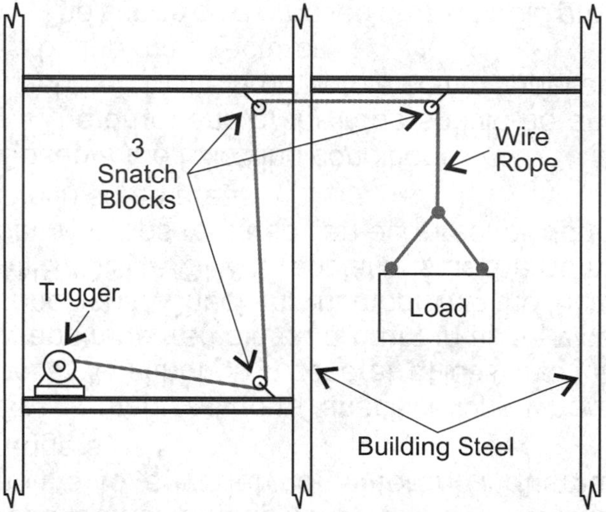
3
Snatch
Blocks
Wire
Rope
Tugger
Load
Building Steel

Illustration #103 - Lifting Construction Loads

A typical air tugger is shown in illustration #104.

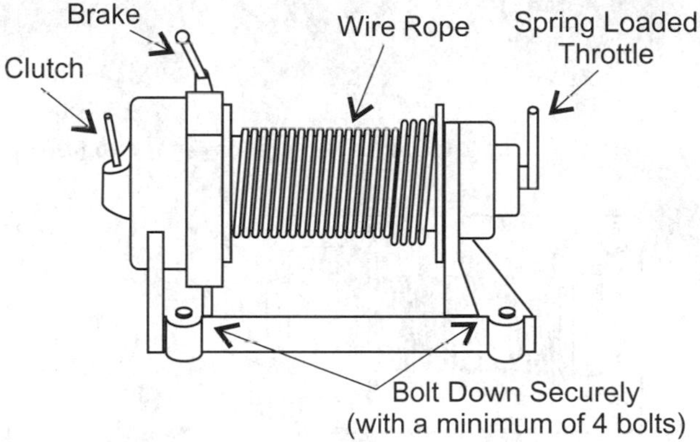
Brake
Wire Rope
Spring Loaded Throttle
Clutch
Bolt Down Securely
(with a minimum of 4 bolts)

Illustration #104 - Typical Air Tugger

- All hoists must have an identification plate with the following information: load rating; drum size (barrel diameter, barrel length, flange diameter); rope size; rope speed; and rated power supply.
- If air powered, the air hose should be blown out to remove excess moisture before attaching to the hoist.
- The wire rope must be attached to the drum by a method approved by the manufacturer. See illustration #105A for an example.
- The base must be bolted down securely
- To maintain proper positioning of the wraps on the drum, the wire rope should be spooled out to a lead sheave aligned with the drum center to maintain the proper fleet angle (illustration #105B).
- A drum with loads suspended for extended periods must have a ratchet and pawl holding method in addition to the brake.
- Never leave a suspended load unattended.
- The operator or someone giving signals must have a clear view of the load at all times.
- The wire rope and other rigging hardware must meet the normal 5:1 WLL (safe working load).

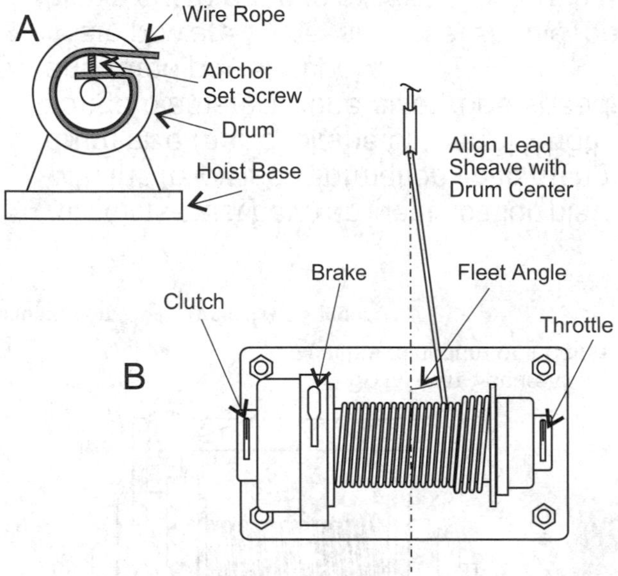
A
Wire Rope
Anchor
Set Screw
Drum
Hoist Base
Align Lead
Sheave with
Drum Center
Brake
Fleet Angle
Clutch
Throttle
B

Illustration #105 -Tugger Connections

- Keep hands and clothing clear of the rope and drum when spooling on.
- Throttle controls are usually spring loaded to return to neutral. Some types of newer model hoists can often be operated by remote control.
- To lock the drum and prevent rotation, the manual brake control lever is pushed down.
- The clutch control lever is pulled up to disengage. This allows the drum to freewheel when unwinding the wire rope by hand.
- All hoist components, including base, motor and controls, drum, and wire rope must be inspected regularly for any signs of wear.

Wire Rope Ultimate Load (Breaking Strength) Formulas

One of the most important requirements to consider when selecting a wire rope is the ultimate load (breaking strength). See table #12. If a chart is not available, a "rule of thumb" formula can be used to give a close approximation.

Ultimate Load
Rule of Thumb Formula

Diameter squared multiplied by the ultimate load (BS) of a one-inch diameter rope.

D^2 x Ultimate Load (BS) of 1 inch wire rope

D^2 x 42 (fiber core - improved plow)

6 x 19 x 1 inch fiber core rope has an ultimate load (breaking strength) of 42 tons.
(chart reading = 41.7 tons - IPS).

D^2 x 45 (wire core - improved plow)

6 x 19 x 1 inch independent wire core rope (IWRC) has an ultimate load (breaking strength) of 45 tons. (chart rating 44.8 tons IPS).

Ultimate Load Examples

1. Fiber Rope Core
   $1/2$ inch fiber rope core
   D^2 x 42 = Ultimate Load
   $1/2 \times 1/2 \times 42 = 42/4 = 10.5$
   Ultimate Load = 10.5 tons
   (chart value = 10.7 tons IPS)

2. Independent Wire Rope Core
   $1/2$ inch independent wire rope core
   D^2 x 45 = Ultimate Load
   $1/2 \times 1/2 \times 45 = 45/4 = 11.25$ tons
   Ultimate Load = 11.25 tons
   (chart value = 11.5 tons IPS)

All ultimate load formulas are based on a diameter of one inch and in a tonnage ratio.

Note: Remember rule of thumb formulas can only give a close approximation, not the exact value and only apply to new or undamaged rope.

Nominal Strengths Of Wire Rope 6 x 19 Classification, IWRC							
Nominal Diameter		Approximate Mass		Nominal Strength			
				Improved Plow		Extra Imp. Plow	
inches	mm	lb/ft	kg/m	tons	Metric tonnes	tons	Metric tonnes
1/4	6.4	0.12	0.17	2.94	2.67	3.40	3.08
5/16	8.0	0.18	0.27	4.58	4.16	5.27	4.78
3/8	9.5	0.26	0.39	6.56	5.95	7.55	6.85
7/16	11.5	0.35	0.52	8.89	8.07	10.2	9.25
1/2	13.0	0.46	0.68	11.5	10.4	13.3	12.1
9/16	14.5	0.59	0.88	14.5	13.2	16.8	15.2
5/8	16	0.72	1.07	17.7	16.2	20.6	18.7
3/4	19	1.04	1.55	25.6	23.2	29.4	26.7
7/8	22	1.42	2.11	34.6	31.4	39.8	36.1
1	26	1.85	2.75	44.9	40.7	51.7	46.9
1 1/8	29	2.34	3.48	56.5	51.3	65.0	59.0
1 1/4	32	2.89	4.30	69.4	63.0	79.9	72.5
1 3/8	35	3.50	5.21	83.5	75.7	96.0	871
1 1/2	38	4.16	6.19	98.9	89.7	114	103
1 5/8	42	4.88	7.26	115	104	132	120
1 3/4	45	5.67	8.44	133	121	153	139
1 7/8	48	6.50	9.67	152	138	174	158
2	52	7.39	11.0	172	156	198	180
2 1/8	54	8.35	12.4	192	174	221	200
2 1/4	57	9.36	13.9	215	195	247	224
2 3/8	60	10.4	15.5	239	217	274	249

Table #12 — Wire Rope Nominal Strengths

Working Load Limit (WLL) or Safe Working Load (SWL)

Most hoisting jobs use a Working Load Limit (Safe Working Load) based on a 5:1 design (safety) factor of the wire rope breaking strength. The 5:1 factor also applies to most rigging hardware when calculating the load weight and equipment required for a hoisting job. This factor should go higher if there is a possibility of injury or death due to breakage. For example elevators, which are usually based on a 20:1 factor. Critical lifts with a danger to personnel should be calculated on a 10:1 factor. If using an ultimate load (breaking strength) chart calculate the WLL (SWL) as follows:

$$WLL\,(SWL) = \frac{Ultimate\,(Breaking)\,Strength}{Design\,(Safety)\,Factor}$$

For example, a one inch IPS core wire rope has an ultimate load of 45 tons

The design (safety) factor is 5:1.

45 tons ÷ 5 = 9 tons WLL (SWL)

Note: See table #13 for an example of a safe working load chart.

Note: Mobile Crane Design (Safety) Factors: The various wire ropes on mobile cranes generally have different factors applied to them than the usual 5:1 (or higher) factor applied to the slings and hardware on the actual load. These crane factors are specified as a minimum by ANSI, OSHA, and CSA. Cranes operating under various jurisdictions or requirements may have to be equipped with higher factor wire rope.

Maximum WLL (SWL) in tons Design Safety Factor = 5				
Rope Diameter (inches)	Grade 100/110 Plow		Grade 110/120 Improved Plow	
	Fibre Core	Steel Core	Fibre Core	Steel Core
3/16	0.26	0.28	0.30	0.32
1/4	0.48	0.52	0.54	0.58
5/16	0.76	0.82	0.82	0.88
3/8	1.08	1.16	1.20	1.28
7/16	1.40	1.50	1.60	1.72
1/2	2.00	2.14	2.20	2.36
9/16	2.34	2.50	2.66	2.86
5/8	3.00	3.22	3.30	3.54
3/4	4.30	4.62	4.76	5.10
7/8	5.66	6.08	6.40	6.89
1	7.60	8.17	8.34	8.96
1 1/8	9.70	10.42	10.60	11.38
1 1/4	12.00	12.90	13.10	14.10
1 3/8	14.70	15.80	16.20	17.40
1 1/2	17.70	19.00	19.20	20.64
1 5/8	20.60	22.14	22.60	24.28
1 3/4	23.80	25.58	26.00	27.94
1 7/8	27.60	29.66	30.40	32.68
2	30.80	33.10	33.80	36.32

Table #13 – Wire Rope Working Load Limits (SWL)

WLL Rule of Thumb

A rule of thumb formula can be used to find the approximate WLL (SWL) for IWRC rope.

The general rule of thumb formula is:

$D^2 \times 45 \div 5$ = load in tons

This load is based on a Design (Safety) Factor of 5

Example 1:

$^1/_2$ inch wire rope

$^1/_2 \times {}^1/_2 \times 45 \div 5$

$= {}^9/_4 = 2\,^1/_4$ tons WLL (SWL)

Example 2:

$^3/_4$ inch wire rope

$^3/_4 \times {}^3/_4 \times 45 \div 5$

$= {}^9/_{16} \times 9 = {}^{81}/_{16} = 5.1$ tons WLL (SWL)

Note: These formulas cannot be used with metric measurements.

Wire Rope Efficiency

A wire rope that bends around a sheave has less strength compared to a straight pull rope. The larger the bending diameter, the more strength or efficiency the rope will have. The efficiency for most 6 x 19 and 6 x 37 rope is shown in table #14. The same condition applies to a wire rope sling bent around the hook of a crane block, a shackle, or a pipe.

Divide the sheave, hook, or pipe diameter by the rope diameter to find a ratio (D/d). Then find the closest ratio in table #14. If the ratio that is worked out doesn't match the table, use the next smaller table ratio number.

Example:

8 inch snatch block

$^7/_8$ inch wire rope

Ratio = 8 inch ÷ $^7/_8$ = 9.14

The ratio is 9.14.

The closest table #6 ratio is 8, and the wire rope strength, or efficiency, is 83%.

Wire Rope Bending Efficiency	
D/d ratio sheave/rope diameter	**% of Strength Efficiency Compared to Catalogue Strength**
40	95
30	93
20	91
15	89
10	86
8	83
6	79
4	75
5	65
1	50

Table #14 - Rope Bending Efficiency

From table #12, a $^7/_8$ inch improved plow rope is rated at 34.6 tons. With an efficiency of 83%, the rating is lowered to 28.7 tons.

A ratio of 1, which means a wire rope bent around an equal size diameter (such as a 1 inch sling and a 1 inch shackle pin) reduces the rope efficiency to 50%.

In comparison, a ratio of 40 (a 1 inch rope around a 40 inch sheave), has an efficiency of 95%. Wire rope manufacturers indicate that any bend will cause a strength reduction. Therefore with anything other than a straight pull, the maximum rope strength will never be rated at 100%.

Note: The working load limit (SWL) of wire rope is shown in table #13. The ultimate load (breaking strength) of IWRC rope is shown in table #12.

Sling Identification Tags

In 2001 it became a requirement that all slings, including wire rope, synthetics, metal mesh, or chain, manufactured under ANSI/ASME guidelines, must have an identification tag. This tag must include the following:

- Name or trademark of the manufacturer
- Diameter or size of the sling
- Type of material used
- Rated load for a given type of hitch
- Lift angle upon which the load rating is based

Note: Sling characteristics are regulated by ANSI B30.9 and CSA.

Note: In the USA, users of alloy chain, wire rope, metal mesh, and ALL types of synthetic slings should refer to ANSI B30.9 for training parameters. These include sling selection, inspection, cautions to personnel, effects of environment, and rigging practices, effective in 2003.

Note: When referring to slings, the "Rated Load" is the maximum allowable working load established by the sling manufacturer. The terms "Rated Capacity" and "Working Load Limit" are commonly used to describe Rated Load in place of the older terminology of "Safe Working Load".

Sling Design (Safety) Factor

As a result of the excessive abuse of slings due to overloading, abrasion, crushing, kinking, and impact loading, a design (safety) factor must be applied to every lift. A common factor is 5:1, although this can vary depending upon the application.

Some specific engineered lifts may have a design (safety) factor lower than 5:1, however most factors that are not 5:1 will be higher. Design (safety) factors that are 6:1, 8:1, 10:1 or higher are not uncommon.

Rule of Thumb WLL (SWL)

The rule of thumb formula to find the working load limit (safe working load) for a wire rope sling is:

$D^2 \times 45 \div 5 =$ WLL (SWL) in tons)

Example: $^1/_2$ inch IWRC sling

$^1/_2 \times {}^1/_2 \times 45 \div 5 = 2.25$ tons WLL (SWL)

This is based on a 5:1 design (safety) factor, however be aware that many sling chart numbers are based on a 6:1 factor, and wire rope sling charts should be based on 95% of the actual rope ultimate strength.

Types of Sling Hitches

Single Vertical Hitch

The total weight of the load is supported by a single sling leg, therefore the load weight can equal the working load limit (safe working load) of the sling, as shown in illustration #106. The load might need a tag line for control.

Illustration #106 - Single Vertical Hitch

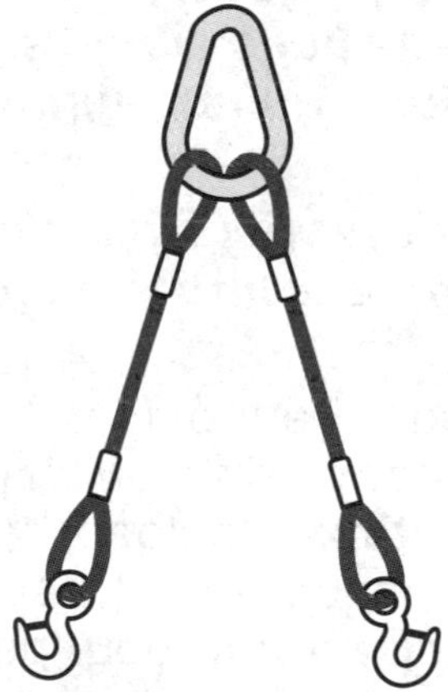

Illustration #107 - 2-Leg Bridle Hitch

Bridle Hitch

A bridle hitch can be made up of a number of legs, usually 2, 3 or 4. See illustration #107 for a two leg bridle.

A bridle hook-up with 2 legs can be straightforward. However a non-symmetrical load, as shown in illustration #108, requires the hook to be positioned over the center of gravity. Some type of adjustment method is needed to increase or decrease one leg length to keep the load level.

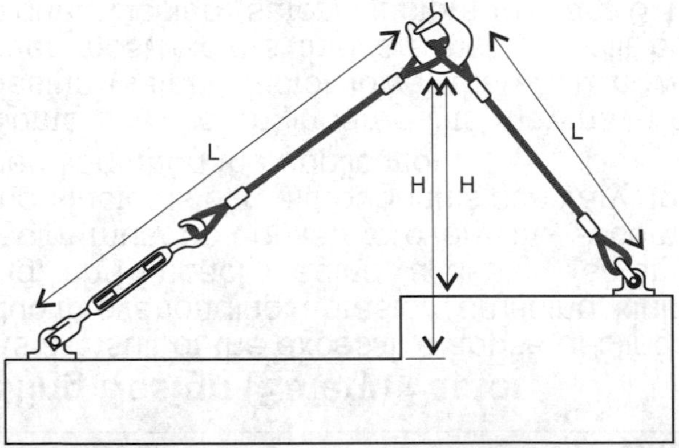
L
L
H
H

Illustration #108 - Non-Symmetrical Bridle Hitch

On lighter loads a turnbuckle, come-a-long, or chain fall can be used, however the last two are not recommended as a number of factors including shock loading, extreme sling lifting angles, or unknown weights could overload the hardware. Getting the proper adjustment is usually not easy.

Note: Some companies require a full length back up sling for a sling leg with an adjuster.

Note: When using a multi-branch sling, the rating shown for the single sling shall not be exceeded for any branch of the multiple branch sling bridle hitch.

A bridle with 3 legs will result in uneven sling leg loading if not properly hooked. See illustration #109. If the pickup points are not evenly spaced and the sling legs are not the same length, the load distribution will have the majority of the load on two legs while the third leg will only act as a balance.

A bridle with four sling legs, as shown in illustration #110, is usually not as simple as it appears. Several factors, including load regidity, can often apply to make equal leg loading difficult or impossible. It is not unusual to have three legs (or possibly only two) carrying the weight, while the third (or third and fourth) balance the load.

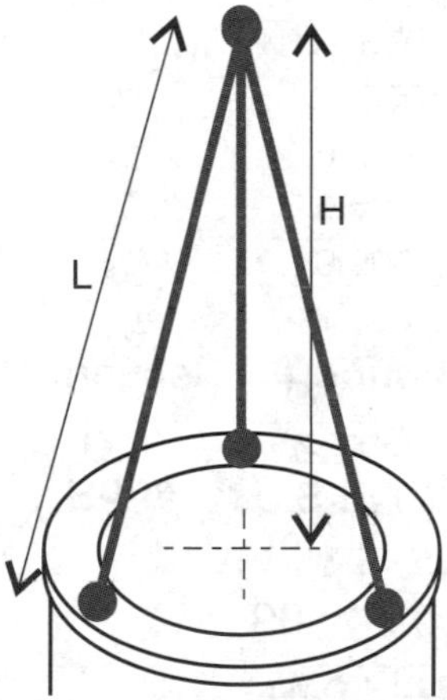
L
H

Illustration #109 - 3-Leg Bridle Hitch

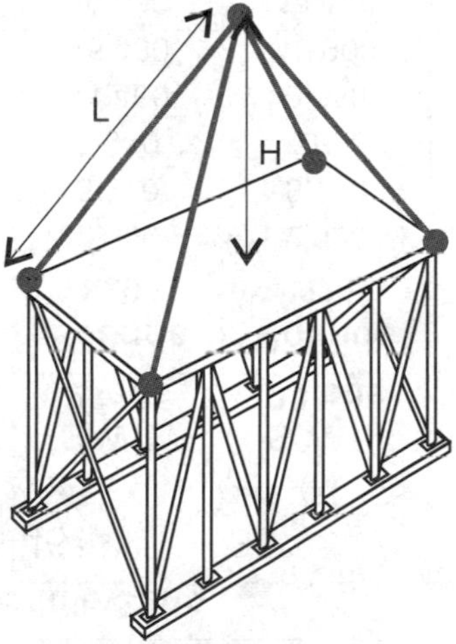
L
H

Illustration #110 - 4-Leg Bridle Hitch

Sling manufacturers may rate a four leg bridle the same as a three leg, or a two leg.

Factors such as different sling leg lengths, stretched sling legs, position of lifting lugs, position of sling eyes in the lifting hook, and a twisted, warped or uneven structure, can change the loading of sling legs.

See tables #15, #16, #17 for bridle sling example capacities based on improved plow wire rope.

Note: If using a four leg bridle, OSHA/OH&S standards require the load to be calculated using three legs.

Note: Multiple loads (e.g. structural steel components) are not permitted during one lift without using an approved hoisting assembly. (Check with the local OSHA/OH&S office).

Note: Angles shown in tables #15, #16, #17 are horizontal angles.

Note: Sling WLL (SWL) in tables #15, #16, #17 is based on 6 to 1 design (safety) factor.

Two Part Bridle Sling			
Rope Dia.	60° S.W.L. 2 Legs	45° S.W.L. 2 legs	30° S.W.L. 2 Legs
Inches	Pounds	Pounds	Pounds
1/4	1,600	1,300	920
3/8	3,500	2,860	2,020
1/2	6,490	5,270	3,740
5/8	9,740	7,910	5,600
3/4	14,020	11,460	8,080
7/8	18,920	15,480	10,900
1	24,600	20,060	14,180
1 1/8	28,900	23,500	16,660
1 1/4	36,000	29,260	20,740
1 3/8	43,880	35,840	25,340
1 1/2	53,040	43,300	30,620
1 5/8	62,180	50,760	35,900
1 3/4	71,280	58,200	41,170
1 7/8	83,680	68,320	48,320
2	91,380	74,600	52,760

Table #15 – Two Part Bridle Sling Working Load Limits

Three Part Bridle Sling			
Rope Dia.	60° S.W.L. 3 Legs	45° S.W.L. 3 Legs	30° S.W.L. 3 Legs
Inches	Pounds	Pounds	Pounds
1/4	2,400	1,950	1,380
3/8	5,250	4,290	3,000
1/2	9,730	7,900	5,600
5/8	14,610	11,860	8,400
3/4	21,030	17,190	12,100
7/8	28,380	23,220	16,300
1	36,900	30,100	21,300
1 1/8	43,350	35,250	25,000
1 1/4	54,000	43,900	31,100
1 3/8	65,820	53,700	38,000
1 1/2	79,560	64,900	45,900
1 3/4	106,920	87,300	61,700

Table #16 – Three Part Bridle Sling Working Load Limits

Four Part Bridle Sling			
Rope Dia.	60° S.W.L. 4 Legs	45° S.W.L. 4 Legs	30° S.W.L. 4 Legs
Inches	Pounds	Pounds	Pounds
1/4	3,200	2,600	1,850
3/8	7,000	5,700	4,000
1/2	13,000	10,500	7,500
5/8	19,500	15,800	11,200
3/4	28,000	22,900	17,000
7/8	37,800	31,000	21,800
1	49,200	40,100	28,300
1 1/8	57,800	47,000	33,300
1 1/4	72,000	58,500	41,500
1 1/8	87,700	71,700	50,600

Table #17 – Four Part Bridle Sling Working Load Limits

Basket Hitch

A basket hitch for supporting a load is shown in illustration #111A. The D/d ratio is the load diameter divided by the sling (wire rope) diameter. To have the full basket hitch sling load rating, the D/d ratio must be 25 :1 for improved plow and extra improved plow wire ropes, or 20:1 for extra-extra improved plow.

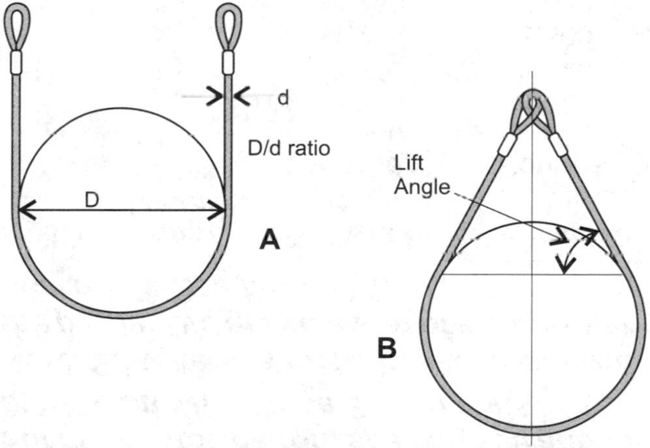
d
D/d ratio
D
A
Lift
Angle
B

Illustration #111 - Basket Hitch

With the proper D/d ratio, and the sling legs vertical, the efficiency of a basket hitch is rated by sling manufacturers' at twice that of a single vertical hitch.

If the sling legs are both attached to one hook, as shown in illustration #111B, the basket capacity is reduced, depending on the lift angle, as shown in table #18.

Angle	Single Leg Capacity
90°	200%
60°	170%
45°	140%
30°	100%

Table #18 - Basket Hitch Capacity

Note: 95% Efficiency – Be aware that wire rope manufacturers state that the maximum efficiency of any wire rope going around a bend is 95% or less. For example, a wire rope hooked around an object of equal diameter (D/d of 1:1) has a strength rating of 50% and as the D/d increases the strength efficiency increases.

For more information, see page 99 and table #14 on Wire Rope Efficiency.

Note: Sling tables rate a basket hitch with the proper D/d at twice that of a single vertical hitch. See table #19.

	Rope Diameter Inches	Basket Hitch	Vertical Lift
		Pounds	Pounds
6 x 19 IWRC	1/4	1,840	920
	3/8	4,040	2020
	1/2	7,470	3,740
	5/8	11,210	5,600
	3/4	16,160	8,080
	7/8	21,790	10,900
	1	28,360	14,180
6 x 37 IWRC	1 1/8	33,320	16,660
	1 1/4	41,480	20,740
	1 3/8	50,680	25,340
	1 1/2	61,240	30,620
	1 5/8	71,800	35,900
	1 3/4	82,330	41,170
	1 7/8	96,640	48,320
	2	105,520	52,760

Table #19 - Vertical Sling & Basket Hitch Safe Working Loads

Note: Table #19 load limits are calculated on improved plow steel 6 x 19 I.W.R.C. from 1/4" diameter to 1" diameter inclusive and improved plow steel 6 x 37 I.W.R.C. from 1 1/8" diameter to 2" diameter inclusive.

Double Basket Hitch

This is a method of supporting a load using two single basket hitches. Do not use this hitch on loads that are difficult to balance as the load could shift and slip out of the sling (see illustration #112).

Do not spread the slings too far apart as the angle will create extra load on the sling legs.

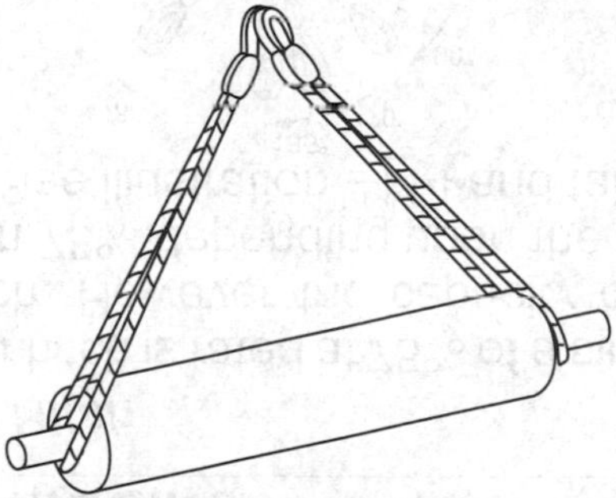

Illustration #112 - Double Basket Hitch

Double Wrap Basket Hitch

This basket hitch is wrapped completely around the load, rather than just supporting it.

It is excellent for pipe and tubing as it exerts a full 360 degree contact and pulls the load together. See illustration #113 for an example of two double wrapped basket hitches.

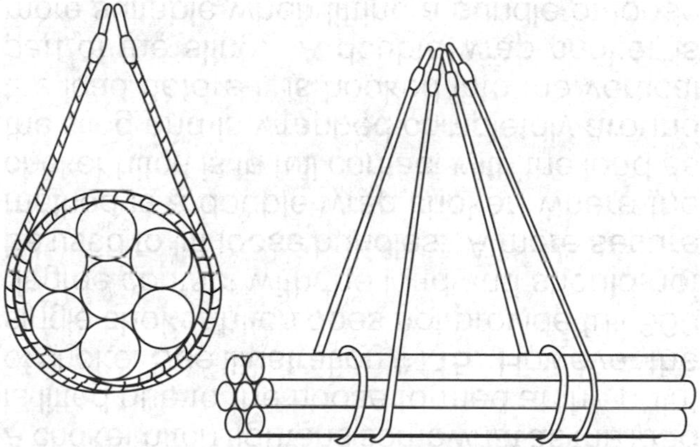

Illustration #113 - Two Double Wrapped Basket Hitches

Choker Hitch

A choker hitch is rated at 75% of a single vertical hitch. However the capacity could be less than 75% depending upon the angle of choke. See illustration #114 and table #20.

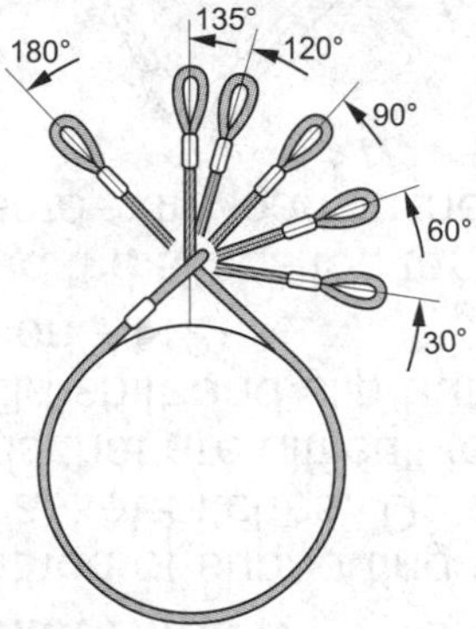
135°
180°
120°
90°
60°
30°

Illustration #114 - Choker Hitch

Angle of Choke	Sling Leg Capacity of Single Vertical Hitch
120° - 180°	75%
90° - 120°	65%
60° - 90°	55%
30° - 60°	40%

Table #20 – Choker Hitch Capacity

Single Choker Hitch

A choker hitch tightens somewhat as the load is lifted due to the noose formed at the point of choke. See illustration #115. However the single choker hitch does not provide full 360 degree contact with the load and should not be used to lift loose bundles. A more secure method is a double wrap choker, where the choker hitch is in full contact with the load as the sling end is wrapped completely around the load before it is hooked into the vertical part of the sling. A double wrap choker is more suitable when lifting a bundle of loose material.

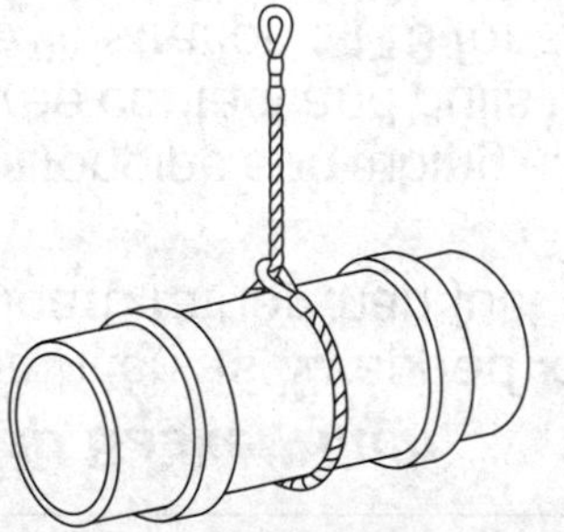

Illustration #115 - Single Choker Hitch

Double Choker Hitches

The double choker hitch is made up of two single chokers that are spread out and attached to the load, making the load more stable. See illustration #116A.

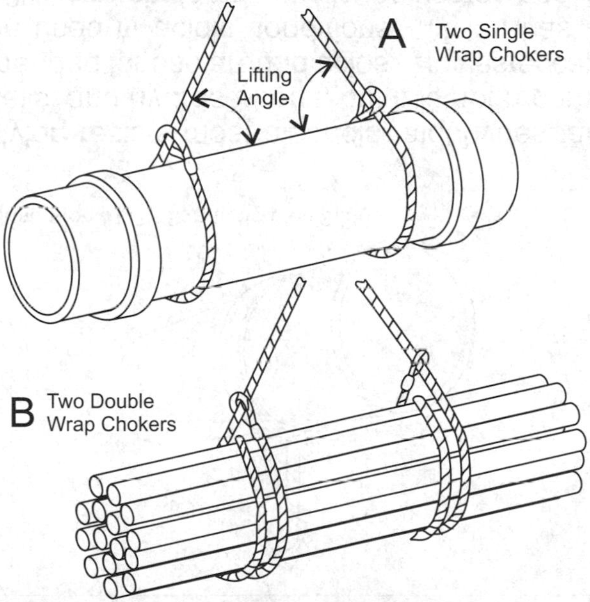
A
Two Single
Wrap Chokers
Lifting
Angle
B
Two Double
Wrap Chokers

Illustration #116 - Double Choker Hitch

The double choker hitch does not provide full 360 degree contact with the load and should not be used to lift loose bundles.

An extra wrap around the load, creating two double wrap chokers should be used when lifting long bundles of loose material, such as pipe or tubing (see illustration #116B).

Note: Two slings in a double choker hitch configuration (illustration #116) will have a reduced lifting capacity as compared to two choker hitches each lifting straight up. The reduced capacity depends upon the lifting angle.

Synthetic Slings

Synthetic Web Slings: offcr good protection for machined parts, are non-sparking, light weight and flexible. It is a flexible flat sling that has the ability to hug the load and keep it more secure from slippage, as indicated in illustration #117. This sling is usually made of nylon or polyester, however other materials are available.

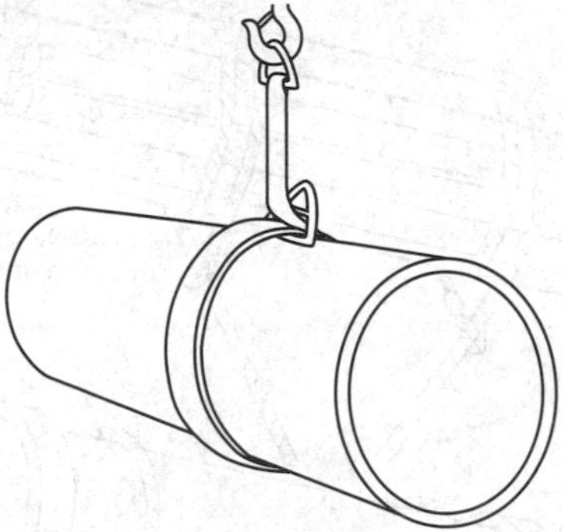

Illustration #117 - Synthetic Web Sling

Nylon resists most alcohols, aldehydes, alkalis, and hydrocarbons, but it is not recommended for use around acids. Polyester can be used in acidic conditions. Nylon has a 10% stretch factor, while polyester has a lower stretch factor.

Both nylon and polyester can be used in temperatures up to 200 degrees F.

Rigging hardware, for example rings and shackles, is available to use with web slings (see the hardware section).

The flat shape of the hardware is more suited to these slings than the usual curved types. Any folding, bunching or pinching in a standard shackle will reduce the rated load of a synthetic sling.

Note: Check with a reputable safety systems distributor for the proper sling material used with specific hazardous products.

Note: Synthetic slings must be removed from service if any of the following conditions are present: acid or caustic burns; melting or charring of any surface part; snags, punctures, tears, or cuts; broken stitches; distorted fittings; or the colored core warning yarns are showing.

Note: All sling types, including synthetic web sling must have the proper identification to show the name of the manufacturer, the rated load, and the type of material used. See illustration #118.

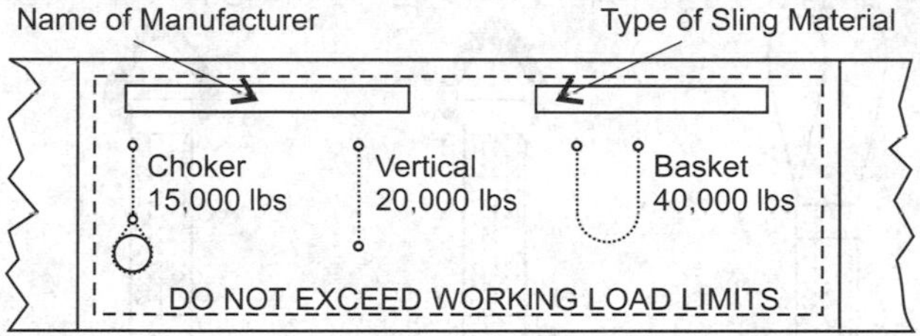
Name of Manufacturer
Type of Sling Material
Choker
15,000 lbs
Vertical
20,000 lbs
Basket
40,000 lbs
DO NOT EXCEED WORKING LOAD LIMITS

Illustration #118 - Synthetic Sling Identification Example

Note: Synthetic slings are manufactured in single and double ply. The double ply capacity ranges from 140% to 200% that of a single ply, depending upon sling type and hook up.

Edge protectors are available. They are the sewn-in, sliding, and replaceable types.

Synthetic web slings are identified by a Type Number, and they are available in a number of eye configurations. See illustration #119.

Synthetic Web Sling Grades

Although most web slings look similar to the untrained eye, they can vary in capacity for several reasons.

- Number of plies
- Grade of webbing material
- Efficiency of sewing

Be aware that a double ply web sling may not necessarily have twice the capacity of a single ply.

Web slings are available in three grades of webbing, and their rating is based on the efficiency of the sewing.

The WLL of a sling is based on the formula:

Material breaking strength x efficiency of sewing ÷ design (safety) factor.

Note: Always refer to the sling identification tag for the sling capacity. If the tag is missing, do not use the sling.

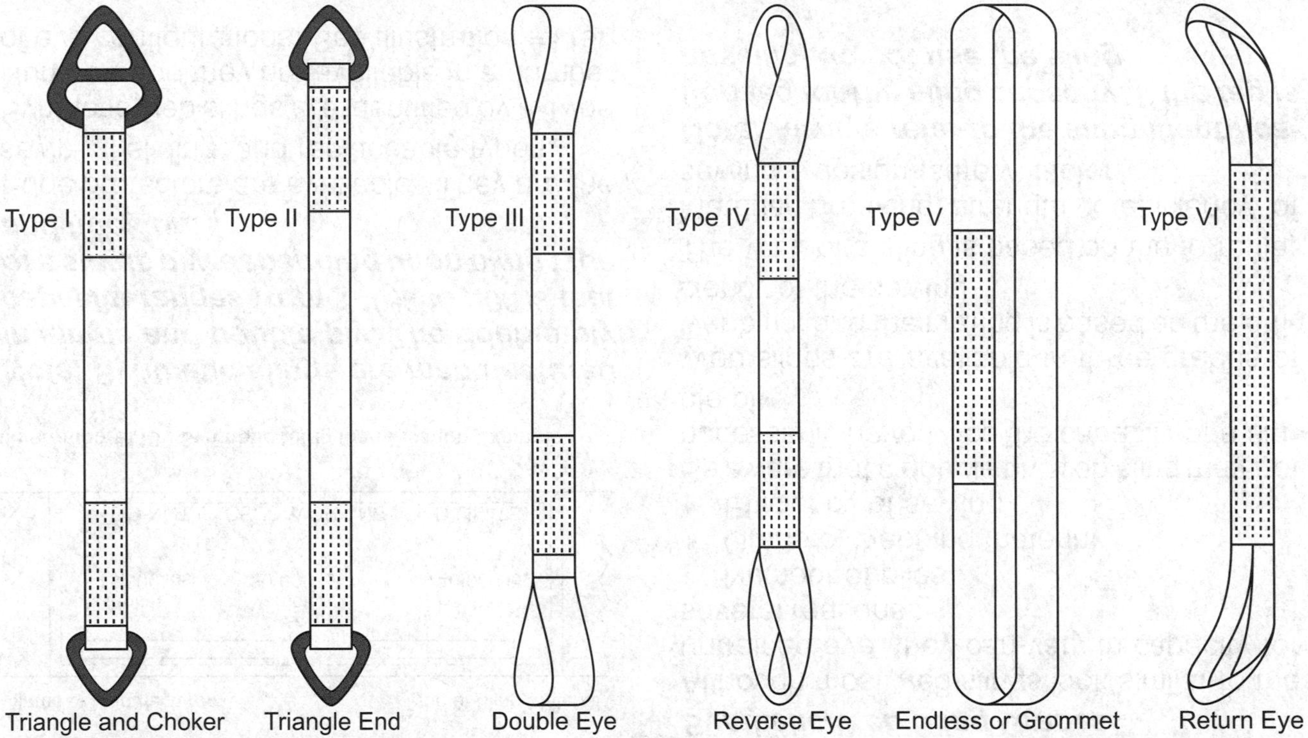
Type I
Type II
Type III
Type IV
Type V
Type VI
Triangle and Choker
Triangle End
Double Eye
Reverse Eye
Endless or Grommet
Return Eye

Illustration #119 - Synthetic Web Sling Types

Synthetic Roundslings: are flexible lightweight slings made up of load carrying fibers covered with a tough non-load carrying cover. They are very flexible with limited stretch. Normal cover wear does not affect the strength, and wear points can be moved around. A safety feature is that the cover will rip when the sling is overloaded and over-stretched. See Illustration #120.

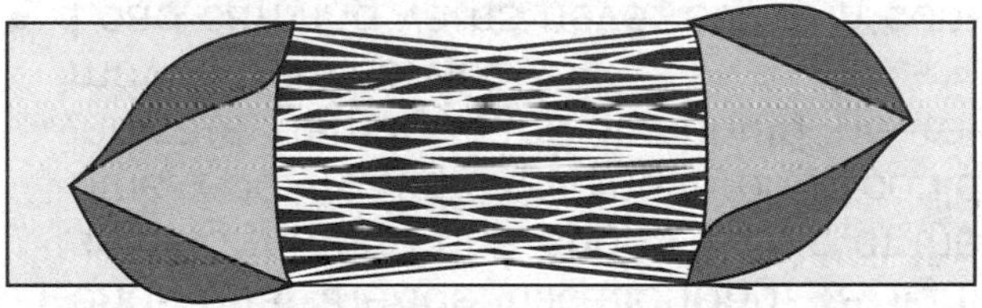

Illustration #120 - Synthetic Roundsling Example

Note: Always refer to the roundsling ID tag. Due to the wide number of manufacturers, there may be discrepancies in sizes and capacities, and color coding of round slings may not be standardized.

New Synthetic Sling Types

Twin Type: is one of the newest designs in slings. It is constructed using two roundsling types encased in an outer cover. See illustration #121 for an end view example.

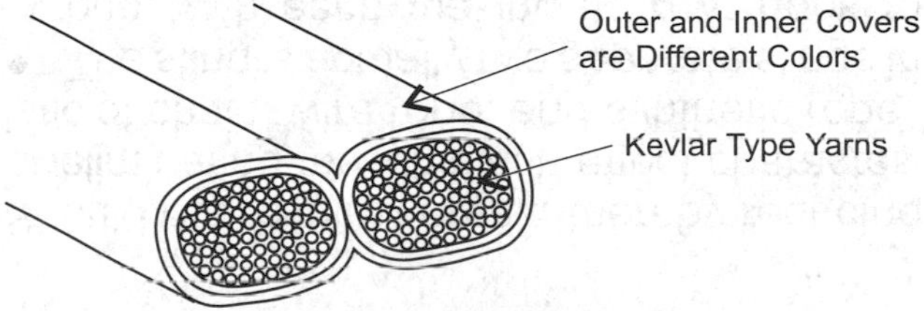
Outer and Inner Covers are Different Colors
Kevlar Type Yarns

Illustration #121 - Twin Type Sling

This sling type is made of fibers from a kevlar typc matcrial which has a better weight to strength ratio than steel. For comparison purposes, one example is a type of 35-foot endless sling used in a basket configuration that has a capacity of 140,000 pounds.

The twin sling only weighs about 60 pounds while a wire rope sling of equal capacity weighs approximately 600 pounds.

Some of the other features of this sling type include:

- Fiber-optic tell-tales: installed with both ends near the identification tag. A light shining through one end is visible at the other end. No light coming through could indicate damage and it should be removed from service.
- Load carrying yarns never come in contact with load. Outer cover material about 4 times more durable than polyester.
- Two inner bundles are covered in a different colored material than the outer cover to provide an instant alert for damage.
- Has overload indicator "tails" that are readily seen, but shrink and disappear when the sling is overloaded (illustration #122).

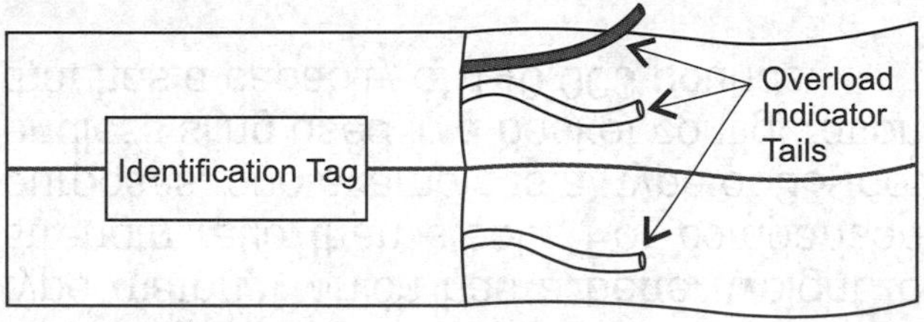
Overload
Indicator
Tails
Identification Tag

Illustration #122 - Twin-Type Sling

Should not recoil at break, thereby reducing or eliminating the whiplash effect characteristic of chain, wire rope, and synthetic rope.

- The sling is actually two separate slings in one, with each making its own hook to load connection.
- Available in a continuous loop sling, two leg bridle sling with hardware, and eye and eye sling.

Sling Lifting Angles

The load imposed on each leg of a bridle sling configuration depends upon the angle to the horizontal formed by the legs lifting the load. Two vertical slings lifting a 1000 pound weight will each carry a load of 500 pounds. See illustration #123B.

When the sling legs are pulled together into a common hook, each sling leg will have a load increase.

This sling leg load increase is often not realized by the person hooking up the load.

At a 60° angle (illustration #123C), the sling leg load is 115%. When the sling angle lowers to 45°, the sling leg load is increased to 141% (illustration #123D), and at a 30° angle the sling load increases to 200% (illustration #123E). In other words, at 30° the load on each sling leg is equal to the actual load weight.

From this point, the load on each sling leg increases rapidly. If the angle could be lowered to 5°, the load on each sling leg would be 5745 pounds, which is almost 6 times the actual load weight.

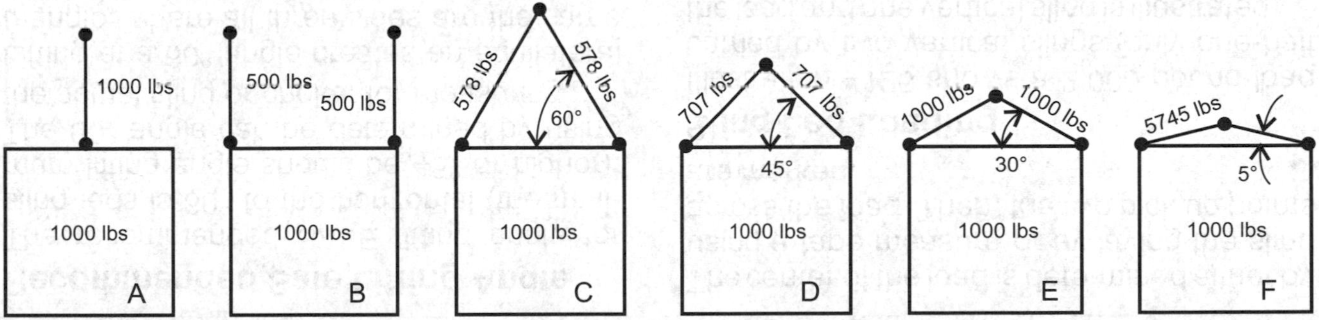
1000 lbs
1000 lbs
A
500 lbs
500 lbs
1000 lbs
B
578 lbs
578 lbs
60°
1000 lbs
C
707 lbs
707 lbs
45°
1000 lbs
D
1000 lbs
1000 lbs
30°
1000 lbs
E
5745 lbs
5°
1000 lbs
F

Illustration #123 - Various Sling Angle Loads

Recommended Safe Lifting Angle

The recommended SAFE lifting angle for sling legs is 60° to the horizontal (the minimum lifting angle should be 45° or higher). The 60° angle can be determined by using the actual sling or choker for measuring.

Lifting at a 60° angle creates an equilateral triangle, where all three sides are the same length. See illustration #124.

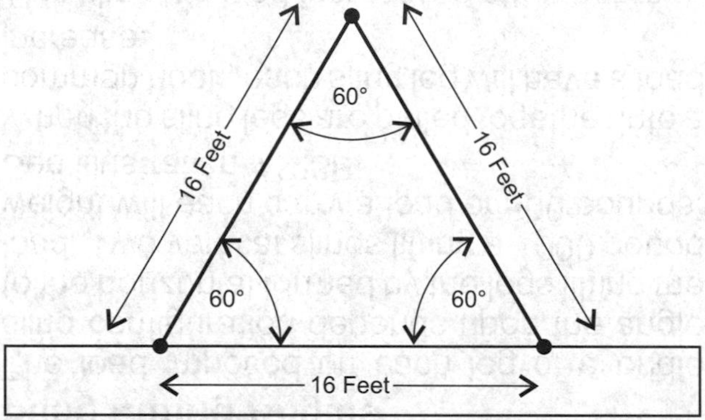
60°
16 Feet
16 Feet
60°
60°
16 Feet

Illustration #124 - Using Sling to Determine Lift Points

The center of the load is determined either by using a tape measure or by laying the sling across the load. Then, the two pick up points are marked.

Sling Leg Loading

Illustration #125 shows a 2,000 pound load carried by two vertical slings (only one-half the load and one vertical sling is illustrated).

The loading on one sling leg as it is moved out to different hookup angles is shown. In a vertical lift one sling carries 1,000 lb (one-half the load weight). When the sling is at a 5° horizontal angle the load on one sling leg is 11,490 lb, or nearly 6 times the load weight. Table #21 shows the Load Angle Factor that matches the applicable sling leg lifting angle.

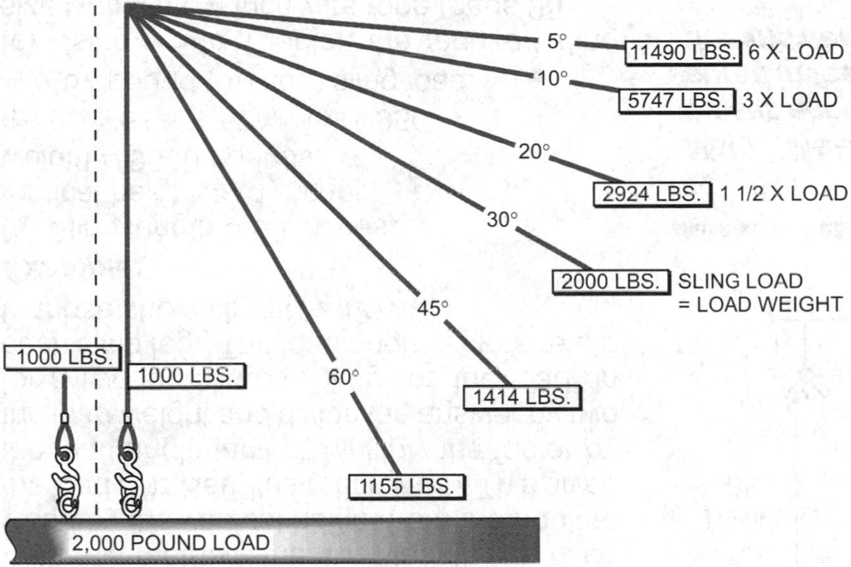
5°
11490 LBS.
6 X LOAD
10°
5747 LBS.
3 X LOAD
20°
2924 LBS.
1 1/2 X LOAD
30°
2000 LBS.
SLING LOAD
= LOAD WEIGHT
45°
1414 LBS.
60°
1155 LBS.
1000 LBS.
1000 LBS.
2,000 POUND LOAD

Illustration #125 - Sling Leg Loading Increases

Sling Angle	Load Angle Factor
5°	11.490
10°	5.747
15°	3.861
20°	2.924
25°	2.364
30°	2.000
35°	1.742
40°	1.555
45°	1.414
50°	1.305
55°	1.221
60°	1.155
65°	1.104
70°	1.064
75°	1.035

Table #21 — Horizontal Sling Angle

Calculating Sling Load

Riggers Rule

With this method, the sling length (L), is divided by the vertical height from the hook to the load (V). See illustration #126. This gives the load angle factor. Multiply the factor by the load weight and divide the answer by two for a two-leg sling. This gives the load on each sling leg. The load angle factors relate to those shown in table #21.

Example:

(a) Sling length = 96 inches,
vertical height = 61 inches,
weight = 9500 pounds.

(b) 96 ÷ 61 = 1.57 factor x 9500 ÷ 2
= 7457 pound (3.7 ton) sling load.

(c) Using a 5 to 1 factor, the required sling size would be ¾ inch wire rope (page 98, table #13) or the equivalent web sling.

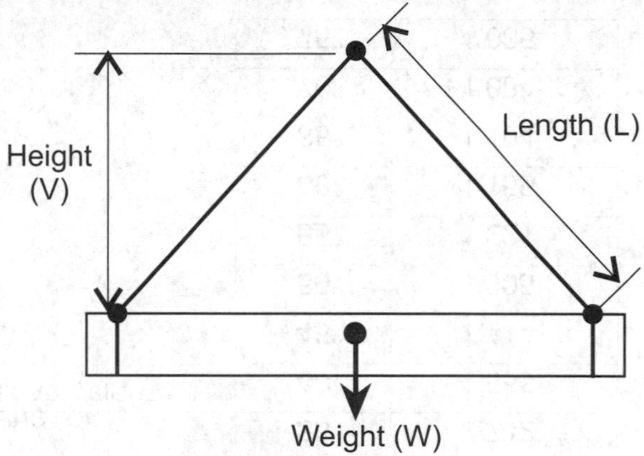
Height
(V)
Length (L)
Weight (W)

Illustration #126 - Sling Load Formula

Note: Measure the lengths in inches for closer accuracy. If the lengths are measured in feet and rounded off to a half foot the answer will only be approximate.

Another version of the rigger's rule is:

$$T\ (tension) = \frac{W\ (weight)}{N\ (\#\ of\ legs)} \times \frac{L\ (length)}{V\ (height)}$$

Unequal Sling Lengths

Centering a Load

When selecting slings for a lift, the main considerations are load weight, load size and the center of gravity of the load. Estimate the center of gravity and spot the hook directly over it. See illustration #127.

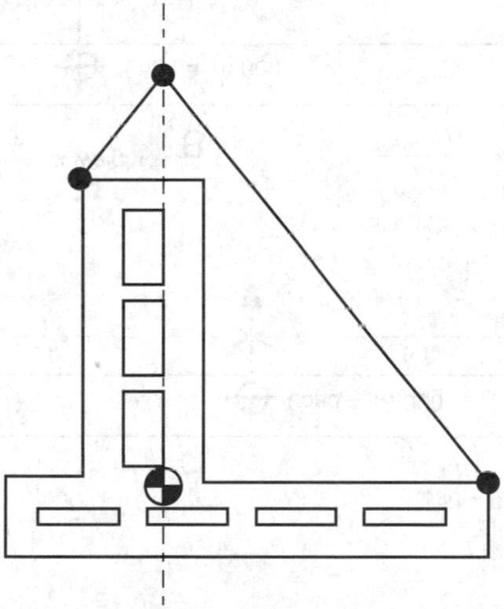

Illustration #127 - Center of Gravity

Note: A load rigged with the hook not positioned directly over the center of gravity will always swing when lifted. This immediately changes the load distribution on the slings. In almost every instance one sling will be carrying more than 50% of the weight. Always attach the slings to the load with the hook directly over the center of gravity. An improperly rigged load could tip or overload one sling.

Sling Loading and Center of Gravity

With two slings lifting vertically, the load will be equally shared if the center of gravity of the load is in the middle. For example, with an 18,000 pound weight, 12 feet long, each sling would carry 9,000 pounds. See illustration #128A.

In illustration #128C, sling 1 has a load of 13,500 pounds, and 4,500 on sling 2.

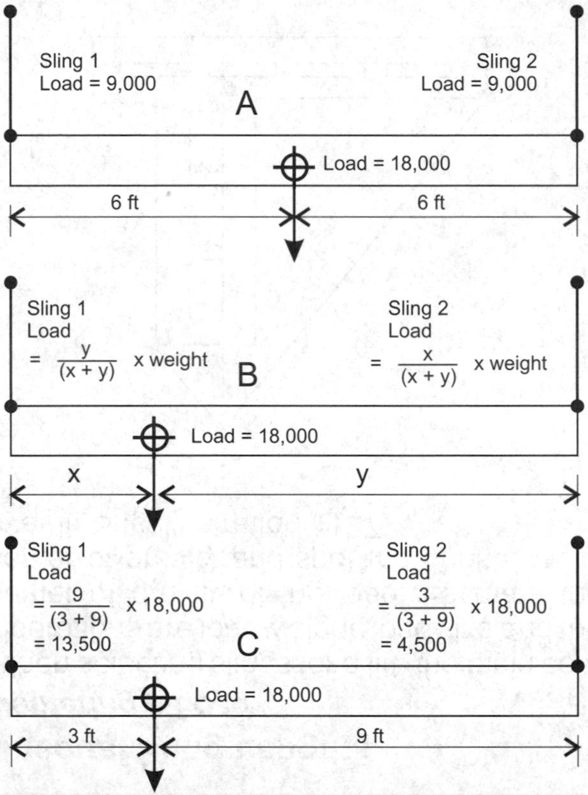
Sling 1
Load = 9,000
Sling 2
Load = 9,000
A
Load = 18,000
6 ft
6 ft
Sling 1
Load
= y/(x + y) x weight
Sling 2
Load
= x/(x + y) x weight
B
Load = 18,000
x
y
Sling 1
Load
= 9/(3 + 9) x 18,000
= 13,500
Sling 2
Load
= 3/(3 + 9) x 18,000
= 4,500
C
Load = 18,000
3 ft
9 ft

Illustration #128 - Off-Center Sling Loads

Softeners

All sharp corners should be covered by pads or softeners to prevent the sling from being bent or cut. These softeners can be made from a split pipe section, padding or blocking, see illustration #129.

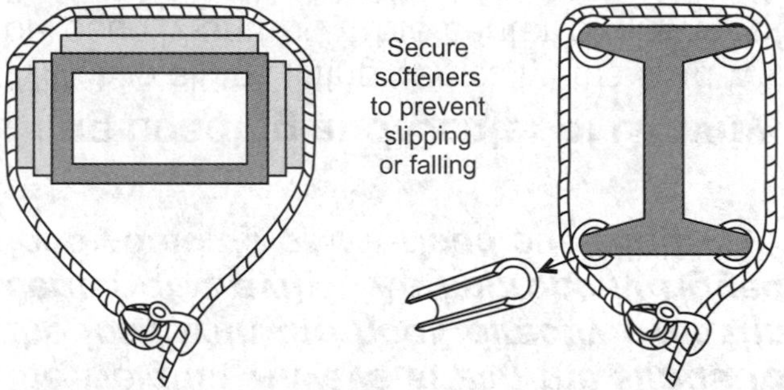
Secure
softeners
to prevent
slipping
or falling

Illustration #129 - Softeners

A good rule to follow is to make sure that the length of contact of the wire rope is equal to one rope lay, or seven times the rope diameter.

Note: see page 99 for wire rope efficiency and bending radius.

Wire Rope Clips

Using wire rope clips is a common method of making an eye or attaching a wire rope to a piece of equipment. The two main types are the U-Bolt and the Fist Grip. See illustration #130 for clip examples. Clips can develop approximately 80% of the wire rope strength when properly applied, but can drop to 40% or less when improperly applied.

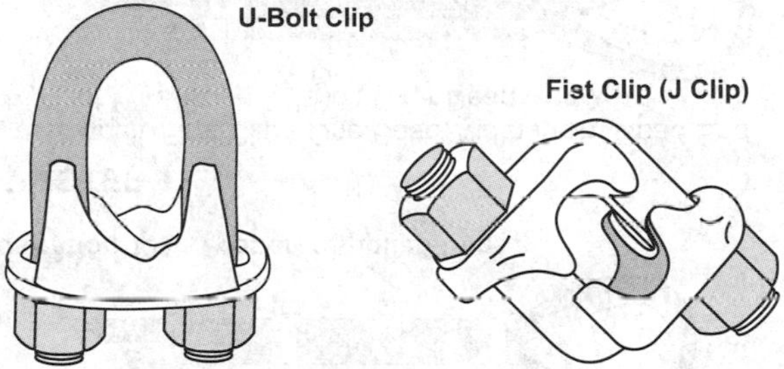
U-Bolt Clip
Fist Clip (J Clip)

Illustration #130 - Types of Clip

Note: ANSI/OHSA/OH&S regulations prohibit the use of clips to make eyes for slings. Sling eyes must be of a type made with a Flemish splice and a hydraulic pressed swaged fitting.

U Bolt Type: When using U-bolt clips, the U section must be on the dead or short end, as indicated in illustration #131.

Fist Grip Type: The fist grip, or J-clip, offers a wide bearing surface for maximum strength and greater holding power as compared to the U-bolt type.

Note: Tighten the clips before tension is placed on the rope. Then re-tighten after a load has been applied to the rope. Clips are usually grooved and it is important to use the correct clip lay grooving to match the lay of the wire rope. See illustration #132 for clip installation and table #22 for manufacturer's chart.

Number of Clips - Rule of Thumb

(use only for $^7/_8$" and under)

Number of wire rope clips = the diameter of the rope x 3 + 1 to the next whole number.

Example: $^1/_2$ inch wire rope:

D x 3 + 1 (NWN) = clips required

$^1/_2$ x 3 + 1 (NWN) = 3 clips

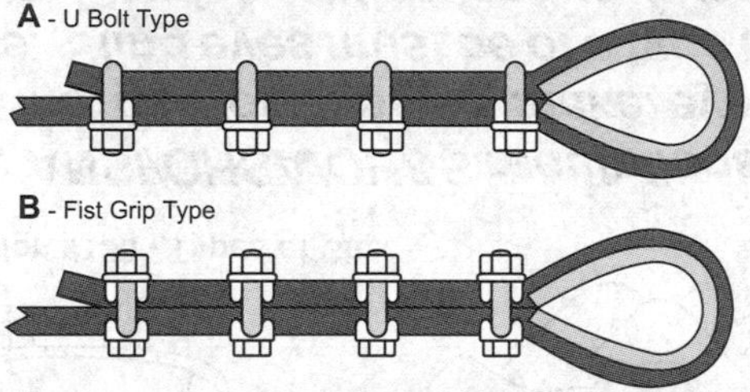
A - U Bolt Type
B - Fist Grip Type

Illustration 131 - Properly Applied Clips

STEP 1

Apply First Clip - One Base Width From Dead End of Wire Rope - U-Bolt Over Dead End.

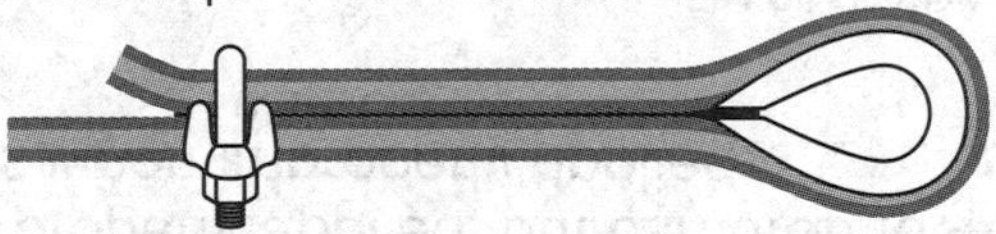

STEP 2

Apply Second Clip - Nearest Eye as Possible
- U-Bolt Over Dead End
- Snug Up Nuts but ***Do Not Tighten***

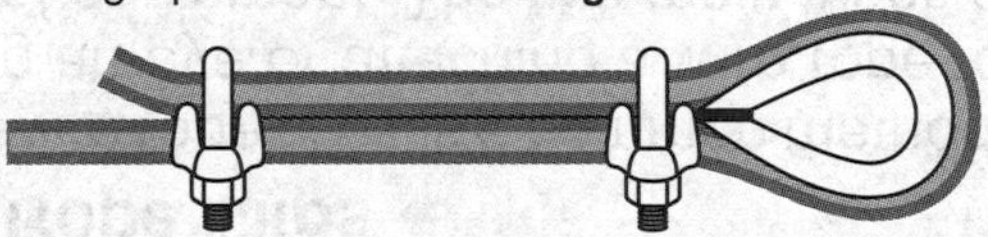

Illustration #132 - Proper Clip Installation

Spacing of Clips - Rule of Thumb

Spacing of wire rope clips
= the diameter of the rope x 6

Example: $^{1}/_{2}$ inch wire rope:
clip spacing = D x 6
$^{1}/_{2}$ x 6 = 3 inch spacing

STEP 3

All Other Clips
- Space Equally Between First Two.

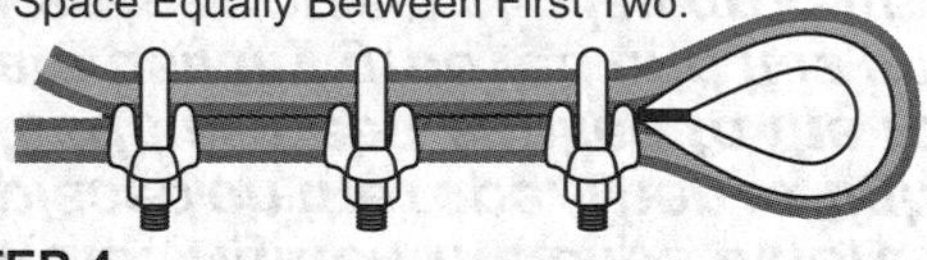

STEP 4

Tighten All Nuts to Recommended Torque.

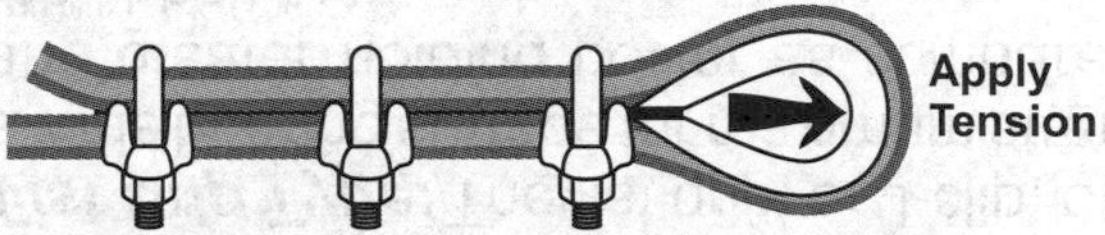
Apply
Tension

STEP 5

Recheck Nut Torque
After Rope Has Been in Operation.

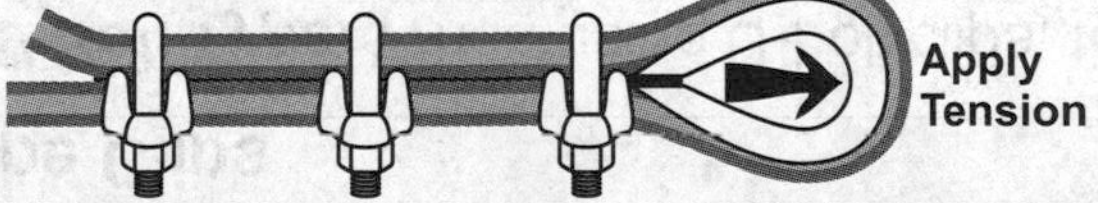
Apply
Tension

Rope Diam. Inches	U-Bolt and Saddle Type			Integral Saddle and Bolt Type		
	Minimum No. of Clips	Amount of Rope to turn back in inches from Thimble	Torque in lbs Foot	Minimum No. of Clips	Amount of Rope to turn back in inches from Thimble	Torque in lbs Foot
1/8	2	3 1/4	—	—	—	—
3/16	2	3 3/4	7.5	2	3 1/4	30
1/4	2	4 3/4	15	2	3 1/4	30
5/16	2	5 1/2	30	2	4	30
3/8	2	6 1/4	45	2	5	45
7/16	2	6 3/4	65	2	5 3/4	65
1/2	3	11	65	3	6 1/2	65
9/16	3	11 1/4	95	3	7 1/4	130
5/8	3	12	95	3	8	130
3/4	4	18	130	3	14	225
7/8	4	21 1/2	225	4	23	225
1	5	24	225	5	26	225
1 1/8	6	28	225	5	29	225
1 1/4	7	30	360	6	40	360
1 3/8	7	37 1/2	360	6	45	500
1 1/2	8	40 1/2	360	7	49	500
1 5/8	8	43 1/2	430			
1 3/4	8	46	590			
2	8	62	750			

Table #22 - Wire Rope Clip Application (revised)

Splicing With Clips

The preferred method of splicing two pieces of wire rope is to use two interlocking thimble eyes. See illustration #133.

Turnback Distance

Illustration #133 - Splicing with Interlocking Eyes

Note: The turnback length is the same as in table #22.

The alternative method has the two ropes parallel with each other. See illustration #134. The overlap length is 2 times the turnback distance. The number of clips is the same as that for the interlocking eye method.

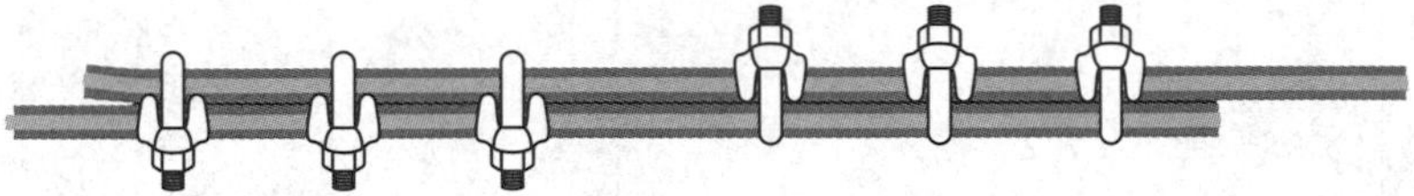

Illustration #134 - Splicing with Parallel Ends

Shackles

The screw pin anchor and the screw pin chain shackle are the most commonly used shackles. The anchor type is better suited for using two slings to lift a load.

The working load limit (SWL) of each shackle should be embossed on the bow section and is rated in tons. The shackle is sized by the diameter of the bow section, not the pin diameter.

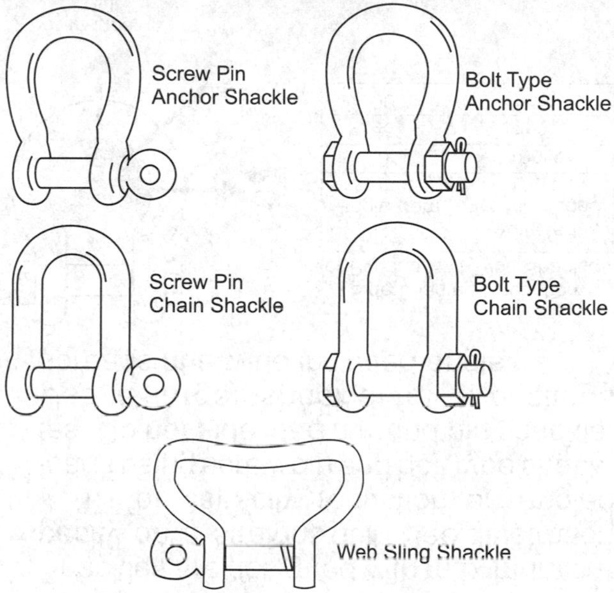
Screw Pin
Anchor Shackle
Bolt Type
Anchor Shackle
Screw Pin
Chain Shackle
Bolt Type
Chain Shackle
Web Sling Shackle

Illustration #135 - Shackle Types

The web sling shackle has increased bow width that gives wider sling bearing area. It also increases web sling efficiency by up to 15%, which brings the sling closer to its rated capacity.

General Shackle Rules

1. Use only a shackle with an embossed rating on the bow.
2. Use only the proper manufacturer's pin, never replace it with a bolt.
3. Never use a screw pin shackle if the pin can roll under load (illustration #136A,C).
4. Always pin the eye of the sling (illustration #136B).
5. Never weld any type of rigging hardware.

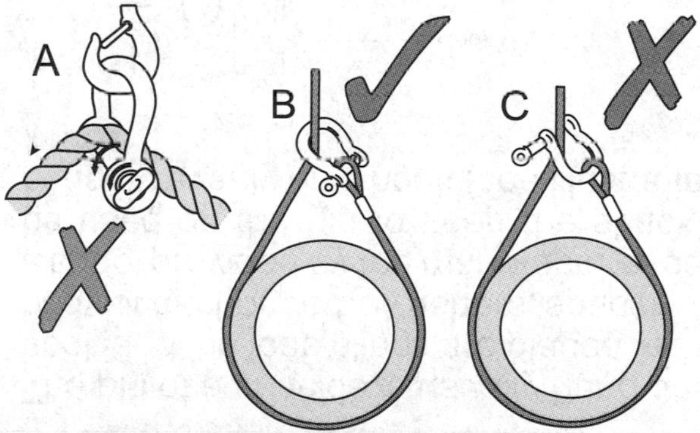
A
B
C

Illustration #136 - Do Not Let Rope Run Over Pin

6. Shackle pins are: $1/16$ inch larger in diameter than the bow on sizes up to $7/16$ inch; $1/8$ inch larger than the bow on sizes $1/2$ inch to 1 $5/8$ inch; $1/4$ inch larger than the bow on sizes 1 $3/4$ and over.
7. Shackles are designed with maximum capacity on a straight pull. See illustration #137 for capacity reduction on angled loads using screw pin and bolt type shackles. Do not side load a round pin shackle. Use a larger shackle for two slings spreads at a wide included angle.

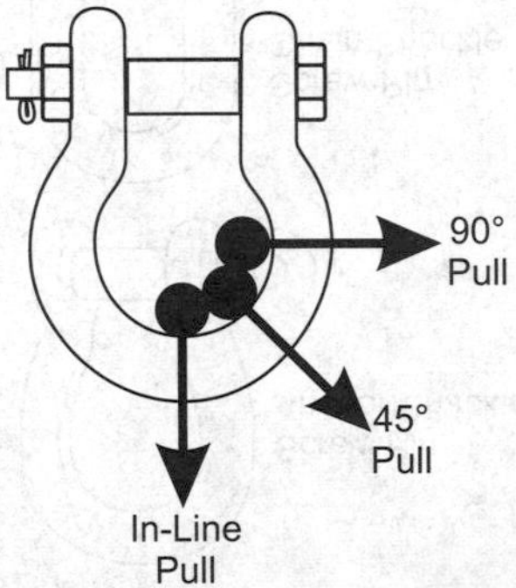
90° Pull
45° Pull
In-Line Pull

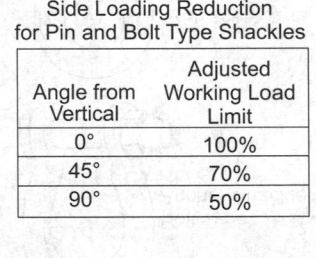

Side Loading Reduction for Pin and Bolt Type Shackles

Angle from Vertical	Adjusted Working Load Limit
0°	100%
45°	70%
90°	50%

Illustration #137 - Shackle Capacity Reduction

8. The pin of a shackle is usually hung on a hook and the load slings are placed in the body or anchor part. Washers, spacers or a spool provided by the manufacturer can be used on the pin to keep the shackle hanging evenly on a hook (see illustration #138).

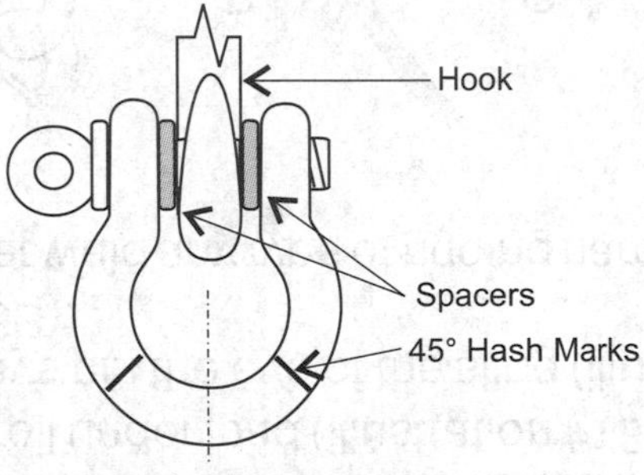
Hook
Spacers
45° Hash Marks

Illustration #138 - Shackle on a Hook

Note: Shackles with 45 degree hash marks on the bow are recommended. These marks indicate that slings hooked up with an included angle greater than 90 degrees have a much reduced capacity.

Shackle Working Load Limits

SHACKLES - Weldless Construction Forged Steel		
Stock Diameter (Inches)	Inside Width At Pin (Inches)	Max. Safe Working Load Single Vertical Pull (Pounds)
3/16	3/8	665
1/4	15/32	1,000
5/16	17/32	1,500
3/8	21/32	2,000
7/16	23/32	3,000
1/2	13/16	4,000
5/8	1 1/16	6,500
3/4	1 1/4	9,500
7/8	1 7/16	13,000
1	1 11/16	17,000
1 1/8	1 13/16	19,000
1 1/4	2 1/32	24,000
1 3/8	2 1/4	27,000
1 1/2	2 3/8	34,000
1 3/4	2 7/8	50,000
2	3 1/4	70,000
2 1/2	4 1/8	100,000
3	5	150,000

Table #23 - Shackle Working Load Limits

Extra Wide Shackle Body

The shackle shown in illustration #139A, designed for higher capacity lifts, has a bow diameter almost twice that of a normal shackle. This increases the D/d ratio (shackle bow diameter to sling diameter), which increases the sling strength efficiency, and reduces the need for a sling thimble. See illustration #139B and #139C for the bow comparison with equal sized pins.

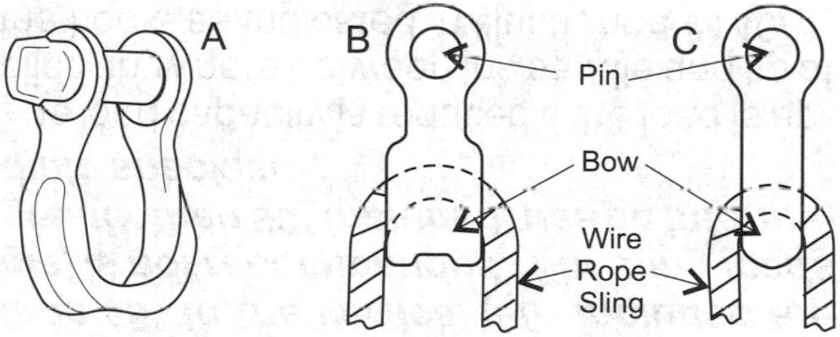
A
B
C
Pin
Bow
Wire
Rope
Sling

Illustration #139 - Large Bow Diameter Shackle

Hooks

All hooks should be made from forged steel and, except grab and sorting types, they should all be equipped with safety catches. Forged hooks with the rating embossed on them are the best quality available.

Note: Inspect hooks regularly and look for wear in the saddle and for cracks, nicks, gouges, or corrosion. Check the hook attachment and securement. Make sure the safety latch is not damaged or malfunctioning.

Do not overload or tip load. OH&S/OSHA/ANSI regulations specify removal from service of any hook with a damaged latch, any cracking, any visible twist or bend, or any increase in the throat opening that exceeds 5% and not to exceed 1/4 inch. A safe practice is to destroy any damaged hook.

Note: The recommended included safe lifting angle for two slings is 60°. Two slings in a hook with an angle greater than 45° to the vertical (90° included angle) is not recommended. For sling loads greater than 90° included, use an intermediate shackle.

The load capacity is reduced if the load is applied anywhere between the saddle and tip of the hook, as indicated in illustration #140.

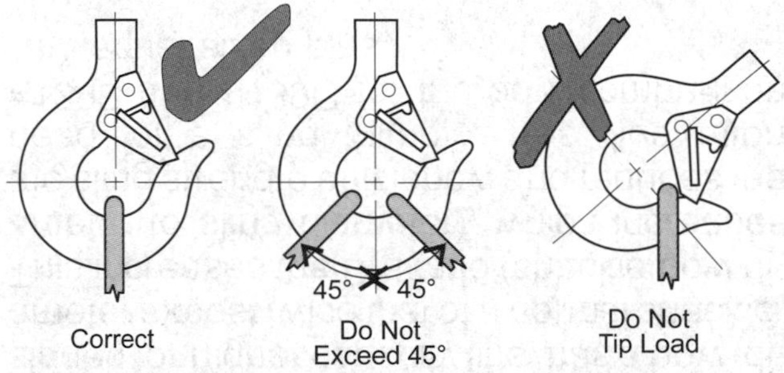
45°
45°
Correct
Do Not
Exceed 45°
Do Not
Tip Load

Illustration #140 - Hook Loading

Do not side load, tip load or back load any hook (see illustration #141).

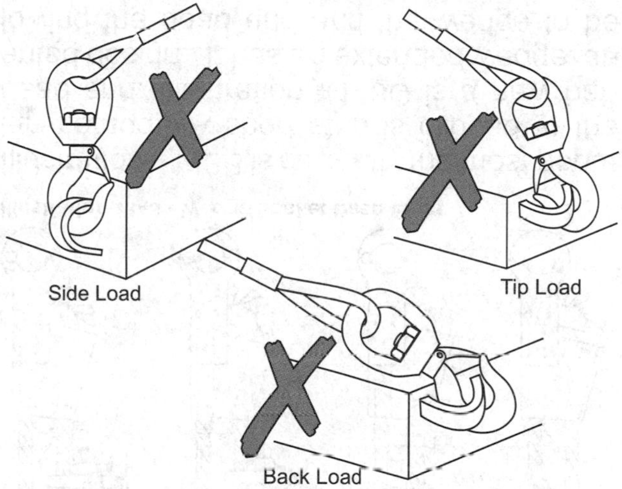
Side Load
Tip Load
Back Load

Illustration #141 - Incorrect Hook Loading Practices

Wedge Sockets

A wedge socket must be attached with the load line pulling in a straight line from the pin. See illustration #142.

Due to core slippage, non-rotating rope is not recommended for use with wedge sockets, however because of the non-rotating benefit, it is commonly used in this application.

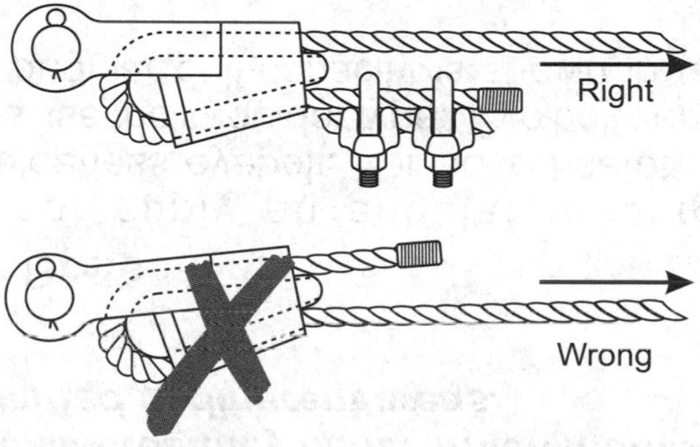
Right
Wrong

Illustration #142 - Correct Wedge Socket Use

Safety regulations vary concerning the attachment of the dead end line. The two approved methods of securing the dead end are shown in illustrations #143A and #143B. Illustration #143A is a method shown in many safety regulations, but sometimes cannot be used when the loop is too big and can snag on projections.

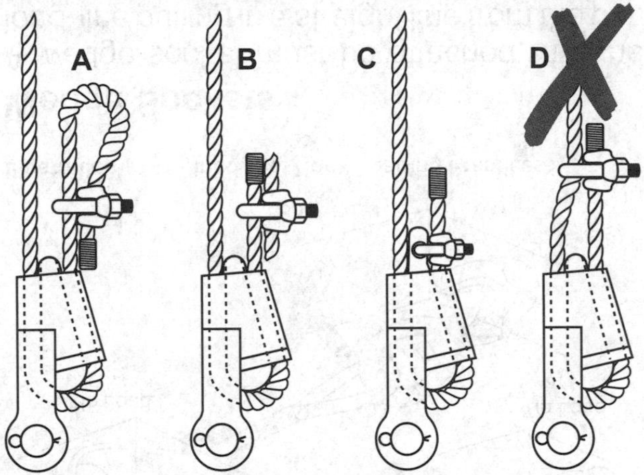
A
B
C
D

Illustration #143 - Wedge Socket Dead Ends

Illustration #143B is currently the most popular method. A short stub is clipped to the dead end. Illustration #143C is a new patented design. It has an extended wedge, allowing the dead end and the wedge to be clipped together.

Clipping the dead end back to the load line is a method that is no longer suggested for use by OHSA or ANSI. This is shown in illustration #143D.

Note: Check with the applicable OH&S/OSHA department concerning wedge socket attachment, as there is a wide discrepancy about which method is permitted in different areas.

Eye Bolts

Do not apply an angular load to a shoulderless eyebolt. For added safety, always use the shoulder type. Eye bolt vertical and angular pull capacity is shown in table #24.

With an angular pull, the capacity drops to 30% of the rated capacity at a 45 degree angle.

Eye Bolt Working Load Limits
- Shoulder Type Only
- Forged Carbon Steel

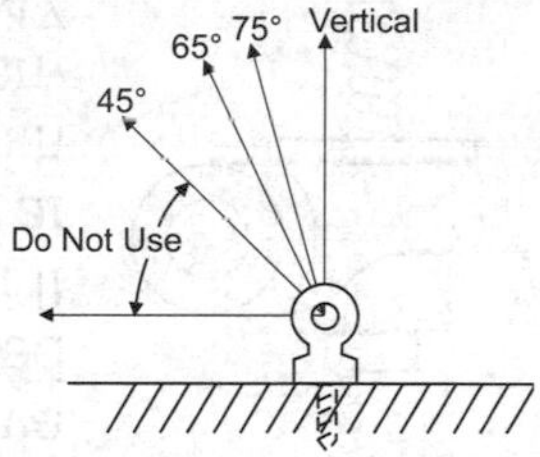
Vertical
75°
65°
45°
Do Not Use

Shank Diameter	Vertical Pull	60° Pull	45° Pull	Under 45°
1/4	650	420	195	160
5/16	1200	780	360	300
3/8	1550	1000	465	380
1/2	2600	1690	780	650
5/8	5200	3380	1560	1300
3/4	7200	4680	2160	1800
7/8	10,600	6890	3180	2650
1	13,300	8645	3990	3325
1 1/4	21,000	13,600	6300	5250
1 1/2	24,000	15,600	7200	6000

Table #24 - Eye Bolt Working Load Limits

For angular pulls, the eye must be aligned as shown in illustration #144. Shims may be needed to align the eye (limit 3 shims).

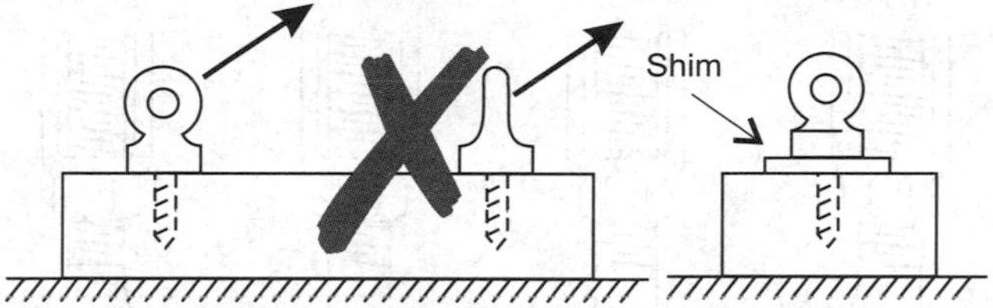
Shim

Illustration #144 - Eye Bolt Alignment

Do not insert a hook tip in the eye. Use a shackle. See illustration #145.

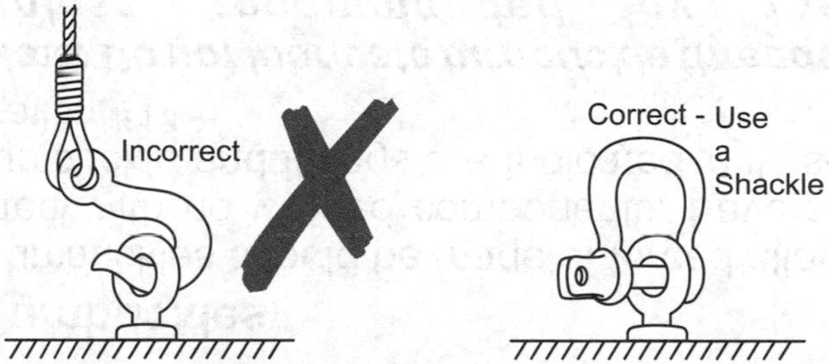
Incorrect
Correct - Use a Shackle

Illustration #145 - Use a Shackle

Swivel Hoist Ring

Swivel rings are a form of eye bolt. The bail (ring) swivels 360 degrees and pivots 180 degrees. In general, the rules concerning eye bolts apply to these rings. They must fit flat against the mounting surface, and be torqued to specification. Never use spacers. Drilled mounting holes must be 90 degrees to the surface. See illustration #146.

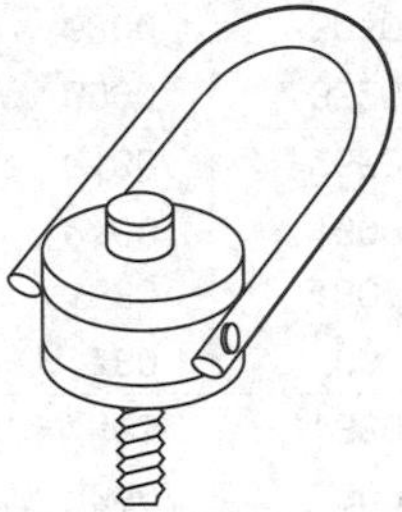
Illustration #146 - Swivel Hoist Ring

Side Pull Hoist Rings

This ring is similar to an eye bolt except it is designed for a 90 degree side pull. It is rated at 100% capacity at 90 degrees. It is used with a shackle for sling attachment. See illustration #147 for an example.

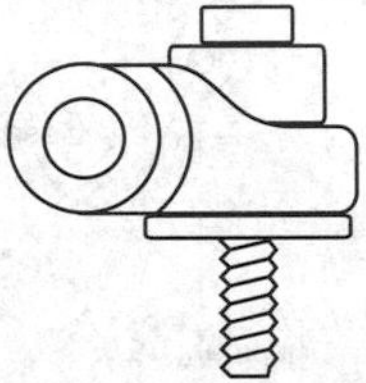
Illustration #147 - Side Pull Ring

Turnbuckles

Turnbuckles should be made of forged alloy steel with no welded components. Several turnbuckle end fittings are indicated in illustration #148.

Note: Do not lubricate turnbuckle threads unless recommended by the manufacturer.

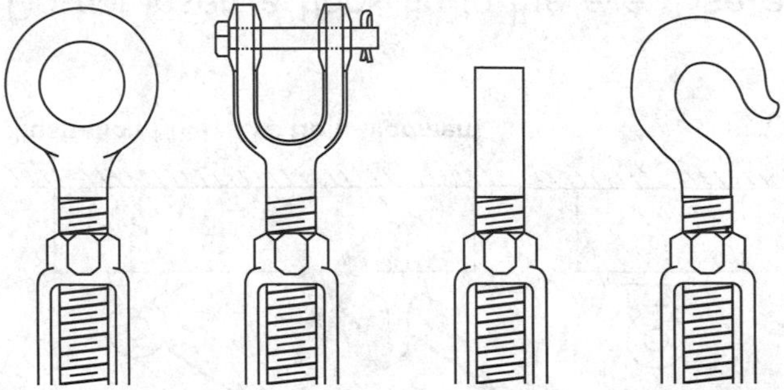
Eye
Jaw
Stub
Hook Has Reduced Capacity
Illustration #148 - Turnbuckle End Fittings

If vibration is present, it is important to lock the frame of the end fitting, as in illustration #149. Do not use jam nuts on turnbuckles that do not come equipped with them as the jam nut will add to the load on the thread.

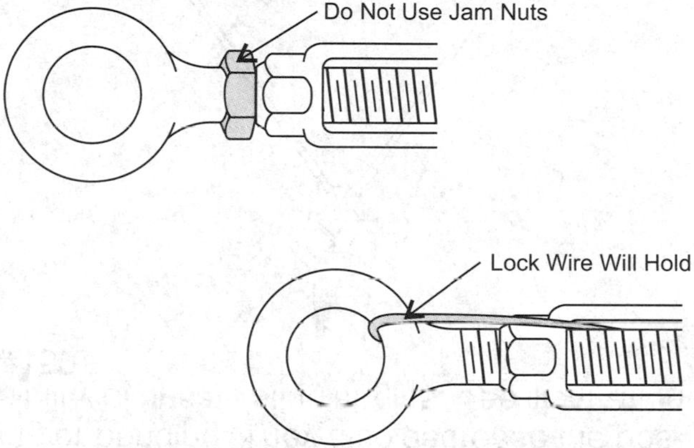
Do Not Use Jam Nuts
Lock Wire Will Hold

Illustration #149 - Turnbuckle Locking

The safe working load depends on the diameter of the threaded portion. The working load limits of turnbuckles are indicated in table #25.

Turnbuckle Working Load Limits

Stock Diameter (Inches)	Jaw, Eye, Stub, End Fittings (Pounds)	Hook End Fitting (Pounds)
1/4	500	400
5/16	800	700
3/8	1,200	1,000
1/2	2,200	1,500
5/8	3,500	2,250
3/4	5,200	3,000
7/8	7,200	4,000
1	10,000	5,000
1 1/4	15,200	5,000
1 1/2	21,400	7,500
1 3/4	28,000	

Table #25 – Turnbuckle Working Load Limits

Spreader Beams

Spreader beams are used to support long, hard-to-handle loads during lifting. The use of these beams eliminates load tipping, sliding or bending. They also decrease the possibility of unsafe sling angles. See illustration #150.

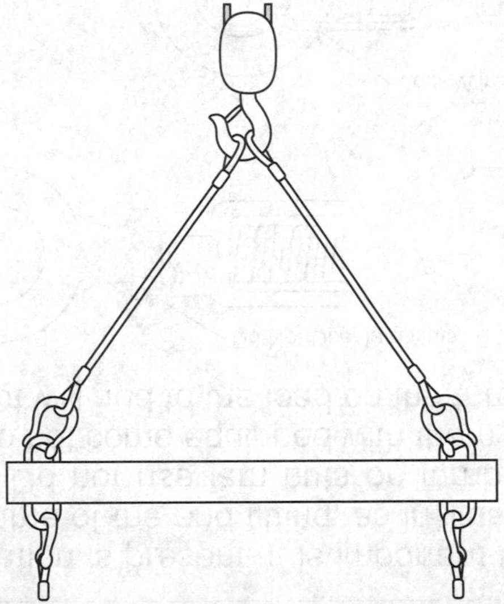

Illustration #150 - Spreader Beam

Equalizer Beams

Equalizer beams are usually used on dual hoist lines to make tandem lifts, but can also be used to equalize the load on sling legs, as in illustration #151.

Note: A custom fabricated lifting beam, or any other lifting device must be designed by an engineer. It should be tested at 125% of rated capacity. The manufacturer, the serial number, the weight and the rated capacity must be clearly indicated on all beams.

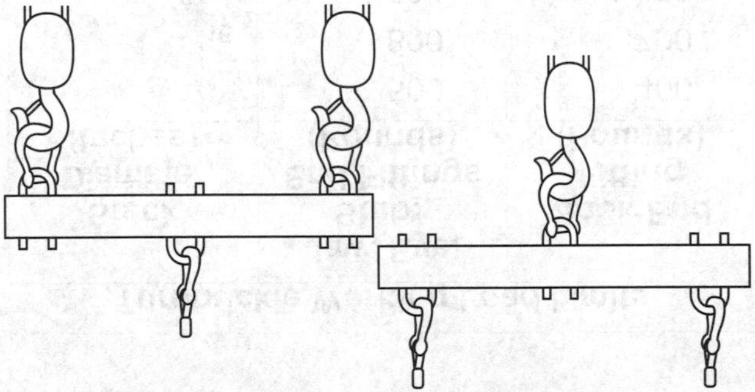

Illustration #151 - Equalizer Beam

Sheaves

Always check the condition and dimensions of sheave grooves before a new wire rope is placed in service. The bottom of the groove should have an arc of support of at least 120° to 150°, as indicated in illustration #152.

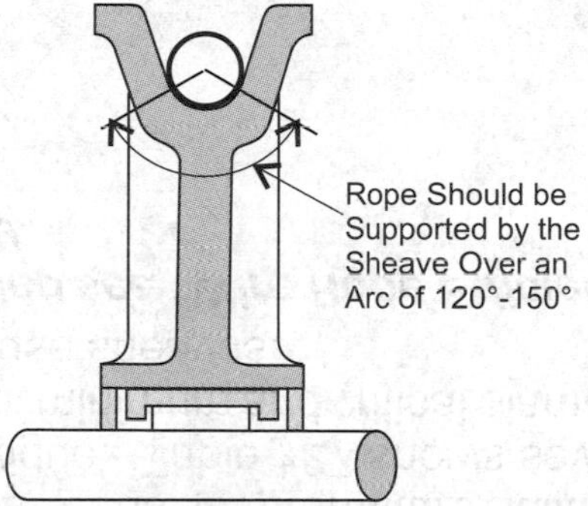
Rope Should be
Supported by the
Sheave Over an
Arc of 120°-150°

Illustration #152 - Sheave Support

To ensure a long and efficient rope life, the grooves should be smoothly contoured, free of surface defects and have rounded edges.

When the groove diameter is worn to less than the minimum values as indicated on table #26, re-groove or replace the sheave.

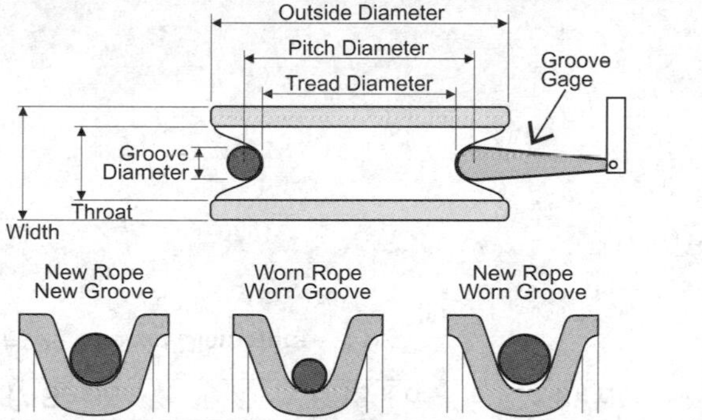
Outside Diameter
Pitch Diameter
Tread Diameter
Groove Gage
Groove Diameter
Throat
Width
New Rope New Groove
Worn Rope Worn Groove
New Rope Worn Groove

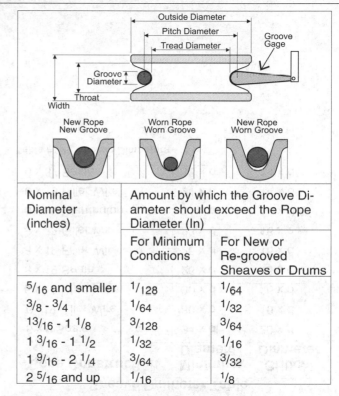

Nominal Diameter (inches)	Amount by which the Groove Diameter should exceed the Rope Diameter (In)	
	For Minimum Conditions	For New or Re-grooved Sheaves or Drums
5/16 and smaller	1/128	1/64
3/8 - 3/4	1/64	1/32
13/16 - 1 1/8	3/128	3/64
1 3/16 - 1 1/2	1/32	1/16
1 9/16 - 2 1/4	3/64	3/32
2 5/16 and up	1/16	1/8

Table #26 – Sheave Groove Conditions

Sheave Diameter

Do not operate wire rope over a sheave smaller than the “critical” diameter. When using small diameter sheaves, the excessive and repeated bending and straightening of the wires leads to premature failure from metal fatigue. Table #27 shows several examples of minimum and critical diameters for general use sheaves.

Note: Also see "Wire Rope Efficiency" on page 99.

Sheave Diameter Table		
Rope Construction	**Minimum Diameter**	**Critical Diameter**
6 x 9 Seale	34 x d	20 x d
6 x19 Filler Wire	30 x d	16 x d
6 x 19 Warrington	30 x d	16 x d
8 x 19 Seale	26 x d	16 x d
8 x 19 Filler Wire	26 x d	16 x d
6 x 22 Filler Wire	23 x d	16 x d
8 x 19 Warrington	21 x d	14 x d
8 x 19 Filler Wire	21 x d	14 x d
6 x 37 Seale	18 x d	14 x d

Table # 27– Sheave Diameters

Sheave and Drum Ratios		
Construction*	**Suggested D/d Ratio****	**Minimum D/d Ratio****
6 x 7	72	42
19 x 7 or 18 x 7 Rotation Resistant	51	34
6 x 19 S	51	34
6 x 25 B Flattened Strand	45	30
6 x 27 H Flattened Strand	45	30
6 x 30 G Flattened Strand	45	30
6 x 21 FW	45	30
6 x 26 WS	45	30
6 x 25 FW	39	26
6 x 31 WS	39	26
6 x 37 SFW	39	26
6 x 36 WS	39	26
6 x 43 FWS	35	23

Sheave and Drum Ratios		
Construction*	**Suggested D/d Ratio****	**Minimum D/d Ratio****
6 x 41 WS	32	21
6 x 41 SWS	32	21
6 x 49 SWS	32	21
6 x 43 FW (2 op)	28	18
6 x 46 SFW	28	18
6 x 46 WS	28	18
8 x 19 S	41	27
8 x 25 FW	32	21
6 x 42 Tiller	21	14

Table #28 – Sheave and Drum Ratios

Wire Rope Blocks

Depending on the capacity, these blocks are much lighter than hook blocks as they are not subjected to the abuse of hook blocks. They are equipped with cheek straps. The cheek straps provide strength between the end attachments and sheave center pins. Two examples of wire rope blocks are shown in illustration #153.

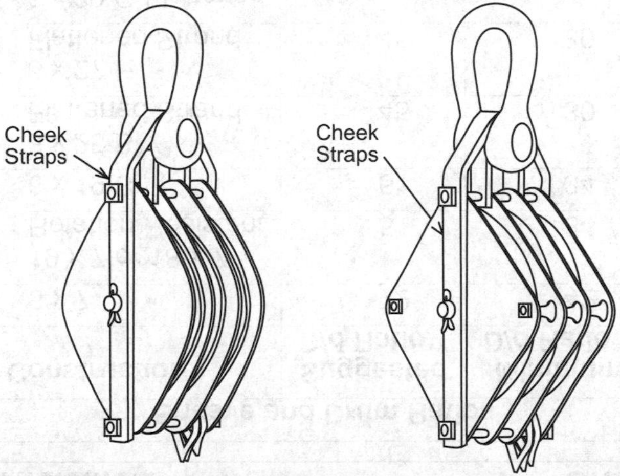
Cheek Straps
Cheek Straps

Illustration #153 - Wire Rope Blocks

Snatch Blocks

Snatch blocks are used to change the pulling direction of a wire rope. The side opens to allow positioning of the rope without having to feed it through the block. See illustration #154.

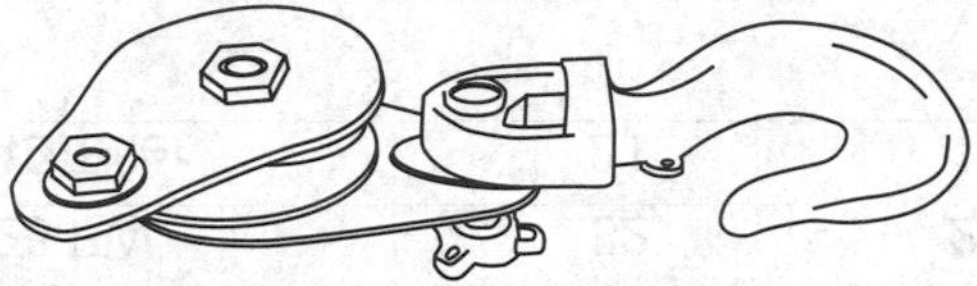

Illustration #154 - Snatch Block Side Plate

The load on the snatch block varies with the angle between the lead and load lines. When both the lead and load lines are parallel, the load on the block hook is double the weight of the load, plus friction when the load is moving. As the angle opens up, the load on the hook is reduced. To determine the load on a block, multiply the pull on the lead line by the applicable factor from table #29.

Multiplication Factors For Snatch Block Loads	
Angle Between Lead and Load Lines	Multiplication Factor
10°	1.99
20°	1.97
30°	1.93
40°	1.87
50°	1.81
60°	1.73
70°	1.64
80°	1.63
90°	1.41
100°	1.29
110°	1.15
120°	1.00
130°	.84
140°	.68
150°	.52
160°	.35
170°	.17
180°	.00

Table #29 – Factors for Snatch Block Loading

Note: On a straight vertical pull (illustration #155A), the block rigging must hold double the load weight.

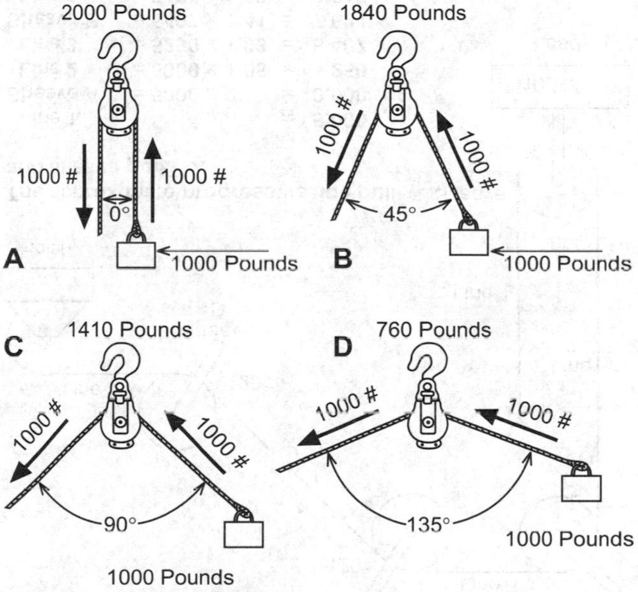
2000 Pounds
1000 #
1000 #
0°
1000 Pounds
A
1840 Pounds
1000 #
1000 #
45°
B
1000 Pounds
C
1410 Pounds
1000 #
1000 #
90°
1000 Pounds
D
760 Pounds
1000 #
1000 #
135°
1000 Pounds

Illustration #155 - Snatch Block Loading

Snatch Block Load Example

Illustration #156 shows a 10,000 pound load being lifted using four snatch blocks.

All wire rope changing direction from a sheave loses efficiency to some degree (more pull required).

The efficiency loss depends on the wire rope to sheave size ratio (D/d), the angle of pull on the sheave (illustration #155), and the type of sheave.

A snatch block with a bronze bushing loses approximately 5% on a 0 degree pull (illustration #155A).

In the example shown in illustration #156 sheave A is based on a 5% (1.05) loss, sheave B at 3% (1.03), and 2% (1.02) for sheaves C and D. Sheaves B, C and D have less efficiency loss because the pull angles are more open.

Note: Line pull numbers are only approximate.

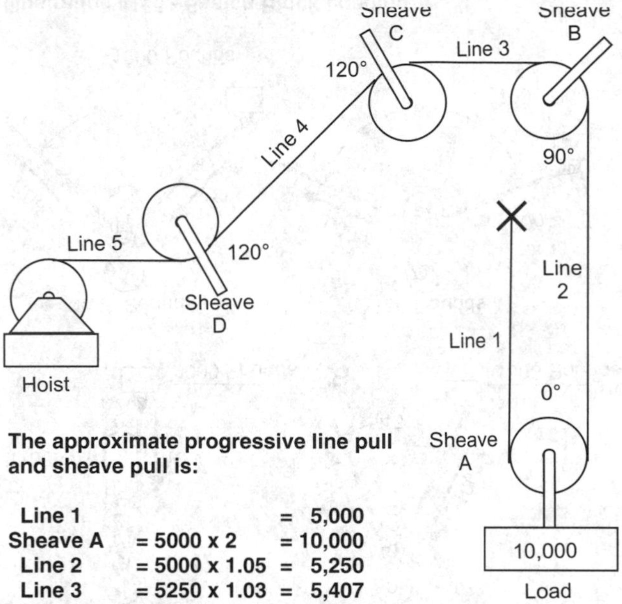
Sheave
C
Sheave
B
Line 3
120°
Line 4
90°
Line 5
120°
Line
2
Sheave
D
Line 1
Hoist
0°
Sheave
A
10,000
Load

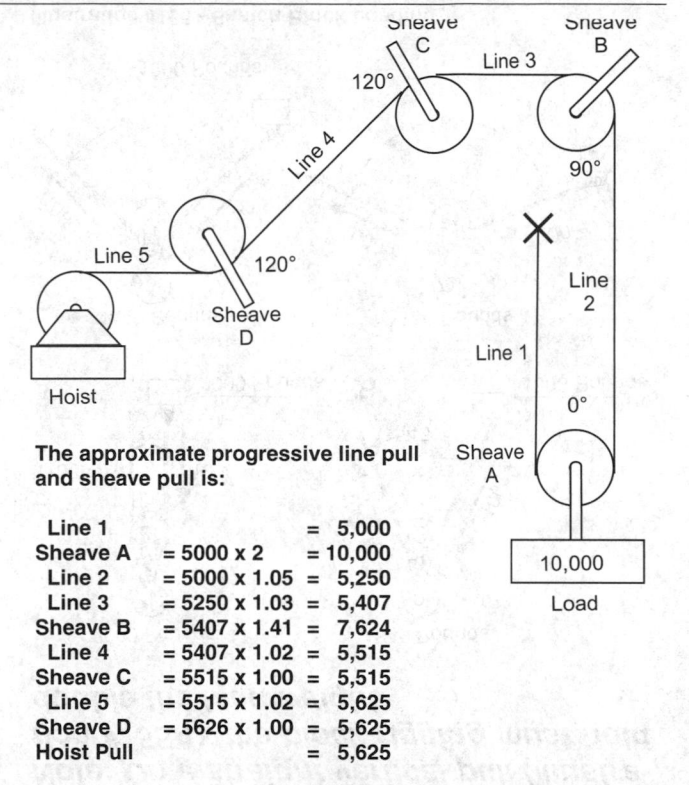

The approximate progressive line pull and sheave pull is:

Line 1		**= 5,000**
Sheave A	**= 5000 x 2**	**= 10,000**
Line 2	**= 5000 x 1.05**	**= 5,250**
Line 3	**= 5250 x 1.03**	**= 5,407**
Sheave B	**= 5407 x 1.41**	**= 7,624**
Line 4	**= 5407 x 1.02**	**= 5,515**
Sheave C	**= 5515 x 1.00**	**= 5,515**
Line 5	**= 5515 x 1.02**	**= 5,625**
Sheave D	**= 5626 x 1.00**	**= 5,625**
Hoist Pull		**= 5,625**

Illustration #156 - Snatch Block Load Example

Block Mechanical Advantage

The mechanical advantage of a machine is the amount by which the machine multiplies the force applied to move a load. Here, the machine is a pulley or a combination of pulleys forming a block and tackle system. Usually this system is used to lift, but it can also be used to move a load laterally across a floor.

The top (fixed) sheaves on the block have no other function than to change the direction of the rope. The sheave on the bottom (travelling) block will create a theoretical mechanical advantage of 2:1 for each sheave.

Calculating Mechanical Advantage:

Count the number of lines supporting the load, with the exception of the lead line when it comes down over the top block. The lead line pulling down is not counted for mechanical advantage (illustration #157A).

If the lead line comes up to the winch from the traveling block it will be counted as a supporting line and included in the mechanical advantage (illustration #157B).

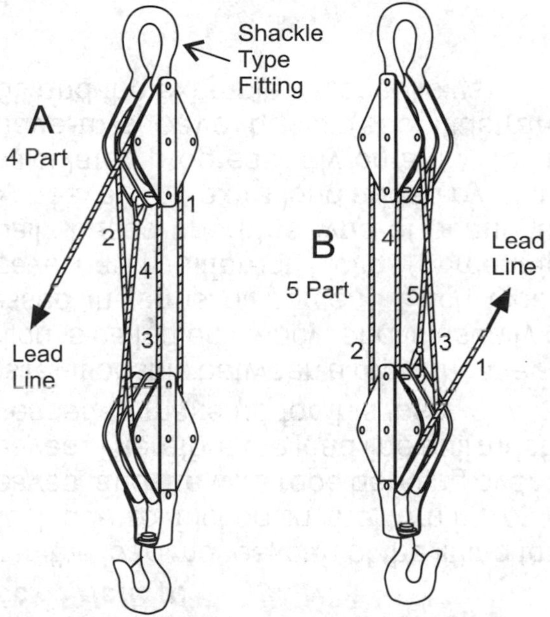
Shackle Type Fitting
A
4 Part
Lead Line
1
2
3
4
B
5 Part
Lead Line
1
2
3
4
5

Illustration #157 - Mechanical Advantage of 4 and 5

Block Speed and Distance:

The speed of the traveling block and the distance of load travel is determined by the mechanical advantage. The speed of the traveling block and the load is calculated by dividing the lead line speed by the number of parts of line, or the mechanical advantage (M/A). Or in other words, using a 5 to 1 M/A, the lead line will travel five feet for every foot the load is lifted, and it will travel five times as fast.

The amount of wire rope needed for the system is determined by measuring the top to traveling block distance and multiplying by the number of parts of line, plus enough wire rope to go to the winch and have at least several full wraps on the winch drum.

Block Friction:

When the load moves, part of the lifting force is lost due to friction in the turning of the sheaves, and the wire rope bending over the sheaves. Therefore the lead line pull must be increased to make up for this loss.

This relationship between a rope sheave and friction is called efficiency, and is usually expressed in terms of percent. Each type of sheave has a different friction percentage, usually based upon the type of bearings in the sheave. The extra load added by friction is calculated progressively on a line to line, sheave-to-sheave basis (see illustration #158 and the example which follows).

Block Friction Example:

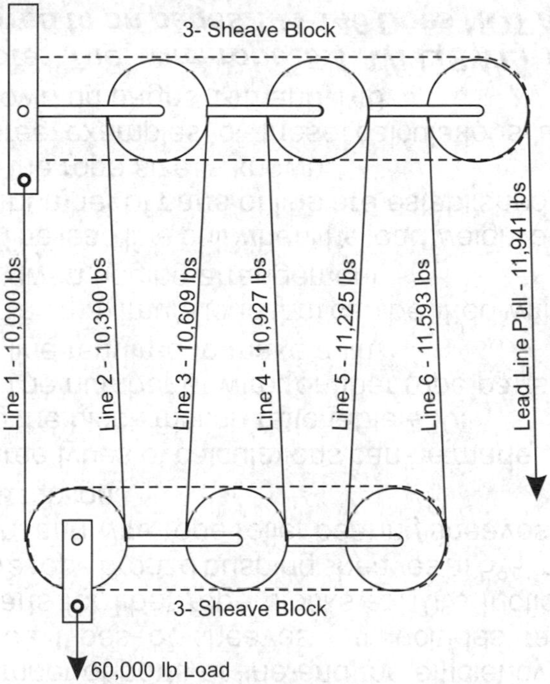
3- Sheave Block
Line 1 - 10,000 lbs
Line 2 - 10,300 lbs
Line 3 - 10,609 lbs
Line 4 - 10,927 lbs
Line 5 - 11,225 lbs
Line 6 - 11,593 lbs
Lead Line Pull - 11,941 lbs
3- Sheave Block
60,000 lb Load

Illustration #158 - Line Friction Example

Load = 60, 000 lbs or 30 tons with a 6 part line

Static load on each line equals:

60,000 / 6 = 10, 000 lbs load on each line

Roller bearing sheaves used (97% efficient - approximately 3% efficiency loss)

Friction Calculation:

Line #1 (becket line) 10,000 lbs

Line #2 10,000 x 1.03 = 10,300 lbs

Line #3 10,300 x 1.03 = 10,609 lbs

Line #4 10,609 x 1.03 = 10,927 lbs

Line #5 10,927 x 1.03 = 11,255 lbs

Line #6 11,255 x 1.03 = 11,593 lbs

Lead line pull = 11,593 x 1.03 = 11,941lbs

The lead line pull would be 11, 941 lbs.

Block Friction Ratio: Table #30 shows the number of parts of line and the efficiency of three types of sheaves. It includes ratio charts for fiber rope blocks at 10% friction, wire rope bronze bushing sheaves at 5% friction, and wire rope roller bearing sheaves at 3% friction.

Three types of calculations can be made using the block friction ratio table #30:

1. The number of wire, or fiber rope parts of line required to make a lift.
2. The maximum load that can be lifted with a given rigging arrangement.
3. The lead line pull when the load weight and number of parts of line are established or the rope size is known.

Three examples of these calculations are shown on pages 145 and 146.

Note: The wire rope 5:1 WLL(SWL) referred to on pages 144-146 Does NOT apply to block systems on cranes.

Ratio Factors To Account For Friction Loads			
# of Parts of Lines	Plain Bore Fibre Rope 10%	Bronze Bushed Wire Rope 5%	Rolling Bearing Wire Rope 3%
1	.91	.95	.97
2	1.65	1.82	1.89
3	2.26	2.59	2.75
4	2.74	3.28	3.54
5	3.11	3.91	4.31
6	3.39	4.48	5.00
7	3.61	4.96	5.69
8	3.74	5.41	6.30
9		5.81	6.87
10		6.13	7.41
11		6.43	7.91
12		6.67	8.39
13		6.88	8.84
14		7.07	9.27
15		7.21	9.62
16		7.34	9.94
17		7.42	10.30
18		7.48	10.59
19		7.51	10.80
20		7.55	11.05

Table #30 – Block Friction Ratios

1. Determine Number of Parts of Line Required:

Determine the WLL (SWL) of the wire rope by chart or rule of thumb.

The rule of thumb formula is:
diameter squared x 8 = WLL (SWL).

Determine the weight of the load.

Load weight / WLL = R (ratio).

Find ratio in table #30.

The number of parts of line is indicated opposite the applicable ratio number.

Example One – Number of Parts of Line:

Size of wire rope = 1 ¼ inch

Load weight = 75 tons

Type of sheaves = roller bearing

WLL (SWL) of 1 ¼ inch rope
= 1.25 x 1.25 x 8 = 12.5 tons

Total weight of load: 75 tons
75 tons / 12.5 = 6 (ratio)

From the column under Roller Bearing wire rope 3%, we read 6.30 as the next highest number over the calculated answer of 6. The first column indicates 8 parts of line.

2. Determine Maximum Load to be Lifted:

The number of parts of line to be used.

Type of sheaves: 3% for roller bearings, 5% for bronze bushing.

The WLL or safe working load of the wire rope to be used or the maximum lead line pull.

The rule of thumb formula = diameter squared x 8 = WLL (SWL)

Use the ratio from table #30 opposite the number of parts of line.

Calculate the maximum WLL (SWL) of the wire rope or the lead line pull x the ratio of the maximum load.

Example Two – Maximum Load:

14 parts of line

roller bearing sheaves = 3%

¾ inch wire rope

Roller bearing sheaves = 3% loss due to friction.

¾ inch wire rope = .75 x .75 x 8 = 4.5 tons WLL (SWL)

Chart ratio opposite 14 parts of line = 9.27 (table #30).

To calculate the maximum load:

WLL x ratio = load

4.5 x 9.27 = 41.715 or 42 ton maximum load.

Block Reeving Methods

Following are several tips to help block reeving:

- If the stationary block has more than two sheaves the lead line should be positioned to come off a center sheave to balance the block under load.
- When both blocks have the same number of sheaves, the rope dead end (becket) is attached to the stationary block. When the number of sheaves per block varies, the becket is attached to the block with the fewer sheaves, which will be the traveling block.
- When reeving, the becket end should be fed through the blocks starting where the lead line exits, and continued on through toward the becket connection to eliminate pulling all of the wire rope through the blocks.
- Before reeving, position the blocks as close together as possible to give less wire rope to pull through.
- The popular methods of arranging wire rope and sheaves to gain mechanical advantage are lacing and square reeving.

Block Lacing

Lacing is the least complicated method of reeving a set of blocks. See illustration #159. The wire rope is fed in through the top outside sheave, goes down to the back of the outside bottom sheave, then progresses from sheave to sheave, from left to right.

The advantages are that it is relatively easy, the blocks will pull quite close together, which creates more lifting height, and there are no reverse bends in the rope.

The disadvantage is that the rope and sheave speed is faster on one side. This causes the blocks to tilt together on one end, resulting in the rope wearing against the sheaves.

Square Reeving

The blocks are positioned with one block turned 90 degrees to the other. The main advantage is that the blocks are brought into balance and run smooth and level.

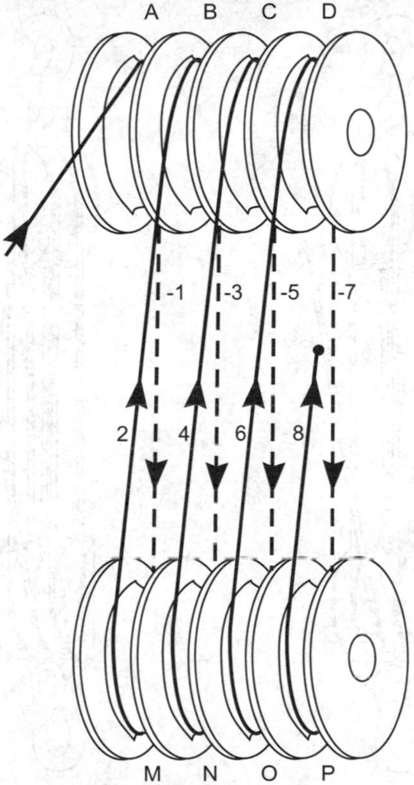
A
B
C
D
-1
-3
-5
-7
2
4
6
8
M
N
O
P

Illustration #159 - Block Lacing

Square reeving has 2 major disadvantages:

1. The blocks cannot come close together due to the positioning of the blocks and wire rope. If attempted, it causes the block-to-block lines to come off the sheaves at excessive angles, resulting in line scrub and sheave wear.
2. Wire rope which is square reeved continually goes through reverse bending. Reverse bending in a wire rope will eventually result in premature fatigue.

Most sets of blocks can be square reeved in two types of patterns. The better method has the lead line coming off one of the center sheaves for balance. The other has the lead line coming off an end sheave, however an uneven block pull is partially offset with the next line coming off the sheave on the opposite end. See illustrations #160 to #163 for examples.

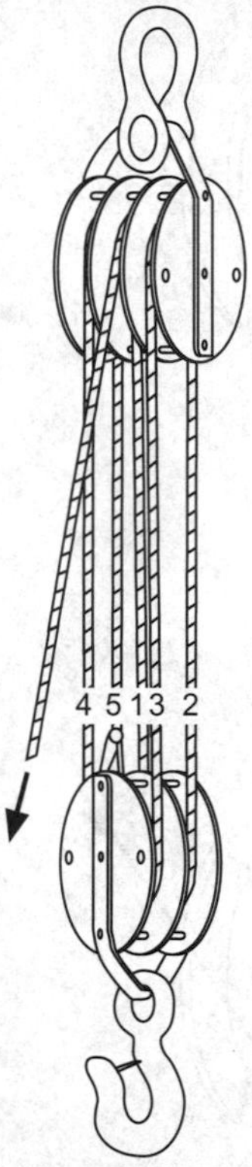
4 5 1 3 2
Illustration #160 - Five Part Reeving

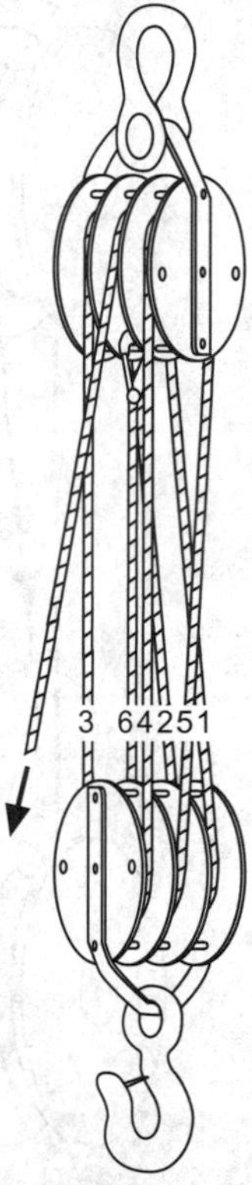
3 6 4 2 5 1
Illustration #161 - Six Part Reeving

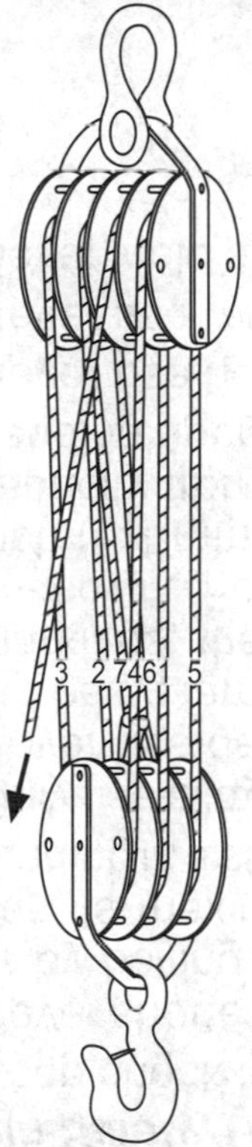
3 2 7 4 6 1 5

Illustration #162 -
Seven Part Reeving

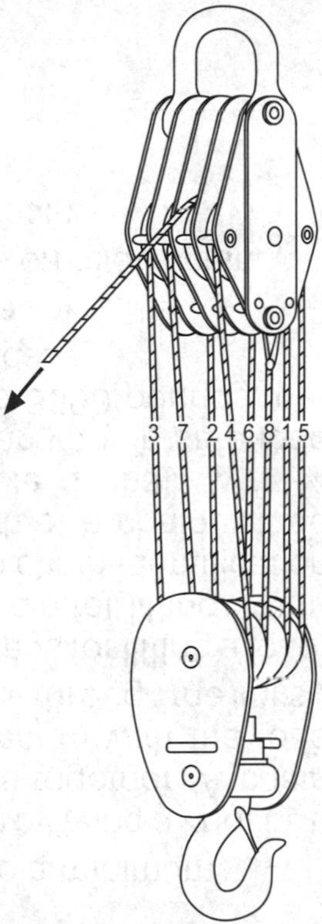
3 7 2 4 6 8 1 5

Illustration #163 -
Eight Part Reeving

Chain Grade Identification

Chain should have an identifying mark embossed regularly on the links, as indicated in illustration #164. Chain quality identification can be confusing as different manufacturers may use their own system of marking. Some of the more common markings for alloy hoisting chain are “A” or a version of the number “8", such as ”80" or “800".

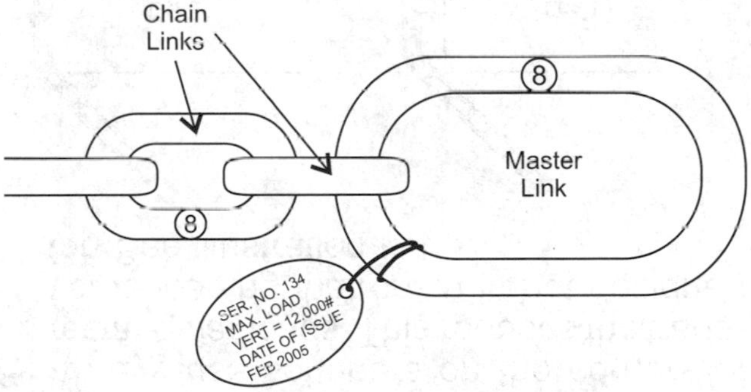
Chain
Links
8
8
Master
Link
SER. NO. 134
MAX. LOAD
VERT = 12,000#
DATE OF ISSUE
FEB 2005

Illustration #164 - Chain Identification

Chain Safety Tips

1. Keep shock loading to a minimum.
2. Never shorten a chain by tying a knot in it, or by bolting two links together. A chain has its maximum strength with the load running in a straight line through the links.
3. Only use alloy hoist slings for lifting a load. Never use decking chain for lifting. Without being familiar with chain identification markings, the strength of a chain will be unknown. For example a chain with ¼ inch (6.4 mm) links can vary in safe load capacity from 1200 to 3500 pounds, depending upon the grade.
4. Never use homemade links.
5. Never use repair links on alloy chain.
6. Never weld an alloy chain.
7. If the links of a chain bind on each other the chain is overstretched.
8. Always use softeners on the corners of rectangular loads. This reduces the transverse loading that chain is not designed for. See illustration #165.

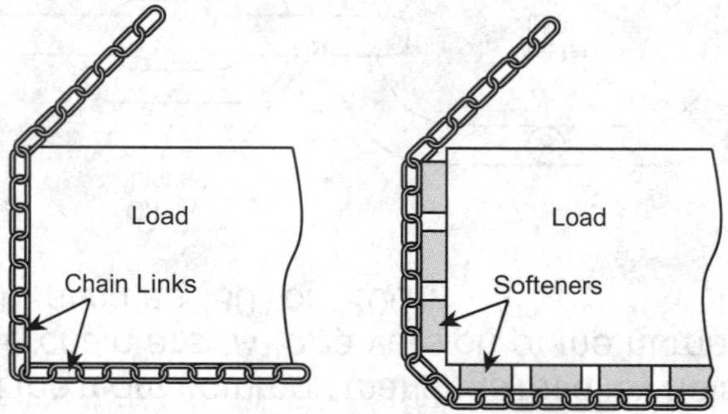
Load
Chain Links
Load
Softeners
Illustration #165 - Chain Bending Around Corners

CHAIN SLINGS - WLL (SWL) BASED ON GRADE 80 ALLOY 4:1 SF							
Nominal Chain Size	Single Chain 90°	Double Chain Slings			Triple & Quad Chain Slings		
		60°(30°)	45°(45°)	30°(60°)	60°(30°)	45°(45°)	30°(60°)
inch	lbs.	lbs.	lbs.	lbs.	lbs.	lbs.	lbs.
9/32 (1/4)	3,500	6,100	4,900	3,500	9,100	7,400	5,200
3/8	7,100	12,300	10,000	7,100	18,400	15,100	10,600
1/2	12,000	20,800	17,000	12,000	31,200	25,500	18,000
5/8	18,100	31,300	25,600	18,100	47,000	38,400	27,100
3/4	28,300	49,000	40,000	28,300	73,500	60,000	42,400
mm	kg	kg	kg	kg	kg	kg	kg
7	1,590	2,700	2,200	1,590	4,100	3,300	2,400
10	3,200	5,500	4,500	3,200	8,300	6,800	4,800
13	5,400	9,400	7,600	5,400	14,000	11,500	8,100
16	8,200	14,200	11,600	8,200	21,300	17,400	12,300
20	12,800	22,300	18,200	12,800	33,500	27,400	19,300

Notes: 1. Quadruple Sling Rating is the same as Triple Sling Rating because lifting practice may not distribute load uniformly. 2. Angles in parentheses are vertical angles.

Table #31 – Grade 80 Chain Sling Capacities

CHAIN SLINGS - WLL (SWL) BASED ON GRADE 100 ALLOY (4:1 SF)							
Nominal Chain Size	Single Chain 90°	Double Chain Slings			Triple and Quad Chain Slings		
		60°(30°)	45°(45°)	30°(60°)	60°(30°)	45°(45°)	30°(60°)
inch	lbs.	lbs.	lbs.	lbs.	lbs.	lbs.	lbs.
9/32(1/4)	4300	7500	6100	4300	11,200	9100	6450
3/8	8800	15,200	12,400	8800	22,800	18,600	13,200
1/2	15,000	26,000	21,200	15,000	39,000	31,800	22,500
5/8	22,600	39,100	32,000	22,600	58,700	47,900	33,900
3/4	35,300	61,100	49,000	35,300	91,700	74,900	53,000
mm	kg	kg	kg	kg	kg	kg	kg
7	1950	3400	2700	1900	5100	4100	2900
10	4000	6900	5600	4060	10,300	8400	6000
13	6800	11,800	9600	6800	17,700	14,400	10,200
16	10,200	17,700	14,500	10,200	26,600	21,700	15,400
20	16,000	27,700	22,600	16,000	41,600	34,000	24,000

Notes: 1. Quadruple Sling Rating is the same as Triple Sling Rating because lifting practice may not distribute load uniformly. 2. Angles in parentheses are vertical angles.

Table #32 – Grade 100 Chain Sling Capacities

SECTION TWO QUESTIONS

Rigging Hardware

1. *Determine if this statement is true or false. The two types of wire rope center core designs are fiber core and independent wire rope core.*

   ❒ true ❒ false

2. *What is the percentage gain in strength using an IWRC versus a fiber core wire rope?*

   ❒ 3.5
   ❒ 5.5
   ❒ 7.5
   ❒ 9.5

3. *What characteristic increases in a wire rope by using a rope with more strands and more wires in the strands?*

   ❒ rigidity
   ❒ breaking strength
   ❒ lubrication
   ❒ flexibility

4. *Determine if this statement is true or false. Grade 110/120 Improved Plow steel has the highest tensile strength for any type of wire rope.*

   ❒ true ❒ false

5. *A regular lay wire rope has strands and wires in the strands that:*

   ❒ are all laid in the right hand direction
   ❒ are all laid in the left hand direction
   ❒ wires and strands laid in opposite directions
   ❒ wires and strands laid in the same direction

6. *Due to its tendency to unwind, which wire rope should NOT be used on single part hoisting lines?*

   ❒ regular lay
   ❒ lang lay
   ❒ alternate lay
   ❒ none of above

7. *Determine if this statement is true or false. A 6 x 19 wire rope classification could have as many as 16 to 26 wires per strand.*

   ❒ true ❒ false

8. *Which rotation-resistant wire rope classification is non-rotating?*
   - ❒ 3 strand
   - ❒ 8 strand
   - ❒ 19 strand
   - ❒ 35 strand

9. *When a non-rotating rope is used in a wedge socket, care must be taken to prevent:*
   - ❒ core slippage
   - ❒ rope from unraveling
   - ❒ wire slippage
   - ❒ strand slippage

10. *When hoisting personnel on a crane equipped with rotating resistant wire rope, what is the Design (safety) Factor required by most safety standards?*
    - ❒ 3.5:1
    - ❒ 5:1
    - ❒ 7:1
    - ❒ 10:1

11. *Newer designs of wire rope with shaped wires and triangular strands are an attempt to prevent rope damage from:*
    - ❒ multiple drum layers
    - ❒ cross winding
    - ❒ improper tensioning
    - ❒ all of the above

12. *Referring to the number of broken wires allowed in a wire rope, The "Rule of Thumb" for determining replacement is:*
    - ❒ 2/6
    - ❒ 3/6
    - ❒ 4/8
    - ❒ 2/12

13. *Wire rope should be replaced if the wear in the outer strand wires exceeds:*
    - ❒ 1/16 of original diameter
    - ❒ 1/8 of original diameter
    - ❒ 1/3 of original diameter
    - ❒ 1/4 of original diameter

14. *When spooling wire rope from a reel to the bottom of a crane or hoist drum, the wire rope must come off which part of the reel?*

❒ top ❒ bottom

15. *When standing behind a drum being overwound with Right Lay Wire Rope, and using the fist method to determine the correct position of the end connection and the winding procedure, the hand would be:*

❒ right hand palm down
❒ right hand palm up
❒ left hand palm down
❒ left hand palm up

16. *If the wire rope hoist line coming off a drum is fed into a sheave, how must the sheave be positioned:*

❒ aligned with the proper fleet angle
❒ aligned with the left drum flange
❒ aligned with the right drum flange
❒ depends on the rope lay

17. *Determine if this statement is true or false. Before using an air operated tugger, the air line should be blown out to remove excess moisture.*

❒ true ❒ false

18. *What is the Rule of Thumb formula to find the Ultimate Load (breaking strength) of an IWRC wire rope?*

❒ D2 x 42
❒ D2 x 45
❒ D2 x 5
❒ D2 x 10

19. *When the Ultimate Load (breaking strength) of a wire rope is divided by a safety (design) factor the result is called the:*

❒ ultimate tensile load
❒ nominal strength of rope
❒ yield strength of rope
❒ working load limit (WLL)

20. *What happens when a wire rope is bent around a sheave or a hook?*

- ❒ nominal strength does not change
- ❒ nominal strength is reduced
- ❒ outside strands are in compression
- ❒ inside strands are in tension

21. *A 1 inch wire rope eye sling (no thimble) lifting a load with a 1 inch shackle will be approximately how efficient?*

- ❒ 100%
- ❒ 75%
- ❒ 50%
- ❒ 25%

22. *Referring to slings, the terms "Rated Capacity" or "Working Load Limit" replaces the old terminology of:*

- ❒ safety factor
- ❒ breaking strength
- ❒ rule of thumb
- ❒ safe working load

23. *What is considered the minimum Design (safety) Factor for general sling use?*

- ❒ 3 to 1
- ❒ 5 to 1
- ❒ 7 to 1
- ❒ 10 to 1

24. *Determine if this statement is true or false. A 4-leg bridle sling will carry the load weight equally on all 4 legs if the load is rigid.*

❒ true ❒ false

25. *With an "improved plow" wire rope sling, the preferred D/d basket hitch ratio is:*

- ❒ 25 to 1
- ❒ 20 to 1
- ❒ 15 to 1
- ❒ 10 to 1

26. *When slinging a bundle of pipe or tubing, which of the following would provide the best contact between sling and load?*

- ❒ double basket
- ❒ bridle hitch
- ❒ two double wrap chokers
- ❒ single leg choker

27. *Determine if this statement is true or false. Synthetic slings can be safely used under any environmental circumstances.*

❒ true ❒ false

28. *Determine if this statement is true or false. Because all web slings are manufactured identically, the ID tag does not indicate the rated load.*

❒ true ❒ false

29. *Referring to the standard format of sling load charts, the angle between the top of the load and the sling leg is called the:*

- ❒ double angle
- ❒ working angle
- ❒ vertical angle
- ❒ horizontal angle

30. *Using two slings to lift a load, at what angle to the horizontal is the load on each sling considered to be equal to the weight of the load?*

- ❒ 15
- ❒ 30
- ❒ 45
- ❒ 60

31. *Calculate using the recommended safe lifting angle, the distance between the lift points connecting the load using two 12 foot slings.*

- ❒ 6 feet
- ❒ 8 feet
- ❒ 10 feet
- ❒ 12 feet

32. *Using the basic "Riggers Rule" (L/V x load/2) calculate the load in pounds on each sling leg, using two 12 foot slings with a vertical distance to hook point of 8 feet, and a load of 8,000 pounds.*
- ❒ 12,000
- ❒ 8,000
- ❒ 6,000
- ❒ 4,000

33. *Determine if this statement is true or false. Safety regulations prohibit the use of clips to make hoisting sling eyes.*
- ❒ true
- ❒ false

34. *Correctly installed U bolt type wire rope clips are installed with the U portion of the clip on the:*
- ❒ dead or short end
- ❒ on the live or long end
- ❒ installed either way
- ❒ alternating up and down

35. *Correctly applied wire rope clips have an efficiency rating of approximately:*
- ❒ 50 percent
- ❒ 80 percent
- ❒ 20 percent
- ❒ 100 percent

36. *When compared to the rated size of the body of a shackle, the diameter of the pin is always:*
- ❒ same size
- ❒ larger than body
- ❒ smaller than body
- ❒ depends on manufacturer

37. *Shackles are only rated for their maximum capacity when used for what type of pull?*
- ❒ straight line pull
- ❒ 90 degree pull
- ❒ 45 degree pull
- ❒ designed for any angle pull

38. *With two shackles or sling eyes in a hook, what is the suggested maximum included lifting angle?*

- ❐ 0 degrees
- ❐ 45 degrees
- ❐ 90 degrees
- ❐ 180 degrees

39. *A wedge socket must be attached with the load line pulling in a straight line from the:*

- ❐ wedge
- ❐ shank
- ❐ point
- ❐ pin

40. *Determine if this statement is true or false. Referring to wedge sockets, it is permitted to clip the wire rope dead end to the load line.*

❐ true ❐ false

41. *Which type of eye-bolt should be used if there is any possibility of an angular load?*

- ❐ shoulder type
- ❐ shoulderless type

42. *Custom fabricated lifting beams or any homemade lifting device must be:*

- ❐ designed by an engineer
- ❐ have the rated capacity clearly stamped
- ❐ be test lifted at 125% of rated capacity
- ❐ all of the above

43. *The main advantage of a side opening snatch block is: (pick the best answer)*

- ❐ change direction of load
- ❐ change direction of wire rope
- ❐ swivel hook
- ❐ ease of installing on wire rope

44. *With the load suspended, a single block hoisting assembly has a lead-line pull of 200 pounds. If the lines are parallel what is the load on the block?*

- ❐ 600 pounds
- ❐ 400 pounds
- ❐ 200 pounds
- ❐ 100 pounds

45. *What is the mechanical advantage ratio created on the top fixed sheave of a two block hoisting system?*

- ❒ none
- ❒ 2 to 1
- ❒ 4 to 1
- ❒ depends on number of sheaves

46. *When determining the number of parts of line needed for rigging a system, what unknown factor makes the use of a ratio chart a necessity?*

- ❒ block weight
- ❒ friction
- ❒ length of wire rope
- ❒ diameter of drum

47. *What is one of the main advantages of lacing a set of blocks?*

- ❒ they can be used in situations where headroom is tight because the blocks can come closer together
- ❒ there are more reverse bends
- ❒ the mechanical advantage is higher than square reeving
- ❒ the blocks are 90° to each other

48. *Determine if this statement is true or false. Load decking chain is the type used for chain hoisting slings.*

❒ true ❒ false

SECTION THREE

FIBER ROPE

Natural & Synthetic Fiber Rope

Fiber Rope: Fiber rope can be made from either natural or synthetic fibers. Natural fiber rope is derived from plants and synthetic rope is made from chemical compounds.

Natural Fiber Rope: The length of the fibers in natural fiber rope is at most a few feet and the effectiveness in this state is very limited. The fibers are first twisted into yarns, which are laid up into strands, and finally three or more strands are formed into a rope, as in illustration #166.

Manila Rope: The only type of natural fiber rope that is used in the construction industry is Number One Grade Manila. Other types of natural fiber rope are not strong enough or deteriorate too quickly.

Number One Natural Manila is strong and durable. It is recognized by its light yellow color. As the grade and strength decreases, the color darkens. A low grade Manila is dark brown. The minimum breaking strength of a one inch diameter manila rope is 9,000 pounds (4,082 kg).

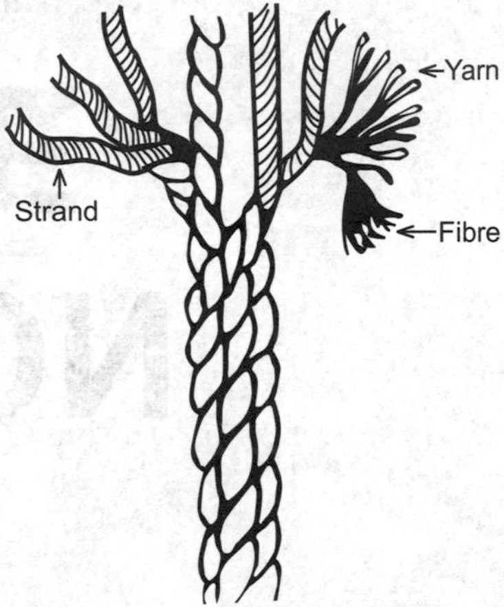
Yarn
Strand
Fibre

Illustration #166 - Fiber Rope Construction

The following types of natural fibre rope are not used in the construction industry due to various undesirable qualities:

1. Hemp: It is the strongest of the natural fiber ropes, however it deteriorates quickly when wet.
2. Sisal: It is approximately 75% the strength of untarred hemp, and will stand exposure to sea water.
3. Coir: It is made from coconut husk fibers. Very elastic, about one-quarter the strength of hemp, and will float.
4. Cotton: It is approximately 60% as strong as hemp.

Synthetic Fiber Rope: Synthetic ropes have individual threads and fibers that run continuously through the rope. All synthetic ropes have the following common characteristics: resistance to rot, mildew, and more strength than natural fiber rope.

Nylon: Other than the Kelvar type materials, Nylon is the strongest rope available. It will absorb greater shock load than any other rope, and outlast all natural fiber ropes by a wide margin. Nylon is flexible, has high abrasion resistance, can be stored wet, resists most alkalis and organic solvents, and will not rot. Nylon rope is ideal for anchor lines, couplers, hawsers, tie-up lines, safety and mountaineering ropes. It is also widely used in commercial fishing.

Polyester (terylene): Polyester is not as strong as Nylon, but is twice the strength of Manila. It stretches far less than Nylon but slightly more than Manila. It has excellent resistance to abrasion, chemicals and weathering. Polyester ropes are recommended wherever minimum stretch, high strength and durability are needed.

Polypropylene: Polypropylene is the lightest, most economical and widely used rope on the market. Strength is far greater than Manila. Other characteristics are long life, ease of handling, flexibility in cold temperatures, excellent resistance to most acids and alkalis and very good impact loading. And it floats! It is supplied in many colors and color combinations.

Polyethylene: Polyethylene is 50% as strong as nylon and resists acids and alkalis.

Uncoiling and Coiling Rope

A new coil of rope should be laid flat, with the inside rope end on the floor. Reach down inside and pull the rope up through, unwinding it in a counter clockwise direction, as in illustration #167.

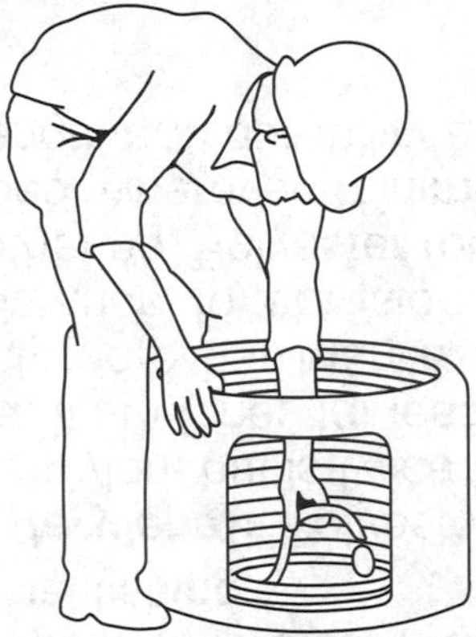

Illustration #167 - Proper Rope Uncoiling

Even when a rope is properly uncoiled, loops and kinks could form. These must be removed to prevent damage.

After use, recoil a rope in a clockwise direction. Loop the rope over your arm and tie with two half hitches. Leave a short end for carrying or hanging from a peg, as in illustration #168.

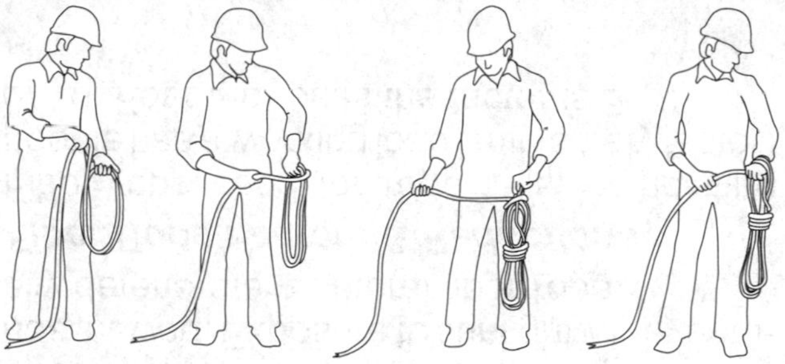

Illustration #168 - Proper Rope Coiling

Rope Ends

Whipping Natural Fiber Rope: When cutting a natural fiber rope, the ends must be taped, or whipped with a small twine to prevent the rope from untwisting. See illustration #169.

Melting Synthetic Fiber Rope: As whipping will not stay in position on synthetic fiber rope, the common practice after cutting is to melt the strands ends together with a torch or lighter to keep the end from untwisting and fraying.

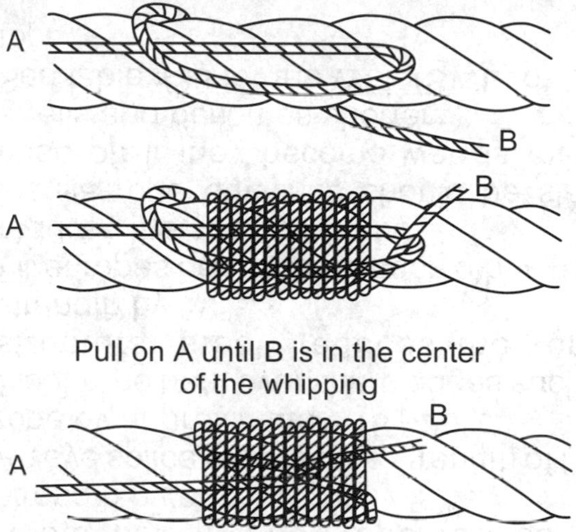
A
B
A
B
Pull on A until B is in the center of the whipping
A
B

Illustration #169 - Fiber Rope Whipping

Fiber Rope Inspection

Every foot of a rope should be inspected, as it is only as strong as its weakest part. Inspect the outer surface for broken yarns or fibers, then untwist the strands and observe the inside.

On manila rope, look for a bright yellow color to indicate good quality. Broken fibers or powder inside a rope indicates the rope has been overloaded. The interior yarns of an overloaded rope will fail first.

With a natural fiber rope, pull out a fiber and try to break it, if it breaks easily the rope has been overloaded or affected by mildew or dry rot.

In northern regions, be careful not to allow natural or synthetic fiber rope to freeze. This causes the separation of yarns and fibers. A frozen rope should not be disturbed until it has thawed. Exposure to sunlight will eventually deteriorate a natural fiber rope.

Fiber Rope Factors & Reductions

Fiber rope used for rope falls, or hoisting people has a working load limit (safety factor) of 10. For other uses the factor is 5.

As the fibers in a Manila rope are short and intertwined, they will pull apart under a continuous load. If loaded to 50% of its breaking strength a Manila rope will fail in several hours, due to fiber creepage, and if loaded to 75% of breaking strength, it will fail in minutes.

- Knots tied in fiber rope reduce the strength by approximately 50%.
- An eye splice reduces the strength of fiber rope by approximately 15 - 20%.
- Fiber rope bent over sharp edges such as structural steel, reduces the ropes strength by 50%.
- Fiber ropes bent around each other in a U reduces the strength by 50%.
- Manila rope guy-lines should be slackened off if they become wet as manila swells and becomes shorter.
- See table #33 for the WLL (SWL) of fiber rope.

Approximate WLL (SWL) of New Fibre Rope (3-Strand Ropes) Design (Safety) Factor of 5											
Rope Diameter		Manila		Nylon		Polypropylene		Polyester		Polyethylene	
Inch	(mm)	lbs	kg	lbs	kg	lbs	kg	lbs	kg	lbs	kg
3/16	(4.82)	100	45.3	200	90.7	150	68.0	200	90.7	150	68.0
1/4	(6.35)	120	54.4	300	136.1	250	113.4	300	136.0	250	113.4
5/16	(7.87)	200	90.7	500	226.8	400	181.4	500	226.8	350	158.8
3/8	(9.53)	270	122.5	700	317.5	500	226.8	700	317.5	500	226.8
1/2	(12.7)	530	240.4	1250	566.9	830	376.5	1200	544.3	800	362.9
5/8	(15.88)	880	399.2	2000	907.2	1300	589.7	1900	861.8	1050	476.3
3/4	(19.05)	1080	489.9	2800	1270.0	1700	771.1	2400	1088.6	1500	680.4
7/8	(22.23)	1540	698.5	3800	1723.6	2200	998.0	3400	1542.2	2100	952.5
1	(25.4)	1800	816.5	4800	2177.2	2900	1315.4	4200	1905.1	2500	1133.9
1 1/8	(28.7)	2400	1088.6	6300	2857.6	3750	1701.0	5600	2540.1	3300	1496.9
1 1/4	(31.75)	2700	1224.7	7200	3265.9	4.200	1905.1	6300	2857.6	3700	1678.3
Rule of Thumb Formula: D^2 = WLL (Working Load Limit)											

Table #33 – Fiber Rope Safe Working Loads

Crown Knot (Back Splice)

The sole purpose of the crown knot (back splice) is to keep the strands at the end of a rope from from unraveling. The one drawback is that it won't fit through a sheave.

- Unlay the strands, as shown in illustration #170, and lay strand A over the center of the rope, then bring B down over A, finally bring C down over B and through the bight of A.
- Pull the strands tight, then tuck each one by passing it over the second strand in the rope and under the third. There should be three tucks in each strand when using natural fibre rope and five tucks when using synthetic fibre rope. Trim the ends after completing the tucks.

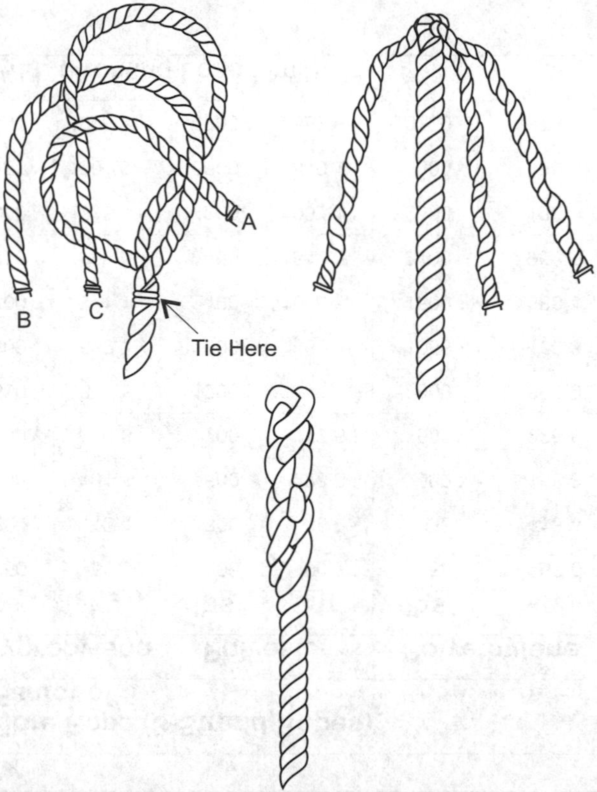
A
B
C
Tie Here

Illustration #170 - Crown Knot (Back Splice)

Fiber Rope Splices & Knots

Short Splice: As a short splice doubles the diameter, it is only used when the rope does not have to pass through a sheave. A short splice is 85% as strong as the original fiber rope.

- Unlay both ends for approximately eight turns. Whip or tape the strand ends, bring them together so they interlock with a strand from one rope between two strands of the other rope (illustration #171A).
- Apply temporary seizing or tape to both ropes after they have been brought closely together.
- Take any one strand and pass it over the strand nearest and tuck it under the next (illustration #171C).
- Tuck all six strands in both ropes at least three times for natural fiber, five times for synthetic. The ends can now be feathered out with several more tucks, then roll the splice to smooth it out (illustration #171E).

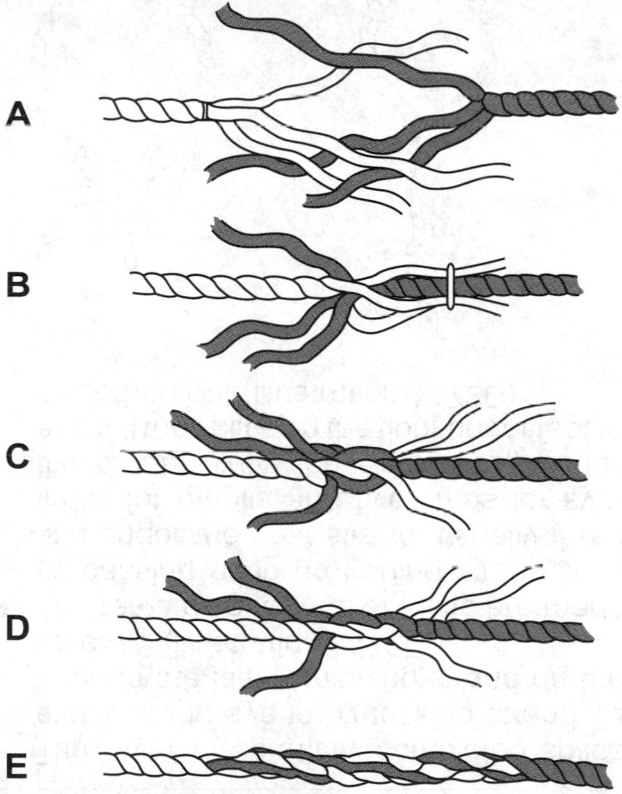
A
B
C
D
E
Illustration #171 - Short Splice

Eye or Side Splice: An eye or side splice is used to make eyes in fiber rope. All eye splices used for lifting should have a metal or nylon thimble.

- Manila rope should be seized or taped six turns from the end (nine for synthetic rope).
- The rope is then untwisted to the seizing.
- Tuck the middle strand, #2, under #5 (illustration #172A).
- Tuck strand #1 under strand #4 (illustration #172B).
- Turn over the partially completed splice and lock the eye in by tucking strand #3 through the last remaining strand on the rope, #6 (illustration #172C).
- The remaining rounds of tucks are made by passing each protruding strand over and under the next strand, usually three times for manila and five times for synthetic. Cut away the remaining strands and roll the splice on the floor under foot to smoothen out (illustration #172D).

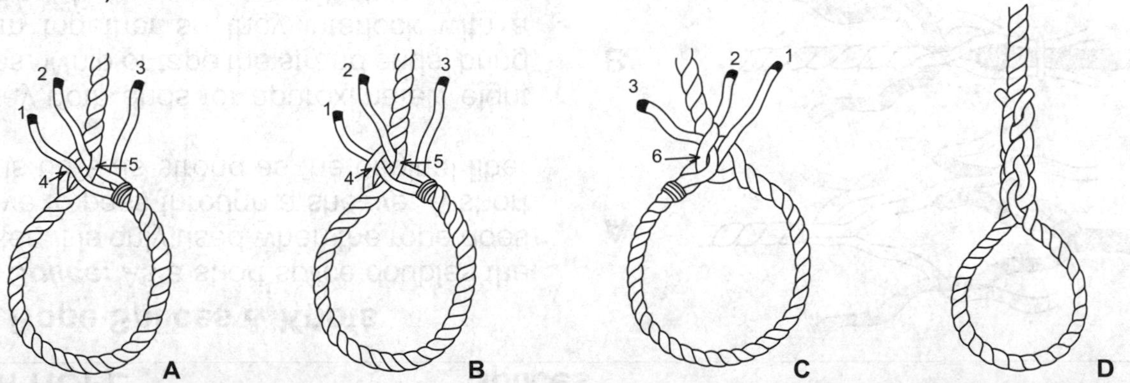
1
2
3
4
5
A
1
2
3
4
5
B
1
2
3
6
C
D

Illustration #172 - Side Splice

Bowline: The bowline is one of the most popular knots. It never jams or slips under load and is easily untied. See illustration #173.

Bowline on the Bight: The bowline on the bight is used to form a non-slipping eye in the middle of a rope. See illustration #174.

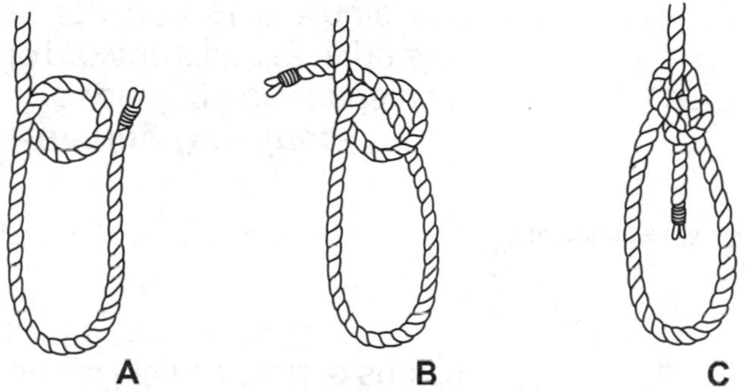
A
B
C

Illustration #173 - Bowline

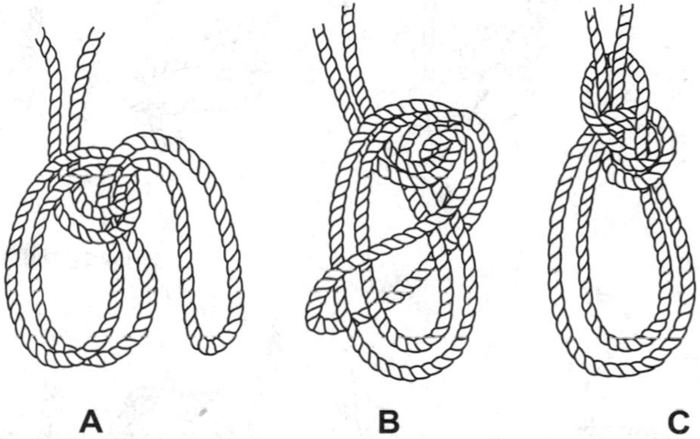
A
B
C

Illustration #174 - Bowline on the Bight

Self-Centering Bowline:

The self-centering bowline is useful when a knot must be tied to center a load with equal load distribution. It compliments a scaffold or barrel hitch, which is shown in illustration #175.

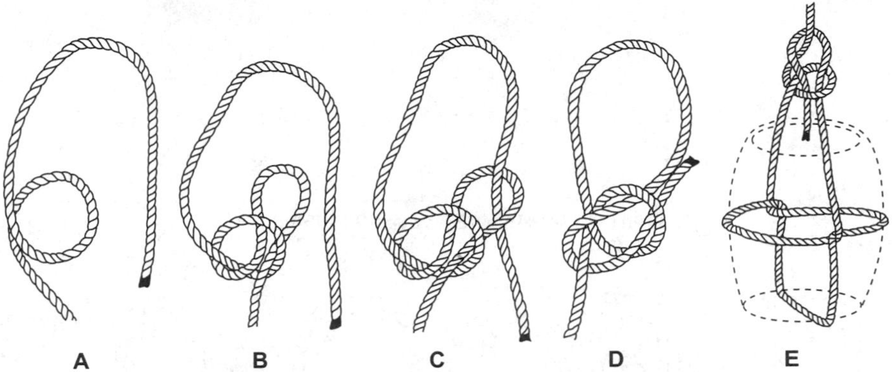
A
B
C
D
E

Illustration #175 - Self-Centering Bowline

Running Bowline:

The running bowline is used to provide a choker type sling at the end of a single line. The knot is made around the standing part of the rope and runs freely. See illustration #176.

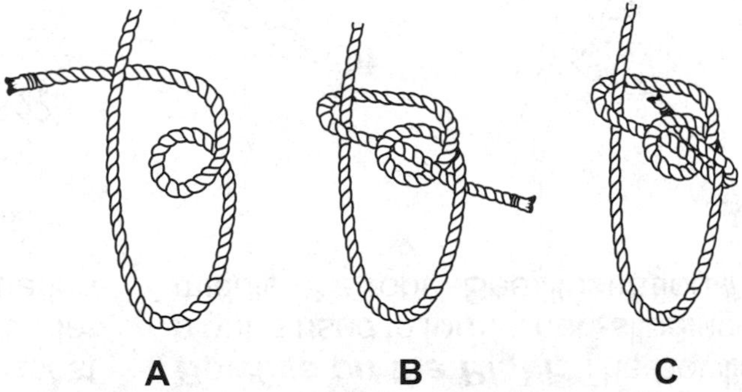
A
B
C

Illustration #176 - Running Bowline

Clove Hitch: The clove hitch is used to tie a rope to a pipe or post. It can be tied in position or slipped over the end. See illustration #177. To prevent loosening it should be finished with a half hitch.

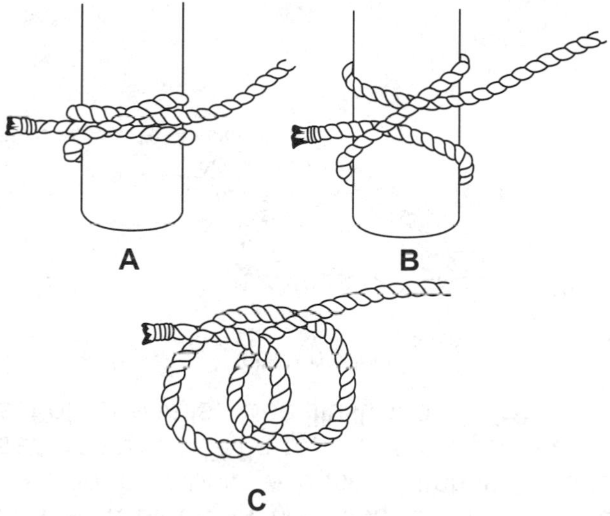
A
B
C

Illustration #177 - Clove Hitch

Rolling Hitch: The rolling hitch is the best simple hitch for lengthwise pull. Ensure that it is laid very carefully and pulled firmly before loading.

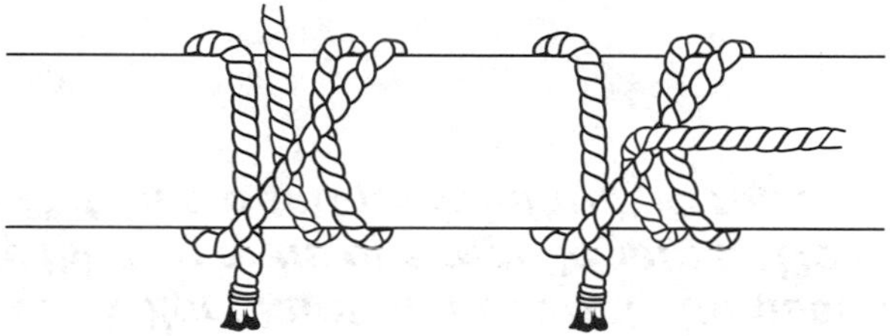

Illustration #178 - Rolling Hitch

Note: Never use a rolling hitch for right angle pull, as it will spill.

Becket Hitch: A becket is the end connection on a block for connecting a rope while reeving the block. A becket hitch is used to secure the end of a rope to the becket on a set of rope falls. See illustration #179.

Becket of Block

Illustration #179 - Becket Hitch

Reef Knot: A reef knot is also referred to as a square knot. See illustration #180.

Illustration #180 - Reef (Deadmans) Knot

Note: This knot is often misused or is not tied properly. It is sometimes referred to as a "killer" knot. It must only be used to tie the two ends of a rope together. Do not use it as a bend for joining two ropes.

Sheet Bend: A sheet bend is used for tying two ropes of unequal diameter together. It is not used on large diameter rope. See illustration #181.

Illustration #181 - Double Sheet Bend

Carrick Bend: A carrick bend is used to tie large diameter ropes together. It will draw up tightly but will not jamb. See illustration #182.

Illustration #182 - Carrick Bend

Catspaw: A catspaw is used to attach a rope to a hook. It is especially useful if the center of the rope is used. See illustration #183.

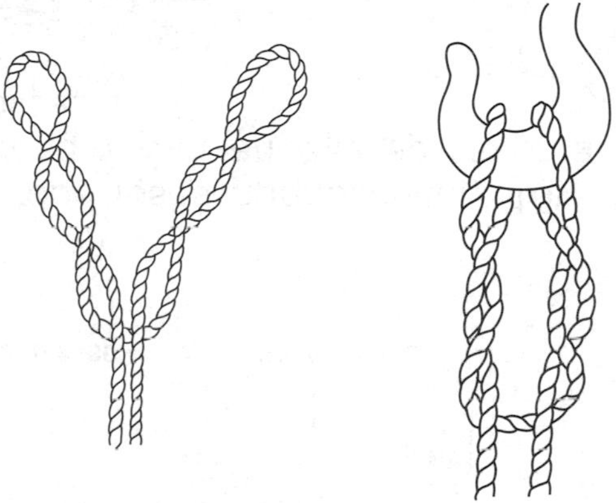

Illustration #183 - Catspaw

Strength of Knots, Bends, Hitches

- Straight lengths of rope without knots or splices represent 100% of its strength.
- When a knot is tied in a rope it loses approximately 50% of its original strength.

Illustration #184 - Knots = 50% Efficiency

- A rope loses 50% of its strength with a bend.

Illustration #185 - Bend = 50% Efficiency

- A rope loses 25% of its strength with a hitch.

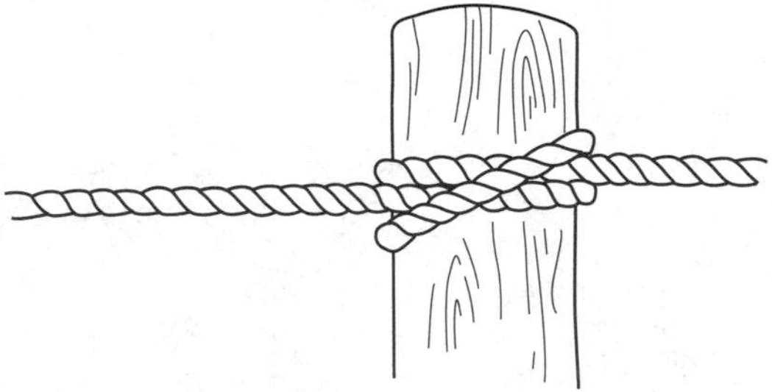

Illustration #186 - Hitch = 75% Efficiency

- A rope loses approximately 15% of its strength with an eye splice or a short splice.

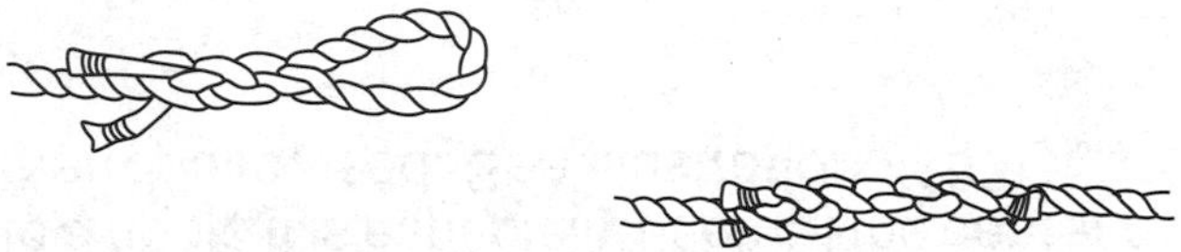

Illustration #187 - Splice = 85% Efficiency

Fiber Rope Tackle Blocks

When reeving a pair of blocks that have more than two sheaves, the hoisting rope should lead from one of the center sheaves on the upper block. The hoist line pull is then placed on the center of the block. This prevents the block from toppling and damaging the fiber rope. The two blocks should be positioned with the sheaves in the upper block at right angles to those in the lower block. See illustration #188.

Note: It is good practice to use the shackle block as the upper block and a hook block as the lower traveling block. A shackle is stronger than a hook of the same size, and the total load on the upper block is considerably more than the lower block load. The lower block supports only the load whereas the upper block carries the load as well as the sheave friction and the lead line pull.

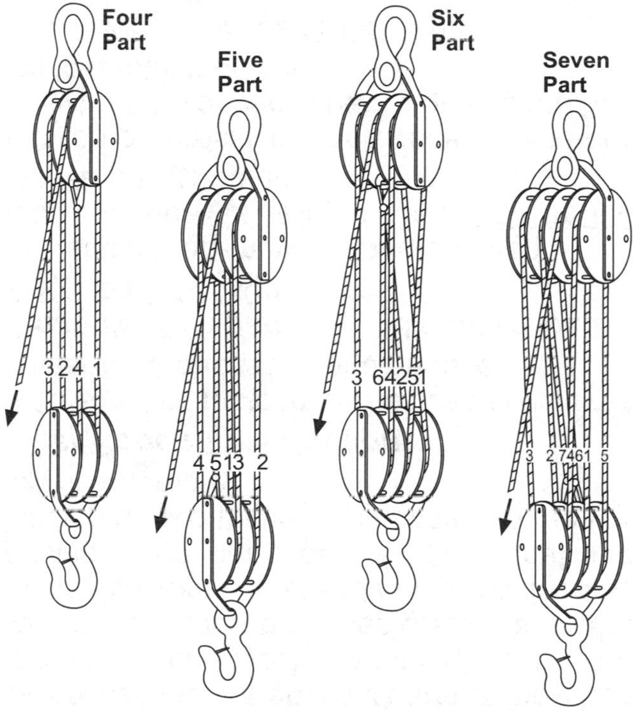
Four Part
3 2 4 1
Five Part
4 5 1 3 2
Six Part
3 6 4 2 5 1
Seven Part
3 2 7 4 6 1 5

Illustration #188 - Fiber Rope Block Reeving

Block Friction

Calculations of Dynamic Loading

Becket Line 1	500 lbs x1.10 550.0 lbs	226.8 kg x1.10 249.4 kg
Line 2	550.0 lbs x1.10 605.0 lbs	249.4 kg x1.10 274.3 kg
Line 3	605.0 lbs x1.10 665.5 lbs	274.3 x1.10 301.7kg
Line 4	665.5 lbs x1.10 732.0 lbs	301.7 kg x1.10 331.9 kg
Line 5	732.0 lbs x1.10 805.2 lbs	331.9 kg x1.10 365.1 kg
Lead Line Pull	805.2 lbs	365.1 kg

Do not use more than eight parts of line when using fiber rope blocks. After eight parts, the increased friction becomes greater than the theoretical mechanical advantage gained by adding more parts of line. Additional line loading due to friction is indicated in the following example.

Fiber Rope Block Friction

A 10% friction factor must be used every time a fiber rope passes over a sheave.

Example: Five part set of falls with a load of 2,500 lbs (1134 kg).

The static (non-moving) load on each line is 2,500 pounds (1134 kg) divided by 5, or 500 lbs (226.8 kg) per line.

Friction progressively increases the line pull an extra 10% at each sheave or an extra 305 lbs to a total lead line pull of:

500 + 305 = 805 lbs (365.1 kg).

SECTION THREE QUESTIONS

Fiber Rope

1. *The two main types of fiber rope are:*
   - ❒ natural and synthetic
   - ❒ nylon and natural
   - ❒ manila and synthetic
   - ❒ none of above

2. *The color of Number One Manila is:*
   - ❒ dark brown
   - ❒ light yellow
   - ❒ silver
   - ❒ depends on manufacturer

3. *Which of these natural fiber ropes is considered to be the strongest?*
   - ❒ hemp
   - ❒ sisal
   - ❒ coir
   - ❒ manila

4. *Which of these synthetic fiber ropes is the strongest?*
   - ❒ polyethylene
   - ❒ polyester
   - ❒ polypropylene
   - ❒ nylon

5. *Determine if the following statement is true or false. The individual strand fibers in a manila rope are full length. Therefore a manila rope is much stronger and elastic than a nylon rope.*
   - ❒ true ❒ false

6. *Determine if the following statement is true or false. If a load equal to 50% of the breaking strength of a manila rope is left hanging for several hours, the rope will pull apart.*
   - ❒ true ❒ false

7. *What is done to prevent the ends of a natural fiber rope from untwisting?*
   - ❒ melt the ends
   - ❒ whip the ends

8. *What is done to prevent the ends of a synthetic fiber rope from untwisting?*
   - ❐ melt the ends
   - ❐ whip the ends

9. *What are the two Design (safety) Factors for fiber rope being used to hoist personnel, and for general use?*
   - ❐ 10 – 1 and 5 – 1
   - ❐ 20 – 1 and 15 – 1
   - ❐ 30 – 1 and 20 – 1
   - ❐ 50 – 1 and 25 – 1

10. *Knots tied in fiber rope reduce the strength by approximately:*
    - ❐ 10%
    - ❐ 25%
    - ❐ 35%
    - ❐ 50%

11. *An eye spliced in a fiber will reduce the rope strength by how much?*
    - ❐ 50 – 60%
    - ❐ 30 – 40%
    - ❐ 15 – 20%
    - ❐ 5 – 10%

12. *The knot used in conjunction with the back splice to keep a rope from unraveling is:*
    - ❐ bowline
    - ❐ clove
    - ❐ crown
    - ❐ reef

13. *How many tucks are required (in total) for a back splice when using natural fibre rope?*
    - ❐ 3
    - ❐ 6
    - ❐ 5
    - ❐ 10

14. *Which splice is used when forming an eye in fiber rope?*
- ❒ side splice
- ❒ short splice
- ❒ long splice
- ❒ bowline splice

15. *Which of the following is used to securely fasten a rope to a pipe?*
- ❒ reef knot
- ❒ bowline
- ❒ self centering bowline
- ❒ clove hitch

16. *This knot is known as a "killer" knot because it is often used improperly.*
- ❒ bowline on the bight
- ❒ spanish bowline
- ❒ reef knot
- ❒ becket hitch

17. *What is used to join two ropes of equal diameter?*
- ❒ sheet bend
- ❒ rolling hitch
- ❒ becket hitch
- ❒ carrick bend

18. *What is the efficiency of a clove hitch?*
- ❒ 25%
- ❒ 50%
- ❒ 75%
- ❒ 100%

19. *In a multi-part fiber rope block system, what is the reason for the hoisting rope to lead from a center sheave of the upper block?*
- ❒ less friction
- ❒ won't topple load as easily
- ❒ keeps blocks from tilting
- ❒ does not really make a difference

20. *What is the accepted amount of friction per block in a multi-part fiber rope system?*
- ❐ 3%
- ❐ 10%
- ❐ 20%
- ❐ 50%

21. *At what point does friction in a multi-part fiber rope system become greater than the theoretical mechanical advantage?*
- ❐ 5 parts of line
- ❐ 8 parts of line
- ❐ 12 parts of line
- ❐ 20 parts of line

SECTION FOUR

LAYOUT

3-4-5 Ratio

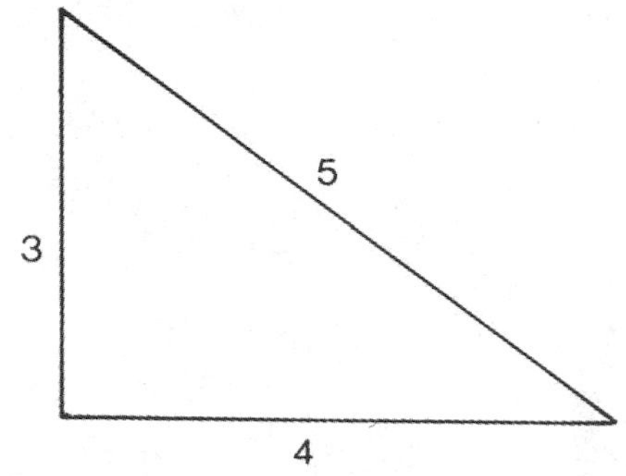
5
3
4

Illustration #189 - Ratio of 3-4-5 Triangle

The ratio of 3, 4, 5 is important to remember in right angle triangles.

Any ratio of these numbers can be used to check or layout a square corner.

Eg: (3-4-5) x 2 = 6-8-10
(3-4-5) x 3 = 9-12-15
(3-4-5) x 4 = 12-16-20

The 3-4-5 ratio can be used with any type of numbers; inches, feet, millimeters, meters, etc.

This ratio is proven through the use of Pythagoras Theorum which is used to calculate the unknown side of a right angle triangle if the other two are known.

This theorum states that the sum of the squares of two sides of a right triangle is equal to the square of the hypotenuse.

Eg: $(3)^2 + (4)^2 = (5)^2$
$9 + 16 = 25$

This ratio sequence has many uses:

- squaring frames
- squaring structural members
- establishing square corners on any type of surface from wallpaper to steel plate.

Rules for Triangles

Two more points that are worthwhile memorizing are the relationship in a right angle triangle, see illustration #190 and #191.

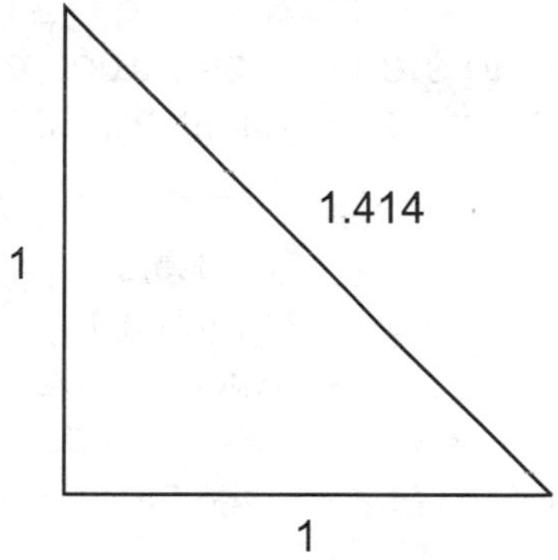
1.414
1
1

Illustration #190 - Ratio of 45° Triangle

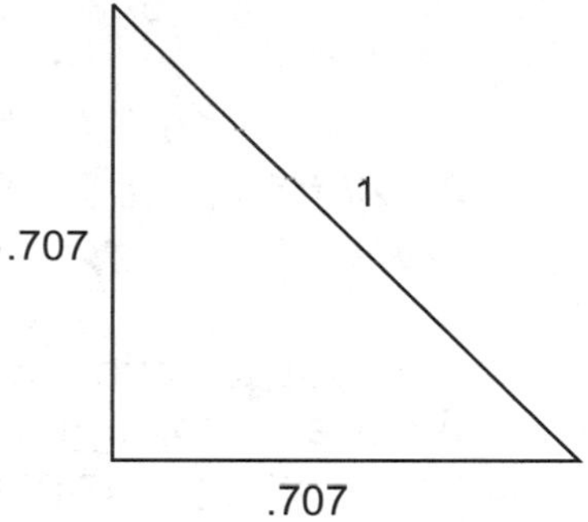
1
.707
.707

Illustration #191 - Ratio of 45° Triangle

If the base or height is known in a 45 degree triangle the hypotenuse can be found by multiplying the base length by 1.414.

Eg: The hypotenuse of a triangle with a base of 15 feet 6 inches would be: 1.414x 15.5 ft = 21.92 ft.

If the hypotenuse of a 45 degree triangle is known, the base or height can be found by multiplying the hypotenuse by .707.

Eg: The base or height of a triangle with a hypotenuse of 8 feet 3 inches would be: 8.25 ft. x .707 = 5.83 ft.

Angles and Circles

If a circle is to be divided, it will be in segments named angles. An angle consists of two straight lines intersecting at a point (the vertex).

Angles are measured in degrees, minutes, and seconds, see illustration #192.

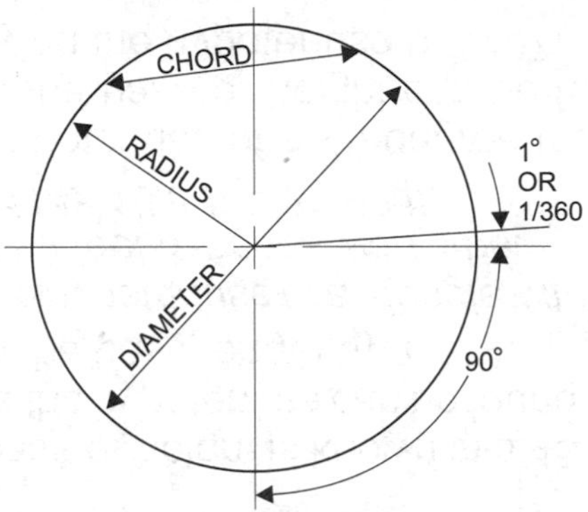
CHORD
RADIUS
DIAMETER
1°
OR
1/360
90°

Illustration #192 - Circle Components

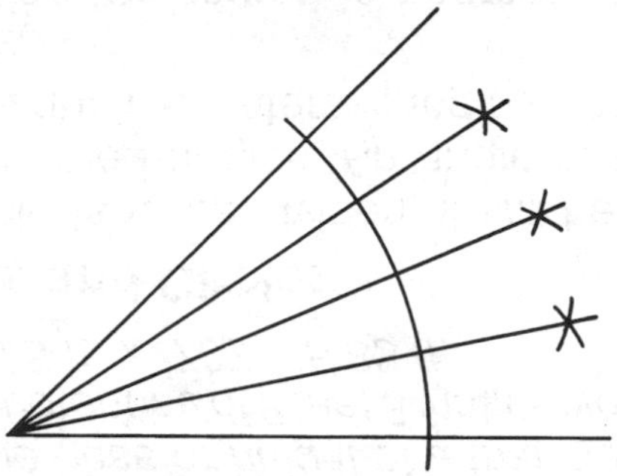

Illustration #193 - Dividing Angles

One complete circle = 360° (degrees)			
1 degree	= 60' (minutes)	1 degree	= $^1/_{360}$ circle
1 minute	= 60" (seconds)	90°	= $^1/_4$ circle
1 second	= $^1/_{60}$ (minute)	180°	= $^1/_2$ circle
1 minute	= $^1/_{360}$ (degree)	270°	= $^3/_4$ circle
		360°	= full circle

An angle can be divided using either a protractor or a compass (dividers on steel), see illustration #193.

This method of dividing angles could be used to layout bolt holes in a flange. The degree spacing for some of the more widely used flanges are:

8 holes = 45° *20 holes = 18°*
12 holes = 30° *24 holes = 15°*
16 holes = 22 $^1/_2$°

Angles and Circles

To construct a perpendicular from a point in a line, see illustration #194.

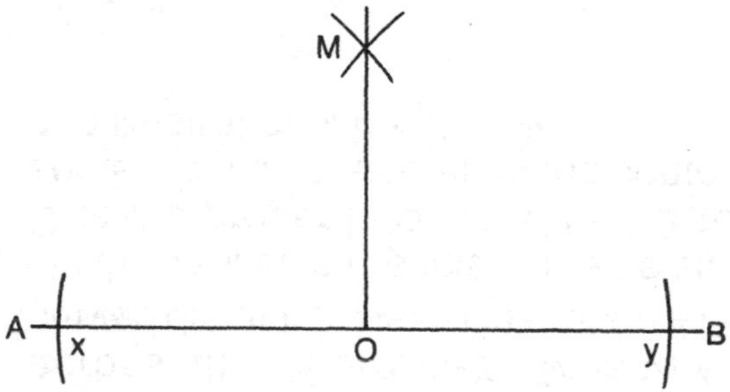
M
A
x
O
y
B

Illustration #194 - Construct a Perpendicular from a Line

If AB is the line, and O is the point in the line, scribe two arcs from O to cut the line AB at points X and Y.

From X and Y swing two arcs to cut each other at M, join MO, this line is perpendicular to AB.

To construct a perpendicular to a line from a point outside the line, see illustration #195.

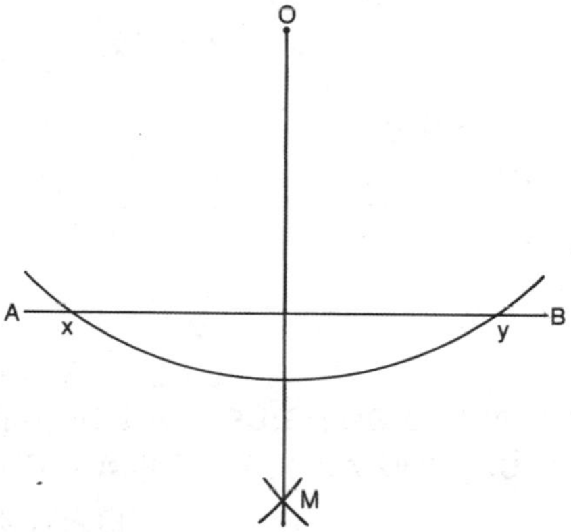
O
A
x
y
B
M

Illustration #195 - Construct a Perpendicular from a Point

Let AB be the line and O the point. From O, swing an arc to cut line AB at X and Y. From X and Y swing two equal arcs to cut at M on the opposite side of the line from O. Join OM, this line is perpendicular to AB. This method is useful if laying out a perpendicular and the point is well beyond the reach of a two foot square.

Layout Large Hole in Vessel

When fitting a large diameter pipe nozzle in a pressure vessel, the large hole usually cannot be scribed as a complete circle as the radius scribed loses distance due to the curvature. See illustration #196A.

1. Use an open shell end or a template to produce a curve similar to the vessel. Measure the pipe outside diameter (O.D.) across the chord X-Y. Measure the curved distance C, see illustration #191 B.
2. On the vessel, strap this curved distance, C at the proper location. D1 - D2 represents the pipe diameter on the centerline, see illustration #196C.
3. Using a set of dividers, establish a point M, on line D1 - D2. This point M, is found by trial and error adjustment of dividers on line D1 - D2 until the dividers will hit points X, Y, and D2, see illustration #196D.
4. Scribe arc X - D2 - Y, then move the dividers to the identical point, N on the other side, and scribe arc X-D1-Y, see illustration #196D.
5. The hole will be cut by holding the torch parallel to the centerline of the intersecting nozzle.

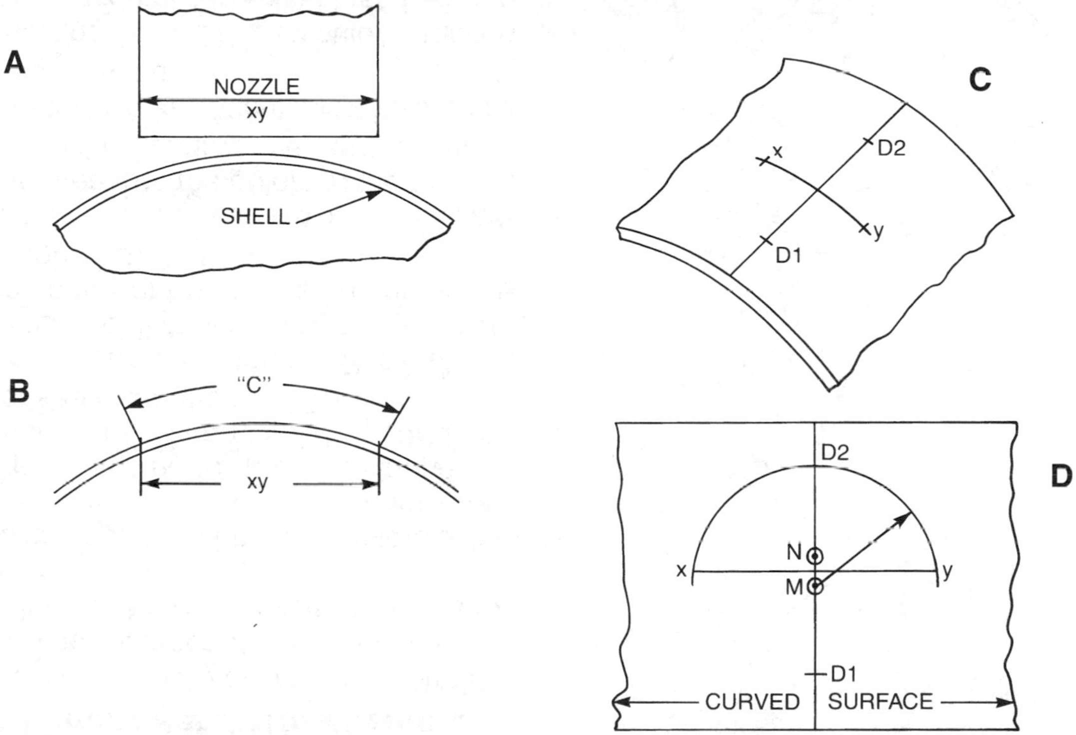
A
NOZZLE
xy
SHELL
B
"C"
xy
C
x
D2
y
D1
D
D2
N
x
y
M
D1
CURVED SURFACE

Illustration #196 - Layout of a Large Hole in a Vessel Shell

Layout A Fitting Parallel to a Centerline

Blueprints will normally only give the straight perpendicular distance X, from a centerline down to the center of a nozzle, see illustration #197A.

1. Using an open shell end or template of the curvature, measure across the chord double the centerline to nozzle distance 2X, measure this distance AB around the curve, see illustration #197B.
2. Divide this curved distance AB in half. DA is the curved distance from the centerline to the center of the nozzle cutout, see illustration #197C.
3. If the curvature is rapid it would be advisable to measure the points to the top and bottom of the fittings as well as the center.
4. Care must be taken to cut this hole parallel to the centerline.
5. When fitting the nozzle, it would be tacked on the horizontal centerline first, then top and bottom.

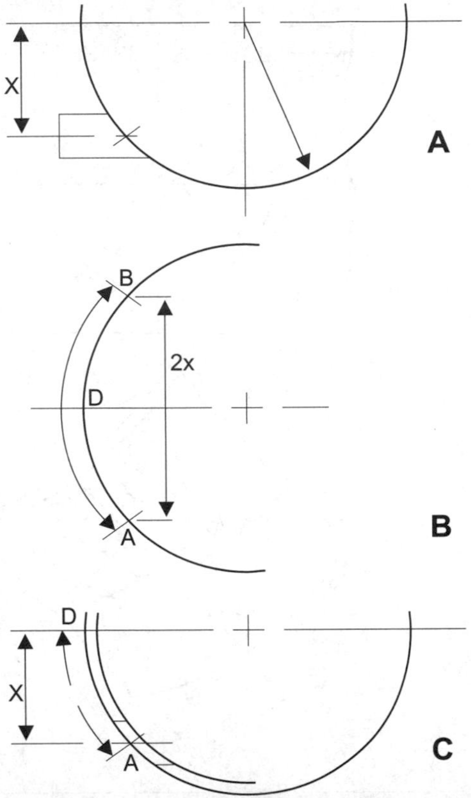
X
A
B
2x
D
A
B
D
X
A
C

Illustration #197 - Layout Fitting Parallel to a Centerline

Layout Hole for Nozzle Entering Shell Parallel to a Centerline

1. Layout one quarter of the shell circumference, draw in the nozzle to the full size in the proper location, see illustration #198A.
2. Draw a circle equal to the pipe diameter on the nozzle centerline.
3. Divide the circle into 12 equal parts and number as per the illustration, with point 1 on top.
4. From points 2, 3, 5 and 6 draw lines parallel to the centerline to intersect the shell. Also draw in lines from the two outside points of 1 and 7 and centerline 4. Letter these intersection points A through G.
5. Develop a stretchout line equal in length to the curve A-G, see illustration #198B. One end will be numbered 7 and the other 1. 7 and A will be on the same point as well as 1 and G. From the curve A-G measure distances A-B, A-C, A-D, A-E, and A-F. Transfer these lengths to the stretchout.
6. From the circle, measure chord distances 2-12, 3-11, 4-10, 5-9, 6-8 and transfer to the appropriate line on the stretchout, *Eg: chord 6-8 will be on stretchout line B.*
7. Remember to cut the hole parallel to the centerline.

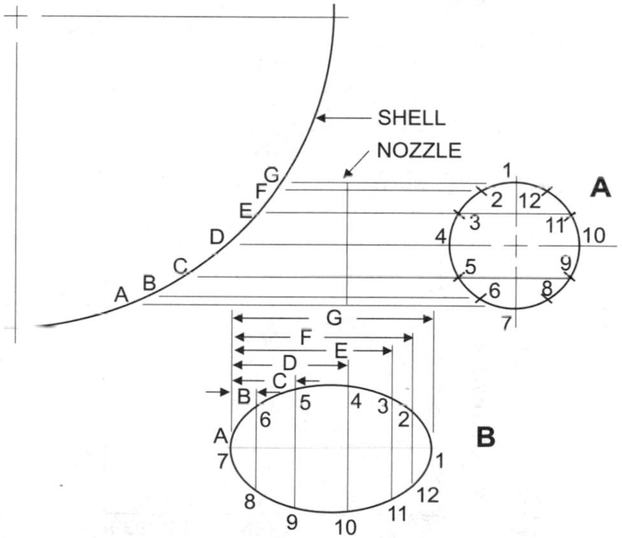
SHELL
NOZZLE
A B C D E F G
1 2 3 4 5 6 7 8 9 10 11 12
A
G
F
E
D
C
B
A
7
1
2 3 4 5 6
8 9 10 11 12
B

Illustration #198 - Layout Hole for Nozzle Parallel to a Centerline

Centerline Layout

The object is to layout centerlines on a rolled cylinder which will become a vessel or tank shell.

1. Most prints will show the two principal views, orientation (end) and elevation (side). The orientation showing the centerlines, weld seam and nozzles will normally be on the left, see illustration #199A, and the elevation view showing the shell length and location of nozzles in relation to a reference line will be on the right, see illustration #199B.
2. The centerlines on the orientation view will be 0°-90°-180°-270° (degrees) in a clockwise direction with 0° at the top.
3. The orientation view may occasionally be shown on the right of the elevation view. The centerlines will then be shown 0°-90°-180°-270° (degrees) in a counter clockwise direction.

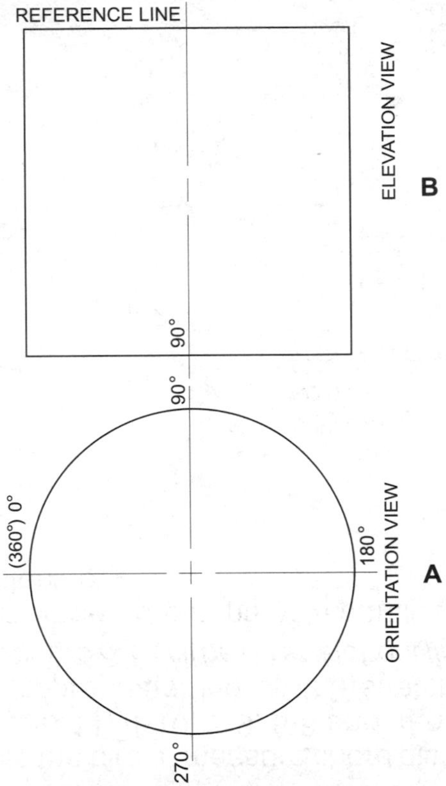
REFERENCE LINE
ELEVATION VIEW
B
90°
90°
(360°) 0°
180°
ORIENTATION VIEW
A
270°

Illustration #199 - Centerline Layout

4. Establish which shell end will be the reference line. Check the open end for roundness. If the ends are round the weld seam can be checked with a tape and level on both ends, see illustration #200A.
5. If the plate was not cut square the seam will spiral after rolling. This could cause problems when fitting two or more shells together. Use a long tape to strap both ends (measure circumference). Divide by four to obtain the distance from one centerline to another. Establish where the seam will be in relation to a centerline, preferably with 0° as a starting point.
6. Remember, if the orientation view is on the left of the elevation view, the centerlines will proceed 0°-90°-180°-270° clockwise, and the reference line should be on the right end of the elevation view where the centerlines will rotate 0°-90°-180°-270° counterclockwise, see illustration #200C.
7. After the centerline locations have been established the points should always be center punched on each end and snapped with a chalk line for easier layout reference.

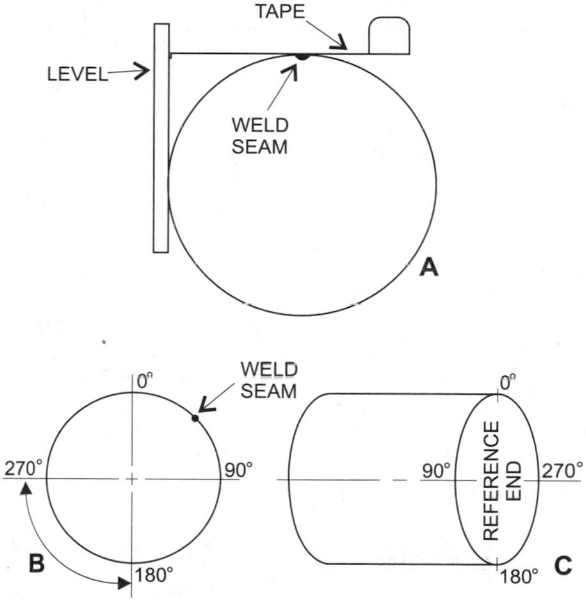
TAPE
LEVEL
WELD SEAM
A
0°
WELD SEAM
270°
90°
180°
B
0°
90°
REFERENCE END
270°
180°
C

Illustration #200 - Centerline Layout

Flat Shell Centerline Layout

The object is to layout the centerlines on a vessel shell prior to rolling. From the print establish the outside diameter. The circumference is diameter times pi, *(pi = 3.1416)* (the symbol is π).

1. The flat length equals the circumference minus pi times one thickness.
   Length = c - π x 1 thickness
2. The flat length is divided by four to establish the distance from one centerline to the next.
3. The distance from the weld seam to the first clockwise centerline (in illustration #201B, the 90° centerline) is found by:
   Number of degrees from seam to 90° centerline = 360 x Flat Length
4. The layout proceeds from right to left in the following order:
   Seam - 90° - 180° - 270° - 0° - seam, see illustration #201B.
5. The plate must be turned over before rolling.

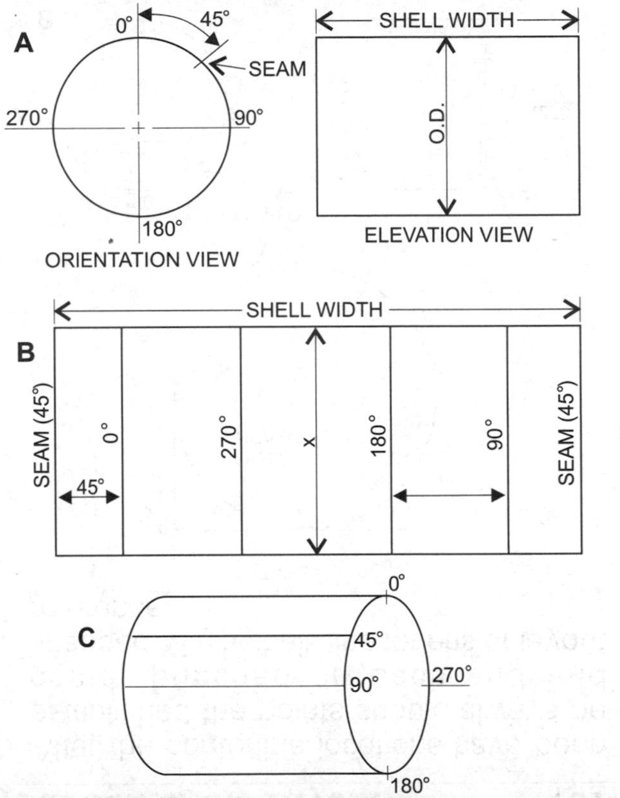
A
0°
45°
SEAM
270°
90°
180°
ORIENTATION VIEW
SHELL WIDTH
O.D.
ELEVATION VIEW
B
SHELL WIDTH
SEAM (45°)
0°
45°
270°
x
180°
90°
SEAM (45°)
C
0°
45°
90°
270°
180°

Illustration #201 - Flat Shell Centerline Layout

Nozzle Location Layout

The orientation view indicates where the nozzles and fittings will be located in relation to the centerlines. The nozzle N1, shown in illustration #202A & B is on the 180° centerline, however the elevation view is needed to show where the nozzle is located along the 180° centerline.

The elevation view may use one of three basic types of reference lines. One is the actual shell end, or weld seam, see illustration #202A.

Another method is a line other than the seam. This could be a reference line or a datum line on the shell, or a tangent line on the vessel head, see illustration #202B. This tangent line is typically 2 inches (50.8 mm) away from the seam, see illustration #202C. The head will have to be cut and beveled to obtain this 2 inch (50.8 mm) tangent point.

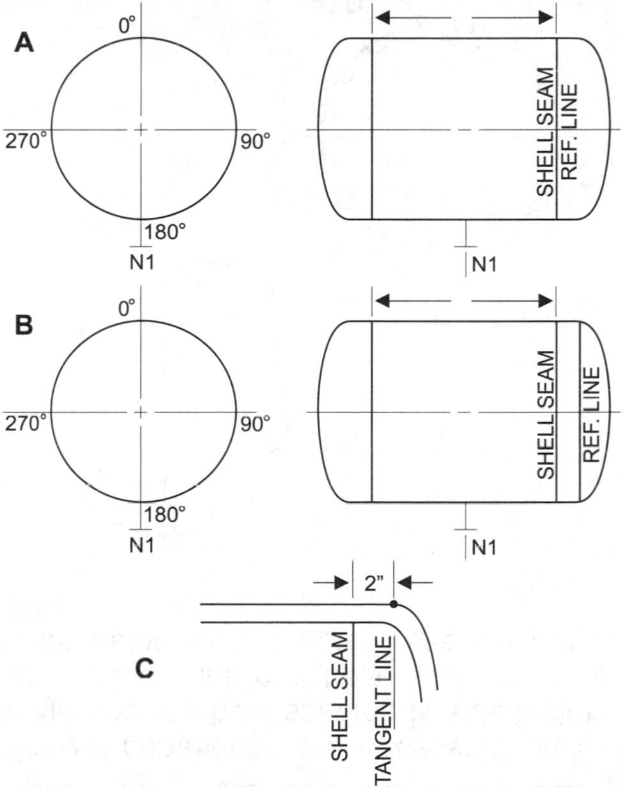
A
0°
270°
90°
180°
N1
SHELL SEAM
REF. LINE
N1
B
0°
270°
90°
180°
N1
SHELL SEAM
REF. LINE
N1
C
2”
SHELL SEAM
TANGENT LINE

Illustration #202 - Nozzle Location Layout

Flange Layout

If the number of holes in a flange is divisible by 4, i.e. 4, 8, 12,16, 20, 24 etc., the holes will straddle both centerlines.

Example: 16 hole flange

1. Layout a line, bisect it to obtain the two centerlines, then scribe the bolt circle.
2. Centerpunch each centerline, see illustration #203A.
3. *16 holes - 4 holes = 12 holes left*
4. *12 holes = 4 quarters = 3 holes per quarter*
5. Four equal spaces are required to layout 3 holes per quarter. Each quarter will be divided into 4 equal spaces by using a protractor, compass or chord chart. Centerpunch lightly. Check by placing a set of dividers in any two holes. Then swing the dividers around from punch mark to punch mark, the distances should all be equal. If not, go back and recheck the work.

If drawn centerlines are necessary on the flange and the hole spacing is satisfactory, the existing lines can be erased, then re-drawn between bolt holes, see illustration #203B.

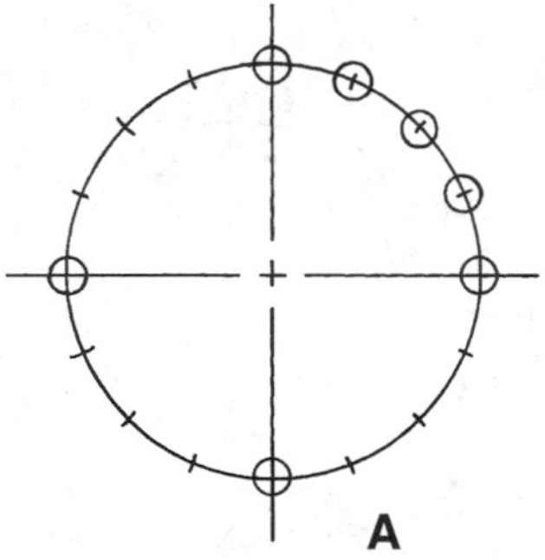
A

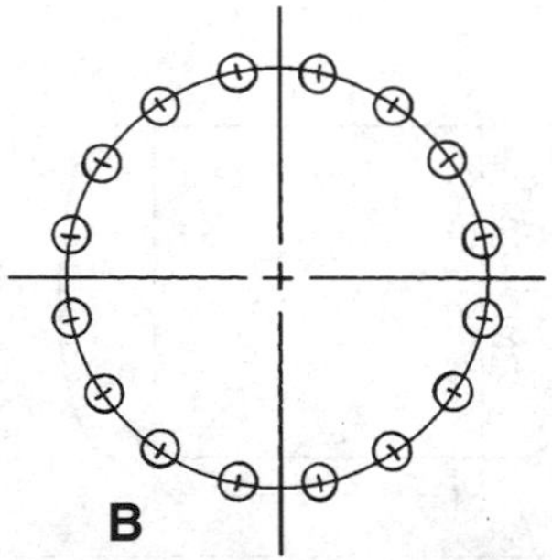
B

Illustration #203 - Flange Layout

If the bolt holes are divisible only by 2, such as 10, 14, 18, 22, etc., the centerlines will straddle the bolt holes on one centerline and go through the holes on the other centerline. These flanges are not common and are made for special application, see illustration #204.

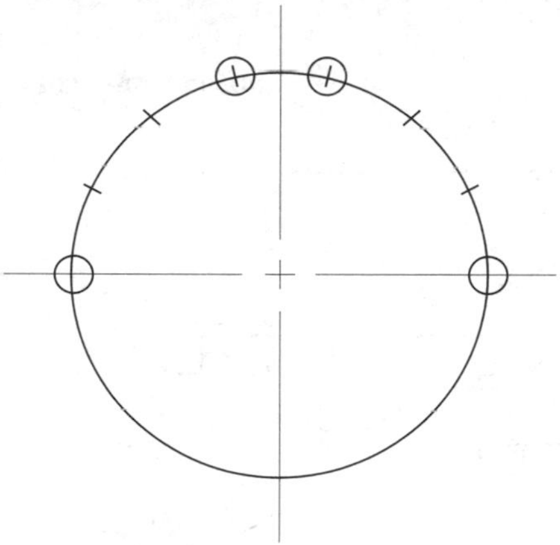

Illustration #204 - Flange Layout

Example: 14 hole flange

1. Layout one centerline, then scribe the bolt circle.
2. Centerpunch two holes on the centerline.
3. *14 holes - 2 holes = 12 holes left*
4. *12 holes = 2 halves = 6 holes per half circle*
5. *7 spaces will be required to obtain 6 holes per half*
6. Divide equally using dividers, protractor or chord chart.
7. Centerpunch lightly and check using a set of dividers.

NOTE: When Installing a flange, most prints will state whether or not the flange bolt holes will straddle the centerline. If the print does not indicate this one way or the other, it will be assumed that the holes will straddle. This is the common procedure and accepted rule.

Head Layout

The head must be strapped to obtain the correct circumference. Divide this distance into four equal spaces to obtain the centerlines.

The center is found by hooking the tape onto the edge of the head at a centerline, then measure the full distance over the head, edge to edge.

Divide this distance by two and mark.

This will be repeated over the other two centerlines. The intersection of the two halfway points should be center.

Another method is to use a tape and a level to measure halfway at each of the four centerlines. *The head must sit level to use this method.* If the head is large both methods should be used as a double check.

The centerlines can be extended up to the center point by using a wrap-around and a soapstone, or if care is taken to ensure a straight line, a tape can be used in place of a wrap-around. The distance from center out to a nozzle can be established with a tape and level. If the nozzle is close to the knuckle on the head it is advisable to measure both outside diameter points of the nozzle as well as the center.

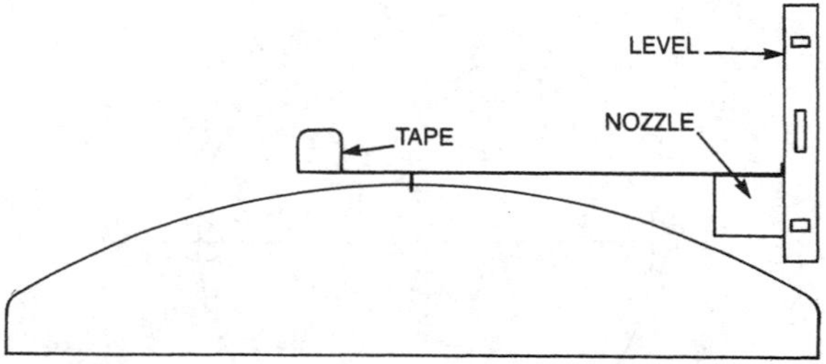
LEVEL
TAPE
NOZZLE

Illustration #205 - Head Layout

Baffle Plate Inside a Head

1. Level the head with the open end up.
2. Place a straight edge across the head in the correct position for the baffle, see illustration #206A. Mark off equal width spaces on the straight edge and measure down to the inside of the head from these points, see illustration #206B.
3. Cut out a plate the correct width and length. Divide the width into spaces equal to the spaces on the straight edge.
4. Transfer the distances, measured from the straight edge to the inside of the head, over to the appropriate lines on the plate, see illustration #206C.

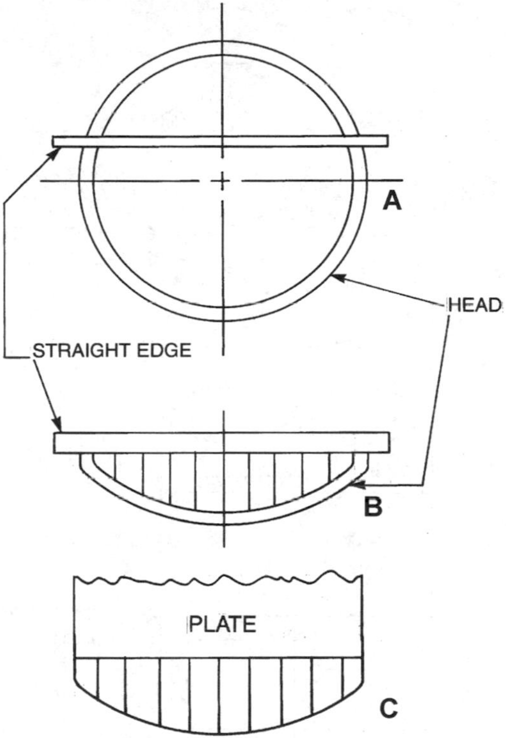
A
HEAD
STRAIGHT EDGE
B
PLATE
C

Illustration #206 - Layout Head Baffle

Semi-Elliptical Head Layout

When laying out material for pressure vessel and head fabrication it is sometimes necessary to know the curvature of a semi-elliptical head when one is not available to obtain such a curve.

1. Layout the vessel diameter with a centerline. Then draw in the weld seam and the tan line, see illustration #207A.
2. Establish the head depth (one quarter of the diameter) from the tan line and draw a horizontal line M N, see illustration #207A.
3. At points M and N draw lines down at 30° to cut the centerline at point O, see illustration #207B.
4. Draw a curve using radius A (the distance from point O to the top of the head) as far around to the side as possible.
5. To complete the curve, draw in radius B, the knuckle of each head.

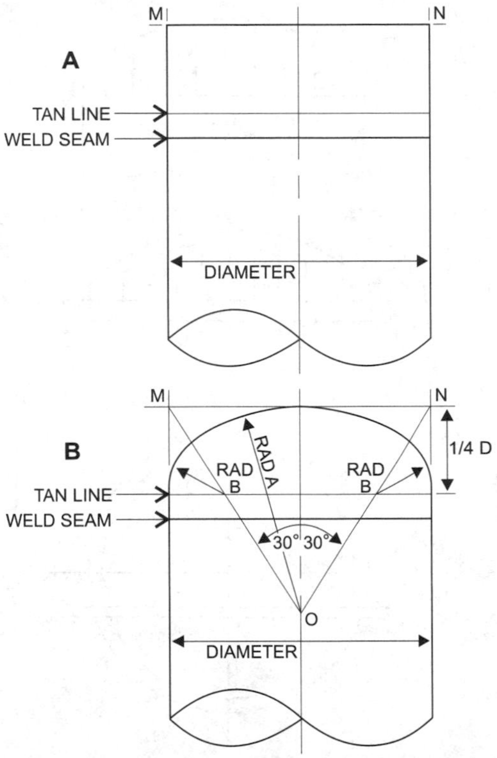
M
N
A
TAN LINE
WELD SEAM
DIAMETER
M
N
B
1/4 D
RAD B
RAD A
RAD B
TAN LINE
WELD SEAM
30° 30°
O
DIAMETER

Illustration #207 - Semi-Elliptical Head

Base Ring Layout

Large base plate rings cut from one full plate are uneconomical due to excess wastage.

1. To conserve plate it is best to make a ring with sections welded together.
2. Most are made from three or four pieces. Three is the easiest to work with as *one radius equals* $^1/_6$ of the chord distance around the ring.
3. In the upper corner of a plate, scribe an arc equal to the outside radius (O.R.) of the ring. Join this point, A to the center punch mark O, see illustration #208.
4. From A swing an arc equal to the radius to point X, from X swing one more radius to B. Join B to O. Now scribe an arc equal to the inside radius (I.R.).
5. Repeat this procedure two more times to layout the other two segments. It may be necessary to tack on a small piece of plate as the center point for the third segment may be off the large plate.
6. These segments must be stitch cut to avoid extreme distortion while the plate is being burned.

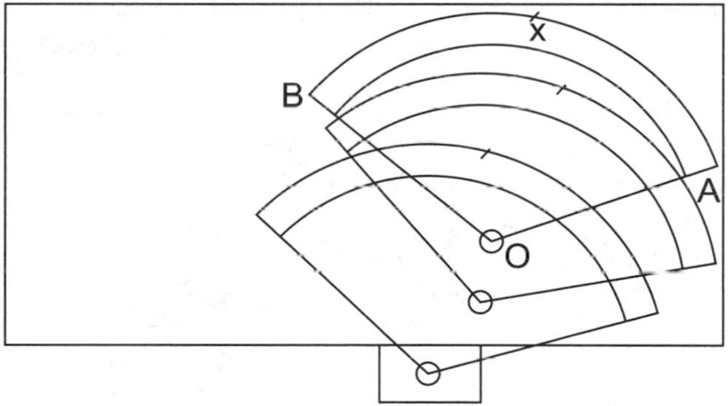
X
B
A
O

Illustration #208 - Base Plate Segments

Elliptical Hole Layout Method

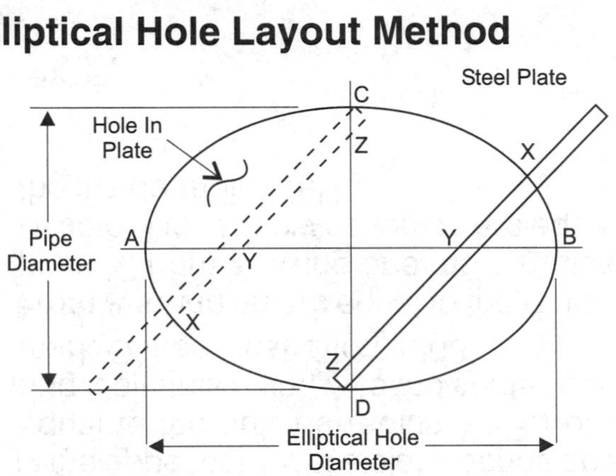
Steel Plate
C
Hole In
Plate
Z
X
Pipe
Diameter
A
Y
Y
B
X
Z
D
Elliptical Hole
Diameter

Illustration #209 - Elliptical Hole Layout

Method of Laying Out An Elliptical Shaped Hole on Steel Plate

Minor diameter = O.D. of pipe

Major diameter = O.D. of pipe x cosecant of angle of pipe to plate

X-Y = one-half of diameter

X-Z = one-half of long diameter

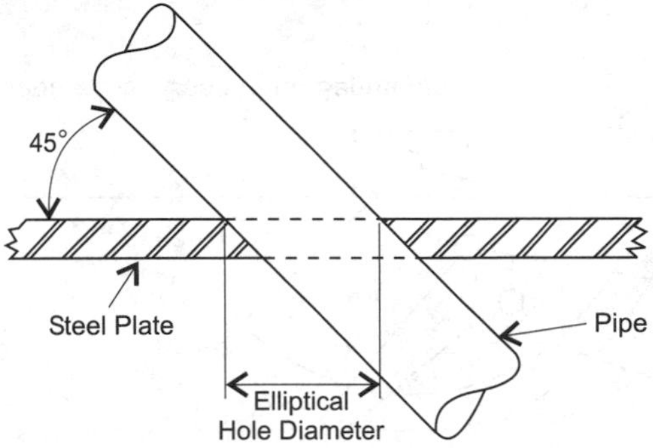
45°
Steel Plate
Pipe
Elliptical
Hole Diameter

Illustration #210

Procedure

1. Lay out lines A-B and C-D at right angles to each other crossing at the center of the opening.
2. Lay out the dimensions X-Y and X-Z on a flat piece of wood.
3. Draw the curved line at point X keeping points Y and Z on lines A-B and C-D as the piece of wood is revolved.

NOTE: When torch cutting, hold the tip at the same angle as the pipe will be when installed in the plate.

Parallel Line Development

Parallel lines is the layout method used on cylindrical objects such as pipe, vessel and tank shells, also on rectangular shapes such as ducting. Illustrations #211A and #211B show a section of rectangular duct with the top cut off at an angle. Illustration #211A is an isometric view showing the duct partially bent up. Points C and C' will match up, as will B and B' and A and A'.

Illustration #211B indicates the general three view method used to layout basic shapes. There is a top view, a front view and a stretchout of the object prior to rolling or bending. The top view shows the shape and is used to calculate the stretchout length. The front view is required for a vertical silhouette. More detailed or complex objects would require at least one additional view, a right side view, to give a clearer picture of the true shape.

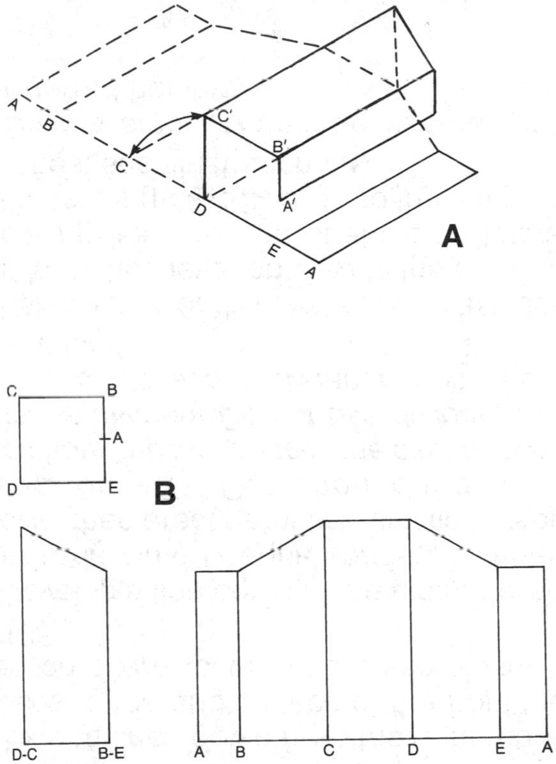
A
B
C
C'
B'
D
A'
E
A
A
C
B
A
D
E
B
D-C
B-E
A
B
C
D
E
A

Illustration #211 - Ducting by Parallel Lines

Two Piece 90° Elbow

A developed two piece 90 degree elbow is shown in illustration #212. Layout of this very basic shape follows the same rules and procedures as the much more complex objects.

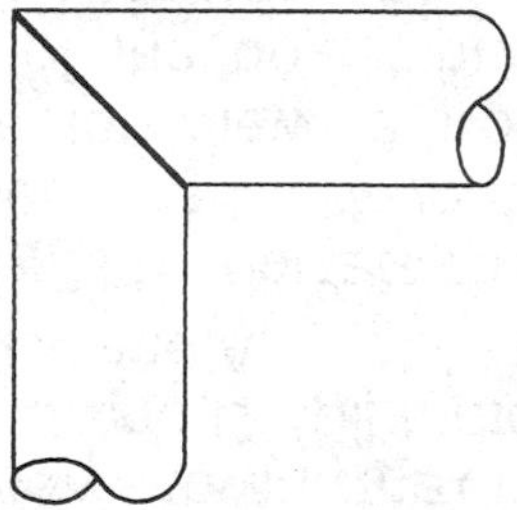

Illustration #212 - Two Piece 90° Elbow

1. Layout two views, top and front, see illustration #213A and #213B.

2. Divide the top view circle into 12 equal parts and number as indicated in illustration #213A.

3. Extend lines down from these numbered spaces to the angled face of the front view, then on down to the base, see illustration #213B.

4. Develop a line equal to the circumference and divide it into 12 equal spaces, number as shown, then erect perpendicular lines, see illustration #213C. *When dividing this stretchout line into spaces the circumference must be divided! Do not use dividers to get the space to space distance from the top view circle!*

5. Using a tape or dividers, transfer the length 1-1' from the elevation view to the two corresponding lines on the stretchout. Transfer the other lengths 2-2', 3-3', to their appropriate lines, see illustration #213C.

6. Draw a *smooth* curve between all of the transferred heights.

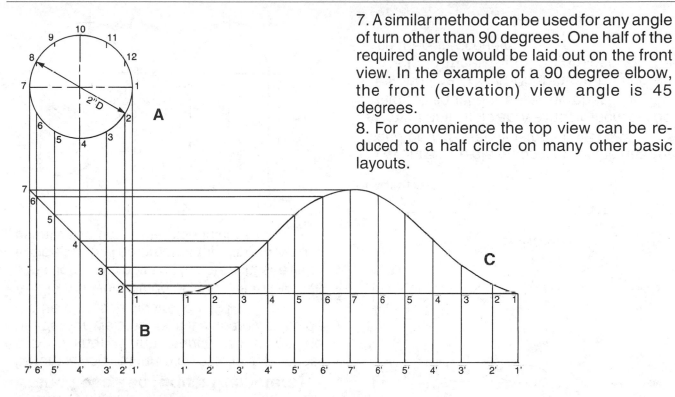

7. A similar method can be used for any angle of turn other than 90 degrees. One half of the required angle would be laid out on the front view. In the example of a 90 degree elbow, the front (elevation) view angle is 45 degrees.

8. For convenience the top view can be reduced to a half circle on many other basic layouts.

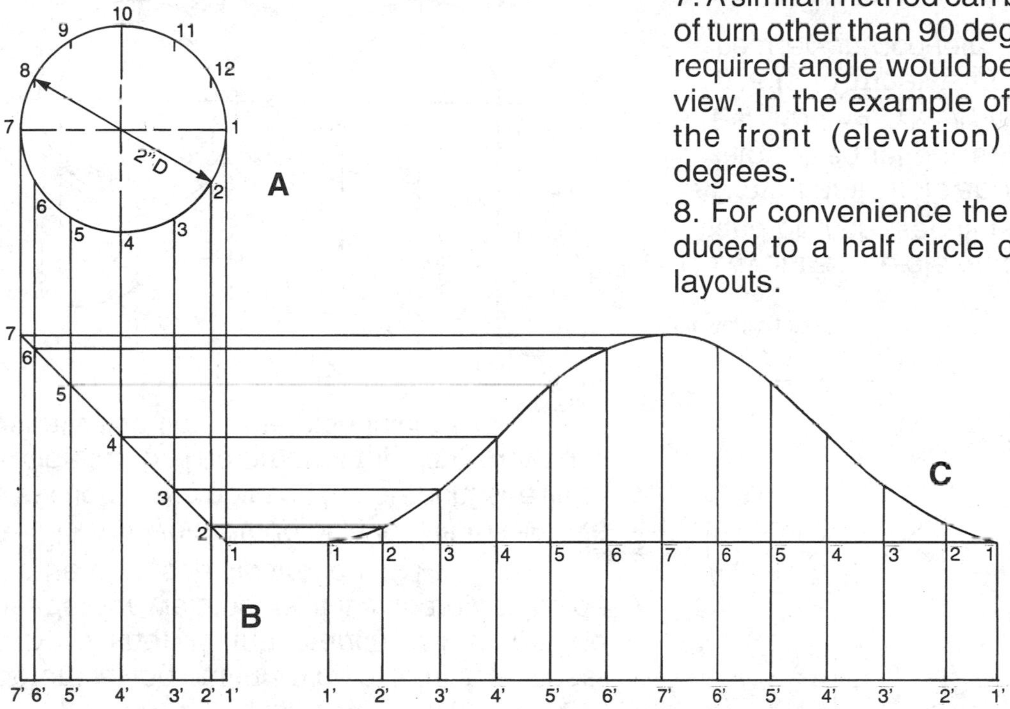
10
9
11
8
12
7
1
2"D
2
6
5
4
3
A
7
6
5
4
3
2
1
B
C
1 2 3 4 5 6 7 6 5 4 3 2 1
7' 6' 5' 4' 3' 2' 1'
1' 2' 3' 4' 5' 6' 7' 6' 5' 4' 3' 2' 1'

Illustration #213- Two Piece 90° Elbow

Branch of a Tee (Equal Diameters)

Before laying out this type of joint it is necessary to know if the branch will sit on the header for welding, or if it will project inside the header, see illustration #214.

An alternative method of layout is to remove a section of the point on the branch, see illustration #215. The amount that is removed is usually two times the pipe thickness.

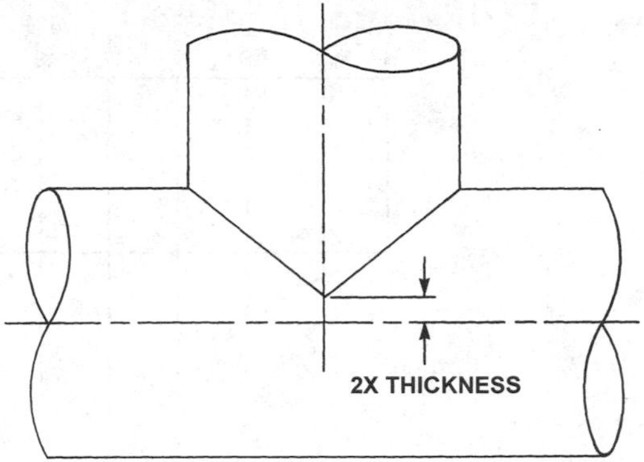
2X THICKNESS

Illustration #215

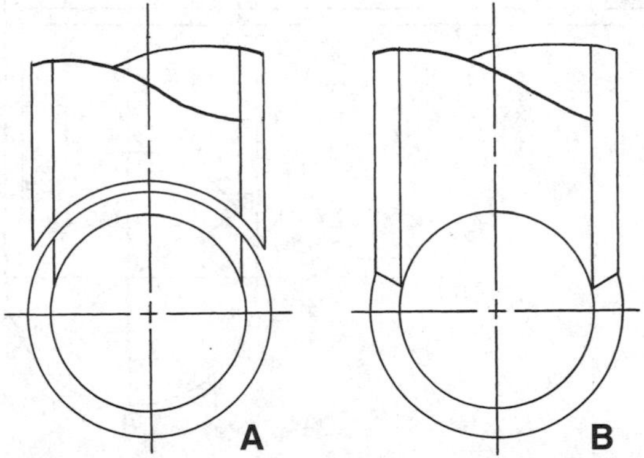
A
B

Illustration #214

1. Layout a side elevation view of the header and branch, see illustration #216A.
2. Draw a half circle above the branch, divide into “6" equal parts and number ”1 to 7".
3. Extend lines down from these numbered points to meet with the cut lines for the header-branch joint.

4. Draw the stretchout at right angles to the branch. This stretchout will be equal to the outside circumference of the pipe.
5. Divide the stretchout into 12 equal parts, extend perpendicular lines and number, see illustration #216B.
6. Transfer the lengths 1-1' to the two appropriate lines, also 7-7', which is identical in length.
7. Next transfer the identical lines of 2-2' and 6-6' to their corresponding lines, as well as 3-3', 4-4' and 5-5'.
8. Connect all points in a smooth curve.

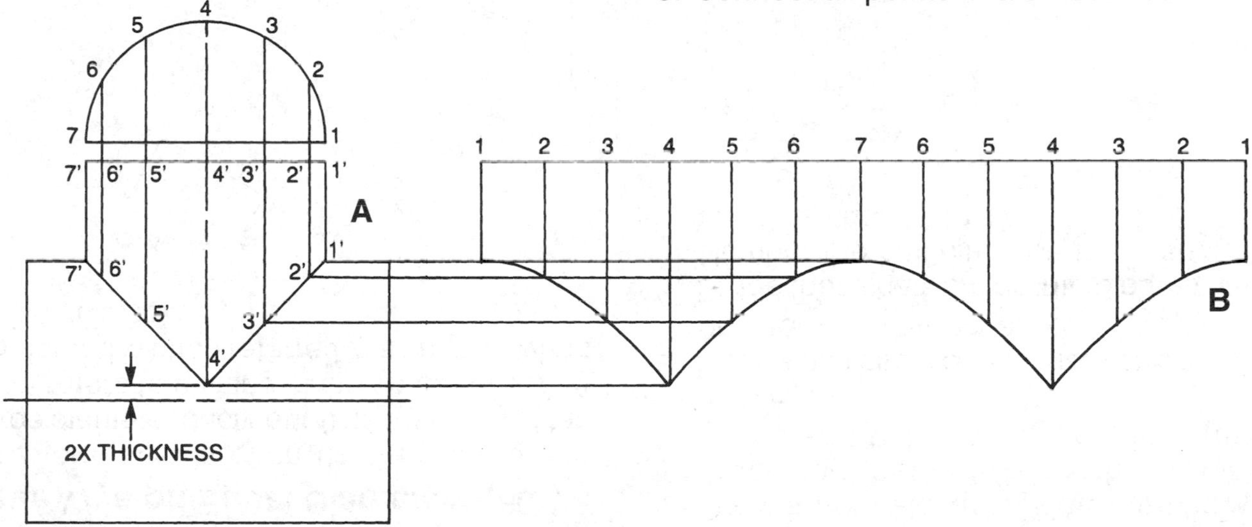
4
5
3
6
2
7
1
7'
6'
5'
4'
3'
2'
1'
A
1'
7'
6'
2'
5'
3'
4'
2X THICKNESS
1 2 3 4 5 6 7 6 5 4 3 2 1
B

Illustration #216 - Branch of a Tee

True Wye on Equal Diameters (60°)

The term wye is often used in piping and large diameter ductwork. The meaning of the term refers to a fitting in the shape of a Y. A 45° lateral is often referred to as a wye, when in fact it is not.

1. Draw a front elevation view starting with the centerlines, then fill in with the outside diameter of the pipe, see illustration #217A.
2. Draw a half circle on the main and another on one of the branches.
3. Divide these half circles into 6 equal parts. Number the half circle on the branch 1-7 and the other 11 to 17.

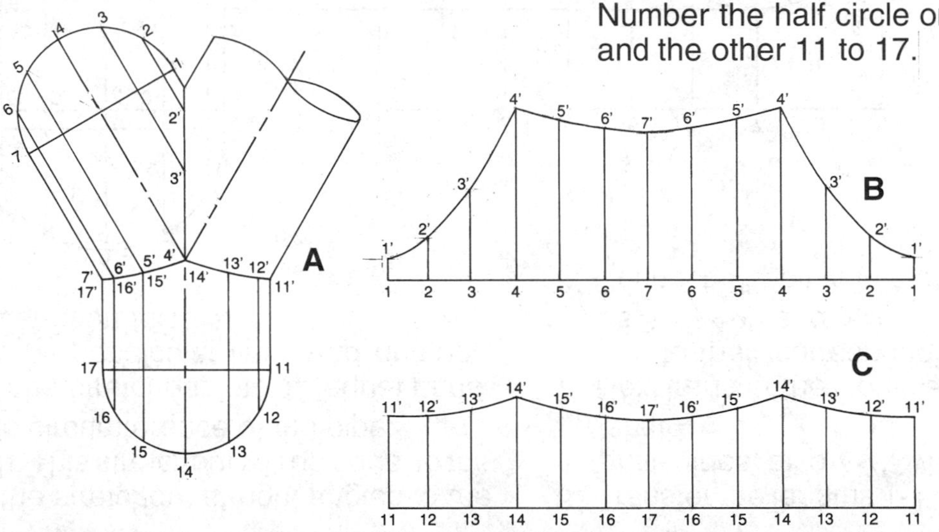
A
B
C

Illustration #217 - True Wye

4. Extend lines from these points to meet the cutlines for the main-branch intersection. If properly drawn the points 6'-16', 5'-15', etc. should meet.
5. This layout will require two stretchouts, one for the branch, see illustration #217B and the other for the main, see illustration #217C.
6. Draw two stretchouts equal to the length of the appropriate circumference, divide both into 12 equal parts and number as shown.
7. Transfer the points 1-1', 2-2' etc. from the branch to the branch stretchout.
8. Transfer the points 11-11', 12-12' etc. from the main to the main stretchout.
9. Connect the points in a smooth curve.
10. The branch layout will work for both branches.
11. For a proper fit up, the four centerlines should be marked on each of the pieces and matched up when fitting (centerlines on the branch will be 1, 4, 7, 4 and 11, 14, 17, 14 on the header).
12. On this layout, as on many others, the circumference has been divided into 12 equal parts as a number of convenience and ease. On larger diameters of pipe with spaces on the stretchout more than 3 inches (76 mm) apart it will be difficult to join the points in the proper curve. The bigger the diameter the more spaces required.

Four Piece 90° Elbow

The layout of any elbow is governed by the angle of turn, the number of sections in the turn, the turn radius and the diameter. All of which will vary with the job requirement.

To layout any elbow it will be necessary to find the number of degrees in the template angle, see illustration #218B. This always depends on the number of sections used to make up the elbow. A five piece elbow will have three full sections and two half sections on the ends. Any elbow will end with two half sections. Also any elbow will have one less joint than there are sections. If the turn angle is 90°, the cut angle will be: 90° ÷ (number of joints x two).

The cut angle for a four piece elbow shown in illustration #218 will be:

90° ÷ 6 = 15°

(6 = 3 joints x 2)

1. Layout the angle of turn (90° in this elbow), see illustration #218A.
2. Layout the throat radius and the heel radius. The heel is found by adding the O.D. of the pipe to the throat radius.
3. Divide the turn angle into 6 spaces (3 joints x 2). Each space will equal 15°.
4. Layout the miter lines so that the two center pieces are twice the two end pieces (30°). Draw lines at right angles to the ends of the turn then outline the two ends (pipe outline). Draw lines at right angles to the centerlines of the two center pieces. This outlines the two full center pieces.
5. There are several methods and possible locations for the next step, which is to draw in a half circle above one of the sections, see illustration #218B and at right angles to the section centerline. Divide the half circle into 6 equal spaces and number.

6. Extend lines down from the numbered points to the face of the section, illustration #218B.
7. Develop a stretchout line equal to the pipe circumference, divide into 12 spaces and number, see illustration #218C.

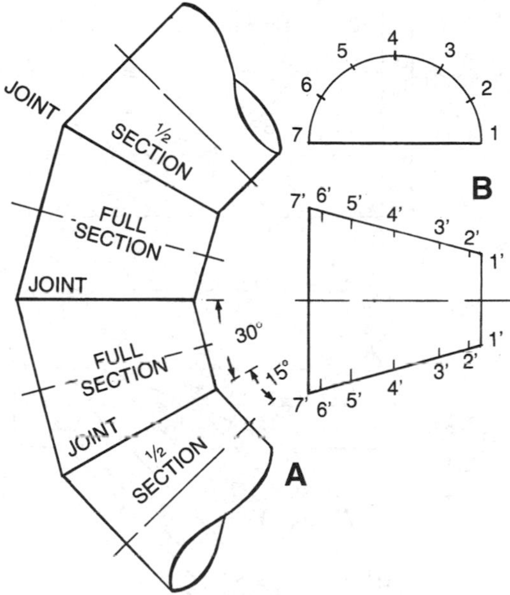
JOINT
½ SECTION
FULL SECTION
JOINT
FULL SECTION
JOINT
½ SECTION
30°
15°
A
7
6
5
4
3
2
1
7' 6' 5' 4' 3' 2' 1'
B

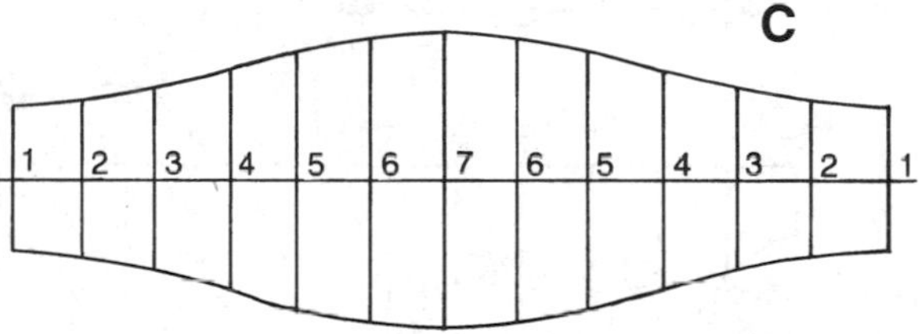
C
1 2 3 4 5 6 7 6 5 4 3 2 1

Illustration #218 - Four Piece Elbow

8. Transfer the lengths of 1-1', 2-2' their corresponding lines on the stretchout.
9. Connect the points in a smooth curve. This lays out one full center section.
10. Centerlines must be marked on each section and used to maintain alignment during fit up.

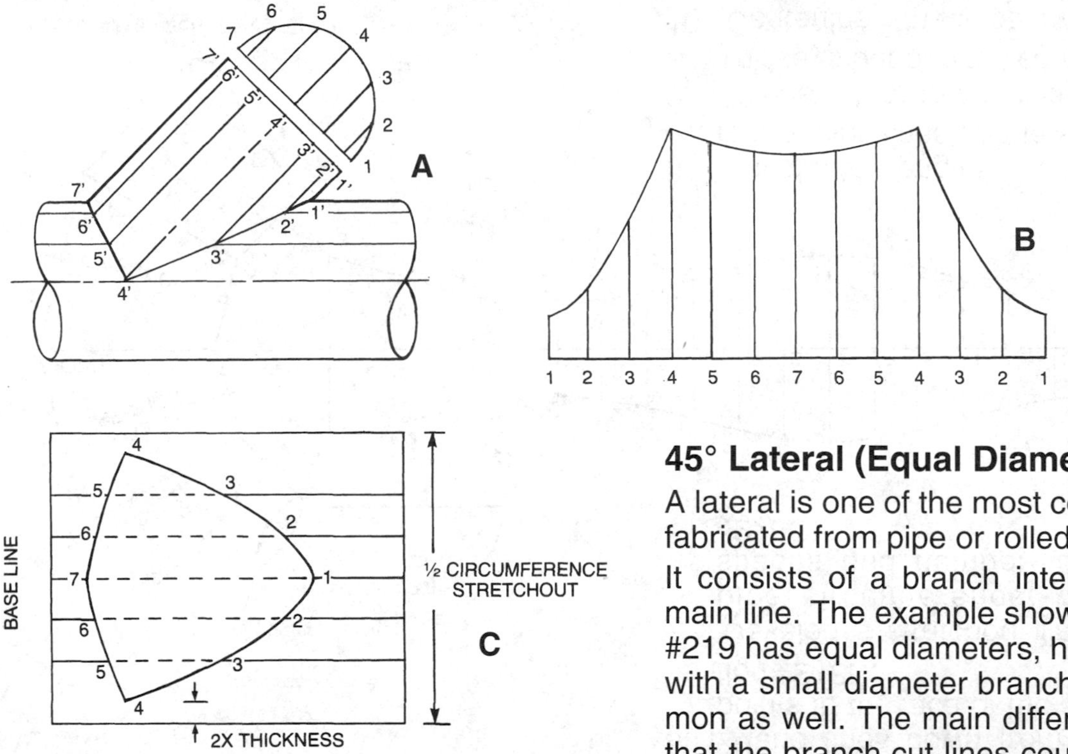
A
B
C
½ CIRCUMFERENCE STRETCHOUT
BASE LINE
2X THICKNESS

Illustration #219 - 45° Lateral

45° Lateral (Equal Diameters)

A lateral is one of the most common layouts fabricated from pipe or rolled plate.

It consists of a branch intersection with a main line. The example shown in illustration #219 has equal diameters, however laterals with a small diameter branch are very common as well. The main difference would be that the branch cut lines could not intersect the main centerline.

1. Layout a side view of the main and the branch using the proper angle (45° in this example), see illustrations #219A.
2. Draw a half circle above the branch, divide into 6 equal spaces and number as shown.
3. Extend lines parallel to the branch from these points to intersect the cut lines.
4. Layout a stretchout line equal to the branch circumference, divide into 12 equal spaces, number and erect perpendiculars, see illustration #219B.
5. Transfer the lines 1-1', 2-2' etc. from the branch to the corresponding stretchout line.
6. Join the points in a smooth curve.

Hole Layout

1. Develop a stretchout equal to one half the main circumference, if possible square or in line with the elevation view, see illustration #219C.
2. Divide into 6 equal spaces, number as shown with 7-1 as the centerline.
3. Using the main base line quarter circle division points and the lines extending from the main base line through to the cut line as distances, transfer these distances to the applicable line on the hole stretchout.
4. Join the points in a smooth curve.

The 'Hole' layout indicates an alternate method of lateral layout to avoid the sharp point at the centerline intersection. This is to move the point, number 4, up 2 thicknesses.

45° Eccentric Lateral (Unequal Diameters)

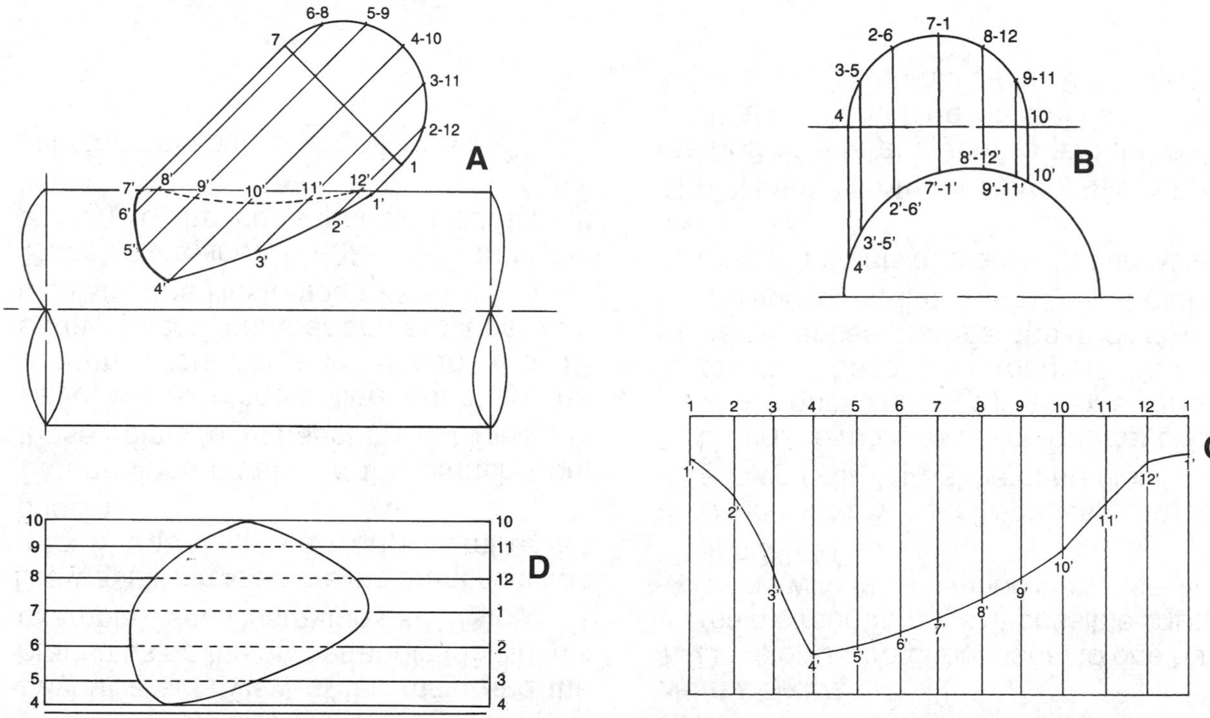
A
7
6-8
5-9
4-10
3-11
2-12
1
7'
8'
9'
10'
11'
12'
1'
6'
5'
4'
3'
2'
B
7-1
2-6
8-12
3-5
9-11
4
10
8'-12'
10'
7'-1'
9'-11'
2'-6'
3'-5'
4'
C
1 2 3 4 5 6 7 8 9 10 11 12 1
1' 2' 3' 4' 5' 6' 7' 8' 9' 10' 11' 12' 1'
D
10 9 8 7 6 5 4
10 11 12 1 2 3 4

Illustration #220 - 45° Eccentric Lateral

1. Layout a side view of the pipe branch using the proper angle, see illustration #220A. The centerline intersection point will only be used as an initial workpoint.
2. Draw a half circle above the branch, divide in 6 equal parts and number 1-12 as shown. Numbers 1 through 7 will refer to the near side of the branch while the remaining numbers will refer to the far side.
3. Extend lines of a yet undetermined length down from these points parallel to the branch centerline.
4. Draw an end view showing the offset centerlines of the main and the branch, to the right of the elevation view and on the same horizontal centerline as the main, see illustration #220B.
5. Draw a half circle above the end view of the branch, illustration #220B, divide it into 6 equal parts. Number from 1-12 as shown. Compare this numbering sequence to the other diagram.
6. Extend vertical lines down from these points to the circumference of the main.
7. Run a horizontal line across from point 4 on the end view to meet line 4 on the side view.
8. Note that points 3' and 5' are at the same location on the main in the end view. From this point run a horizontal line across to intersect lines 3' and 5' on the elevation view in their appropriate location.
9. These three points, 3', 4', 5' should be the lowest points on the branch-main cut line, illustration #220A.

10. Transfer the remainder of the points on the end view over to the elevation view.
11. Develop a stretchout line of the branch. Divide into 12 equal sections and number 1-12. Draw perpendicular lines from these points, see illustration #220C. Note that the base line is on the top.
12. Transfer the lengths 1-1', 2-2' etc. from the branch side view to the appropriate lines on the stretchout. Draw a smooth curve through these points to complete the pattern.
13. A stretchout for the hole should be drawn perpendicular to the main. Measure the curved distance from point 4' to point 10' on the main end view. This will be the length of the stretchout, see illustration #220D.
14. Point 7'-1' on the main end view will be the starting point and will be the center-line on the hole stretchout. Measure the curved distance from 7'-1' to 2'-6', 7-1' to 3'-5' and 7'-1' to 4' on the main end view. These curved distances will be transferred to the hole stretchout. They will be the distance from line 7-1 on the stretchout to lines 2-6, 3-5 and 4-4. Line 4-4 must be on the bottom of the layout.
15. Carry out the same procedure by measuring from 7'-1' on the main end view to points 8'-12', 9'-11' and 10' to arrive at lines 8-12, 9-11 and 10-10 on the stretchout, illustration #220D.
16. With #220D directly under (perpendicular to) #220A, transfer the cut line points on #220A down to their appropriate line on #220D. Eg: Point 4' on the side view is the bottom point and therefore is on line 4-4 and is the bottom point of the hole layout.

Pipe Centerlines

There are two easy methods of establishing the four centerlines on a pipe.

One is to strap (measure with a tape) the circumference, divide the distance by four, then wrap the tape around and mark the centerline points.

This method works on larger diameters of pipe but does not work as well when using a wide tape measure on smaller diameters. Another efficient method is to wrap a narrow strip of paper around the pipe, mark and then cut off the overlap. Fold the paper in half and mark the crease, then fold the two halves thereby dividing the strip into four equal sections.

The paper is now the exact length of the pipe circumference and is equally divided in four parts.

Marking Centerlines

It is normally a difficult task to mark the centerlines on a pipe and keep the lines parallel to the centerline.

A simple method of accomplishing this can be used with a piece of angle iron.

First divide the pipe circumference in four and mark the centerlines, then either place the pipe inside the open V of the angle, or place the inverted angle on top of the pipe. Line up the toe of the angle iron with a centerline mark, then draw in the centerline the length required.

Rotate the pipe to mark all four centerlines in a similar manner.

Cut Angles of Pipe

A fast and easy method of laying out a pipe which has to be cut off at a specific angle is to use a factor chart, see table #34, and a pipe wrap around.

The initial work points on each side are established by making four centerlines on the pipe and then by drawing a line around the pipe with a wrap around.

In this example, illustration #221A, a cut of 30° is required on a 6 inch (152.4 mm) pipe. The chart gives a factor number of .57735 for 30°, which is multiplied by the diameter of 6.625 inches (168.3 mm):

(6.625 inches x .57735 = 3.82 inches) (97 mm)

Divide this by two:

(3.82 inches = 2 = 1.91 inches) (48.5 mm)

1.91 inches = 1 15/16 inches. This is the factor measurement indicated by X on the top and bottom of illustration #221A. Mark these distances, hold a pipe wrap around in place and draw in the upper half of the cut line.

Rotate the pipe and draw in the bottom half, see illustration #221B.

A

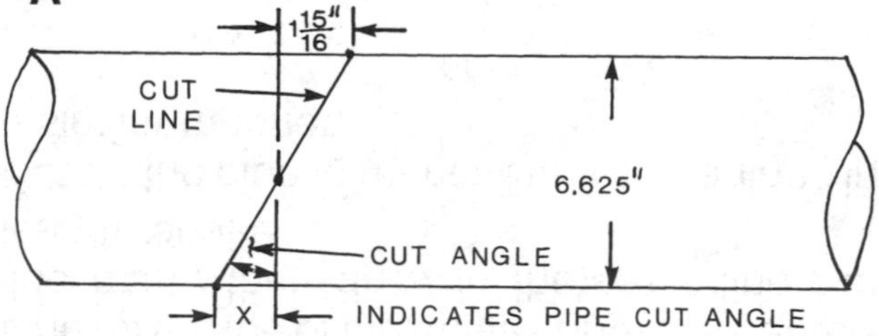

1 15/16"
CUT LINE
6.625"
CUT ANGLE
X
INDICATES PIPE CUT ANGLE

B

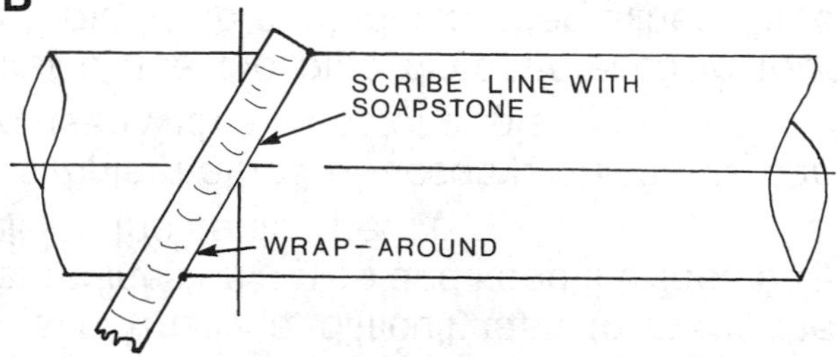

SCRIBE LINE WITH SOAPSTONE
WRAP-AROUND

Illustration #221 - Cut Angle of Pipe

CUT ANGLE FACTORS											
Cut Angle		Factor	Cut Angle		Factor	Cut Angle		Factor	Cut Angle		Factor
5°		.08749	15°		.26795	25°		.46631	35°		.70021
5°	30'	.09629	15°	30'	.27732	25°	30'	.47697	35°	30'	.71329
6		.10510	16		.28674	26		.48773	36		.72654
6	30	.11393	16	30	.29621	26	30	.49858	36	30	.73996
7		.12278	17		.30573	27		.50952	37		.75355
7	30	.13165	17	30	.31530	27	30	.52057	37	30	.76733
8		.14054	18		.32492	28		.53171	38		.78128
8	30	.14945	18	30	.33459	28	30	.54295	38	30	.79543
9		.15838	19		.34433	29		.55431	39		.80978
9	30	.16734	19	30	.35412	29	30	.56577	39	30	.82424
10		.17633	20		.36397	30		.57735	40		.83910
10	30	.18534	20	30	.37388	30	30	.58904	40	30	.85408
11		.19438	21		.38386	31		.60086	41		.86929
11	30	.20345	21	30	.39391	31	30	.61280	41	30	.88472
12		.21256	22		.40403	32		.62487	42		.90040
12	30	.22169	22	30	.41421	32	30	.63707	42	30	.91633
13		.23087	23		.42447	33		.64941	43		.93251
13	30	.24008	23	30	.43481	33	30	.66188	43	30	.94896
14		.24933	24		.44523	34		.67451	44		.96569
14	30	.25862	24	30	.45573	34	30	.68728	44	30	1.00000

Table #34 - Cut Angle Factors

Reducing Lateral

Header Layout

A quick method of laying out a reducing lateral on smaller pipe diameters is indicated in illustration #222.

Establish the correct angle of the branch and hold it in place with a brace tacked to the header and the branch.

Hold a long sharpened soapstone on the branch, see illustration #222A, then move the soapstone around the branch, keeping the point against the header and draw a smooth curved cut line on the header.

Branch Layout

With the branch still tacked in position, establish distance D on both the top and bottom of the branch, see illustration #222B. This will establish point A.

Lay a small straight edge on top of the branch touching the header.

Mark point A on the straight edge, then move it around the branch, keeping the end against the header and transferring point "A" around the branch in the form of a smooth curved cut line.

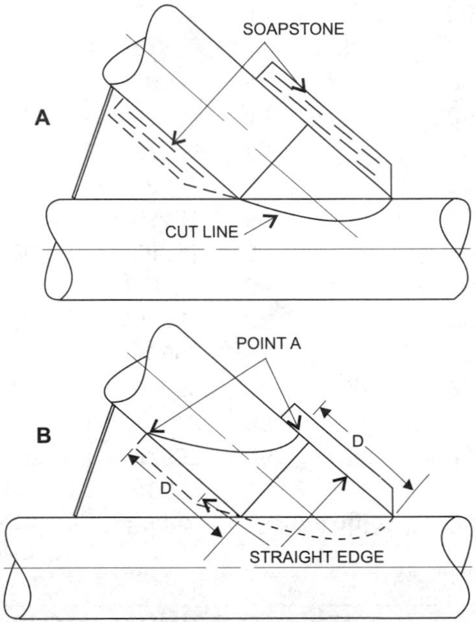
SOAPSTONE
A
CUT LINE
POINT A
B
D
D
STRAIGHT EDGE

Illustration #222 - Reducing Pipe Lateral

Orange Peel Layout

A method of capping off the end of a pipe when a weld cap is not available is by laying out, cutting and welding a cap made from the pipe.

Table #35 will determine the number of sections for the applicable pipe diameter. Divide the pipe end into the correct number of sections, extend reference lines down to reach a base line, the distance of which is also determined by the table.

Pipe Size in Inches	No. of Sections	X in inches	D in inches	C in inches	B in inches
2	4	1 7/8	1 7/8	1 5/8	15/16
4	4	3 1/2	3 17/32	3 1/16	1 3/4
6	5	5 1/4	4 1/8	3 5/8	2 1/16
8	5	6 3/4	5 3/8	4 3/4	2 11/16
10	7	8 1/2	4 13/16	4 1/4	2 3/8
12	8	10	5	4 3/8	2 1/2

Table #35 - Orange Peel Layout Data

A template common to each section is made up by using data from the table applicable to the diameter.

Mark out each section with the template and a soapstone, cut the pipe, heat the sections cherry red, bend and weld them into a cap.

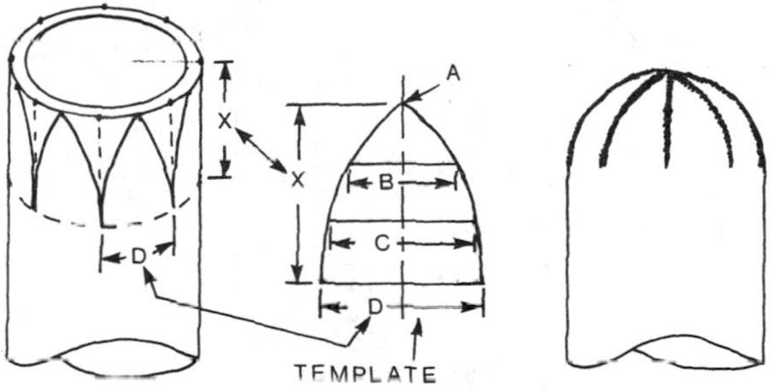
A
X
X
B
C
D
D
TEMPLATE

Illustration #223 - Orange Peel Pipe Cap

Right Cone (Radial Lines)

1. Layout a side view of the cone, letter it A,B,X,Y, see illustration #224A. Extend the centerline and both slanted sides to meet at O.
2. Using distance O-B', illustration #224B, swing a long arc. Calculate the cone bottom circumference ($C = \pi D$) and measure this distance around the bottom of the arc.
3. From distance O-A on the side view swing another arc on the cone layout.
4. This gives the full cone development A',B',X',Y', illustration #224B, prior to rolling or bending.
5. If the cone is to be bent up with a brake, the bend lines should be marked out before the cone is cut from the plate.

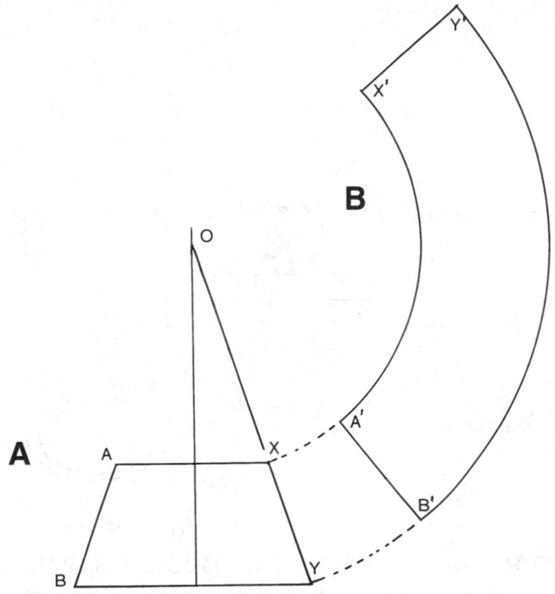

A
B
O
A
B
X
Y
A'
B'
X'
Y'

Illustration #224 - Right Cone

Triangulation

Triangulation is a layout method used when other easier methods cannot be adapted to do the job.

In this method, an object is divided into triangles on a flat surface, then the triangles are transferred to the correct size and position on a flat plate. The plate is either rolled or broken at the bend lines to make up the required object. *The reason for using triangulation is that an object which has an oblique shape does not show the correct true lengths of its sides when displayed on a flat sheet or is drawn on paper.*

An example of this is shown in illustration #225, a wide flange brace. The side elevation and plan views do not show the true length of the brace. The principle of establishing a true length is that a plan (top view) length placed at a right angle to its true vertical height will produce a diagonal equal to its true length. For an example illustration #225 shows three views.

When the plan length L is placed against the true vertical height H, the true length X of the brace is established. This is checked by comparing the true length in the elevation view with the length of X. The principle still applies if the brace is offset.

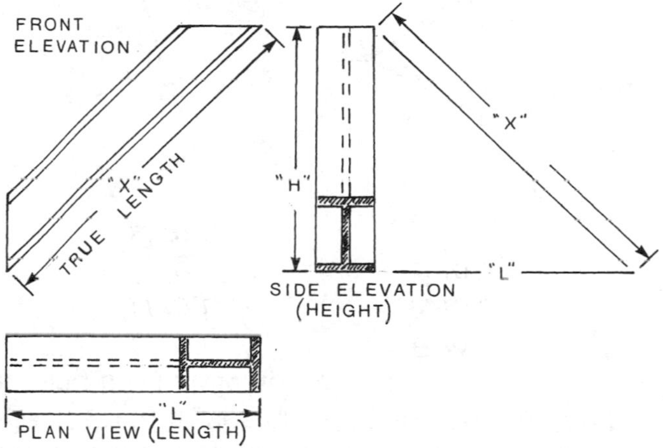
FRONT
ELEVATION
"X" TRUE LENGTH
"H"
"X"
"L"
SIDE ELEVATION
(HEIGHT)
"L"
PLAN VIEW (LENGTH)

Illustration #225 - Flange Brace by Triangulation

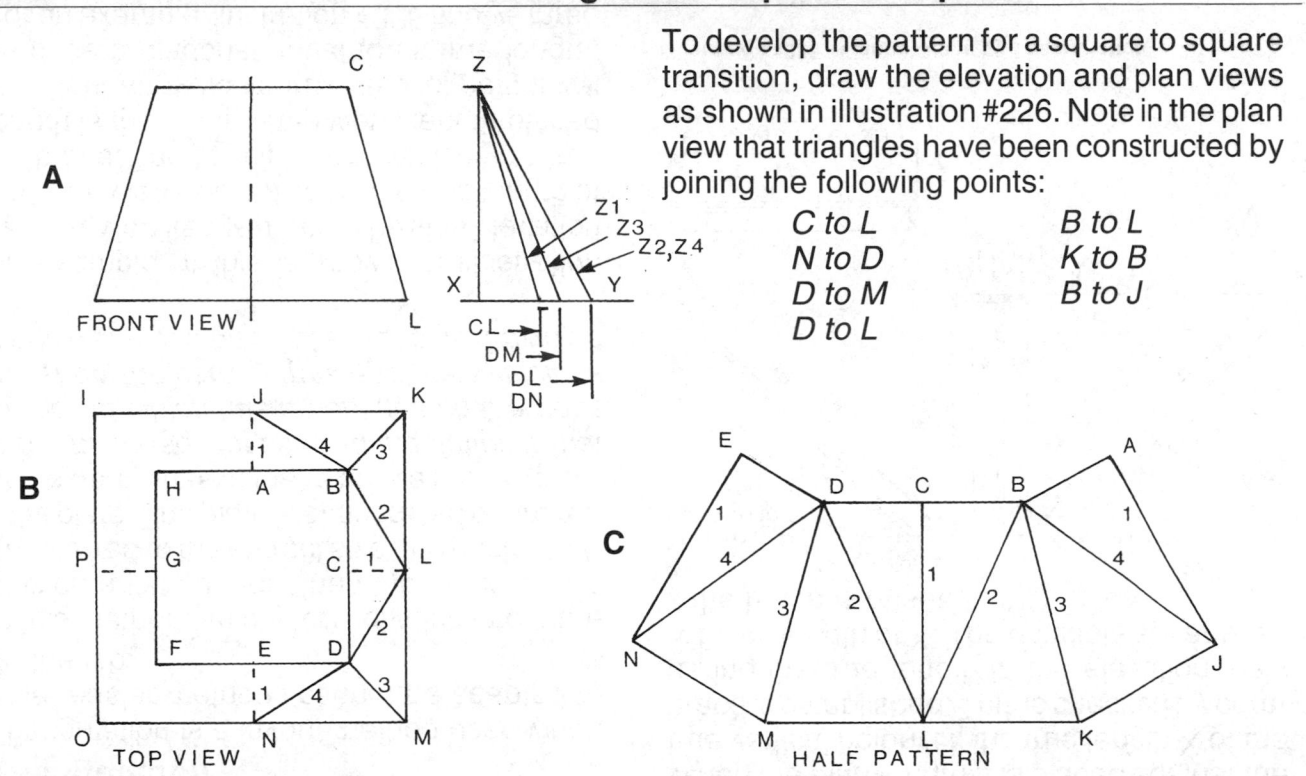

To develop the pattern for a square to square transition, draw the elevation and plan views as shown in illustration #226. Note in the plan view that triangles have been constructed by joining the following points:

C to L	*B to L*
N to D	*K to B*
D to M	*B to J*
D to L	

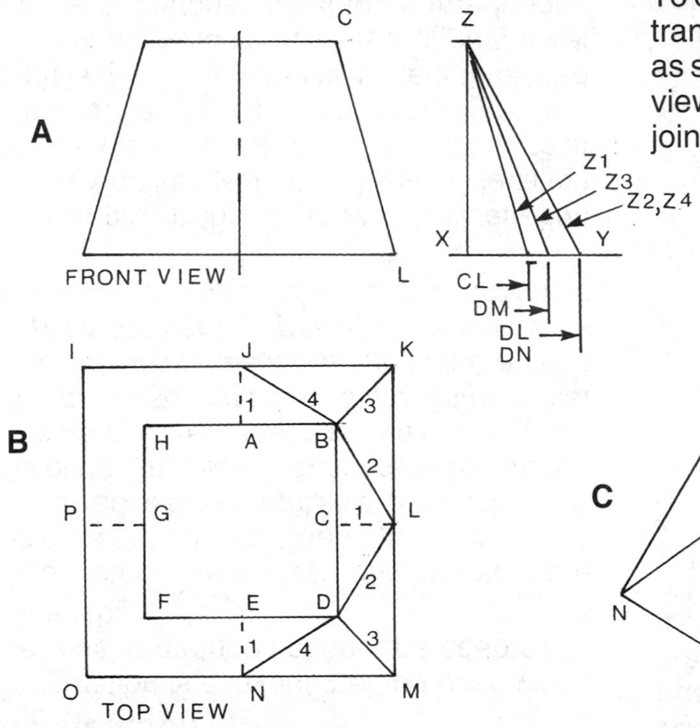
A
C
Z
Z1
Z3
Z2,Z4
X
Y
FRONT VIEW
L
CL
DM
DL
DN
B
I
J
K
H
A
B
P
G
C
L
F
E
D
O
N
M
1
4
3
2
1
2
1
4
3
TOP VIEW

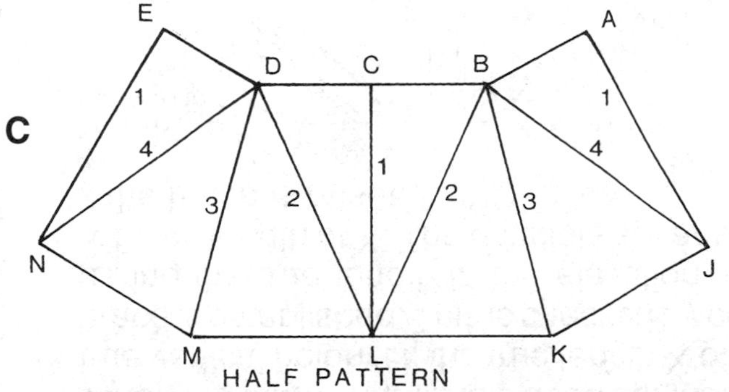
C
E
D
C
B
A
1
4
3
2
1
2
3
4
1
N
J
M
L
K
HALF PATTERN

illustration #226 - Square to Square by Triangulation

Square to Square Transition

1. To determine the bend line true lengths, draw the right triangle X-Y-Z, with Z-X equal to the vertical height of the transition piece (transferred from the elevation view), see illustration #226A.
2. From the plan view, illustration #226B measure lengths C L, D M and D L. Transfer these lengths to line X Y, as shown in illustration #226A. Connect these points on line X Y to point Z. These lines are the true lengths of the plan view lines. As the triangle is symmetrical, these three triangles in one quarter of the plan view will be equal to the triangles in the other three sections.
3. To develop the pattern, draw line M K in illustration #226C equal to M K in the plan view. From L erect a perpendicular equal to C L in the elevation view which is a true length. This line should be equal to line Z 1, illustration #226A.
4. To locate points B and D on the pattern, scribe arcs from center C using lengths C D and B C from the plan view. With center L and length Z 2 draw two arcs to cut at B and D. Join B and D through C. This line should be parallel to line M K.
5. To establish points N and J, scribe arcs from centers M and K with length MN and KJ from the plan view. With centers B and D and length Z2, scribe arcs to cut at N and J. Join MN and KJ.
6. To locate points A and E, scribe arcs from the centers N and J with true length CL from the elevation view (Z1). With centers B and D and true lengths ED (or AB) from the plan view, draw arcs to cut at A and E. Draw in lines, DE, EN, AB and AJ. Check that angles AJK and ENM are 90° angles.

This pattern will develop one half of the required transition.

1. Draw the front elevation as shown in illustration #227A. As the transition is symmetrical, a full plan view is not required. A half plan view is used to illustrate the numbering and lettering sequence. The half circle in the plan view is divided into 12 equal parts. The division points are numbered and connected to B and D, see illustration #227B.

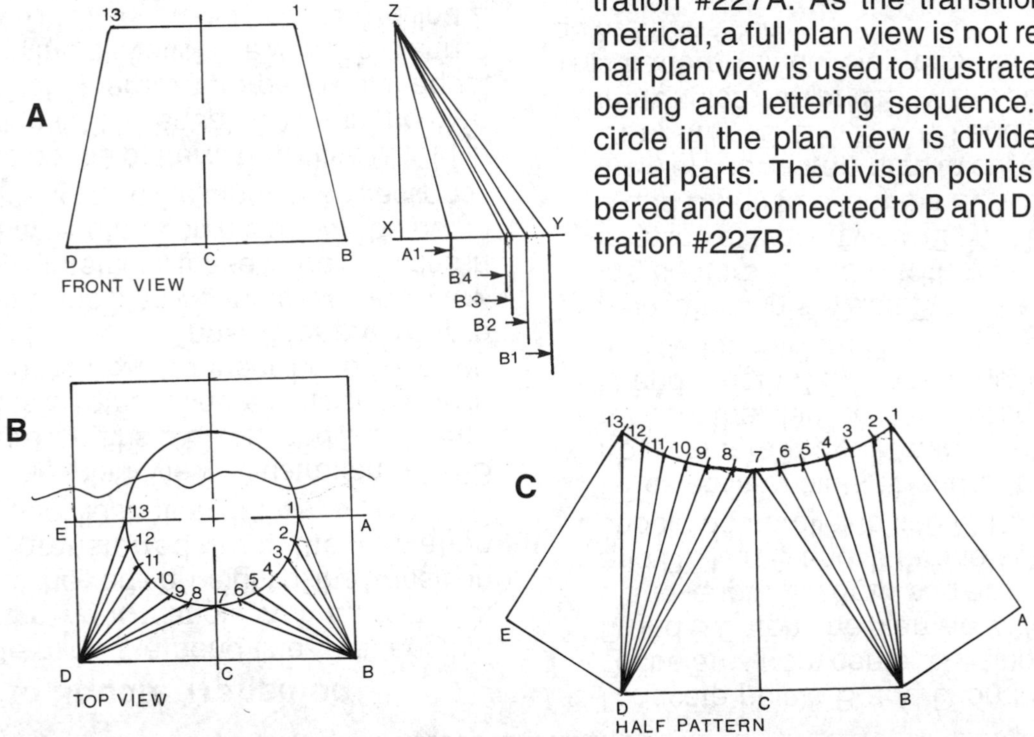
A
13
1
D
C
B
FRONT VIEW
Z
X
Y
A1
B4
B3
B2
B1
B
E
A
13
12
11
10
9
8
7
6
5
4
3
2
1
D
C
B
TOP VIEW
C
13
12
11
10
9
8
7
6
5
4
3
2
1
E
A
D
C
B
HALF PATTERN

Illustration #227 - Square to Round Transition

Square to Round Transition

2. To develop the true length lines, construct the true length triangle XYZ with ZX equal to the vertical height of the transition in the elevation view. From the half plan view, transfer the plan lengths A1, B1, B2, B3 and B4 to the base of the right angle triangle and connect the points to apex Z.
   Line B1 will equal lines B7, D7, D13. Line B2 equals B6, D8 and D12. B3 equals B5, D9 and D11.
3. To develop the pattern, draw base line BCD equal in length to BCD in the plan view. From C erect a perpendicular C7, equal to the true length A1 in the front elevation. This true length applies to lines A1, C7 and E13 in the plan view.
4. Transfer arc length 7-6 from the plan view to the pattern and swing off from point 7 on both sides, (this length is constant for the entire pattern).
5. From the true length triangle, transfer line B2 to the pattern by scribing arcs from centres B and D to intersect at arcs 6 and 8. (This length equals the true length of lines B6 and D8 in the plan).
6. Scribe arcs from 6 and 8 equal to the arcs scribed from point 7. With centers B and D and length B3 from the true length triangle, draw arcs to intersect at arcs "5 and 9". (This length equals the true lengths of line B5 and D9 in the plan).
7. Continue the procedure using true length lines to correspond with the plan view, to locate points 4,10, 3, 11, 2, 12, 1 and 13.
8. To locate points A and E on the pattern, use centres B and D with length AB or DE from the plan view and scribe arcs.
   With points 1 and 13 and pattern length C7 (previously stated as equal to true lengths A1 and E13), draw arcs to intersect at A and E.
9. Connect all points as shown in the pattern. Angles 1 AB and 13ED are 90° angles.

Neutral Diameter

Workers unfamiliar with rolled plate often cut the flat length either too long or too short the first time they calculate the length by using the formula:

Circumference = π x diameter.

Example: Shell inside diameter of 54 inches using $^3/_8$ inch plate.

Using the formula $C = \pi D$, a flat plate cut to this formula, 3.1416 x 54 inches, (using the inside diameter) will be 169 $^5/_8$ inches, see illustration #228A. However after rolling, the shell will actually have an inside diameter of only 53 $^5/_8$ inches, not 54 inches. The reason is as follows: the length of a piece of plate is only constant for both sides as long as it is flat. When it is rolled, its length (or the circumference of the arc or circle it describes) becomes longer on the outside and shorter on the inside, see illustration #228B.

The only portion of the plate that retains the original length is the middle of the plate thickness, referred to as the mean or neutral length of circumference.

In the example, the inside diameter of the rolled plate reflects the shortening of the inside circumference resulting from rolling.

To obtain the required inside diameter of 54 inches, the circumference must be calculated by using 54 $^3/_8$ inches, (the inside diameter plus one thickness of plate), see illustration #228C.

This would result in a necessary flat length of 170$^{13}/_{16}$ inches.

Conversely, when the outside diameter is the critical measurement, the neutral diameter is found by subtracting one thickness from the outside diameter.

From these examples, a rule of thumb can be developed to ensure precise finished dimensions for rolled plate:

For exact O.D. subtract one plate thickness from the specified diameter and calculate the required flat length as:

$C = \pi$(D - one plate thickness)

For exact I.D. add one plate thickness to the specified number and calculate the required flat length as:

$C = \pi(D + \text{one plate thickness})$

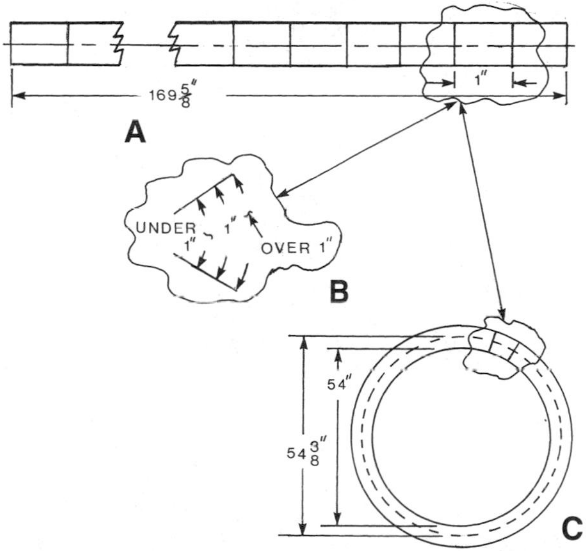
169 5/8"
1"
A
UNDER 1"
1"
OVER 1"
B
54"
54 3/8"
C

Illustration #228 - Rolling Plate

PLATE DEVELOPMENT SYMBOLS AND ABBREVIATIONS			
PL	PLATE	CL	CENTRE LINE
W.L.	WORK LINE	Sec.	SECTION
W.P.	WORK POINT	Elev.	ELEVATION
B.L.	BEND LINE	Dev.L.	DEVELOPED LENGTH
In.S.	INSIDE	T.L.	TRUE LENGTH
O.S.	OUTSIDE	Ref.L.	REFERENCE LINE
O.D.	OUTSIDE DIAMETER	Cir.	CIRCUMFERENCE
I.D.	INSIDE DIAMETER	Dia.	DIAMETER
Bev.	BEVEL	M.Dia.	MEAN DIAMETER
Temp.	TEMPLATE	Rad.	RADIUS
	BEND SYMBOL	M.Rad.	MEAN RADIUS
SQ. (Sq.)	SQUARE		

Table #36 - Plate Development Symbols & Abbreviations

SECTION FOUR QUESTIONS

Layout

1. *Which of the following is a correct ratio of a 3-4-5 triangle?*
   - ❒ 12-16-20
   - ❒ 9-16-20
   - ❒ 6-8-12
   - ❒ 27-36-45

2. *The layout mechanic can use the 3-4-5 method to check if the ends are __________ to the sides of large plates and also to __________ up frames or structural members.*
   - ❒ plumb
   - ❒ aligned
   - ❒ level
   - ❒ square

3. *What would be the height and diagonal length of a 45 degree triangle with a base of 10 inches?*
   - ❒ height 14.14, diagonal 10
   - ❒ height 10, diagonal 14.14
   - ❒ height 10, diagonal 10
   - ❒ height 14.14, diagonal 14.14

4. *270 degrees is what part of a circle?*
   - ❒ 3/4 circle
   - ❒ 1/4 circle
   - ❒ 1/2 circle
   - ❒ full circle

5. *What is a straight line called that touches two points on the circumference of a circle?*
   - ❒ degree
   - ❒ circumference
   - ❒ radius
   - ❒ chord

6. *The term "strapping" refers to:*
   - ❒ checking for square
   - ❒ measuring the circumference
   - ❒ measuring the perimeter
   - ❒ determining high/low

7. *A pressure vessel has an outside circumference measurement of 2540 mm. What would be the length of the arc length from the 0 degree centerline to the 90 degree centerline.*
   - ❒ 2540
   - ❒ 1905
   - ❒ 1270
   - ❒ 635

8. *Determine if the following statement is true or false. A flange having 16 bolt holes will also have a total of 16 spaces between each bolt hole.*
   - ❒ true ❒ false

9. *Determine if the following statement is true or false. The common procedure when installing a flange on a pipe or in a vessel is to have the bolt holes straddle the centerline.*
   - ❒ true ❒ false

10. *A vessel base ring is being layed out in 3 pieces. An arc, with a radius equal to the outside ring radius, is scribed for each piece. How many distances equal to the ring outside radius are scribed on each arc?*
    - ❒ 4
    - ❒ 3
    - ❒ 2
    - ❒ 1

11. *Parallel Line Development would not be suitable to use as a method of layout on:*
    - ❒ cones
    - ❒ pipe
    - ❒ square ducting
    - ❒ tubing

12. *The outside diameter of a pipe measures 3 1/2 inches. Determine the length of the stretch out line necessary to develop a template for a two piece 90 degree elbow.*
    - ❒ 3 1/2
    - ❒ 22/7
    - ❒ 10 31/32
    - ❒ 14

13. *Referring to page 196, illustration #217, the required radius used to develop the semi-plan view of the true wye would be equal to:*
- ❒ O.D. of pipe
- ❒ O.D. of pipe divided by 2
- ❒ I.D. of pipe
- ❒ I.D. of pipe divided by 2

14. *The correct cut angle for a 3 piece 90 degree turn using 3 inch N.P.S. pipe schedule 40 wall would be:*
- ❒ 45 degrees
- ❒ 15 degrees
- ❒ 30 degrees
- ❒ 22 1/2 degrees

15. *When laying out the surface of a pipe, an angle iron can be used to help keep which of the following going parallel and in a straight line?*
- ❒ chords
- ❒ diameter
- ❒ radial lines
- ❒ centerlines

16. *Referring to illustration 221 on page 206 and table #34, determine the measure back distance for a 4 inch pipe to be torch cut at an angle of 35 degrees. (Note: Refer to Pipe Schedules Chart for actual 0.D. of 4 inch pipe)*
- ❒ 1.58
- ❒ 3.15
- ❒ 1.40
- ❒ 1.30

17. *Refer to the chart on page 209. When making a pipe cap by the orange peel layout method on an 8 inch pipe, how many sections should the pipe end be divided into?*
- ❒ 3
- ❒ 5
- ❒ 7
- ❒ 9

18. *When laying out a reducing cone that has a 6 ft. bottom diameter, a 4 ft. top diameter, and is 3 ft. high; the first arc that is scribed will be equal to what length?*
- ❒ top circumference
- ❒ bottom circumference
- ❒ height
- ❒ none of above

19. *The principle of triangulation is to establish a plan view length placed at a right angle to the actual vertical height, this will produce a diagonal equal to what length?*
    - ❒ radial length
    - ❒ plan length
    - ❒ elevation length
    - ❒ true length

20. *Referring to illustration #227 on page 214, the reason for developing only a half pattern of this transition is because it is:*
    - ❒ conical
    - ❒ semi-elliptical
    - ❒ right cone
    - ❒ symmetrical

21. *The outside diameter of a cylinder is known. The correct formula to calculate the required length of plate would be:*
    - ❒ O.D. minus one T x pi
    - ❒ O.D. minus two T x pi
    - ❒ I.D. plus two T x pi
    - ❒ O.D. x pi (T = thickness)

22. *The required length of plate needed to roll a 48 inch O.D. shell using 1/4 inch plate would be:*
    - ❒ 150.80 inches
    - ❒ 149.23 inches
    - ❒ 150 inches
    - ❒ 147.65 inches

23. *The abbreviation W.P. refers to:*

    ____

24. *The abbreviation C.L. refers to:*

    ____

25. *The abbreviation SQ. refers to:*

    ____

SECTION
FIVE
BULK STORAGE TANKS

Foundations

A level foundation may not appear necessary on a large bulk tank, however a tank, like any other structure, must have a level base to be erected properly.

The usual requirement of a tank pad is, *plus or minus, 1/4 inch (6.4 mm), high to low.*

The three most common types of pads are:

1. Concrete Ringwall
2. Asphalt
3. Sandpad

The type most widely used is the sandpad which is oiled to prevent erosion.

A solid foundation is important, as a tank exerts head pressure on the pad and could result in the necessity of piles.

Centerlines

It will always be necessary to have the four centerlines established on the pad prior to laying any plate, see illustration #229.

Laying Floor Plates

It is impossible to set out many procedures for laying the floor plates of a tank due to the different procedures followed by various companies. For the exact procedure, the floor layout print will outline the necessary steps. However, some of the basic steps are standard.

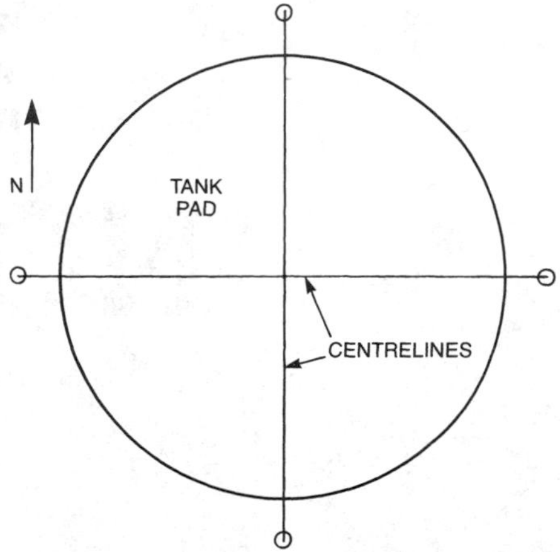
N
TANK PAD
CENTRELINES

Illustration #229 - Tank Centerlines

1. Move plate #1 into position, straddling the four centerlines. Tack a welding rod to the center of the plate.
2. Remove the four lines, then lay plates #2, #3, #4 and #5 with an overlap of at least 5 times the plate thickness. Nuts tacked to the last positioned plate can be used to maintain this lap. Occasionally check with the centerline to ensure that the plates are running square.
3. On large tanks there will be a large number of plates extending out from center similar to plates #1 and #2 in the diagram. A simple check method to ensure the plates are running square is to measure from the outside edge to the center pin. If they are not square a heavier lap on one end will bring the last plate back into line.
4. Next lay the four centerline sketch plates at #6, #7, #8, #9, #10 and #11. The sketch plates between the centerlines, at #12 through #19 will be laid last, see illustration #230.

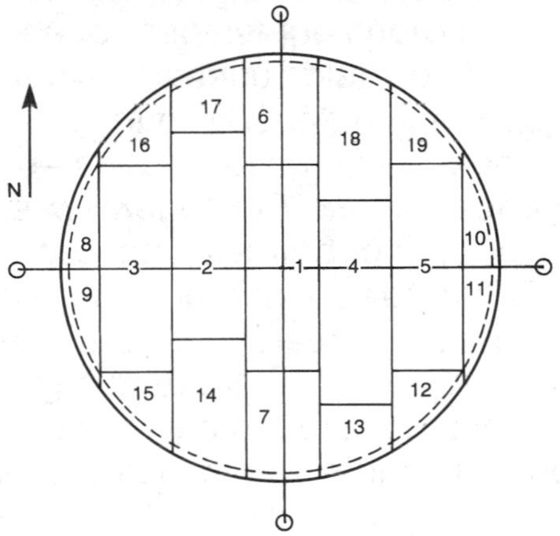
N
1
2
3
4
5
6
7
8
9
10
11
12
13
14
15
16
17
18
19
FLOOR PLATE ORIENTATION

Illustration #230 - Laying Tank Floor

5. On a larger tank it is advisable to keep the outside edge at least 1/2 inch (13 mm) larger than the indicated outside radius. This allows extra room for tacking on fitting aids such as nuts, and it also compensates for weld shrinkage in the floor. For methods of fitting up the floor plates, see illustrations #231 and #232.

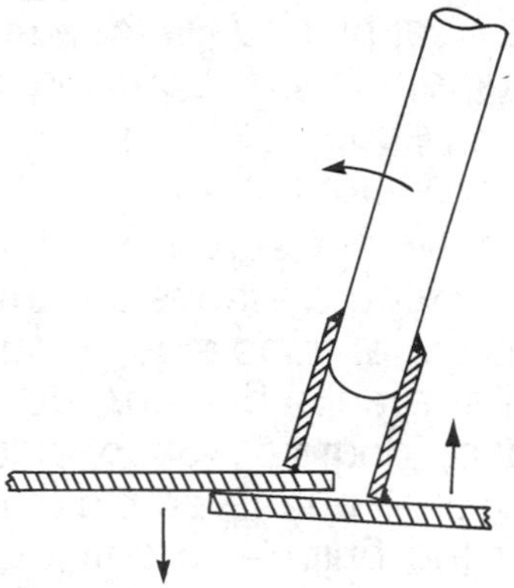

Illustration #231 - Fit Up of Floor Plates

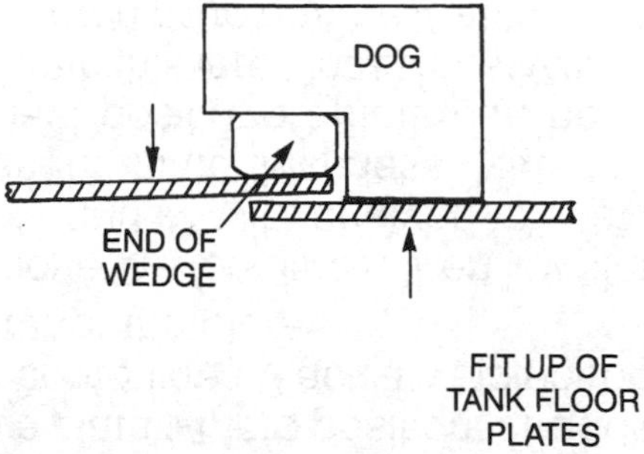
DOG
END OF WEDGE
FIT UP OF TANK FLOOR PLATES

Illustration #232 - Dog and Wedge

First Ring Layout

- Scribe a circle equal to the inside radius of the first ring, using a steel tape and soapstone, see illustration #233.
- The starting point of a joint in the first ring will be established from the orientation view.
- The chord distance of a plate should be indicated on a detail print, see illustration #234.
- At the starting point, swing a series of arcs, equal to the chord to cut the scribed circle. The number of arcs will be equal to the number of shell plates in one ring. Layout the circle in two halves going each way from the starting point. The two halves will very likely overlap each other or come short of each other. If so, divide the discrepancy by the number of chords and then move each point the appropriate distance to readjust the chord length.
- Each point will be the exact location of every shell seam joint.

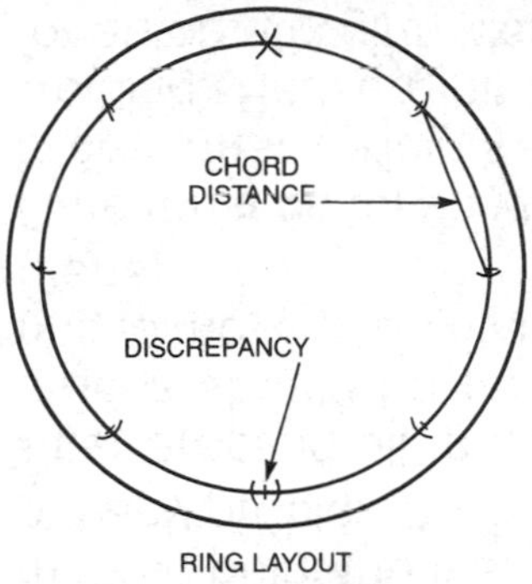
CHORD
DISTANCE
DISCREPANCY
RING LAYOUT

Illustration #233 - Chord Layout

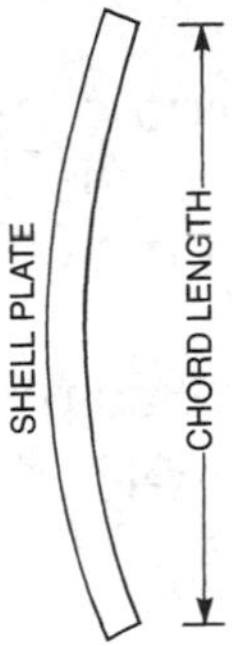
SHELL PLATE
CHORD LENGTH

Illustration #234 - Chord Length

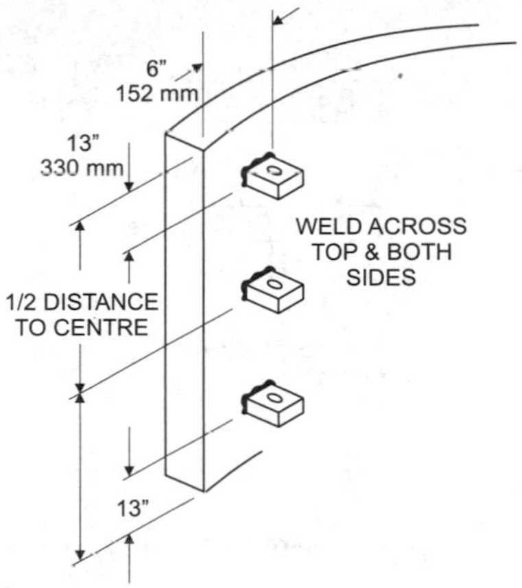
6"
152 mm
13"
330 mm
WELD ACROSS
TOP & BOTH
SIDES
1/2 DISTANCE
TO CENTRE
13"

Illustration #235 - Key Plate Nut Locations

Shell Plates

The erection nuts or lugs and the scaffold brackets should be welded on while the plates are lying on the ground, see illustration #235. Then weld on scaffold bracket clips.

Scaffold Bracket Clip Welding: Usually uphand weld starting in a short distance from the 2 outside bottom corners, then proceed up and around top corners and continue along top. See illustration #236.

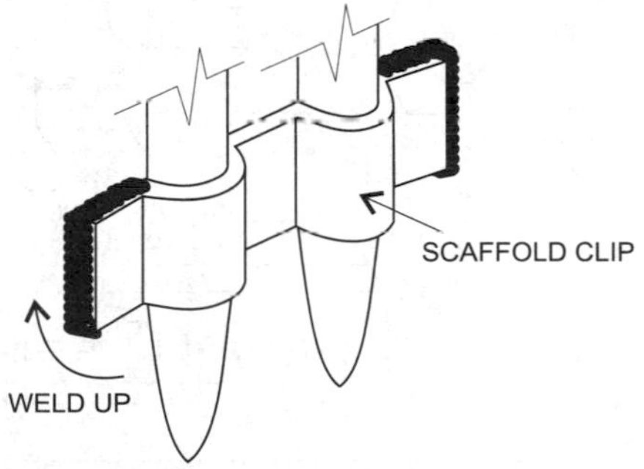
SCAFFOLD CLIP
WELD UP

Illustration #236 - Scaffold Clip

First Ring Erection

1. Position the end of plate #1 on the starting point. Tack this end then force the plate out to the scribed circle.
2. Bull pins and nuts are used to move the plate in or out. Brace securely in position. Move plate #2 into position and attach it to plate #1 with key plates. Each joint is pulled up fairly tight and each plate should be plumb.
3. If every plate end is placed on each marked point the last plate will fit in without any problem.
4. After erecting all the plates any tacks or braces should be removed to allow the ring to move while fitting the vertical joints (verts).
5. Care must be taken when fitting the verts in order that the joints are not peaked after welding. Peaked joints create problems for automatic girth welders.

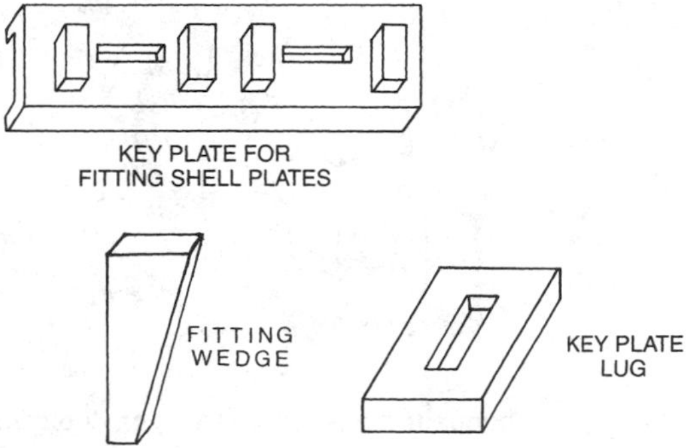
KEY PLATE FOR
FITTING SHELL PLATES
FITTING
WEDGE
KEY PLATE
LUG

Illustration #237 - Key Plate Hardware

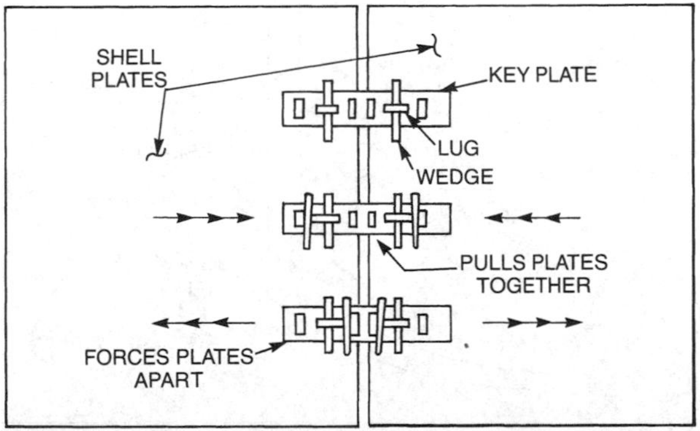
SHELL
PLATES
KEY PLATE
LUG
WEDGE
PULLS PLATES
TOGETHER
FORCES PLATES
APART

Illustration #238 - Key Plate Arrangements

Shell to Floor Welding

The shell should not be welded to the floor until after the shell verts and the floor lap joints have been welded. Various floor sizes and plate layouts will have different weld procedures to minimize shrinkage and buckling. The shell must be rounded out as closely as possible to the original line, then tacked and welded on the outside. The weld can be tested by spraying the joint liberally with oil on the inside, then watching for oil seepage on the outside, or by a magnetic flux test.

Tank Leveling

Erecting the first ring on an off level base will cause various problems throughout the remainder of construction. These will include flat spots and buckles in the shell and difficulty in fitting up roof rafters. A transit should be used to check the tank for level after the first ring is up. If necessary the floor will have to be jacked up and grout forced between the base and the floor. A jacking frame is indicated in illustration #239.

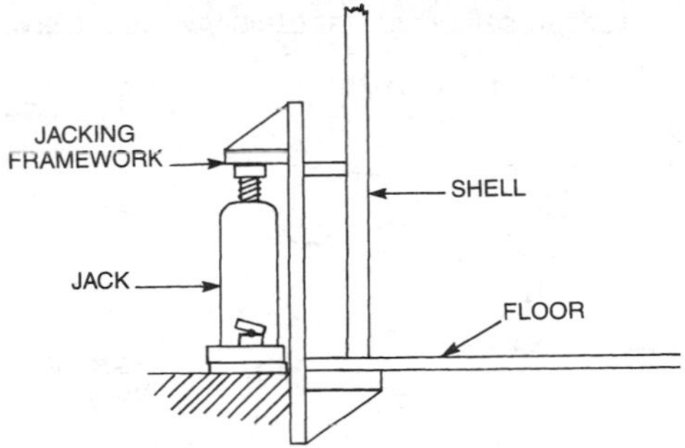
JACKING FRAMEWORK
SHELL
JACK
FLOOR

Illustration #239 - Jacking Framework

Succeeding Rings

Several methods can be used to gap and hold the second shell course on top of the first: (1) Gap shims with pins inside and out, illustration #241, or (2) beads of weld on top of the first ring, along with a U bar and pin system on both plates, see illustrations #240 and #242.

Most shell seams are offset by 1/3 the length of one plate. To maintain the distance for ring erection the top of plates are marked at 1/3 spacings, see illustration #242.

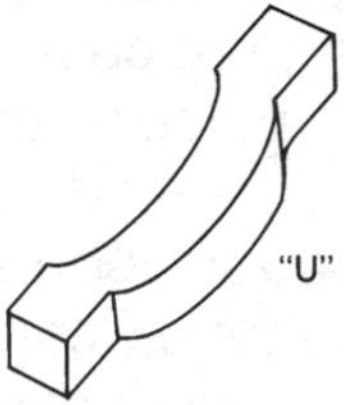
"U" BAR

Illustration #240 - U-Bar

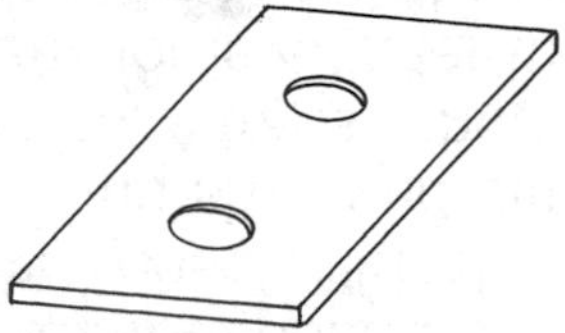
SHIM FOR GAPPING PLATE

Illustration #241 - Gapping Shim

Fitting Horizontal Seams

One very important consideration when fitting horizontal seams is that the vertical seam welding must keep ahead of horizontal seam fitting. This is because of the vertical seam shrinkage from welding. On large tanks with many seams, this shrinkage could add up to a considerable distance. Care must also be taken when fitting to keep the vertical joints on the 1/3 plate marks. See illustration #243.

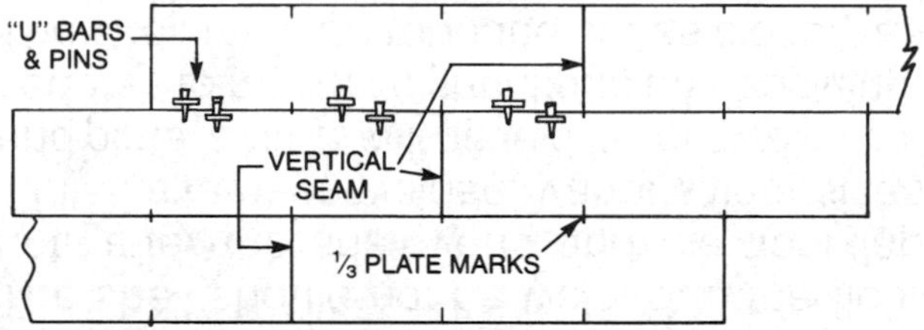
"U" BARS
& PINS
VERTICAL
SEAM
⅓ PLATE MARKS

Illustration #242 - 1/3 Plate Marks

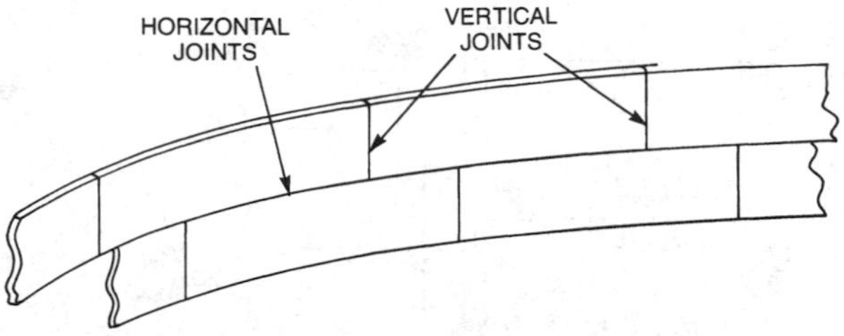
HORIZONTAL
JOINTS
VERTICAL
JOINTS
WELD VERTICAL JOINTS BEFORE HORIZONTAL JOINTS

Illustration #243 - Horizontal and Vertical Seams

Barrel Roll

Some pre-rolled plates will have a built in barrel roll, see illustration #244. If, during fit up of vertical joints, the top and bottom of two plates with barrel rolls are tacked first it will be almost impossible to pull in the center.

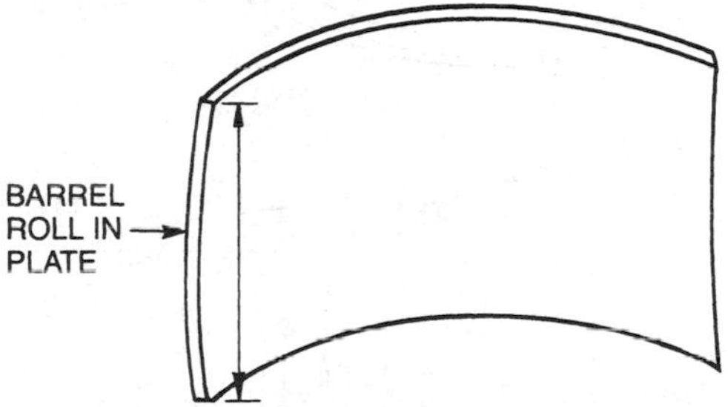
BARREL
ROLL IN
PLATE

Illustration #244 - Barrel Roll

The correct method is to first pull in the center to the right gap, tack weld, then the remainder of the seam will be easily forced out to position and the two ends will have the proper gap.

Rim Angle

The top or rim angle is usually fitted up prior to erecting any of the rafters. This angle helps to round out the tank top, however it should not be welded until the rafters are on. Welding will make the top rigid and could cause rafter fitting difficulties, see illustration #245 and 246.

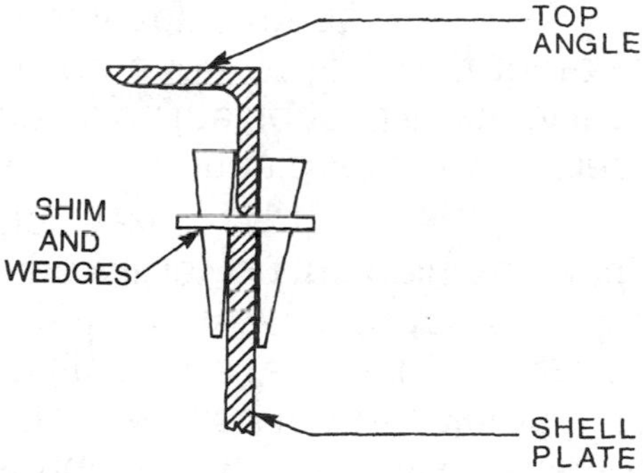
TOP
ANGLE
SHIM
AND
WEDGES
SHELL
PLATE

Illustration #245

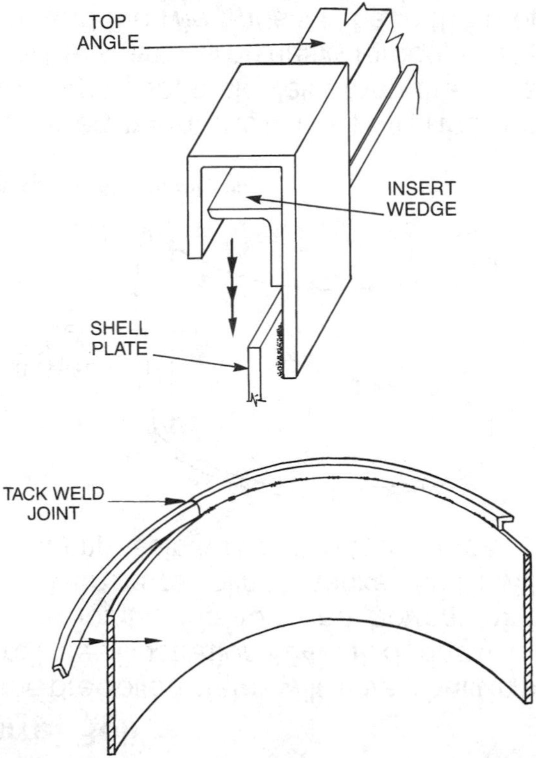
TOP ANGLE
INSERT WEDGE
SHELL PLATE
TACK WELD JOINT

Illustration #246 - Rim Angle

Roof Framework

Single Column

On a single column roof two rafters are securely tack welded to the column in the correct position. The remaining rafters are then positioned and welded to the shell lugs, the other end will lay on the column head, see illustration #247.

These rafters should all be pre-marked for positioning on the head. If some of the rafters appear too short or too long there are two methods of adjustment.

1. Pulling in the short rafters to position should force the long rafters out.
2. Place jacks under the tank floor in vertical line with the short rafters. This will push the short rafters in and move the long ones out. If this method is used grout will have to be forced under the floor for support.

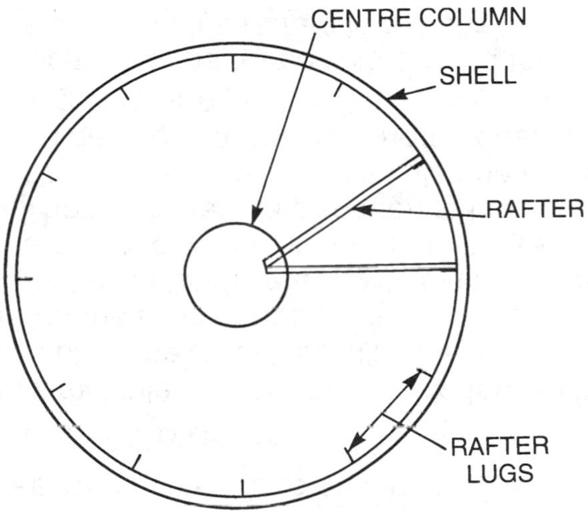
CENTRE COLUMN
SHELL
RAFTER
RAFTER
LUGS

Illustration #247 - Single Column Roof

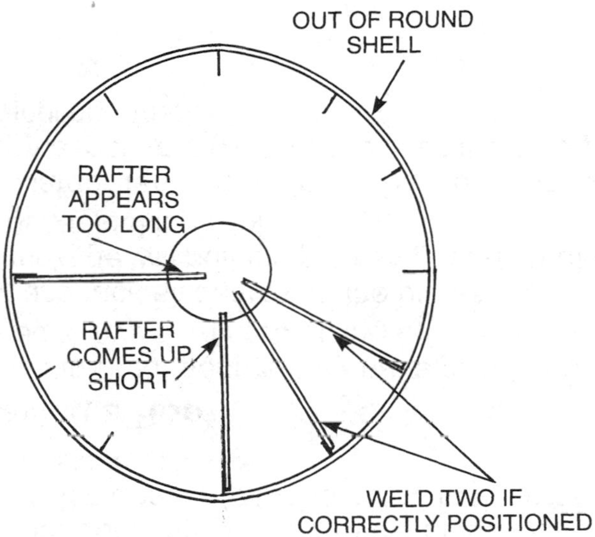
OUT OF ROUND
SHELL
RAFTER
APPEARS
TOO LONG
RAFTER
COMES UP
SHORT
WELD TWO IF
CORRECTLY POSITIONED

Illustration #248 - Misalignment of Rafters

It is possible that all the rafters will be short. This could happen if the crown in the tank was too high thereby creating an excessive roof pitch and an extra long distance between the center head and the tank shell.

Multiple Columns

On a multiple column framework, the shell is laid out for the rafter lugs, also the floor is laid out for the column positions.

1. At the shell side, erect two columns, a column to column girder and the rafters. Then weld securely enough to hold in position. The girders should also be tied off on each end to prevent them from spiralling and falling in.
2. Complete the framework around the outside. Weld the rafters to the shell lugs.
3. Erect the center column and the inside rafters. Bolt or weld (as required) the inside and outside rafters together (to form single shell to center column rafters).
4. Weld the rafters which are correctly positioned to the center head. Pull in the rafters which are short of the correct position; this should force those rafters which appear too long out to their correct position.

Laying a Roof

The tank roof seams may have to be orientated to avoid any roof fittings.

Fit and tack all seams as the plates are laid. Shrinkage will pull the plates tight and make a better looking roof.

On larger tanks it will probably be easier to lay the roof from two sides to keep the natural shingling effect.

Types of Joints

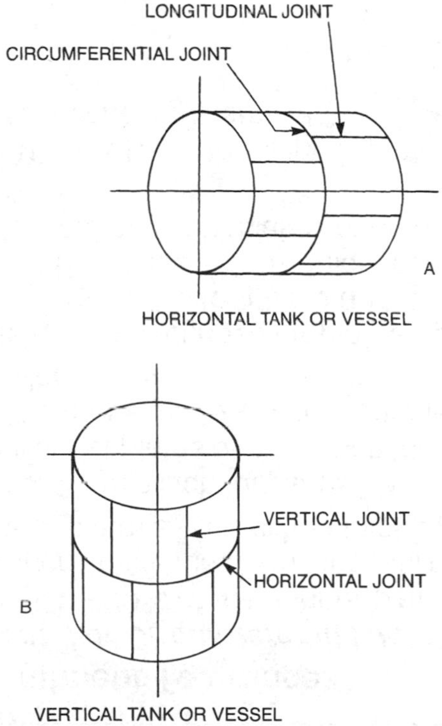
LONGITUDINAL JOINT
CIRCUMFERENTIAL JOINT
A
HORIZONTAL TANK OR VESSEL
VERTICAL JOINT
HORIZONTAL JOINT
B
VERTICAL TANK OR VESSEL

Illustration #249 - Tank Joints

Misalignment Tolerances

Vertical or Longitudinal Joints

- **API 650** - 10% of plate thickness, or 1/16 inch, whichever is larger.
- **API 620** - 1/16 inch for plate 1/4 inch thick and less. For plates over 1/4 inch thick, 25% of plate thickness or 1/8 inch, whichever is less.
- **ASME** - 1/4 of the thickness for plates up to 1/2 inch thick. 1/8 of the thickness for plates 1/2 inch to 2 inches thick. The lesser of 1/16 thickness or 3/8 inch for plates over 2 inches thick.
- **AWWA** - 10% of the thinner plate, or 1/16 inch, whichever is larger.

Misalignment Tolerances

Horizontal or Circumferential Joints

- **API 650** - 20% of the thinner plate with a 1/8 inch maximum. 1/16 inch allowed if thinner plate is 5/16 inches thick or less.
- **API 620** - 1/16 inch for plates 1/4 inch thick or less. For plates over 1/4 inch thick, 25% of thickness or 1/8 inch, whichever is smaller.
- **ASME** - 1/4 thickness for plates up to 3/4 inch. 3/16 inches for plates up to 2 inches thick. The lesser of 1/8 thickness or 3/4 inch maximum for plates over 3 inches thick.
- **AWWA** - 20% of the thinner plate, or 1/8 inch, whichever is smaller.

ROUNDNESS

- **API 650** - 0 to 40 feet diameter, 1/2 inch +/-.
- **API 620** - 40 to 150 feet diameter, 3/4 inch +/-.

Measured - 150 to 250 feet diameter,
One Foot 1 inch +/-.

Above The - 250 feet and up,
Floor. 1 1/4 inches +/-.

- **ASME** - Difference between maximum and minimum inside diameter shall not exceed 1% of the nominal diameter.

NOTE: Metric conversion - to convert fractions of an inch to millimeters multiply the decimal equivalent of the fraction by 25.4.

Scaffold Safety

Included in the important items on any tank equipment list are the parts that make up the scaffolding.

Many injuries and fatalities have occurred due to faulty, improperly erected or carelessly-used scaffolds.

Several often overlooked safety features are listed below:

- *Third hand line.*
- *Correct bracket alignment.*
- Proper storage containers.
- *Proper location of storage containers on the scaffold.*
- *Testing of scaffold planks.*

Third Hand Line

Most tank erectors insist on two outside hand lines. Many serious injuries caused by snapped scaffold planks can be avoided with the use of a third line running around the tank connected to the scaffold brackets at the tank-bracket intersection point, see illustration #250.

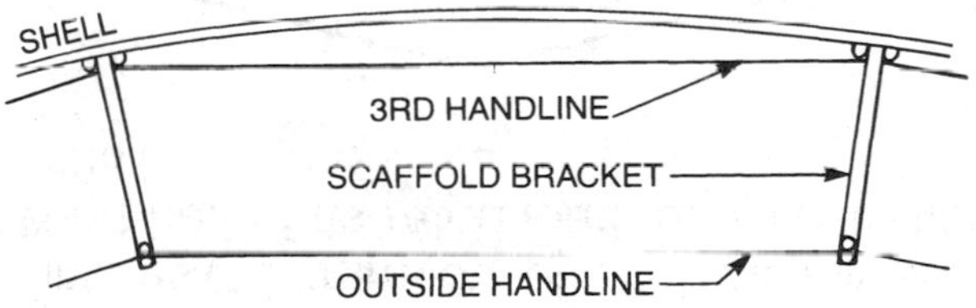
SHELL
3RD HANDLINE
SCAFFOLD BRACKET
OUTSIDE HANDLINE

Illustration #250 - Third Hand Line

Several other points concerning hand lines are:

- Hand lines should be $^3/_8$ inch (9.5 mm) wire rope or $^3/_4$ inch (19 mm) Manila rope.
- The outside hand lines should be kept taut and well secured to each post.
- The third hand line is a must if the space between the shell and the planks is over 12 inches (305 mm).

Bracket Clips

Points on Bracket Safety are:

- *A second person should check the welding of a clip to the shell plate.*

Clip welding has occasionally been overlooked after the clip has been tacked on.

- Bracket clips should be installed an equal distance down from the top of the shell plate. Up and down clips create a roller coaster effect.
- Bracket clips must be plumb. A bracket 5 inches (127 mm) out of level will only support half of its rated load, see illustration #251.

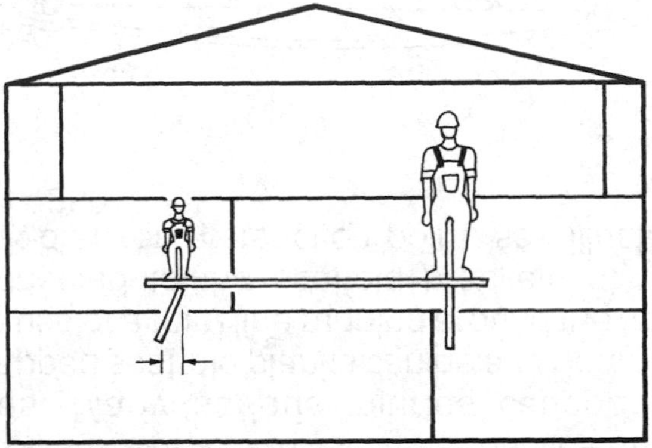

Illustration #251 - Bracket Alignment

Planks

- The strength of a scaffold plank will vary depending on the type of lumber. To ensure maximum safety only first grade lumber should be used.
- It is recommended that the end of each plank be banded or bolted through to prevent splitting.
- Inspect scaffolds and planks daily for any required maintenance prior to commencing work.
- Planks should be jump tested before erection, by two workers weighing a total of approximately 375 pounds (170.5 kg), over two six inch by six inch (152 x 152 mm) blocks, see illustration #252.

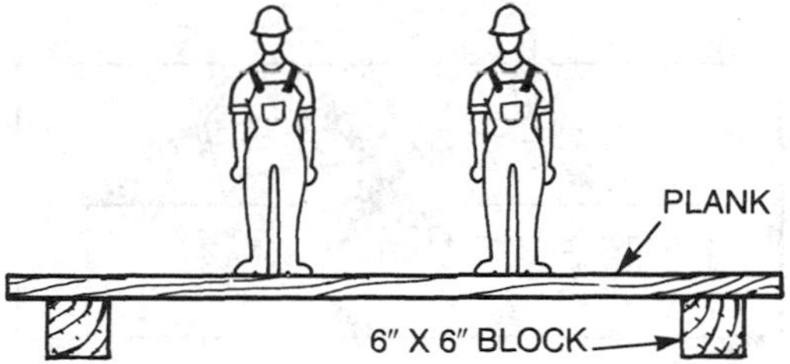
PLANK
6″ X 6″ BLOCK

Illustration #252 - Plank Jump Test

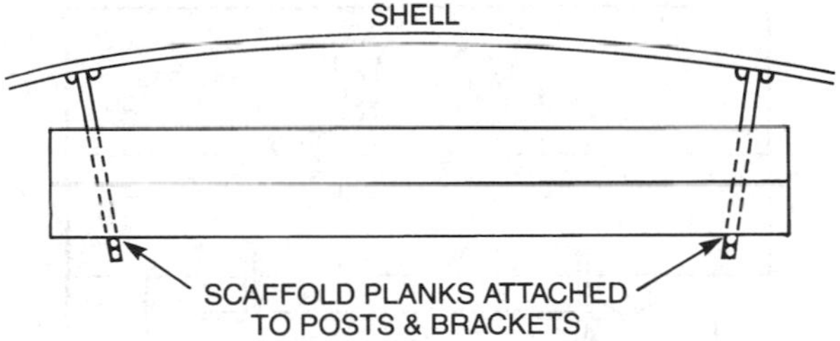
SHELL
SCAFFOLD PLANKS ATTACHED
TO POSTS & BRACKETS

Illustration #253 - Attaching Planks to Brackets

Containers

Scaffold planks constantly accumulate an assortment of underfoot hazards. Pins, bars, hammers and miscellaneous hardware can be dropped or kicked off the scaffold.

A worker can be thrown off a scaffold by stepping on a rolling bar or pin.

A proper container should be kept up on the scaffold to collect those loose items.

A five gallon pail is not a proper container as the handle may pull off, see illustration #254. A small barrel is more suitable, however do not fill it over half way as it will become too heavy. Place it over the bracket, not on the middle of the planks, see illustration #255.

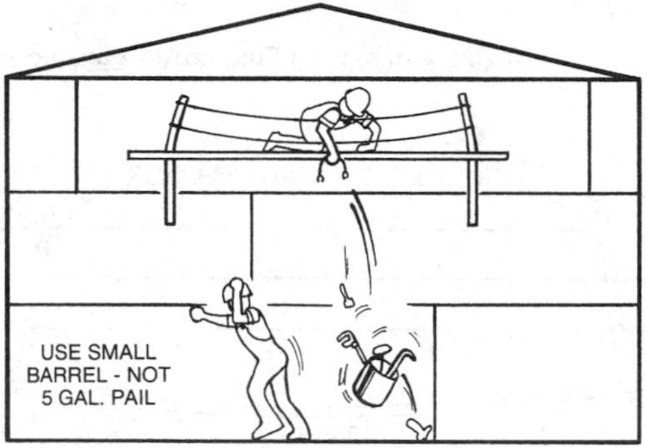
USE SMALL
BARREL - NOT
5 GAL. PAIL

Illustration #254 - Proper Container

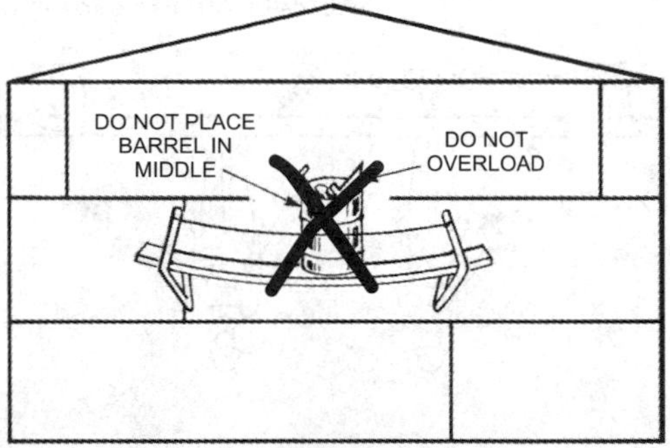
DO NOT PLACE
BARREL IN
MIDDLE
DO NOT
OVERLOAD

Illustration #255 - Container Location

Jumping Scaffold

Start at the ladder when jumping scaffold from one ring up to the next.

Use three extra brackets, A-B-C, see illustration #256.

Planks from lower spaces (1) and (2) go to the upper spaces (1) and (2). Bracket (D) is now free and goes to location (D) above.

This bracket is removed from its lower clip by the worker above with a hook and rope who then passes it to the worker below for relocation.

Planks from space (3) can now go up to space (3) above.

This procedure will continue around the tank. Both workers should stand with their backs to the shell to avoid falling over if a plank gets out of control during lifting.

The safety posts and lines should also be lifted as the planks go up, space by space, to give protection to both workers.

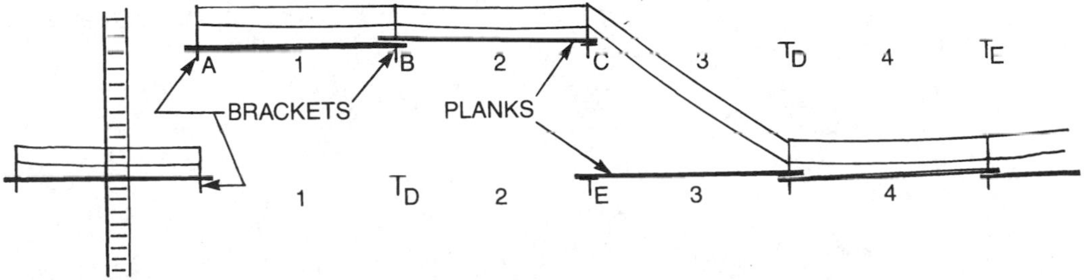
A
1
B
2
C
3
D
4
E
BRACKETS
PLANKS
1
D
2
E
3
4

Illustration #256 - Jumping Scaffold

SECTION FIVE QUESTIONS
Tanks

1. *The base or pad of a tank should be level to within:*
   - ❐ ± 0
   - ❐ ± 1/4 inch
   - ❐ ± 1/2 inch
   - ❐ is not a concern

2. *What plate should be set first when laying out tank floor plates?*
   - ❐ centerplate
   - ❐ circumference plates
   - ❐ sketch plates
   - ❐ longitudinal plates

3. *What is the suggested minimum overlap when laying or fitting floor plates?*
   - ❐ 3 inches
   - ❐ 2 inches
   - ❐ 5 times the plate thickness
   - ❐ 2 times the plate thickness

4. *What simple method is used to ensure that plates are running square while laying out the tank floor?*
   - ❐ use a transit
   - ❐ use a level
   - ❐ measure from outside plate edge to tank circumference
   - ❐ measure from outside plate edge to center pin

5. *A basic method of keeping floor plates square to a centerline is to:*
   - ❐ trim them
   - ❐ allow a larger overlap
   - ❐ reset all other plates
   - ❐ re-square at sketch plates

6. *To allow for the use of fitting aids and compensate for weld shrinkage of floor plates on larger tanks, approximately how much longer should the outside floor radius be compared to the indicated radius?*
   - ❐ 2 inches
   - ❐ 1 inch
   - ❐ 1/2 inch
   - ❐ 1/4 inch

7. *When measuring the chord length along the shell ring layout circle, each point will be the exact location of the:*
   - ❐ floor plate
   - ❐ sketch plate
   - ❐ key plate
   - ❐ shell seam joint

8. *Referring to illustration #236 on page 223, the distance measured from the plate edge to the key plate nut center is:*
   - ❐ 6 inches
   - ❐ 13 inches
   - ❐ 1/2 distance to center
   - ❐ 330 mm

9. *Determine if the following statement is true or false. To allow for movement and shrinkage, the shell will not be welded to the floor plates until after vertical joint fit-up and welding.*
   - ❐ true ❐ false

10. *What problem(s) can occur if the first ring is erected on an off-level base?*
   - ❐ flat spots in shell
   - ❐ buckles in shell
   - ❐ roof rafter difficulties
   - ❐ all of above

11. *If a shell plate measured 21 feet, what would be the usual vertical seam offset required when erecting the next ring?*
   - ❐ one plate thickness
   - ❐ O.D. divided by 3
   - ❐ 7 feet
   - ❐ minimum one foot

12. *When welding the tank shell plates, what process is first in the order of joint fitting and welding?*
   - ❐ vertical joint welding, then horizontal joint fitting
   - ❐ horizontal joint welding, then vertical joint fitting
   - ❐ tank shell to floor plates
   - ❐ whatever is most convenient for crew

13. *To simplify vertical seam fit-up with plates that have a barrel roll, the seams should be tacked first at:*
- ❒ top
- ❒ bottom
- ❒ 1/3 up
- ❒ center

14. *Determine if the following statement is true or false. The reason the rim angle is welded before the roof rafters are in place is to avoid rafter fitting difficulties.*
- ❒ true ❒ false

15. *The out-of-round roof rafter problem encountered in illustration #248 on page 229 can be avoided by:*
- ❒ proper leveling of the base
- ❒ proper ring layout
- ❒ re-checking level after first ring erection
- ❒ all of the above

16. *The maximum allowable seam misalignment tolerance for a vertical joint built according to the API 650 standard is:: (plate thickness = 3/8 inch)*
- ❒ 1/16 inch
- ❒ 3/32 inch
- ❒ 1/8 inch
- ❒ 3/16 inch

17. *Determine if the following statement is true or false. It is acceptable for a 55 foot diameter tank built to the API 620 standard to measure 1/2 inch out of round.*
- ❒ true ❒ false

18. *What is the minimum size for tank scaffold safety hand lines?*
- ❒ 3/4 wire rope or 1 1/4 inch manila
- ❒ 1/2 wire rope or 1 inch manila
- ❒ 3/8 wire rope or 3/4 manila
- ❒ 1/4 wire rope or 1/2 manila

19. *Which of the following is a necessary safety step when installing scaffold bracket clips?*
   - ❒ second person to check clip welding
   - ❒ clips must be equal distance down from top
   - ❒ clips must be plumb
   - ❒ all of above

20. *Determine if the following statement is true or false. A container on a scaffold to hold possible underfoot hazards should be positioned between two scaffold brackets.*
   - ❒ true ❒ false

21. *Determine if the following statement is true or false. A five gallon pail is the most suitable type of scaffold container because of its handle and convenient size.*
   - ❒ true ❒ false

22. *To help avoid falling when jumping scaffolds from one elevation to another, both workers should:*
   - ❒ stand with backs to the tank shell
   - ❒ stand with backs to the handline
   - ❒ use ladders
   - ❒ hang onto safety line at all times

SECTION SIX

TOWERS

Inspection

This section on distillation trays will mention important considerations for proper and quicker traying of both old and new towers. One of the most common questions is when should a tower be re-trayed. For a unit that is on stream and operating this can be a difficult question without a good prior inspection report.

Inspection should include:

- Cleanliness of trays.
- Cleanliness of sump and seals.
- Condition of hardware.
- Micrometer measurement of tray floor thickness.
- Measurement of weir height and clearance of underdowncomer.
- Amount of tray corrosion, as well as area of tray that is corroded.
- Amount of shell corrosion, pitting above tray floor or in downcomer, also condition of support rings.
- Condition of feed pipe, spargers, etc.
- Perforated Trays - size of holes in tray may be excessive due to corrosion. Operating or engineering staff will have to determine whether some holes will be blanked off or welded to reduce diameter in order to reestablish the proper total area of the holes.
- Float Valve Trays - legs must be checked for corrosion and ensure that the valves are in place and can't be dislodged.
- Bubble Caps - check for corrosion of risers and caps, and that caps and risers are bolted tightly.

Trays

The three most common types of trays are: Float Valve, Sieve and Bubble Cap.

Single Pass Tray:

Illustration #257 indicates a type of single pass tray and the process flow.

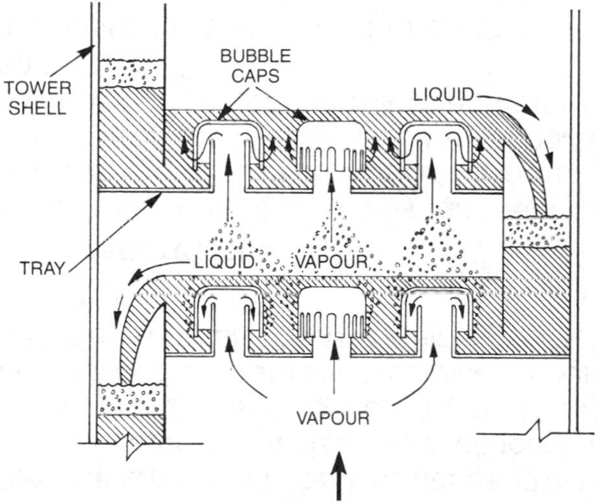
TOWER SHELL
BUBBLE CAPS
LIQUID
TRAY
LIQUID
VAPOUR
VAPOUR

Illustration #257 - Single Pass Tray

Double Pass Tray:

Illustration #258 indicates the flow pattern of one pass versus two pass trays.

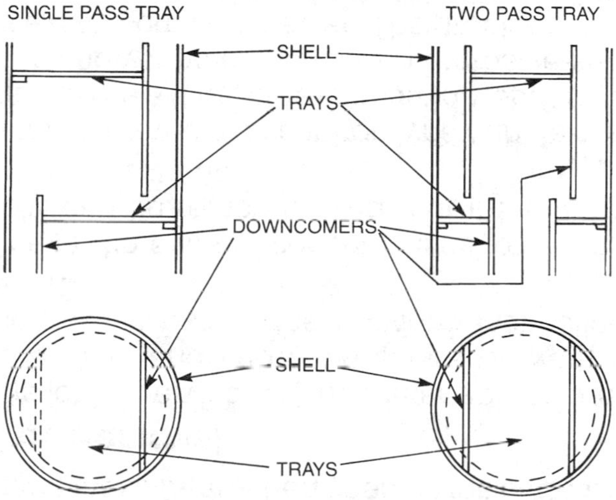
SINGLE PASS TRAY
TWO PASS TRAY
SHELL
TRAYS
DOWNCOMERS
SHELL
TRAYS

Illustration #258 - Single Pass Compared to Two Pass

Most trays are made of light gauge (10-14 gauge) carbon or stainless steel although a few of the old, heavy 1/2 inch (13 mm) trays with cast iron caps are still in service. Bubble caps are less popular due to their high installation time.

Job Preparation

Regardless of the type of tray job, be it removal and installation on an existing tower or a new tower, the job supervisor must be familiar with the job and the equipment required.

The prints must be studied to establish the complete assembly of the tray and its parts. The crates holding the parts should be set up by the tower, the hoist must be rigged and any scaffolds as well as internal bulkheads should be made up or prepared.

Tray crates contain many small parts, therefore caution should be used to avoid losing any of these parts when opening the crates.

Tray Removal

The job supervisor will be better able to prepare tools and know the scope of work if there is access to the previous inspection report.

One of the primary concerns is whether the bolts can be removed readily or if the trays are to be cut out.

Removal of the old cast-iron type bubble cap tray can be a dirty, time consuming job. Trays of the newer types used for a corrosive service may come out easier. The problem here lies in the corrosion of the bolt heads. This means that a wide variety of sockets must be available.

Oxy-acetylene cutting or carbon-arc gouging of trays or support bars will require a good air supply as well as an exhaust fan and a fire extinguisher.

Tray support and downcomer bars are not usually cut and ground flush with the shell, but are cut $^{3}/_{8}$ to $^{1}/_{2}$ inch (9.5 to 13 mm) out from the shell.

New support bars must be installed dead level to ensure an efficient operating tray. Bar installation in a standing tower on a hot sunny day can be affected by expansion. The side facing the sun could expand and give an untrue reading of the actual bar elevation.

Pre-assembly

It is much easier to work on the ground rather than inside a tower, therefore each tray should be assembled on the ground to the extent necessary to check on all the correct parts. Pre-assemble whatever will fit through the tower manway.

Care must be exercised with valve trays as the legs are easily bent and the valve may fall out, also two valve trays can lock together causing damage, see illustration #259.

Installation

The individual pieces or pre-assembled parts should be hoisted into the tower in the correct installation sequence to make the work go more efficiently; that is downcomer, underdowncomers, tray floors and the manway last.

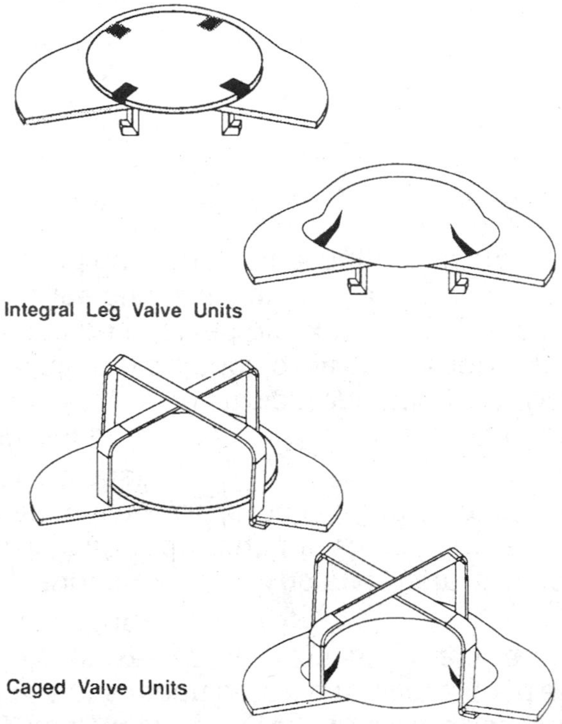
Integral Leg Valve Units
Caged Valve Units

Illustration #259 - Types of Valves Caps

Installation

The installation always starts at the bottom of the tower with the downcomers of the first tray. The parts are lowered in from the top manway. Two critical measurements are the underdowncomer clearance and the tray floor weir height. The underdowncomer clearance can be maintained by using wooden spacer blocks.

The tray floor sections are usually installed in the following order:

1. No. 1 is positioned and loosely clamped.
2. Do likewise with no. 2.
3. No. 3 is positioned and bolted to no. 2.
4. No. 4 is positioned and bolted to no. 3.
5. This procedure will continue up to the manway sections.
6. The manway opening width is checked and if it is satisfactory all the bolting is tightened to the correct torque. See illustration #260 for sequence.

7. The common trend is for tray suppliers to use very few welded nuts or tapped holes. This will mean an extra person under the tray to hold nuts on the downcomers and around the tray support bar.

Bulkheads

The location of the tower manways may allow a bulkhead to be installed and for two crews to work inside the tower at different elevations. The manway locations would be top, center and bottom.

A wooden bulkhead is securely built directly below the center manway to act as a working platform. The tray above the manway is then installed, see illustration #261. Half the bulkhead is now relocated below the top manway.

A smaller, movable safety bulkhead is placed above the workers' heads on a support ring. This will give protection from falling pieces in the possibility of an accident while lowering of components, see illustration #262.

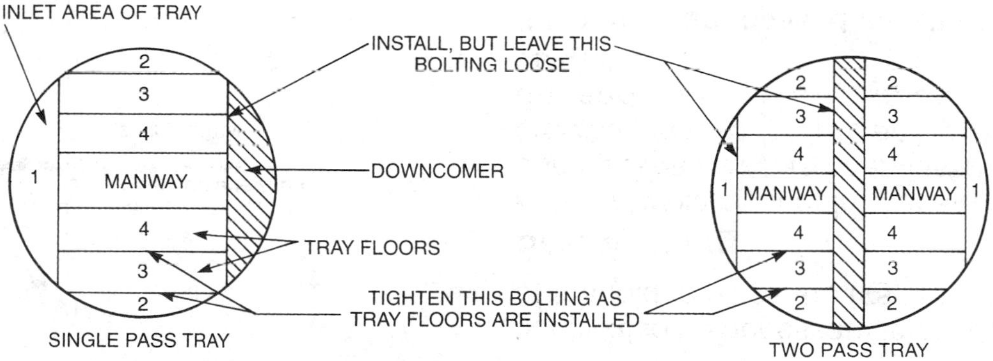
INLET AREA OF TRAY
INSTALL, BUT LEAVE THIS BOLTING LOOSE
DOWNCOMER
TRAY FLOORS
TIGHTEN THIS BOLTING AS TRAY FLOORS ARE INSTALLED
1
2
3
4
MANWAY
SINGLE PASS TRAY
TWO PASS TRAY

Illustration #260 - Installation Sequence

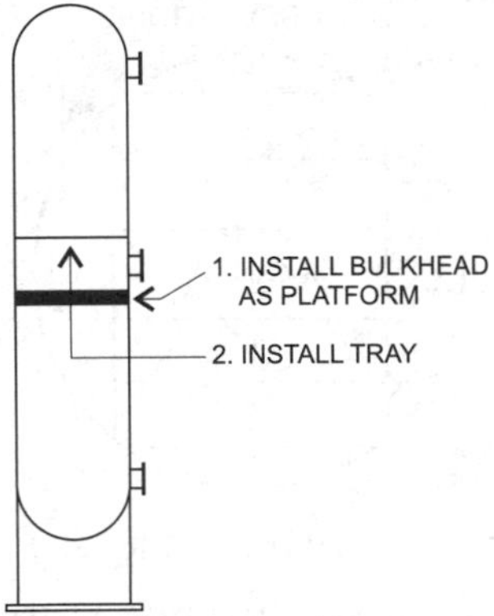
1. INSTALL BULKHEAD
AS PLATFORM
2. INSTALL TRAY

Illustration #261 - Bulkhead as a Platform

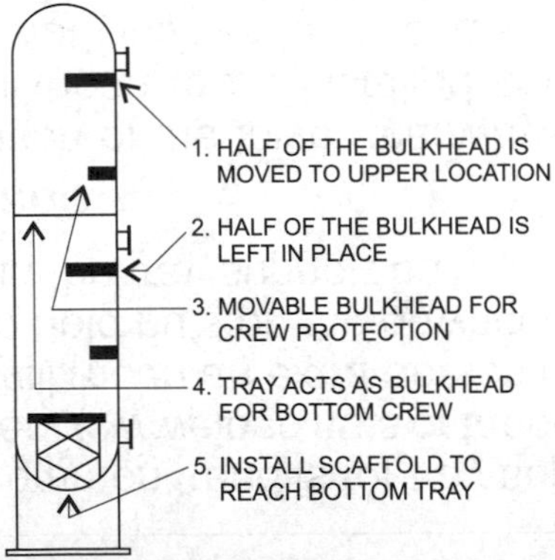
1. HALF OF THE BULKHEAD IS
MOVED TO UPPER LOCATION
2. HALF OF THE BULKHEAD IS
LEFT IN PLACE
3. MOVABLE BULKHEAD FOR
CREW PROTECTION
4. TRAY ACTS AS BULKHEAD
FOR BOTTOM CREW
5. INSTALL SCAFFOLD TO
REACH BOTTOM TRAY

Illustration #262 - Safety Bulkhead

It may also be necessary to build some type of scaffold to place the first tray in position.

Seal Welding

Any seal welding should, if at all possible, be done after a tray has been installed and the crew has moved on. The ability to do this will depend on the tray spacing and on ventilation.

If the trays are spaced less than 24 inches (610 mm) apart, the crawl space is very tight for a welder to work.

Any welding in such a confined area will require smoke removal and possibly a fresh air supply, with a fan set up by a manway.

If conditions limit the work ability of a welder, it may be necessary to seal weld the trays as they are installed.

A water test will be necessary to check for leaks.

Safety Points

- Prior to any work or entry, a safe entry and hot work permit must be obtained from the operational personnel in either an operating plant or in a recently shut down unit.
- Valves, plus other inlets and outlets must be blanked off with a plate blind prior to opening manways or entering the unit.
- Check whether the unit has been steamed. Check the air quality before entering if it has been assumed that conditions are safe without an adequate life support system.
- Ensure that a constant manwatch is maintained at the tower manway opening.
- If proceeding downward through the tray manways on an inspection of a shut down tower, check the condition of the next tray down before dropping down through the manway. Tray support bars, bolts, etc., sometimes corrode and the entire tray or series of trays may collapse on the bottom of the tower.
- Air impact guns are often used for bolt removal and replacement. If using a screwed hose to gun attachment, tighten the connection with a wrench.
- Opening of the top and bottom manways usually results in natural air circulation. A fan system may also be required to circulate air if cutting, gouging or welding.
- Removal of catalyst from vessels, towers or reactors containing inert gases should be performed by workers trained in the use of self-contained breathing apparatus (SCBA).

SECTION SIX QUESTIONS
Towers

1. *What is used to measure the thickness of a tray floor?*
   - ❒ tape measure
   - ❒ micrometer
   - ❒ depth gauge
   - ❒ all of the above

2. *When visually inspecting a tower, list three things to watch for:*

   ____

   ____

   ____

3. *What is the most common type of tray?*
   - ❒ float valve
   - ❒ sieve
   - ❒ bubble cap
   - ❒ all of the above

4. *Determine if the following statement is true or false. Most trays are normally made of carbon steel or stainless steel.*

   ❒ true ❒ false

5. *Determine if the following statement is true or false. As most tray components are made up of large pieces, keeping track of the individual tray parts is a non-issue for whoever is in charge.*

   ❒ true ❒ false

6. *Which of the following items is not necessary if removing trays by the oxy-acetylene cutting or carbon arc gouging process?*
   - ❒ good air supply
   - ❒ an exhaust fan
   - ❒ fire extinguisher
   - ❒ welding rod oven

7. *What atmospheric condition can make it difficult to properly level new support bars when retraying a tower?*
   - ❒ humidity
   - ❒ cloudiness
   - ❒ rain
   - ❒ sunshine

8. *What factor determines the degree a tray can be pre-assembled before installation into the tower?*
   - ❒ tower manway size
   - ❒ hoist capabilities
   - ❒ bulkhead location
   - ❒ depth of sump

9. *Determine if the following statement is true or false. Tray installation starts at the upper part of the tower with the work progressing down.*
   - ❒ true ❒ false

10. *Determine the tray part that will be installed last:*
    - ❒ weir
    - ❒ downcomer
    - ❒ tray floor manway
    - ❒ under-downcomer

11. *What allows for more than one crew to safely work inside a tower at different elevations when installing new trays?*
    - ❒ downcomers
    - ❒ manways
    - ❒ bulkheads
    - ❒ trays

12. *What smaller safety device is placed above workers heads when tray parts are being lowered.*
    - ❒ safety net
    - ❒ scaffold plank
    - ❒ moveable bulkhead
    - ❒ not necessary

13. *Which of these safety points is attended to first before work or entry can start on a tower?*
    - ❒ valves blanked off
    - ❒ check air quality
    - ❒ unit is shutdown
    - ❒ safe entry and hot work permits

14. *What two procedures will stop hazardous vapors from entering a tower past leaking valves and clear the air inside the tower?*

    ____

    ____

15. *In the event of an accident inside the tower, a necessary safety precaution is to:*

- ❒ provide a manwatch
- ❒ use of bulkheads
- ❒ wear safety glasses
- ❒ keep both manways open

SECTION SEVEN

HEAT EXCHANGERS

Introduction

A conventional tube and shell heat exchanger consists of a grouping of tubes enclosed in a container. Usually a cylindrical pressure vessel shell with removable heads. The purpose of a heat exchanger is either to heat or to cool a liquid, see illustration #263 for a typical heat exchanger.

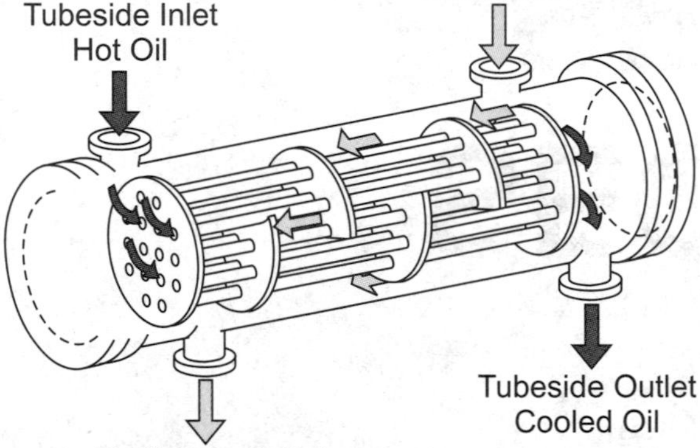
Shell Side Inlet
Cold Water
Tubeside Inlet
Hot Oil
Tubeside Outlet
Cooled Oil
Shell Side Outlet
Warm Water

Illustration #263 - Typical Heat Exchanger

In this example, hot product enters into the tube side inlet, passes through the tubes where the temperature is reduced by the cool water on the shell side, then exits through the tube side outlet.

Other types of exchangers could have the product entering the shell side or use steam to heat rather than water to cool the product.

The greater the surface area of a conductor, the more quickly heat is conducted. A bundle of small tubes is more efficient than one large tube.

Depending on the purpose of a heat exchanger, the tubes may be of a non-corrosive material such as brass, copper, a variety of stainless steel types, or carbon steel.

The tubes of an exchanger are typically anchored between two tubesheets or are of the U tube type with one tubesheet. The combination of tubes and tubesheets is called a tube bundle.

Nearly all tubes are attached to the tubesheet by the tube expanding process. Some exchangers will have tubes that are seal welded as well as being expanded.

The tube bundle in illustration #264 is fixed to the shell and cannot be removed.

The tube bundle in illustration #265 is a U type and is removable. The complete bundle can be pulled out of the tubesheet for repair or cleaning.

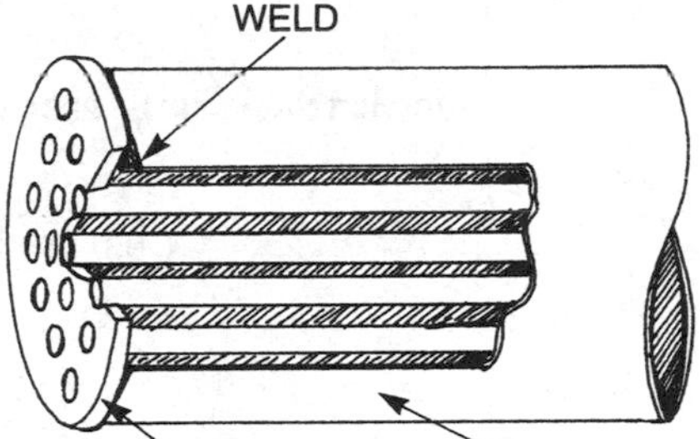
WELD
TUBE SHEET
SHELL

Illustration #264 - Fixed Bundle

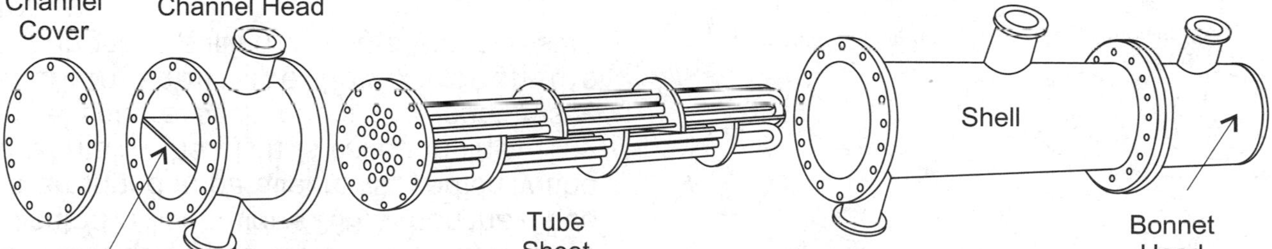
Channel Cover
Channel Head
Channel Baffle
Tube Sheet
Shell
Bonnet Head

Illustration #265 - Removable Bundle

Tubesheet Layout

The four basic types of tubesheet layouts are indicated in illustration #266. When the tubes are arranged in parallel rows, vertically and horizontally, the pitch is called in-line. The in-line square pitch offers the least resistance to shell side flow through the exchanger, resulting in a greater pressure drop.

Staggering the tubes, as shown in the other three types, allows more tubes in a given area than the in line square.

The more tubes in a given area, the greater the heat transfer rate. The triangular pitch gives a greater heat transfer but does not allow as much pressure drop through the shell.

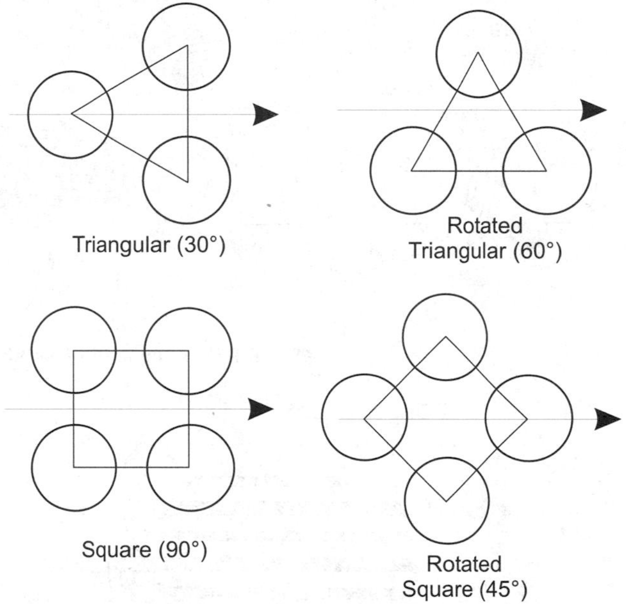
Triangular (30°)
Rotated
Triangular (60°)
Square (90°)
Rotated
Square (45°)

Illustration #266 - Tubesheet Layout

Baffles

The longer the tubes in an exchanger the heavier they are.

Baffles are used to prevent sagging from the weight, and also to help relieve stress on the tubes and tubesheet, see illustration #267.

Baffles also assist the heat transfer in laminar flow exchangers. A layer of liquid surrounds each tube acting as an insulator. The layer is thicker in a laminar flow but is broken up by the baffles.

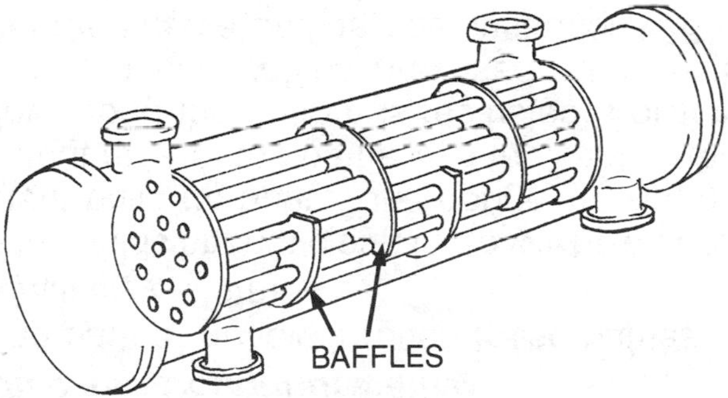
BAFFLES

Illustration #267 -Typical Baffle Plates

Segmental Baffles

A segmental baffle is a circle from which either a vertical or horizontal portion has been cut. Segmental baffles are positioned so that the cut out areas face in alternate directions. Alternating the baffles causes the flow to cross the tubes a number of times, see illustration #268.

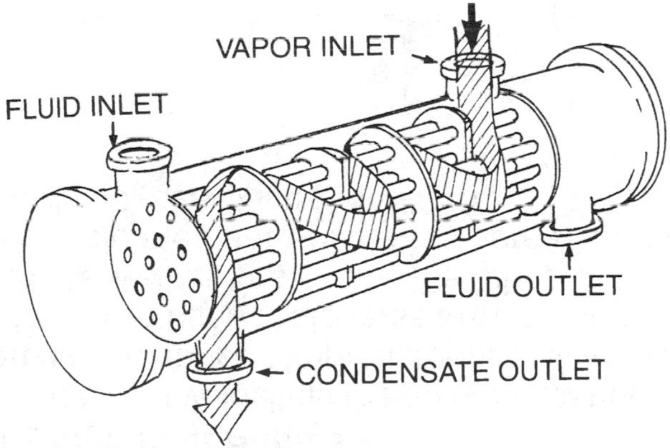
VAPOR INLET
FLUID INLET
FLUID OUTLET
CONDENSATE OUTLET

Illustration #268 - Segment Baffles

Disc and Doughnut Baffles

The pattern of flow through these baffles is relatively uniform.

If the fluids are not clean there will be a sediment build up behind the doughnut. As the cutout area of the baffle is in the center, the flow along the bottom is restricted. For this reason these baffles are used much less than segmental baffles, see illustration #269.

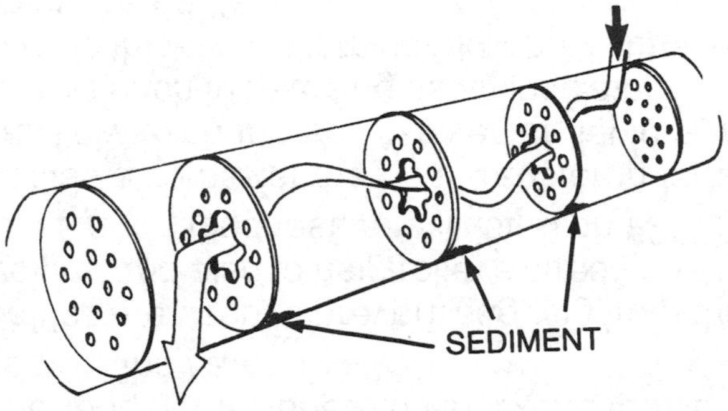
SEDIMENT

Illustration #269 - Disc and Doughnut Baffles

Impingement Baffles

At high inlet velocities the fluid can seriously erode the tubes. Impingement baffles are sometimes used to disperse the incoming liquid. As well as protecting the tubes this will also help the heat transfer by spreading out the liquid, see illustration #270.

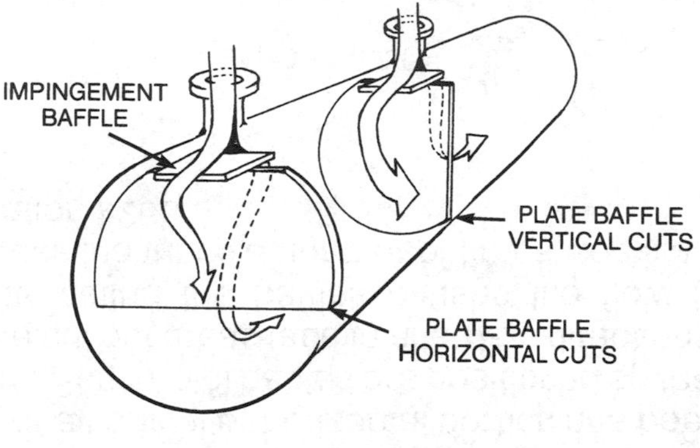
IMPINGEMENT
BAFFLE
PLATE BAFFLE
VERTICAL CUTS
PLATE BAFFLE
HORIZONTAL CUTS

Illustration #270 - Impingement Baffles

Longitudinal Baffles

These baffles are sometimes used to split the shell side flow into two or more passes.

The baffle is somewhat shorter than the exchanger allowing for the return or double pass through the exchanger, see illustration #271.

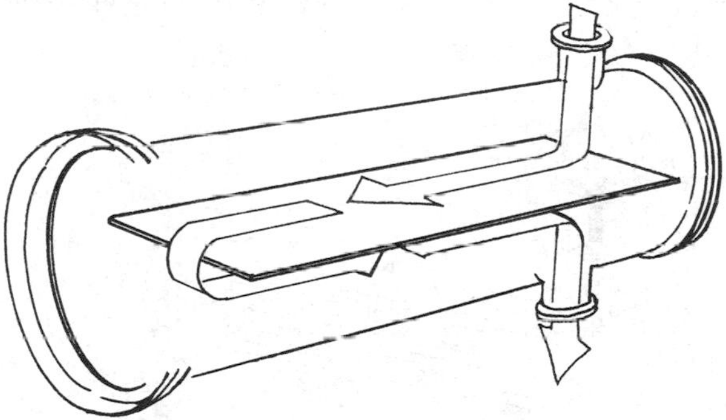

Illustration #271 - Longitudinal Baffles

Three longitudinal baffles would provide for four passes through the exchanger, see illustration #272.

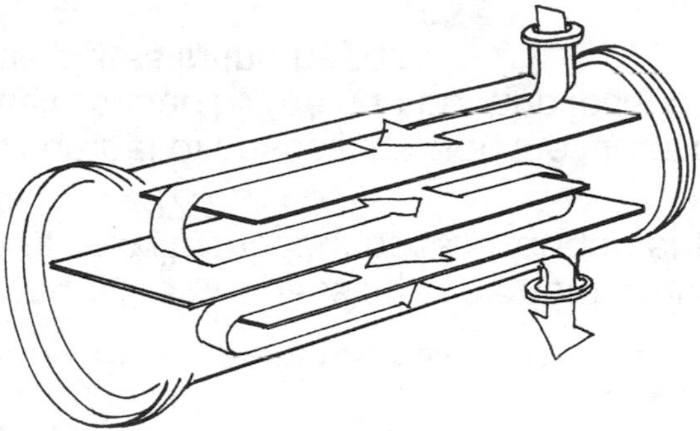

Illustration #272 - Four Pass Baffles

Tube Side Flow

Illustration #273 indicates a single pass tube arrangement. The tube side fluid enters one end of the exchanger through the head, flows through all the tubes in the same direction and leaves at the opposite end.

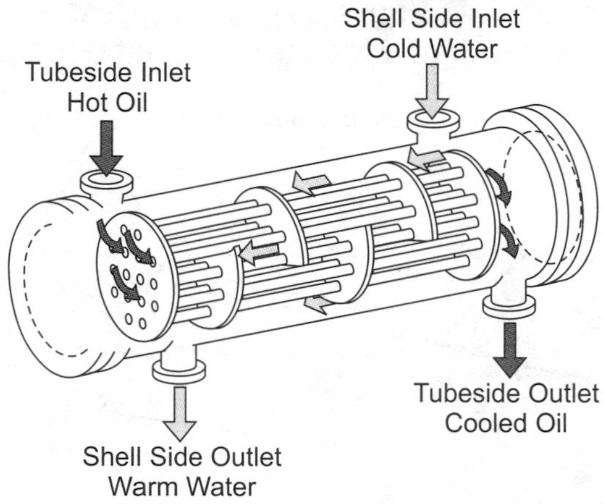
Shell Side Inlet
Cold Water
Tubeside Inlet
Hot Oil
Tubeside Outlet
Cooled Oil
Shell Side Outlet
Warm Water

Illustration #273 - Single Pass Tube Side

Illustration #274 indicates a two pass tube arrangement. A baffle in the head redirects the flow through the tubes. The liquid enters through one head and can only flow one way through half of the tubes because of the baffle in the head. The liquid will then return in the opposite direction through the other half of the tubes.

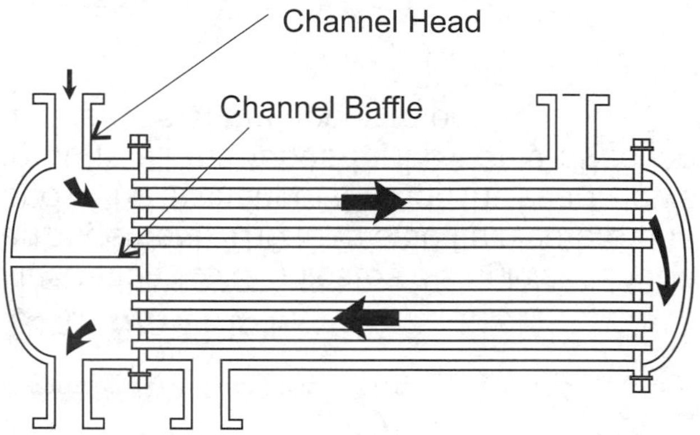
Channel Head
Channel Baffle

Illustration #274 - Two Pass Tube Side

Compare the two pass arrangement, illustration #274, with the four pass arrangement, illustration #275.

The number of passes through the tubes can be determined by the number and location of baffle plates in the head.

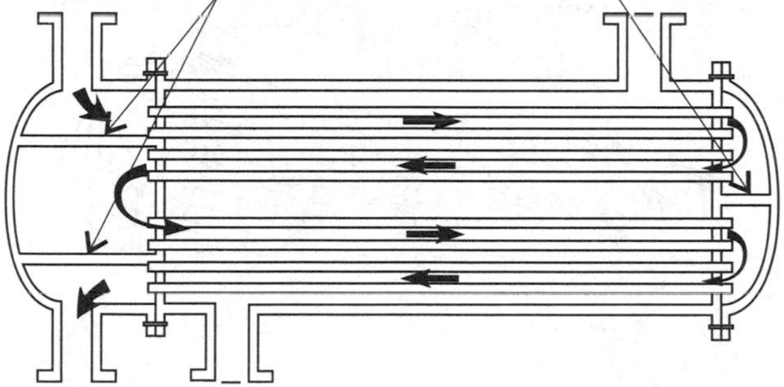
Channel Baffles
Head Baffle

Illustration #275 - Four Pass Tube Side

Note: Care must be taken when making gaskets for multi pass heads as the gasket must fit over the baffles perfectly or leakage from one side to another will lower the efficiency.

Fixed Tubesheet

In the fixed tubesheet type, the tubesheet is welded directly to the shell. The tube bundle is permanently installed. Temperature changes cause stress in the shell and bundle through expansion and contraction. Stress is partially absorbed in these types through the use of an expansion joint in the shell. This allows the shell to expand along with the tubes, see illustration #276.

Exchangers of this type require shell side cleaning by chemical process as the tube bundle is not removable.

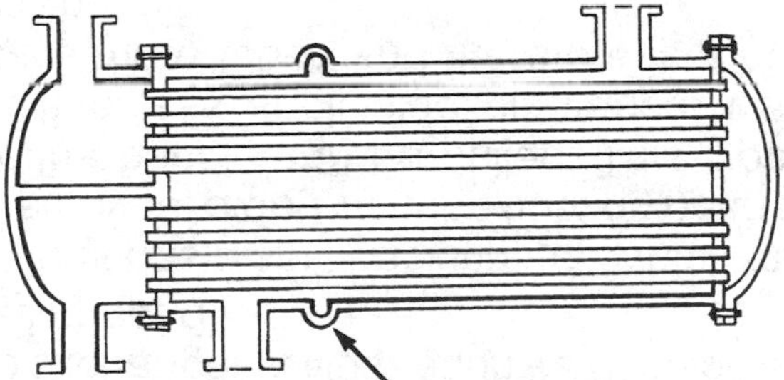
EXPANSION JOINT

Illustration #276 - Fixed Tubesheet

Floating Heads

This particular type of exchanger, see illustration #277, has a tubesheet on the front end that is bolted between the shell and the head.

The tubesheet on the other end, along with a cover, floats horizontally inside the shell. After unbolting the front head flange, the bundle and the floating head can be pulled as one unit.

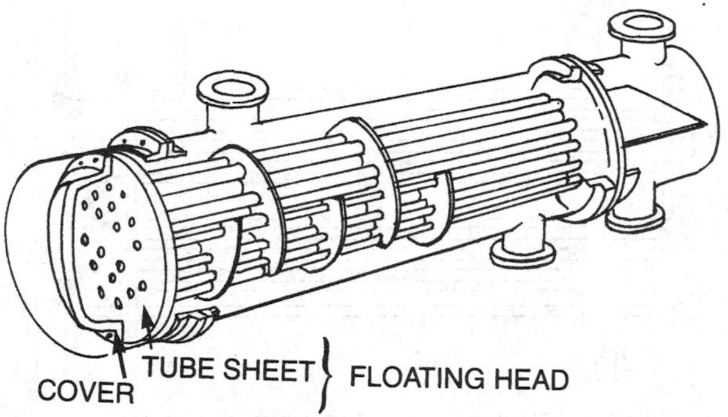
COVER
TUBE SHEET
FLOATING HEAD

Illustration #277 - Floating Head

The exchanger in illustration #278 also has a floating head.

This unit has a split backing ring which must be removed, along with the floating head before the bundle can be pulled. This type of unit has less shell side clearance, which means more tubes and therefore is a more efficient unit.

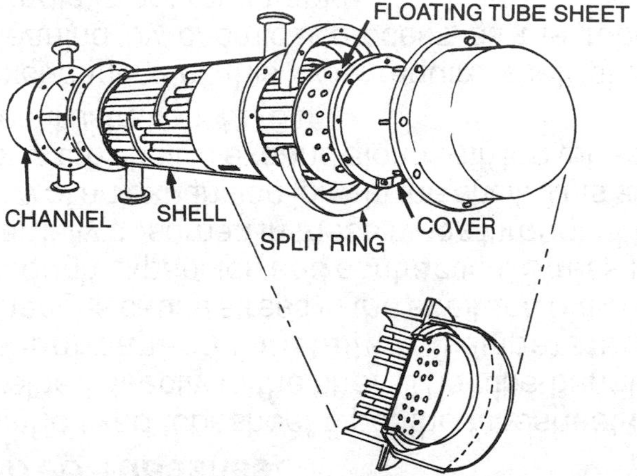
FLOATING TUBE SHEET
CHANNEL
SHELL
SPLIT RING
COVER

Illustration #278 - Floating Head with Split Backing Ring

Exchanger Sizes and Type Designation

The shell diameter and the tube length in inches are the governing factors in determining the size of an exchanger as specified by TEMA. (Tubular Exchanger Manufacturer's Association).

The shell diameter is specified first, therefore in a 23 - 192 exchanger, the diameter is 23 inches (584 mm) and the tubes are 192 inches (4 877 mm) long. Fractional sizes are rounded off to the nearest number.

The designation of an exchanger depends on three variables:

- the type of front stationary head
- the type of shell
- the type of rear head

Designations are specified by letters of the alphabet.

The front head uses the letters:
A, B, C, D, or N
see illustration #279

Shell types use:
E, F, G, H, J, K or X.
see illustration #280

The rear head uses:
L, M, N, P, S, T, U or W.
see illustration #281

Illustrations #279 through #285 are reproduced compliments of the Tubular Exchanger Manufacturers Association (TEMA).

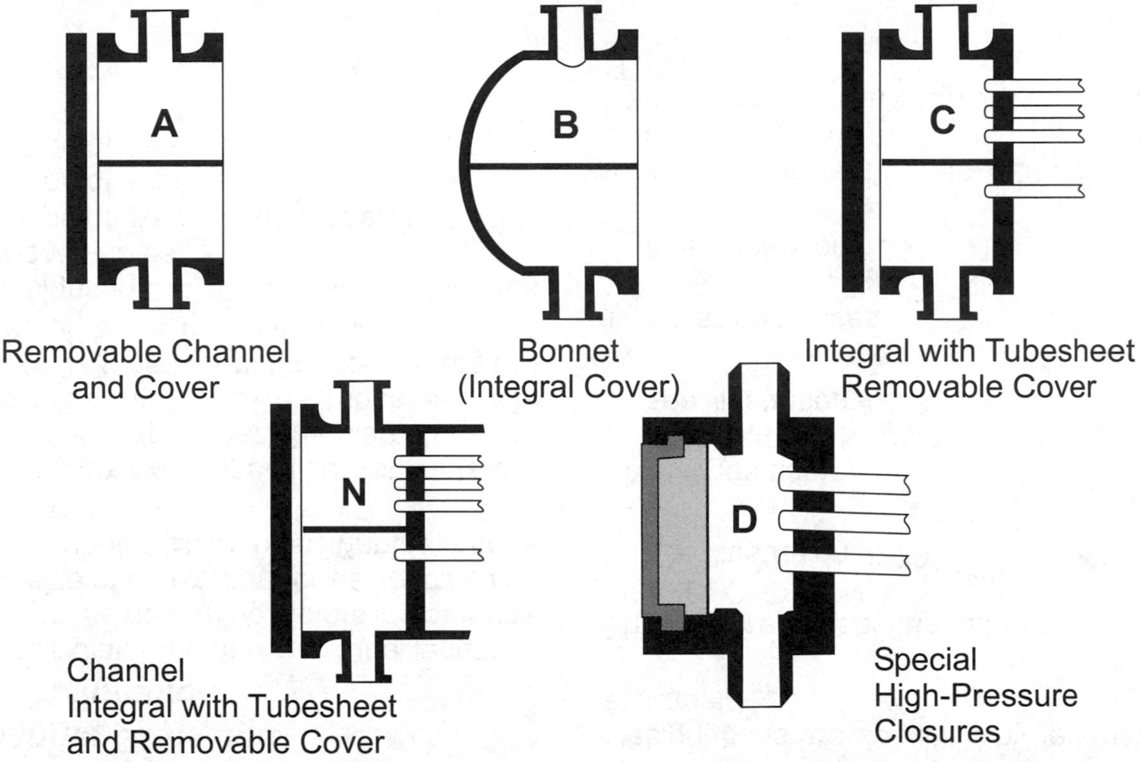
A
Removable Channel
and Cover
B
Bonnet
(Integral Cover)
C
Integral with Tubesheet
Removable Cover
N
Channel
Integral with Tubesheet
and Removable Cover
D
Special
High-Pressure
Closures

Illustration #279 - Front Head Design Designations

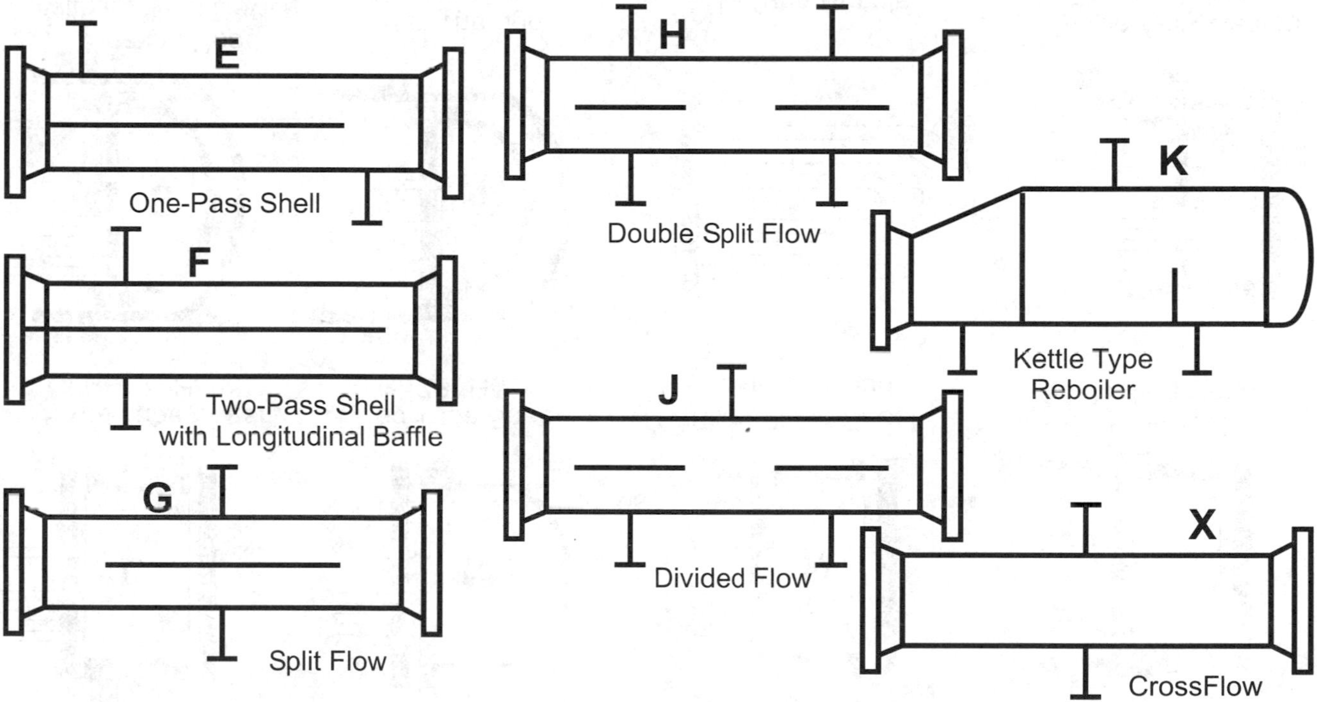
E
One-Pass Shell
F
Two-Pass Shell
with Longitudinal Baffle
G
Split Flow
H
Double Split Flow
K
Kettle Type
Reboiler
J
Divided Flow
X
CrossFlow

Illustration #280 - Shell Type Designations

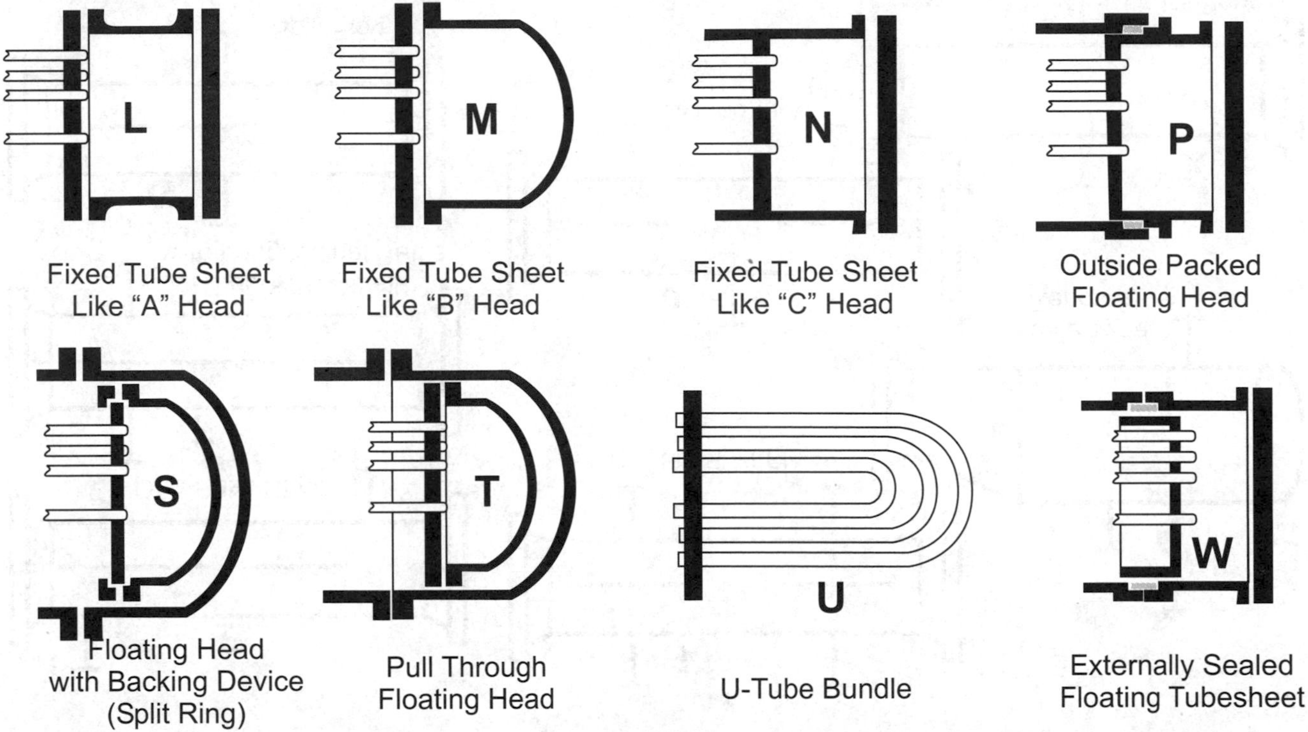
L
Fixed Tube Sheet
Like "A" Head
M
Fixed Tube Sheet
Like "B" Head
N
Fixed Tube Sheet
Like "C" Head
P
Outside Packed
Floating Head
S
Floating Head
with Backing Device
(Split Ring)
T
Pull Through
Floating Head
U
U-Tube Bundle
W
Externally Sealed
Floating Tubesheet

Illustration #281 - Rear Head Design Designations

Heat Exchanger Examples

Examples of various heat exchanger types are shown with illustrations #282, #283, #284, #285.

Illustration #282 (BEB) is a basic fixed tubesheet type with two type B bonnet heads, with one pass through the tubes.

The shell type is an E, with no baffle, but does have an expansion joint.

Illustration #283 (BEU) is a type E, one pass shell heat exchanger. It has one welded hemispherical head, and it has a type B bonnet head with a two pass baffle. The removable tube bundle is a two pass U tube type.

Illustration #284 (AES) is a type E, one pass shell heat exchanger. The front head is a type A channel with a two pass baffle. It has a type S rear floating head with a split backing ring, and a larger bonnet type cover head. The removable bundle is a two-pass with a rear tubesheet.

Illustration #285 (AKT) is a divided flow type K, kettle reboiler heat exchanger. The front head is a type A channel with a two-pass baffle. The rear head is a type T pull through floating head. The removable tube bundle is a two-pass with a head cover bolted to the tubesheet.

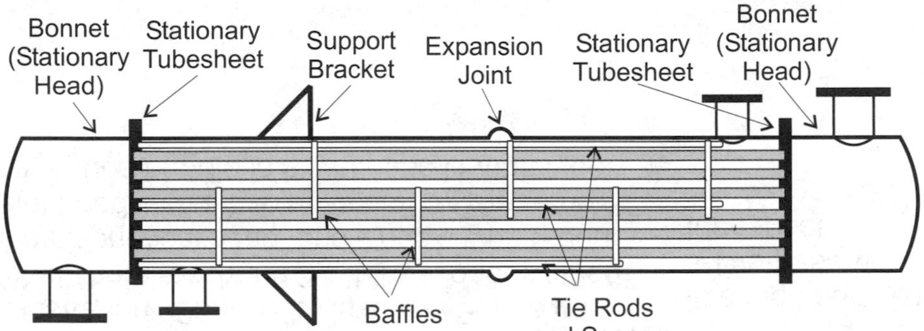
Bonnet (Stationary Head)
Stationary Tubesheet
Support Bracket
Expansion Joint
Stationary Tubesheet
Bonnet (Stationary Head)
Baffles
Tie Rods and Spacers

Illustration #282 - Type BEB

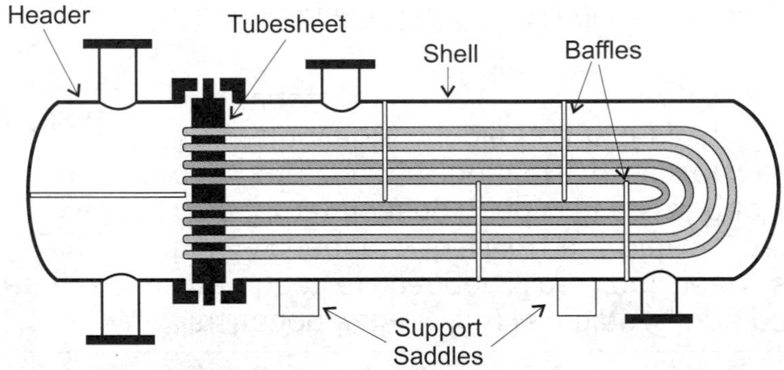
Header
Tubesheet
Shell
Baffles
Support Saddles

Illustration #283 - Type BEU

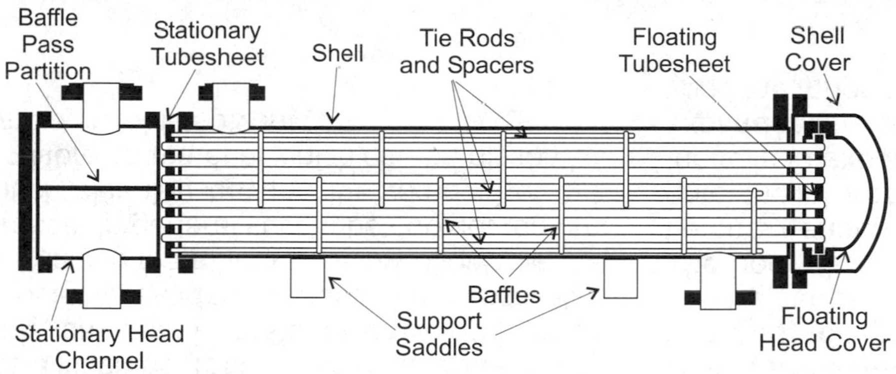
Baffle
Pass
Partition
Stationary
Tubesheet
Shell
Tie Rods
and Spacers
Floating
Tubesheet
Shell
Cover
Baffles
Support
Saddles
Stationary Head
Channel
Floating
Head Cover

Illustration #284 - Type AES

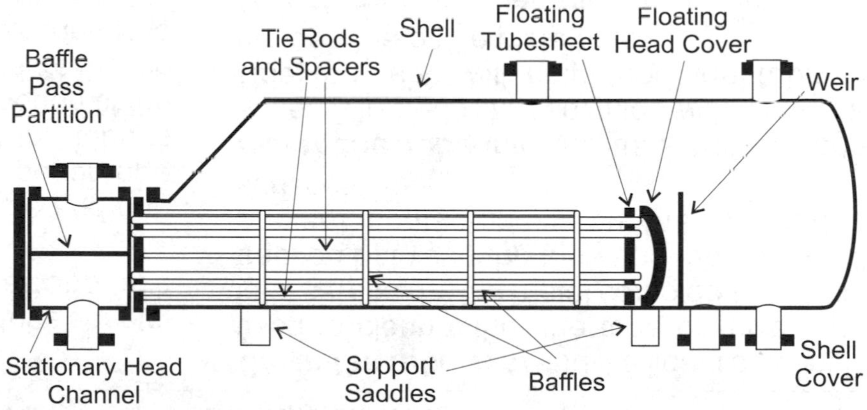
Tie Rods
and Spacers
Shell
Floating
Tubesheet
Floating
Head Cover
Baffle
Pass
Partition
Weir
Stationary Head
Channel
Support
Saddles
Baffles
Shell
Cover

Illustration #285 - Type AKT

Tube Installation

To install and expand tubes into tube sheets, the following general operations are necessary.

Clean the end of the tube inside and outside with a wire brush, abrasive paper, or a liquid cleaner until the metal of the tube is free of all foreign substances. Enough of the tube end should be cleaned to ensure that no foreign matter can get into the seat during the installation operation. Use of abrasive materials on electric resistance welded tubes should be avoided because of the possibility of thinning the tube wall below allowable tolerance. In general such tubes do not require much cleaning beyond the removal of dirt and foreign material which can be dissolved with a suitable solvent.

Clean the tube seat and if a liquid solvent is used to clean either the tube or tube seat, take care to dry the metal completely. Liquid trapped between the tube and tube seat will prevent contact between the two metal surfaces.

Insert the tube into the tube hole of one sheet. A torpedo shaped guide with a stub inside the tube will help feed the tube in through the baffle plate holes.

Select the expander with the correct length and body diameter. The length of the expander varies to suit the width of tube seat. The body diameter of the expander should be small enough to permit the expander to enter the tube and yet large enough to permit the rolls to expand the tube completely. The expander should not expand the tube beyond the inner edge of the tubesheet.

Secure the tube so that it will not rotate with the expander body as the expanding process is carried on. A tube clamp or some other suitable device can be arranged to prevent the tube from moving.

Lubricate the inside of the tube with a suitable compound. There are several lubricants available. The tubes should be expanded from the bottom rows up to avoid having the excess lubricant run onto the unrolled tubes (first end only).

Roll miscellaneous tack tubes on the second tubesheet. This helps avoid tube sheet deflection on thin sheets due to the extrusion of expanded tubes. For more details see the section on Tube Expanding.

Stud Tightening Procedure

It is important that all bolted joints be tightened uniformly and in a diametrically staggered pattern, except for special extra high pressure closures when the instructions of the manufacturer should be followed.

The bolt pattern in illustration #286 is one of the primary suggested methods of bolting flanges. It is however a bit complicated.

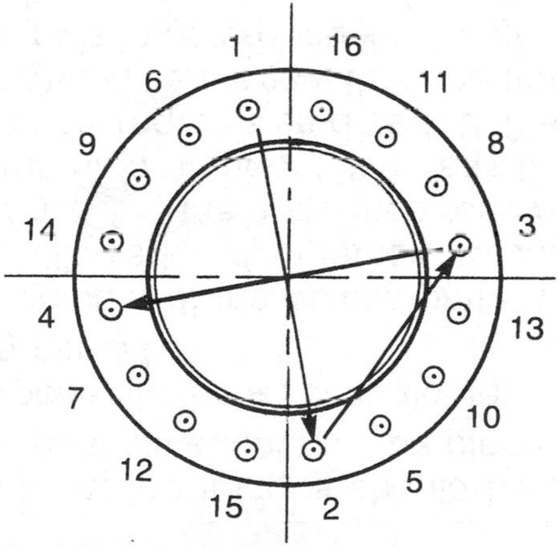
1
16
6
11
9
8
3
14
4
13
7
10
12
5
15
2

IIIllustration #286 - High Pressure Flange Tightening

The most commonly used method on low pressure joints is shown in illustration #287. For either method, start at the widest gap between the flanges (stud #1). Tighten lightly until flanges touch then go to stud #2 and tighten.

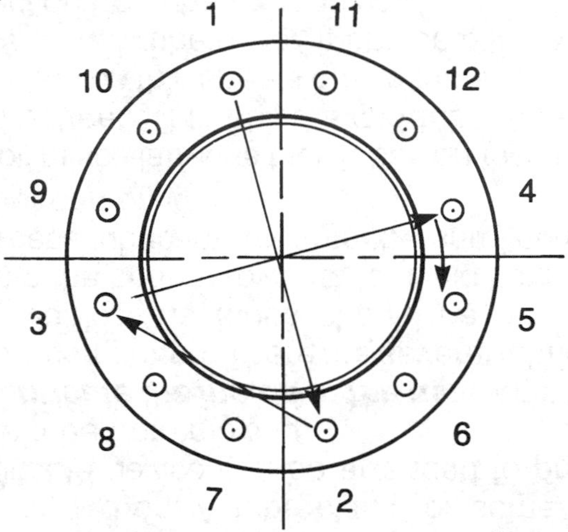
1
11
10
12
9
4
3
5
8
6
7
2
Illustration #287 - Normal Flange Tightening

At this point the flanges should be parallel and the gaskets should not be pinched.

Now proceed to the #3 stud, tighten it lightly, then tighten #4.

The remainder of the bolting pattern should now be followed. In the method indicated in illustration #286, the sequence required is to follow the stud numbers, whereas the other method only requires stud #s 1, 2, 3 and 4 to be followed in sequence, then the tightening procedure is to go around the flange, stud to stud.

Go around as many times as necessary to sufficiently tighten all studs. At least two threads on the studs should project out from the nuts, excess threads on the studs should be at the rear of the head when possible.

Care should also be taken to avoid over tightening joints. Studs stretched beyond the allowable limits are difficult to remove and should not be reused.

Inspection for Tube Leakage

The following procedures should be followed to enable inspection of the tubes for leaks or for cleaning, see illustration #288 for an indication of a leak.

Front Head:

- Type A, C and D - remove cover only.
- Type B - remove bonnet.

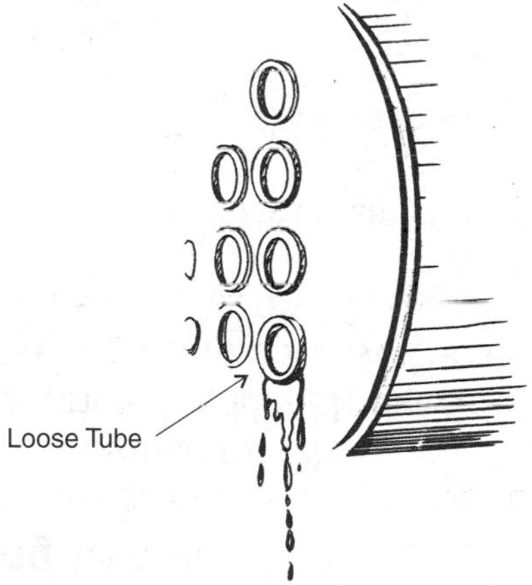
Loose Tube

Illustratiion #288 - Leaky Tube

Rear Head:

- Type L, N and P - remove cover only.
- Type M - remove bonnet.
- Type S and T - remove shell cover and floating head cover.
- Type W - remove channel and cover or bonnet.

CAUTION: Prior to loosening the head studs, be absolutely sure that the unit has been depressurized, vented and drained.

The studs at the bottom of the head flange should be loosened first. If the unit is still pressurized this will allow any liquid under pressure to spray down toward the floor rather than out on the worker's face.

Locating Leaks

- For channel heads - remove the cover and hydrostatic test the shell.
- For bonnet heads with fixed tubesheets remove the head and hydrostatic test the shell, see illustration #289.

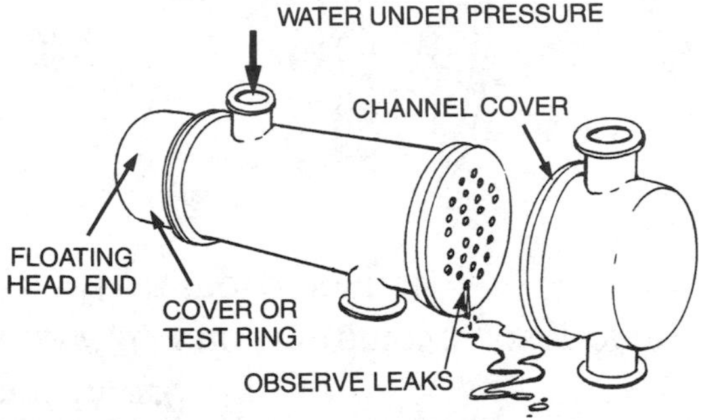
WATER UNDER PRESSURE
CHANNEL COVER
FLOATING HEAD END
COVER OR TEST RING
OBSERVE LEAKS

Illustration #289 – Remove Head and Pressurize

- On removable bundle types - remove the bonnet and rebolt the tubesheet to the shell flange using a test flange or a test gland, see illustration #290, then hydrostatic test the shell.

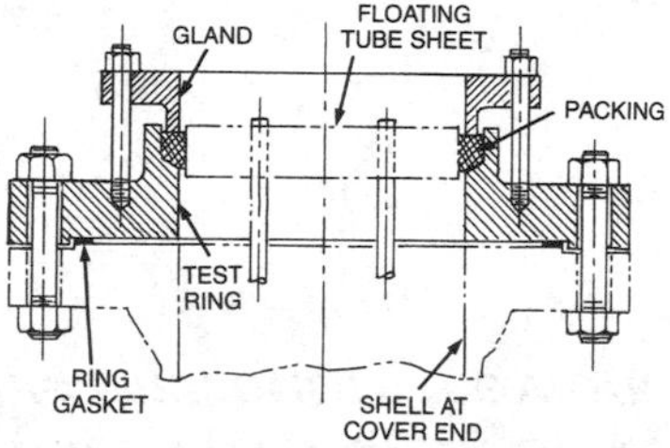
GLAND
FLOATING TUBE SHEET
PACKING
TEST RING
RING GASKET
SHELL AT COVER END

Illustration #290 - Test Flange

- On S or T floating heads - remove the head and floating head cover, then install a test ring and hydrostatic test the shell.

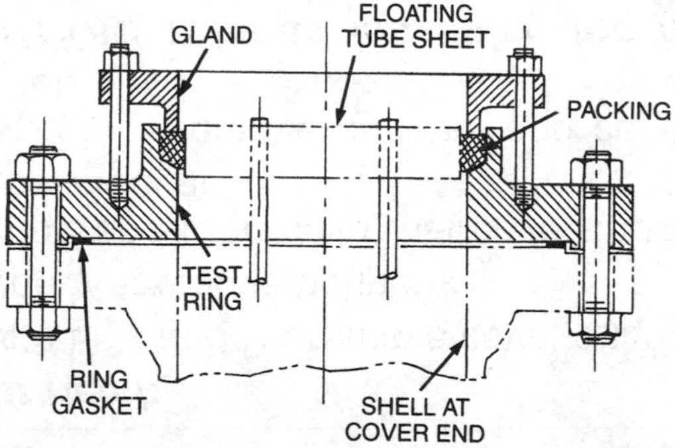
GLAND
FLOATING TUBE SHEET
PACKING
TEST RING
RING GASKET
SHELL AT COVER END

Illustration #291 – Test Gland

Tube Plugs

Temporary repair of a split tube can sometimes be accomplished by firmly driving plugs into each end of the damaged tube. To do this, both ends of the exchanger bundle must be accessible and it must be remembered that each plugged tube lowers the unit's efficiency.

The plug material must be compatible to the tube material and the product, i.e: don't use carbon steel plugs in stainless tubes containing highly corrosive product.

Some applications require puncturing the tube before plugging to allow drainage of flammable liquids or to avoid pressure build-up.

Tube Removal

Tube removal methods will vary depending on whether the bundle is fixed or removable, the size and type of tubes, and on possible seal welding. The number of tubes to be removed can also be a factor.

1. ***Punching*** - this method can be used by inserting a tube punch into the tube and hitting it with a hammer. When it projects out of the other end several inches, the tube can be pulled by some outside factor.

   A variation of this is to drill the tube the thickness of the tubesheet with a drill slightly smaller than the tube O.D., then punch as usual.

2. ***Tap and Draw*** - this method uses a type of tap that is screwed into the tube, then is pulled out by an outside force. A fly cutter can also be used to cut off the tube on the inside. The tube and the stub are then pulled separately.

3. ***Hydraulic*** - the fastest and most efficient method is to use a hydraulic tube puller. This tool has jaws which are inserted inside the tube. When pressure is exerted, the jaws activate against the tube and rams push against the tubesheet to pull the tube out several inches.

An outside force is again used to pull the tube completely out. Depending on the degree of difficulty encountered, it may be easier, or necessary, to use a flycutter to cut off the tube and remove from both ends.

Bundle Removal & Handling

Removal - Care should be exercised when removing a tube bundle from the shell, otherwise the bundle or the shell may be damaged. The pulling cable should be attached to eye bolts screwed into the tubesheet. Steel rods or cables inserted through the tubes and attached to bearing plates may be used where tubesheets are not tapped for eye bolts. The tube bundle should always be supported on the baffles or the tubesheet. Never support the bundle directly on the tubes.

CAUTION: Ensure there are no explosive vapours inside the shell prior to pulling. Sparks could cause an explosion.

Handling - Tube bundles should not be handled with hooks or other devices which might damage the tubes. Bundles should be supported on cradles or skids.

Horizontal bundles should be lifted by means of suitable web or steel mesh slings.

Bundles can be bent and damaged by dragging over a rough surface. All gaskets and packing contact surfaces should be protected from damage as these areas are difficult to repair

Cleaning Tube Bundles

The heat transfer surfaces of heat exchangers should be kept reasonably clean to assure satisfactory performance.

Heat exchangers may be cleaned by either chemical or mechanical methods. The method selected must be chosen by the plant supervisor and will depend on the type of deposits and the facilities available. Following are several cleaning procedures that may be considered.

- Circulating hot wash oil or light distillate through tubes or shell at high velocity will effectively remove sludge or similar soft deposits.
- Some salt deposits may be washed out by circulating hot fresh water.
- Cleaning compounds are available for removing sludge or scale provided hot wash oil or water is not available or does not give satisfactory results.
- Fixed tubesheet types must be chemically cleaned on the shell side of the tubes.
- Turbine type tube cleaners can be used for removal of deposits inside of tubes.
- Scrapers, rotating wire brushes and other mechanical means can be used for removing hard scale, coke or other deposits.
- Employ the services of a qualified organization that provides cleaning services. These organizations will check the nature of the deposits to be removed, furnish proper solvents and/or acid solutions containing inhibitors for the complete cleaning job.

Cleaning Precautions

- Tubes should not be cleaned by blowing steam through individual tubes as this overheats the tube and results in severe expansion strain.
- When mechanically cleaning a tube bundle care should be exercised to avoid damaging the tubes.

Gaskets

Gasket and gasket surfaces should be thoroughly cleaned and should be free of scratches and other defects. Gaskets should be properly positioned before attempting to tighten studs. It is recommended that when a heat exchanger is dismantled for any reason it must be reassembled with new gaskets.

This will tend to prevent future leaks and/or damage to the gasket seating surfaces of the heat exchangers. Composition gaskets become dried out and brittle and therefore they do not always provide an effective seal when reused.

Metal or metal jacketed gaskets, when compressed initially, flow to match their contact surfaces. In so doing they are work hardened and, if reused, may provide an imperfect seal or result in deformation and damage to the gasket contact surfaces of the exchanger.

Gasket Installation

When installing a gasket in an exchanger ensure the gasket remains in the proper position. If the gasket crossbars don't line up with the baffle plates in the exchanger head there will be a leak from one process side to another.

If tape is used to hold gaskets in place for installation, the tape should not cross the face of the gaskets as it could very well leak along the edge of the tape. Steel gaskets are especially hard to keep tight with tape across them. Garlock fiber gaskets can sometimes be tightened enough to keep them from leaking but it is not advised to put tape across the face.

Hydrostatic Testing

One of the most important steps in checking for leaks before and after repair of a heat exchanger or pressure vessel is hydrostatic testing.

- Before hydro testing of an exchanger or vessel, blank off all flanges and valves with plates and gaskets.
- The highest point must be vented. Any amount of air trapped inside will make the testing extremely difficult if not impossible.
- Pump the water in through a valved inlet.
- After filling, close the inlet valve, blank the vented outlet and hook up a pump to the water inlet.
- Open the inlet valve and start the pump.
- A pressure gauge should be attached to the pump and vessel to determine pressure.
- Most tests are conducted at $1^1/_2$ times the normal working pressure, although many plants and companies may have other specifications to follow.
- After inspecting for leaks, close the inlet valve and crack open the blanked off outlet vent on the top or high point of the exchanger or vessel.
- After the pressure has dropped to zero the exchanger or vessel can be drained, leave the vent open while draining.
- In cold weather always drain the exchanger or vessel. There have been countless severely damaged pieces of equipment due to water freezing after testing.

SECTION SEVEN QUESTIONS

Heat Exchangers

1. *Determine if the following statement is true or false. A heat exchanger could be used to either heat or cool a liquid.*
   - ❒ true ❒ false

2. *Determine if the following statement is true or false. A combination of tubes and tubesheet is called a tube bundle.*
   - ❒ true ❒ false

3. *By what process are tubes normally attached to the tubesheet?*
   - ❒ welding
   - ❒ expanding
   - ❒ retracting
   - ❒ swedging

4. *Which of the following is not a method of tubesheet layout?*
   - ❒ twisted square
   - ❒ rotated square
   - ❒ triangular
   - ❒ rotated triangular

5. *What is not a reason for having baffles in the shell side of a heat exchanger?*
   - ❒ prevent tube sagging
   - ❒ increases inlet velocity
   - ❒ relieve stress on tubes
   - ❒ assist in heat transfer

6. *Which baffle helps reduce velocity?*
   - ❒ segmental
   - ❒ doughnut
   - ❒ impingement
   - ❒ longitudinal

7. *If the shell side of a heat exchanger has a single, center longitudinal baffle, and with the inlet and outlet nozzles at the same end, the shellside flow would be called a:*
   - ❒ one pass
   - ❒ two pass
   - ❒ three pass
   - ❒ four pass

8. *If the front head of a heat exchanger has two baffle plates, the tubeside flow would be a:*
   - ❒ one pass
   - ❒ two pass
   - ❒ three pass
   - ❒ four pass

9. *Determine if the following statement is true or false. Leakage between baffles occurred on a multi-pass exchanger head. This problem was likely caused because of an improper fitting gasket.*

   ❒ true ❒ false

10. *Determine if the following statement is true or false. The term "fixed tubesheet" means the tubesheet is welded directly to the shell.*

    ❒ true ❒ false

11. *Determine if the following statement is true or false. On a floating head exchanger, the tubesheet and inside rear head can be pulled when the front head has been removed.*

    ❒ true ❒ false

12. *Determine if the following statement is true or false. An exchanger specified as a 36-145 would have a shell diameter of 36 inches and a tube length of 145 inches.*

    ❒ true ❒ false

13. *What shell type usually does not have a removable rear head?*
    - ❒ type E, one-pass
    - ❒ type G, split flow
    - ❒ type K, kettle reboiler
    - ❒ type X, cross flow

14. *What must be done to prepare tubes for installation in a heat exchanger tubesheet?*
- ❒ score the ends
- ❒ polish the ends
- ❒ clean the ends
- ❒ all of above

15. *If the tubesheet thickness of an exchanger is one inch, how far must the tube ends be cleaned before installation?*
- ❒ half the tubesheet thickness
- ❒ equal to tubesheet thickness
- ❒ triple the tubesheet thickness
- ❒ enough to ensure a clean seat

16. *Determine if the following statement is true or false. Before installing tubes, it is not necessary to eliminate any moisture trapped between the tube and the tubeseat.*
- ❒ true ❒ false

17. *Determine if the following statement is true or false. When expanding tubes into the first tubesheet, the expanding operation usually proceeds from the top to the bottom.*
- ❒ true ❒ false

18. *Determine if the following statement is true or false. When expanding the second tubesheet, the usual first step is to expand a number of scattered location tack tubes to help prevent tubesheet deflection.*
- ❒ true ❒ false

19. *Determine if the following statement is true or false. All bolted joints must be tightened using one universal accepted method, including low and high pressure joints.*
- ❒ true ❒ false

20. *What must be checked when inspecting a heat exchanger for tube leakage, before loosening the head studs?*
- ❒ unit has been depressurized
- ❒ unit has been vented
- ❒ unit has drained
- ❒ all of above

21 *As a safety precaution, what studs should be removed first when removing a heat exchanger head for inspection?*

- ❐ top
- ❐ left side
- ❐ right side
- ❐ bottom

22. *A temporary method of fixing leaking tubes in a heat exchanger is to:*

- ❐ remove tubes and plug holes
- ❐ use tube plugs
- ❐ gasket off tube area
- ❐ remove tubes and replace

23. *What method is the fastest and most efficient way of removing tubes from a tube sheet?*

- ❐ hydraulic method
- ❐ tap and draw method
- ❐ punching
- ❐ drilling

24. *Which of the following precautions should be observed when pulling a tube bundle?*

- ❐ pull using eyebolts
- ❐ support bundle on baffles
- ❐ ensure no explosive vapors are present
- ❐ all of the above

25. *Determine if the following statement is true or false. Gasket surfaces are easy to repair if damaged during bundle removal.*

❐ true ❐ false

26. *Determine if the following statement is true or false. Both metal and composition gasket material is designed to permit being reused without losing efficiency.*

❐ true ❐ false

27. *Determine if the following statement is true or false. When installing a new gasket, the use of tape across a gasket face to hold the gasket in place is permitted as the tape will compress enough to allow a tight joint.*

❐ true ❐ false

28. *A vessel to be hydro tested operates at 275 PSI. What would be the recommended test pressure?*

- ❒ 412.5 p.s.i.
- ❒ 275 p.s.i.
- ❒ 137.5 p.s.i
- ❒ 250 p.s.i.

29. *When filling or draining a vessel for a hydrostatic test, it should be vented to avoid potential problems.*

❒ true ❒ false

SECTION EIGHT

TUBE EXPANSION

Introduction

ASME Codes establish definite design standards for boilers and unfired pressure vessels, but do not cover the actual expansion of rolled joints. Thus, this important matter is left to the judgement of individuals who may be inexperienced, and consequently joints that are well designed may be rolled improperly and give unsatisfactory service.

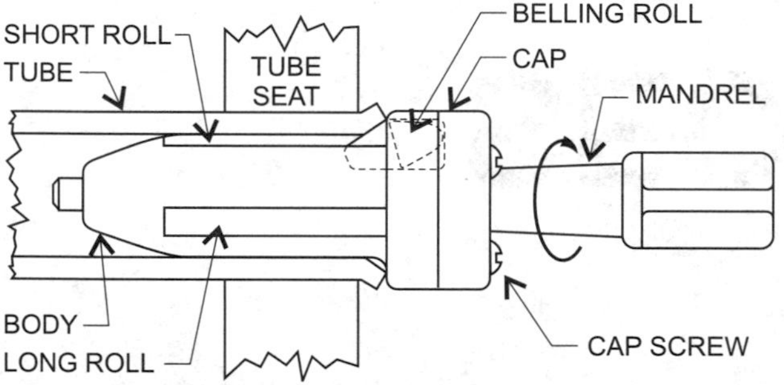
SHORT ROLL
TUBE
TUBE SEAT
BELLING ROLL
CAP
MANDREL
BODY
LONG ROLL
CAP SCREW

Illustration #292 - Typical Tube Expander

It is apparent, therefore, that in order to prevent service interruptions, shutdowns and repairs, the rolling-in of tubes should proceed in the best possible manner.

When rolling tubes, an expander is inserted into the tube end and a tapered mandrel is rotated. Feeding the mandrel inward causes the expander rollers to be forced apart and by rolling over the inside tube surface, coldwork the tube metal. The tube is enlarged and contacts the tube hole surface, then, because the tube hole is a restraining barrier, further expanding deforms the tube metal and forces it into more intimate contact with the metal of the tube hole. The increase of tube size deforms the metal around the tube hole, with a resultant elastic reaction against the tube, holding it in place with great strength and resistance to leakage. Since all displaced tube metal cannot escape radially, it flows from the center to each end of the rolled joint. This outward tube flow is called extrusion.

The metal surrounding the tube hole is also affected, and the hole is slightly enlarged. The net result of the expanding operation is a joint condition similar to a shrink-fitted shaft coupling.

Joint Preparation

Cleanliness is one of the basic requirements for making good joints. Both tube holes and tube ends should be well cleaned of scale, dust and dirt before assembly and care should be taken to keep oil, soap and other lubricants out of the unrolled joint. Tube holes in tube sheets, baffles and support plates must be free from burrs in order to prevent longitudinal scratching of the tube ends, should the tube be fed through such holes at assembly.

End scratches and tube hole toolmarks are a major cause of leaky joints. It must be realized that if longitudinal nicks or scratches remain on the outside of the tube over the area which is to be rolled in, there is an excellent chance for a leak as it may not be possible to have the groove or nick rolled out during expanding. For final cleaning of boiler tube ends in the field, emery cloth should be used and the rubbing must be circumferentially rather than longitudinally, in order that scratches remaining from the emery cloth will run around the circumference of the tube and not in line with the tube axis.

Tube Preparation

When cleaning the tube ends, it is important to only polish the number of tubes that can be installed in one day. It is not advisable to have tubes with bare polished ends stored away for two or three days before the tubes are inserted in the boiler. After the final cleaning, no oil or other protective coating must be used on the polished ends. If the raw metal is exposed to the atmosphere for several days it will rust and the purpose of polishing is defeated.

Erection should be scheduled in order that tube end cleaning and inserting of tubes into the boiler proceed in parallel, to the extent job conditions permit.

If possible, the most ideal procedure would be to have each tube inserted in the boiler immediately after the ends are cleaned and to follow at once with the expanding.

Occasionally tube end polishing discloses cracks and laminations near the tube end. These are residual faults produced in the manufacturing of the tube. Hair line cracks running longitudinally in the tube are laminations caused by folding the metal when the tube is being manufactured and will produce leaks in the tube joints. The cracks will open up during rolling-in of the tubes and the tube may split at the end while being expanded. If any defect is found during final cleaning of the tubes in the field, the tube must be placed aside.

Boilers - Expanding Equipment

A boiler tube expander is usually made up of three expanding rolls and one or two belling rolls, held in place by a body and a tapered mandrel. The rolls are set at an angle to the centerline of the body, so that when the mandrel is rotated in a clockwise direction it feeds into the body, pushing the rolls out against the inside of the tube.

The expanders must be designed to suit the size and gauge of the tubes and the thickness of the tubesheet. Rolls should be tapered to expand the tubes parallel to the tubesheet. The rolls should be long enough to expand the tubes from 1/4 inch to 1/2 inch (6-13 mm) past the outside edge of the seat. This gives the tubes a slight bulge at the outside edge of the seat and prevents them from pushing into the drum. The large end of the rolls should be rounded off to prevent digging into the tube as the expander moves forward.

The belling rolls flare or bell the tube ends projecting inside the drum or header. Uniform tube joints are only possible if the compressed air supply is continuous and of reasonably constant pressure. When portable air compressors are used it is advisable that the compressor supplying air to the rolling motors not be connected with any other machine such as an air hoist, etc. The air compressor should be located close to the worksite in order that the air hoses are as short as possible.

When the air compressor cannot be located near the tube rolling operation, a pressure gauge mounted on a manifold or on a separate receiving tank close to the boiler should be provided. The compressed air is then piped up to the manifold or receiving tank and all tube rolling motors will receive compressed air from the common source.

The air pressure indicated by the gauge must be carefully noted and if for some reason the air pressure should drop below a pre-determined point, the tube rolling operation must be stopped immediately.

The rolling motor must have sufficient power to complete the rolling operation. This is important! Never roll a tube until the motor stalls. If the extent of tube rolling is governed by the strength of the motor, it is not possible to obtain uniformly rolled joints. The air pressure supplied to the rolling motor is rarely constant and if it is attempted to roll a tube end until the motor stalls, one joint may be severely over-rolled because high air pressure was available while the next may be under-rolled because the air pressure has dropped.

Boilers - Tube Expanding

When beginning to expand a tube, the expander should be set so that the small end of the belling roll has just started to enter the tube.

The expander body will move into the tube as the mandrel is rotated in a clockwise direction, see illustration #293. The proper setting of the expander can be determined only by experience, as it is necessary to set the expander back further from the end of the tube when expanding into a thin tube sheet. If the expander has been properly set, the tube should be properly expanded when the small end of the belling roll reaches the inside edge of the seat. Do not let the small end of the belling roll pass the inside edge of the seat as it will cut the tube or pull it into the drum, see illustration #294.

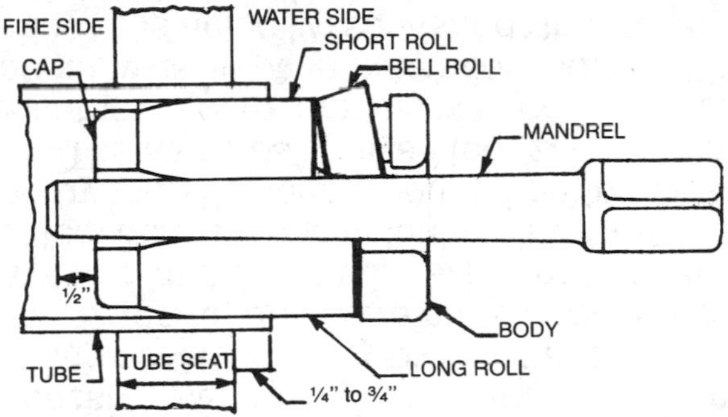
FIRE SIDE
WATER SIDE
SHORT ROLL
BELL ROLL
CAP
MANDREL
½"
BODY
TUBE
TUBE SEAT
LONG ROLL
¼" to ¾"

Illustration #293 - Setting Expander

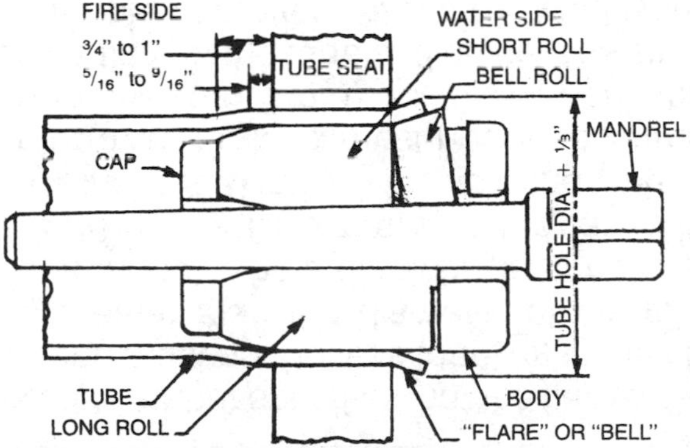
FIRE SIDE
WATER SIDE
¾" to 1"
SHORT ROLL
TUBE SEAT
5/16" to 9/16"
BELL ROLL
MANDREL
CAP
TUBE HOLE DIA. + ⅓"
TUBE
BODY
LONG ROLL
"FLARE" OR "BELL"

Illustration #294 - Expander Flaring the Tube

The expander is removed from the tube by rotating the mandrel in a counter-clockwise direction. If the tube has not been sufficiently expanded when the small end of the belling roll reaches the inside edge of the seat, the expander should be removed and the operation repeated. The expanding operation should be slow enough to prevent the tubes from heating up while being expanded. A tube that heats up while being expanded may shrink away from the seat when it cools off. The ASME Boiler Code specifications state that the projection of the tube ends in boiler drums and headers shall not be less than 1/4 inches (6 mm) and not more than 3/8 inches (19 mm) and are measured on the high side of the drum shell and before the tube end is flared. It is advisable to attempt to hold this protection to 3/8 inches (10 mm) (water tube boilers only).

The code further specifies that the flare of the tube end must not be less than 1/8 inches (3 mm) greater than the diameter of the tube hole. If the tube hole diameter is, for example, 3.28 inches (83.3 mm) as in the case with a 3 1/4 inch (82.6 mm) O.D. tube, then the diameter over the flare must not be less than 3.405 inches (86.5 mm). It is highly desirable that the flare of the tube end be kept as small as possible to prevent excessive cold working on the tube end, which in some cases splits the end of the tube.

Excessive flaring may actually reduce the holding power and may produce a leaky tube joint. Some tube ends removed from boilers have shown that the tube expander was prevented from traveling further into the tube end by the shoulder produced on the flared end. The samples showed that after the correct amount of expanding was done, the expander was kept in operation so that the flaring rolls actually "squashed" the metal of the tube against the inner edge of the tube hole.

Probably the most controversial issue connected with tube expanding of all types is the practical determination of the point in the expanding operation at which optimum results are obtained. In other words, at what point in the expanding operation shall it be stopped? That point is reached when the seat metal surrounding the tube exerts an elastic reaction slightly below the elastic limit of the metal. It has been found that to have this result, after release of expanding pressures and withdrawal of the mandrel, it is necessary to deform the seat plastically by application of the expanding pressure. This is often undesirable because of its effect on adjacent tube holes and expanded joints. The amount a tube should be expanded can be determined only by experience and care must be taken to prevent over-rolling the tubes. It is better to have the tubes slightly under-rolled than over-rolled as the under-rolled tubes can be re-rolled, while over-rolled tubes will have to be removed.

Boilers - Maximum Expansion

Over the years many methods have been used, most with limited success, to attempt to measure the amount of expansion required for boiler tubes.

Some of the methods include: measuring tube extrusion, limiting the amount of mandrel travel and power input cutoff.

Some of the more practical methods used with a better success rate are:

1. Compound Tube Gauge

This tool is inserted into the tube and a dial indicates the difference between the rolled and unrolled tube I.D., see illustration #295.

2. Snap Gauge

This is a practical method of determining optimum expanding with the use of a gauge to measure the O.D. of a tube. When a tube has been properly expanded, it will have a slight bulge for a distance of at least 1/4 inch (6 mm) past the outside edge of the seat.

The tube is expanded until the gauge will not slip over the tube as gauged immediately outside the header. The gauges are made for each tube O.D. used and with recognition of the following factors: (1) whether the tube is in a drum or a header, (2) what the pressure of the boilers will be.

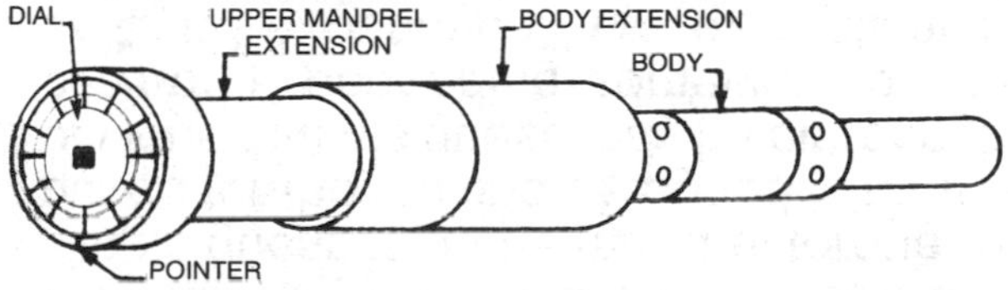
DIAL
UPPER MANDREL EXTENSION
BODY EXTENSION
BODY
POINTER

Illustration #295 - Compound Tube Gauge

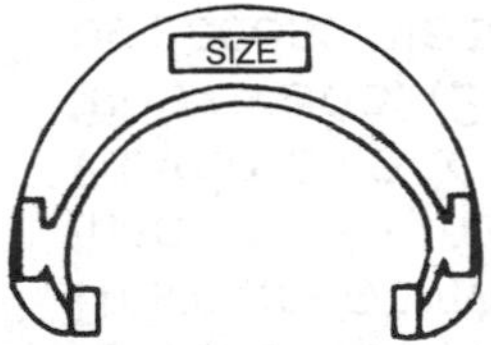
SIZE

Illustration #296 - Snap Gauge

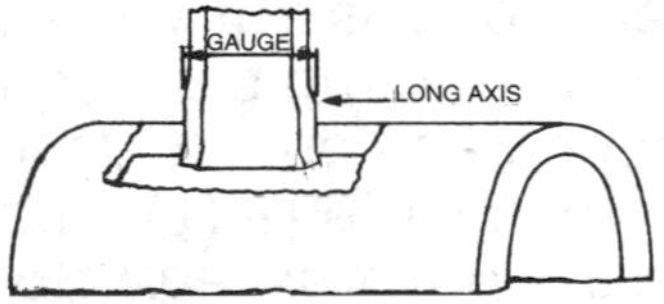
GAUGE
LONG AXIS

Illustration #297 - Snap Gauge Application

A point of importance in connection with this gauge is that when used for checking tubes in headers it must be used to measure the O.D. of the tube in line with the longitudinal axis of the header. The reason for this is that during the expanding operation the header opens up quickly in a circumferential direction, whereas it is much more rigid in the longitudinal direction. Consequently the gauge is quickly satisfied in the circumferential direction but this is no indication that the tube is completely expanded.

3. Mill Scale

One method that works fairly well on certain boiler drums is the cracking of mill scale. When a tube has been sufficiently expanded, there will be a slight indication of flaking of the mill scale or paint around the outside of the tube hole. Excessive flaking of this mill scale or paint generally indicates over-rolling.

4. Feel Method

There are obvious drawbacks to the use of these three methods. (1) The holes may vary in size too much for the compound tube gauge. (2) Tubes in a drum may not be accessible to check with a snap gauge. (3) There may not be any mill scale or paint on the drum to crack. Probably the most widely practiced rolling method is the manual “feel” method. The operator simply guesses at the mandrel torque required for the making of a good joint. It is obvious that his guess may be either right or wrong, depending somewhat on his skill and experience. It is evident, also, that an operator’s “feel” may vary considerably during a day’s work, nor is it the same day after day. Further, the “feel” of different operators varies and it is not often they agree on how much to roll. Thus, many joints rolled in this manner are of questionable stability.

Even though this method is the least technical of all, it is used more on boiler tube expansion than any other method.

Table #37 shows the suggested minimum tube O.D. enlargement immediately outside the tube seat.

MEASUREMENTS FOR THE TUBE O.D. IN INCHES			
Tube Diameter	Drums	Headers Under 500 PSI	Headers Over 500 PSI
2"	2.055	2.061	2.071
2 1/2"	2.561	2.569	2.581
3"	3.067	3.076	3.091
3 1/4"	3.320	3.330	3.346
4"	4.079	4.091	4.111
4 1/2"	4.599	4.599	4.621

Table #37 - Outside Tube Enlargement. All figures are based on a tube hole clearance of .031 inches.

METRIC CONVERSION:

1 inch = 25.4 mm

To convert decimals of an inch to metric, for example: 3/4 inch is 0.75 inches,

0 .75 inches x 25.4 = 19.05 (approx 19 mm)

Expanding Lubricant

To obtain parallel rolling, the rolls and the mandrel are tapered evenly in opposite directions. Obviously the surface speed of the rolls must be faster at one end than at the other.

This means slippage which produces friction and heat at great pressure. To avoid tube surface flaking a proper lubricant must be used. This lubricant must be boiled out by water before the boiler goes into operation. Mineral oil of any type can not be used. Castor and other vegetable oils are partially satisfactory but will oxidize after sitting a short time.

Only use commercial products as a tube rolling lubricant. They give satisfactory lubrication and are water soluble.

Heat Exchanger Expanding

Tube ends and holes must be cleaned of rust, dirt, grease, etc. Care must be taken not to scratch the tube ends longitudinally.

The tube rolling equipment is basically identical to that used for boilers, except that the tubes are normally smaller in diameter and thinner in tube wall thickness, resulting in equipment smaller in size and lighter in design.

The process of tube expansion is again similar to that of rolling boiler tubes, however, the main differences are: (1) the amount of expansion, due to the thinner tubes and normally thinner tube sheets, (2) the length of tube expanded in relation to the tube sheet. The length of expansion is one of the prime differences between boilers and heat exchangers. Boiler tubes are expanded at least 1/4 inch (6 mm) beyond the tube sheet, creating a slight "bulge" in the tubes.

Heat exchangers must not normally be rolled this far. The expansion should stop approximately 1/8 inch (3 mm) from the inside edge of the tube sheet. See illustration #298.

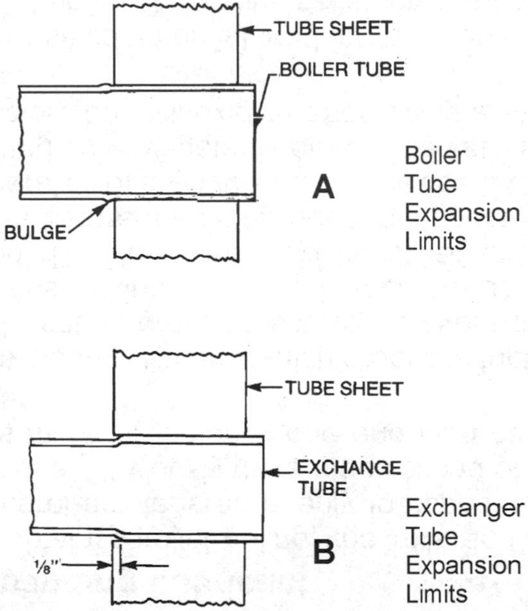
TUBE SHEET
BOILER TUBE
BULGE
A
Boiler Tube Expansion Limits
TUBE SHEET
EXCHANGE TUBE
1/8"
B
Exchanger Tube Expansion Limits

Illustration #298 - Boiler vs Exchanger Expansion

Tack Tubes

The procedure for expanding tubes in exchangers with two flat tube sheets is to expand all of the tubes on one sheet first. Usually the rolling will proceed from the bottom to the top, row by row. The excess tube rolling lubricant, which will run out of the holes, will not foul the clean unrolled tubes if this procedure is followed.

Then proceed to the other tube sheet with the unrolled tubes. When a tube is rolled, the tube wall becomes thinner. This is similar to squeezing a rubber ball; the ball becomes flatter but also bigger in diameter. Likewise with a tube; it becomes thinner but increases in length.

If the tubes in the second tube sheet are rolled similar to the first, row by row, the extrusion creates structural stresses in both the tube and the tube sheet and in some cases this stress could deform the tube sheet.

To avoid this sheet deflection, roll a line of tack tubes vertically and horizontally, plus one row around the circumference.

The remaining tubes are then rolled from the center out.

The stress is still created but the tube sheet deflection will be eliminated or reduced by the use of tack tubes. An indication of the stress in each individual tube can be seen by looking in the end of a tube. Instead of seeing the round end of a tube, all that can normally be seen is a crescent of light. This is due to a bow or deflection of the tube, see illustration #299.

Improperly aligned baffles will also cause a similar appearance; this is nothing more than a fabrication error, while bowing from extrusion cannot be avoided.

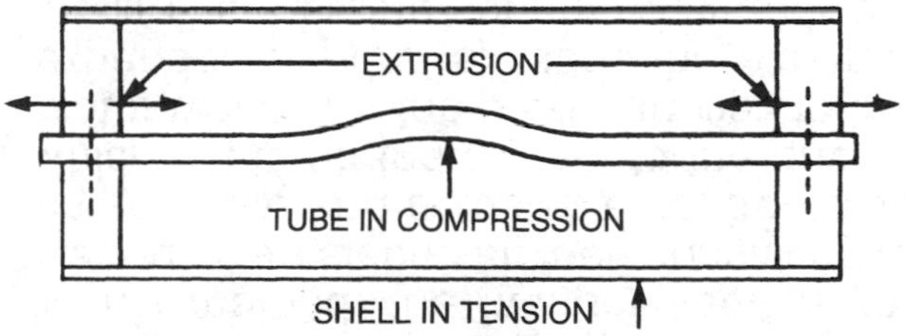
EXTRUSION
TUBE IN COMPRESSION
SHELL IN TENSION

Illustration #299 - Tube Bowed from Extrusion

Exchangers Maximum Expansion

As in the expansion of boiler tubes, there are several methods of finding the correct amount of heat exchanger tube expansion. However, the most common methods used are not the same as those used for rolling boiler tubes.

1. **Feel Method**

   This method, which is widely used in the expansion of boiler tubes, is extremely unreliable for heat exchangers. There is a certain point in the rolling of boiler tubes which gives the maximum holding power. However, a good joint can be obtained over or under this point due to the thickness of the tube and tube sheet. There is also a point to be reached for maximum holding power in heat exchangers; but, due to the thinner tubes and tube sheets this point is hard to hit and it is very easy to under-roll or over-roll a joint.

2. **Electric Expanders**

   This is the best type of expander and the one most commonly used in rolling heat exchanger tubes.

   In this method, the manual "feel" is replaced by an electrical "feel" consisting of an accurate and adjustable control relay which shuts off the current to the driving motor whenever the power applied to the expander mandrel exceeds the expanding limit set by the control relay and rolling-in torque requirements. These units are readily adaptable in varying types of rolling conditions.

3. **Expansion Formula**

   A method which can be used to check for the correct amount of expansion is a formula which indicates the amount of tube wall thinning to obtain the correct degree of expansion. This method would not be used on every hole.

   Instead, a few holes are picked at random, and the hole I.D. is measured with a micrometer and telescoping gauge. After the tubes have been inserted and expanded in these same holes the tube I.D. is then measured. The formula will indicate what the expanded tube I.D. would be, see illustration #300.

The formula is based on increasing the original tube inside diameter by 5% plus filling the clearancc space between tube and tubesheet (steel tubes).

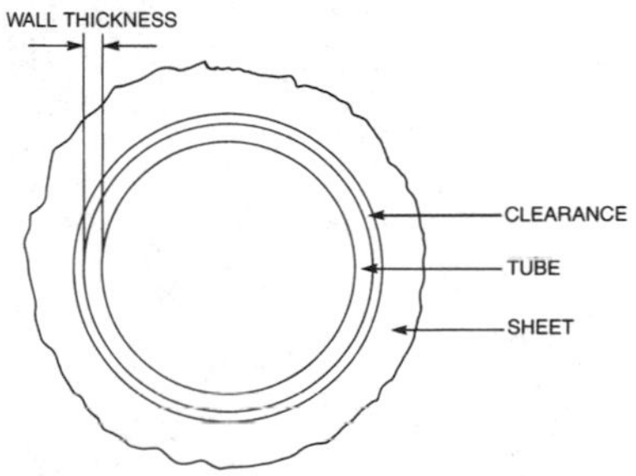
WALL THICKNESS
CLEARANCE
TUBE
SHEET

Illustration #300 - Expanding Formula

Example One: The following is an example using a 3/4 inch (19.3 mm) steel tube.

1. I.D. of tubesheet hole = .760" (19.3 mm)
2. O.D. of tube = .750" (19 mm)
3. Clearance = .010" (.3 mm)
4. I.D. of tube = .584" (14.8 mm)
5. 10% of <u>one</u> wall thickness = .008" (.2 mm)
6. Final I.D. = .602" (15.3 mm)
7. .602" = .584" (I.D.) + .010" (clearance) + .008" (10% of <u>one</u> wall thickness)

The 10% of wall thickness is derived by:

- Subtracting the I.D. of .584 inches from the 0. D. of .750 inches.
- This indicates a combined wall thickness of both tube walls of .166 inches.
- One wall thickness would be half of this, or .083 inches. 10% of .083 is .008 inches. (.166 x 5% = .008)

Table #38 indicates the percentage of wall thickness reduction for various materials to obtain a strong joint.

Carbon steel & Stainless steel	10%
Monel	12%
Nickel	14%
Aluminum brass	16%
Muntz brass	18%
Red brass	18%
Copper	20%

Table #38 -Tube Wall Thinning Percentages

NOTE: Most exchanger manufacturers attempt to drill tube holes in the 3/4 inch to 1 inch (19 to 25.4 mm) diameter range with a clearance of .008 inches (.2 mm) to .010 inches (.3 mm).

SECTION EIGHT QUESTIONS
Tube Expanding

1. *Determine if the following statement is true or false. The entire piece of equipment used in the tube expanding process is called a mandrel.*
   ❒ true ❒ false

2. *The tube expanding rolls are forced outwards against the tube by rotating a tapered:*
   ❒ short roll
   ❒ mandrel
   ❒ cap screw
   ❒ long roll

3. *During the expanding process, the inside and outside diameter of the tube increases, while the thickness of the tube wall:*
   ❒ increases
   ❒ stays the same
   ❒ decreases
   ❒ expands

4. *The tube expanding process is also called:*
   ❒ tube rolling
   ❒ tube belling
   ❒ tube cleaning
   ❒ tube polishing

5. *What term describes the movement of the displaced tube material during the expanding process?*
   ❒ radial
   ❒ extrusion
   ❒ expansion
   ❒ contraction

6. *Determine if the following statement is true or false. The first basic requirement of making a good expanded joint is joint and tube cleanliness.*
   ❒ true ❒ false

7. *Which of the following is the most important item to remove from the tube end and the tube hole?*
   ❒ mill scale
   ❒ rust
   ❒ expanding lubricant
   ❒ all of the above

8. *What type of scratches in a tube cause problems as they cannot be rolled out?*
   - ❒ radial
   - ❒ longitudinal
   - ❒ residual
   - ❒ hairline

9. *Emery cloth should be used for the final cleaning of tube ends, and is best used in what type of motion?*
   - ❒ diagonal
   - ❒ circumferential
   - ❒ longitudinal
   - ❒ crosshatch pattern

10. *Preferably, how far in advance should the tube cleaning process be compared to the installation process?*
   - ❒ same day
   - ❒ several days
   - ❒ one week
   - ❒ no time limit

11. *What should be done if a defect or crack is discovered in a tube end that is to be expanded?*
   - ❒ weld and repair tube
   - ❒ cutoff cracked portion
   - ❒ install it
   - ❒ discard tube

12. *Boiler tube expanders are usually made up of how many expanding rolls?*
   - ❒ two
   - ❒ three
   - ❒ four
   - ❒ five

13. *The long roll of a boiler tube expander should be of sufficient length to roll the complete thickness of the drum plus an additional distance of:*
   - ❒ 1/8 to 1/4 inches past
   - ❒ 1/4 to 1/2 inches past
   - ❒ 1/2 to 5/8 inches past
   - ❒ 5/8 to 3/4 inches past

14. *What creates a flare in the tube portion that projects inside a drum or header?*
- ❒ long rolls
- ❒ short rolls
- ❒ belling rolls
- ❒ horizontal rolls

15. *Determine if the following statement is true or false. The compressed air supply for the rolling process must be continuous and of constant pressure.*
- ❒ true ❒ false

16. *Determine if the following statement is true or false. To expand tubes enough, it is always advisable to roll until the air motor stalls.*
- ❒ true ❒ false

17. *When beginning the expanding process on boiler tubes, and with a bell roll expander, how far should the small end of the roll be set into the tube?*
- ❒ at beginning of tube
- ❒ halfway through tubesheet
- ❒ at the inside edge of tubesheet
- ❒ depends on the air supply

18. *Determine if the following statement is true or false. A belling roll that expands too far past the inside edge of the tubesheet could cut the tube.*
- ❒ true ❒ false

19. *Determine if the following statement is true or false. If an expanded tube pulls away from the tubesheet, it could be caused by cooling contraction if the expanding process was too fast.*
- ❒ true ❒ false

20. *For water tube boilers, the internal projection of the tube into the drum is best kept to:*
- ❒ 1/8 inch
- ❒ 1/4 inch
- ❒ 3/8 inch
- ❒ 3/4 inch

21. *If a boiler is tube is expanded into a tube hole measuring 2 3/8 inches, what will be the minimum flare of the tube end to meet code requirements?*
- ❒ 2 1/4 inches
- ❒ 2 3/8 inches
- ❒ 2 1/2 inches
- ❒ 2 5/8 inches

22. *What tool measures the difference between the rolled and unrolled tube inside tube diameter?*
- ❒ micrometer
- ❒ tape measure
- ❒ snap gauge
- ❒ compound tube gauge

23. *What tool measures the expanded tube outside diameter outside of a drum or header?*
- ❒ micrometer
- ❒ tape measure
- ❒ snap gauge
- ❒ compound tube gauge

24. *Referring to table #37 on page 285, in order for this table to be accurate, the tube hole clearance must be:*
- ❒ .031
- ❒ .061
- ❒ .075
- ❒ .081

25. *Determine if the following statement is true or false. Mineral oil works very satisfactorily as a rolling lubricant.*
- ❒ true ❒ false

26. *Determine if the following statement is true or false. As boiler tubes and drums, and heat exchanger tubes and tubesheets are similar in size, the expanding equipment is interchangeable.*
- ❒ true ❒ false

27. *If the tubesheet thickness of a heat exchanger is 1 inch, the tube expanded joint length should be approximately:*
- ❒ 7/8 inch
- ❒ 1 inch
- ❒ 1 1/8 inches
- ❒ 1 1/4 inches

28. *The tack tube procedure is used to help reduce the effect of:*

- ❐ mill scale
- ❐ expansion
- ❐ contraction
- ❐ extrusion

29. *Which type of expander motor is most commonly used for rolling heat exchanger tubes?*

- ❐ air
- ❐ electric
- ❐ hydraulic
- ❐ hydrostatic

30. *What is the final inside diameter of a 1 inch outside diameter stainless steel tube to be rolled into a tube hole that measured 1.010 in diameter and the tube I.D. was 0.834 inches?*

- ❐ 0.834 inches
- ❐ 0.844 inches
- ❐ 0.852 inches
- ❐ 0.860 inches

SECTION NINE

PIPING

Pipe Standards and Specifications

Seamless and seam welded pipe and tube are manufactured to various pipe standards and specifications.

Some of the more common international and national standards and specifications for pipe and tube are listed in table #39.

National and International Pipe Standards & Specifications	
API-AMERICAN PETROLEUM INSTITUTE	
API 5L	Line Pipe
API 5LX	High Test Line Pipe
API 5LS	Spiral Weld Line Pipe
ASTM-AMERICAN SOCIETY FOR TESTING AND MATERIALS	
ASTM A53	Welded and Seamless Steel Pipe
ASTM A106	Seamless Carbon Steel Pipe for High-Temperature Service
ASTM A120	Black and Hot Dipped Zinc Coating (Galvanized) Welded and Seamless Steel Pipe for Ordinary Use

Table #39 - National and International Pipe Standards and Specifications

National and International Pipe Standards & Specifications	
ASTM A134	Electric-Fusion (ARC) Welded Steel Plate (Sizes 16 in. and Over)
ASTM A135	Electric-Resistance-Welded Steel Pipe
ASTM A139	Electric-Fusion (Arc)-Welded Steel Plate Pipe (Size 4 in. and Over)
ASTM A211	Spiral-Welded Steel or Iron Pipe
ASTM A312	Seamless and Welded Austenitic Stainless Steel Pipe
ASTM A333	Seamless and Welded Steel Pipe for Low-Temperature Service
ASTM A335	Seamless Ferritic Alloy Steel Pipe for High-Temperature Service
ASTM A358	Electric-Fusion-Welded Austenitic Chromium-Nickel Alloy Steel Pipe for High-Temperature Service
ASTM A369	Carbon and Ferritic Alloy Steel Forged and Bored Pipe for High-Temperature Service
ASTM A376	Seamless Austenitic Steel Pipe for High-Temperature Central-Station Service

Table #39 cont.- National and International Pipe Standards and Specifications

National and International Pipe Standards & Specifications	
ASTM A381	Metal-Arc-Welded Steel Pipe for High-Pressure Systems
ASTM A405	Seamless Ferritic Alloy Steel Pipe Specially Heat Treated for High-Temperature Service
ASTM A409	Welded Large Diameter Austenitic Steel Pipe for Corrosive or High-Temperature Service
ASTM A430	Austenitic Steel Forged and Bored Pipe for High Temperature Service
ASTM A523	Plain End Seamless and Electric-Resistance-Welded Steel Pipe for High Pressure Pipe-Type Cable Circuits
ASTM A524	Seamless Carbon Steel Pipe for Process Piping
ASTM A530	General Requirements for Specialized Carbon and Alloy Steel Pipe
ASTM A671	Electric-Fusion-Welded Steel Pipe for Atmospheric and Lower Temperatures

Table #39 cont.- National and International Pipe Standards and Specifications

National and International Pipe Standards & Specifications	
ASTM A672	Electric-Fusion-Welded Steel Pipe for High-Pressure Service at Moderate Temperatures
ASTM A691	Carbon and Alloy Steel Pipe, Electric-Fusion-Welded for High-Pressure Service at High Temperatures
ASTM A714	High Strength Low-Alloy Welded and Seamless Steel Pipe
ASTM A731	Seamless and Welded Ferritic Stainless Steel Pipe
ASTM A790	Seamless and Welded Ferritic/ Austenitic Stainless Steel Pipe
ASTM A795	Black and Hot-Dipped Zinc-Coated (Galvanized) Welded and Seamless Pipe for Fire Protection
AWWA-AMERICAN WATER WORKS ASSOCIATION	
AWWA C200	Steel Water Pipe, 6 Inches and Larger
AWWA C203	Standard for Coal-Tar Enamel Protective Coatings for Steel Water Pipe

Table #39 cont.- National and International Pipe Standards and Specifications

National and International Pipe Standards & Specifications	
CSA-CANADIAN STANDARD ASSOCIATION	
CSA Z245.1	Steel Line Pipe
CSA Z245.2	High Strength Steel Line Pipe 18 Inches and Larger in Diameter
CSA Z245.3	Low Strength Steel Line Pipe Less Than 18 Inches in Diameter
CSA Z245.4	Low Strength Steel Line Pipe 18 Inches and Larger in Diameter
CSA Z245.5	High Strength Steel Line Pipe Less Than 18 Inches in Diameter
ISO-INTERNATIONAL ORGANIZATION FOR STANDARDIZATION	
IOS 65	Steel Tubes Suitable for Screwing in accordance with International Standards IS07/1.

Table #39 cont.- National and International Pipe Standards and Specifications

Note: Many of the standards and specifications correspond between countries and/or agencies.

Pipe Properties & Characteristics

Standards and/or specifications for pipe indicate pipe grade designations, intended use, testing practices, manufacturing methods, chemical properties and various physical characteristics of the pipe. Examples of chemical properties and physical characteristics of ASTM (A-53) and API (5L) specified pipe are shown in table #40.

Even though steel pipe is available in various grades, the most common grades used are: Grade A and B, and the less common Grade C. It is important that the grade be specified for each application.

Even though Grade B may have a higher tensile strength than Grade A, Grade A pipe may be preferred in some applications.

(See table #40 for tensile strengths). Grade A is preferred where close coiling or cold bending of pipe is required because of its lower carbon content which makes it more ductile and less brittle.

Chemical Composition and Tensile Strength of Grade A and Grade B Steel Pipe							
Chemical Composition						**Tensile Properties**	
Designation	**Grade**	**C**	**Mn**	**P**	**S**	**min. yield strength psi (MPa)**	**min. tensile strength psi (MPa)**
ASTM A-53	A	0.25	0.95	0.05	0.06	30,000 (205)	48,000 (330)
	B	0.30	1.2	0.05	0.06	35,000 (240)	60,000 (415)
API 5L	A	0.22	0.9	0.04	0.05	30,000 (205)	48,000 (330)
	B	0.27	1.15	0.04	0.05	35,000 (240)	60,000 (415)
C = Carbon	Mn = Manganese		P = Phosphorous		S = Sulfur		

Table #40 - Grade A and B Pipe Chemical Composition

Weights and Schedule Numbers

Steel pipe is produced in three weights or general wall thickness classifications:

- Standard (Std.)
- Extra Strong (XS) or Extra Heavy (XH).
- Double Extra Strong (XXS) or Double Extra Heavy (XXH).

Note: Designations of Strong and Heavy are interchangeable in the weight classifications.

Light wall, light weight or light gage pipe, as it may be referred to, is another weight classification sometimes given to steel pipe. This pipe classification is used extensively in many sprinkler installations and other applications where a thinner wall pipe may be preferred. The light wall pipe designation corresponds to schedule number 10 for steel pipe in most sizes.

Note: The weight classification denotes the wall thickness of the pipe.

For any pipe size, the outside diameter is constant and the inside diameter varies with the wall thickness. Pipe dies and fittings therefore remain the same for specific sizes of pipe, no matter what the weight.

Because of the variation in inside diameter, pipe sizes from 1/8 inch (6 mm) to 12 inches (300 mm) are designated by nominal inside diameter (ID), not by the actual inside diameter. Nominal sizes are referred to as Nominal Pipe Size (NPS) and less commonly, Iron Pipe Size (IPS). Pipe sizes over 12 inch (300 mm) are classified by actual outside diameter (OD).

Schedule Numbers

To further broaden the range of wall thicknesses for specific applications and various pressures, steel pipe is manufactured in assorted schedule numbers. These schedule numbers range from 10 through to 160 and are commercially available in schedules: 10, 20, 30, 40, 60, 80, 100, 120, 140, and 160.

Pipe Sizes

Carbon steel pipe is commercially available in nominal pipe sizes ranging from 1/8 inch (6 mm) through to 42 inches (1050 mm). The following nominal pipe sizes are available within this range. Outside diameter (OD) designations are also given because of varying trade practices in specifying some line pipe by OD measurements. See table #41 for actual and nominal pipe sizes.

Note:

1. ***Metric nominal pipe sizes are based on International Organization for Standardization (ISO).***
2. ***For specific sizes, dimensions, weights, and schedule numbers of steel pipe refer to tables #42 (imperial) and #43 (metric).***

Nominal Pipe Size (NPS) 1 inch (25mm)

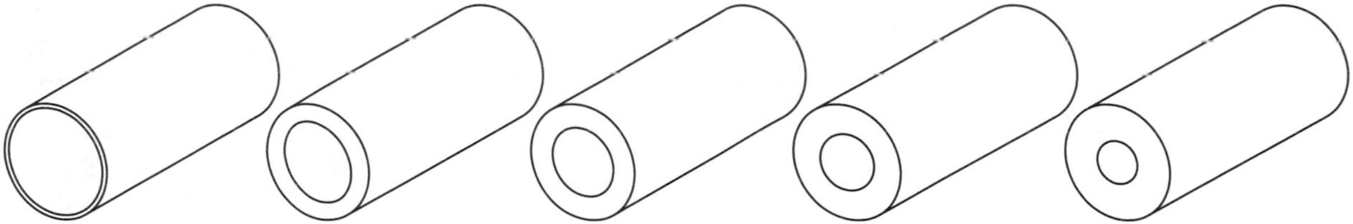

	Light Wall Schedule #10	Standard Schedule #40	Extra Strong Schedule #80	Schedule #160	Extra Extra Strong
Outside Diameter	1.315" (33.4mm)	1.315" (33.4mm)	1.315" (33.4mm)	1.315" (33.4mm)	1.315" (33.4mm)
Inside Diameter	1.097" (27.864mm)	1.049" (26.65mm)	0.957" (24.31mm)	0.815" (20.7mm)	0.599" (15.2mm)
Wall Thickness	0.109" (2.769mm)	0.133" (3.4mm)	0.179" (4.6mm)	0.250" (6.35mm)	0.358" (9.093mm)

$$\text{Wall Thickness} = \frac{\text{Outside Diameter} - \text{Inside Diameter}}{2}$$

Illustration #301 - Wall Thickness and Schedule Numbers

Actual and Nominal Pipe Sizes			
Actual OD		Nominal Sizes	
inches	(mm)	inches	(mm)
0.405	10.3	1/8	6
0.540	13.7	1/4	8
0.675	17.1	3/8	10
0.840	21.3	1/2	15
1.050	26.7	3/4	20
1.315	33.4	1	25
1.660	42.2	1 1/4	32
1.900	48.3	1 1/2	40
2.375	60.3	2	50
2.875	73.0	2 1/2	65
3.500	88.9	3	80
4.000	101.6	3 1/2	90
4.500	114.3	4	100
5.563	141.3	5	125
6.625	168.3	6	150
8.625	219.1	8	200
10.750	273.1	10	250

Actual and Nominal Pipe Sizes			
Actual OD		Nominal Sizes	
inches	(mm)	inches	(mm)
12.750	323.9	12	300
14.000	355.6	14	350
16.000	406.4	16	400
18.000	457.0	18	450
20.000	508.0	20	500
22.000	559.0	22	550
24.000	610.0	24	600
26.000	660.0	26	650
28.000	711.0	28	700
30.000	762.0	30	750
32.000	813.0	32	800
34.000	864.0	34	850
36.000	914.0	36	900
38.000	965.0	38	950
40.000	1016.0	40	1000
42.000	1067.0	42	1050

Table #41 - Actual vs. Nominal Pipe Sizes

NOM. PIPE SIZE	OUT-SIDE DIAM.	NOMINAL WALL THICKNESS													
		Sched. 5	Sched. 10	Sched. 20	Sched. 30	Stand-ard	Sched. 40	Sched. 60	Extra Strong	Sched. 80	Sched. 100	Sched. 120	Sched. 140	Sched. 160	XX Strong
3/4	1.050	0.065	0.083	-	-	0.113	0.113	-	0.154	0.154	-	-	-	0.218	0.308
1	1.315	0.065	0.109	-	-	0.133	0.133	-	0.179	0.179	-	-	-	0.250	0.358
1 1/4	1.660	0.065	0.109	-	-	0.140	0.140	-	0.191	0.191	-	-	-	0.250	0.382
1 1/2	1.900	0.065	0.109	-	-	0.145	0.145	-	0.200	0.200	-	-	-	0.281	0.400
2	2.375	0.065	0.109	-	-	0.154	0.154	-	0.218	0.218	-	-	-	0.343	0.436
2 1/2	2.875	0.083	0.120	-	-	0.203	0.203	-	0.276	0.276	-	-	-	0.375	0.552
3	3.5	0.083	0.120	-	-	0.216	0.216	-	0.300	0.300	-	-	-	0.438	0.600
3 1/2	4.0	0.083	0.120	-	-	0.226	0.226	-	0.318	0.318	-	-	-	-	-
4	4.5	0.083	0.120	-	-	0.237	0.237	-	0.337	0.337	-	0.438	-	0.531	0.674
5	5.563	0.109	0.134	-	-	0.258	0.258	-	0.375	0.375	-	0.500	-	0.625	0.750
6	6.625	0.109	0.134	-	-	0.280	0.280	-	0.432	0.432	-	0.562	-	0.718	0.864
8	8.625	0.109	0.148	0.250	0.277	0.322	0.322	0.406	0.500	0.500	0.593	0.718	0.812	0.906	0.875
10	10.75	0.134	0.165	0.250	0.307	0.365	0.365	0.500	0.500	0.593	0.718	0.843	1.000	1.125	-
12	12.75	0.156	0.180	0.250	0.330	0.375	0.406	0.562	0.500	0.687	0.843	1.000	1.125	1.312	-
14 OD	14.0	-	0.250	0.312	0.375	0.375	0.438	0.593	0.500	0.750	0.937	1.093	1.250	1.406	-
16 OD	16.0	-	0.250	0.312	0.375	0.375	0.500	0.656	0.500	0.843	1.031	1.218	1.438	1.593	-
18 OD	18.0	-	0.250	0.312	0.438	0.375	0.562	0.750	0.500	0.937	1.156	1.375	1.562	1.781	-
20 OD	20.0	-	0.250	0.375	0.500	0.375	0.593	0.812	0.500	1.031	1.281	1.500	1.750	1.968	-
22 OD	22.0	-	0.250	-	-	0.375	-	-	0.500	-	-	-	-	-	-
24 OD	24.0	-	0.250	0.375	0.562	0.375	0.687	0.968	0.500	1.218	1.531	1.812	2.062	2.343	-
26 OD	26.0	-	-	-	-	0.375	-	-	0.500	-	-	-	-	-	-
30 OD	30.0	-	0.312	0.500	0.625	0.375	-	-	0.500	-	-	-	-	-	-
34 OD	34.0	-	-	-	-	0.375	-	-	0.500	-	-	-	-	-	-
36 OD	36.0	-	-	-	-	0.375	-	-	0.500	-	-	-	-	-	-
All dimensions given in decimals of an inch of the nominal pipe sizes. Thicknesses may vary due to mill tolerance.															

Table #42 - Pipe Schedules (Imperial)

NOM. PIPE SIZE	OUT-SIDE DIAM.	NOMINAL WALL THICKNESS														
		Sched 5S	Sched 10S	Sched 10	Sched. 20	Sched 30	Stand-ard	Sched. 40	Sched. 60	Extra Strong	Sched. 80	Sched. 100	Sched. 120	Sched. 140	Sched .160	XX Strong
20 mm	26.670	1.651	2.108	-	-	-	2.870	2.870	-	3.912	3.912	-	-	-	5.563	7.823
25 mm	33.401	1.651	2.769	-	-	-	3.378	3.378	-	4.547	4.547	-	-	-	6.350	9.093
32 mm	42.164	1.651	2.769	-	-	-	3.556	3.556	-	4.851	4.851	-	-	-	6.350	9.703
40 mm	48.260	1.651	2.769	-	-	-	3.683	3.683	-	5.080	5.080	-	-	-	7.137	10.160
50 mm	60.325	1.651	2.769	-	-	-	3.912	3.912	-	5.537	5.537	-	-	-	8.738	11.074
65 mm	73.025	2.108	3.048	-	-	-	5.156	5.156	-	7.010	7.010	-	-	-	9.525	14.021
80 mm	88.900	2.108	3.048	-	-	-	5.486	5.486	-	7.620	7.620	-	-	-	11.125	15.240
90 mm	101.600	2.108	3.048	-	-	-	5.740	5.740	-	8.077	8.077	-	-	-	-	-
100mm	114.300	2.108	3.048	-	-	-	6.020	6.020	-	8.560	8.560	-	11.125	-	13.487	17.120
125mm	141.300	2.769	3.404	-	-	-	6.553	6.553	-	9.525	9.525	-	12.700	-	15.875	19.050
150mm	168.275	2.769	3.404	-	-	-	7.112	7.112	-	10.973	10.973	-	14.275	-	18.263	21.946
200mm	219.075	2.769	3.759	-	6.350	7.036	8.179	8.179	10.312	12.700	12.700	15.088	18.263	20.625	23.012	22.225
250mm	273.050	3.404	4.191	-	6.350	7.798	9.271	9.271	12.700	12.700	15.088	18.263	21.438	25.400	28.575	25.400
300mm	323.850	3.962	4.572	-	6.350	8.382	9.525	10.312	14.275	12.700	17.475	21.438	25.400	28.575	33.325	25.400
350mm	355.600	3.962	4.775	6.350	7.925	9.525	9.525	11.125	15.088	12.700	19.050	23.925	27.788	31.750	35.712	-
400mm	406.400	4.191	4.775	6.350	7.925	9.525	9.525	12.700	16.662	12.700	21.438	26.187	30.963	36.525	40.488	-
450mm	457.200	4.191	4.775	6.350	7.925	11.125	9.525	14.275	19.050	12.700	23.825	29.362	34.925	39.675	45.237	-
500mm	508.000	4.775	5.537	6.350	9.525	12.700	9.525	15.088	20.625	12.700	26.187	32.537	38.100	44.450	50.013	-
550mm	558.800	4.775	5.537	6.350	9.525	12.700	9.525	-	22.225	12.700	28.575	34.925	41.275	47.625	53.975	-
600mm	609.600	5.337	6.350	6.350	9.525	14.275	9.525	17.475	24.613	12.700	30.963	38.887	46.025	52.375	59.538	-
650mm	660.400	-	-	7.925	12.700	-	9.525	-	-	12.700	-	-	-	-	-	-
750mm	762.000	6.350	7.925	7.925	12.700	15.875	9.525	-	-	12.700	-	-	-	-	-	-
850mm	863.600	-	-	7.925	12.700	15.875	9.525	-	-	12.700	-	-	-	-	-	-
900mm	914.400	-	-	7.925	12.700	15.875	9.525	19.050	-	12.700	-	-	-	-	-	-

All dimensions given in decimals of an inch of the nominal pipe sizes. Thicknesses may vary due to mill tolerance.

Table #43 - Pipe Schedules (Metric)

Flanges

Flanges connect piping and components together in a system with the use of bolted connections. This type of connection eases the disassembling and separation of piping, and equipment for repair and regular maintenance.

Illustrations #302 through #307 show different types of flange styles that are available. The following gives a brief description of each.

Welding-neck Flange

This flange type is designed to be connected by butt-welding the protruding neck of the flange to either a fitting, pipe, or equipment requiring a flanged joint. Welding-neck flanges provide good service under a wide range of temperature and pressure conditions in both static or intermittent flows (illustration #302).

Slip-on Flange

The slip-on flange is designed to slip over the end of the pipe. It allows easy positioning before welding. Both the inside and outside of the flange is fillet welded to the pipe. The inside weld is accomplished by pulling the pipe back (approximately the wall thickness of the pipe) from the end of the flange and welding the end of the pipe to the inside of the flange (illustration #303).

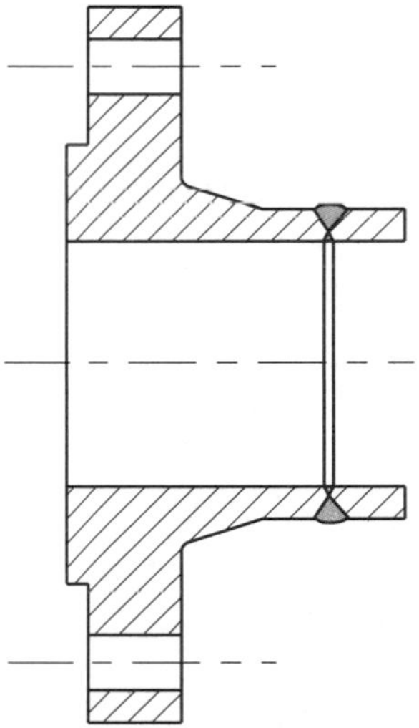

Illustration #302 - Weld-Neck Flange

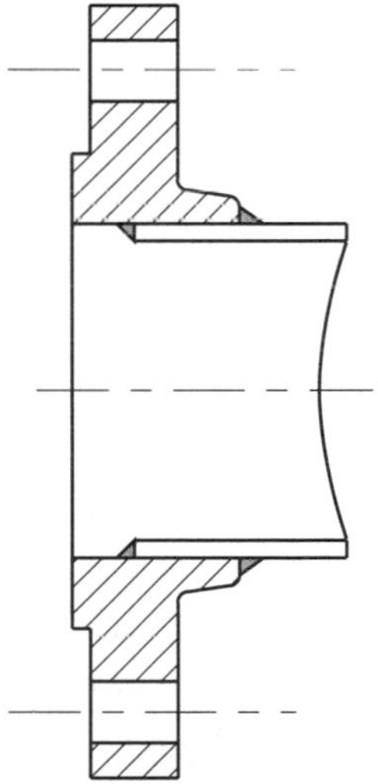

Illustration #303 - Slip-On Flange

Lap-joint (Van Stone Flange)

This flange arrangement consists of both a stub end and a flange. The flange itself is not welded but slips over the stub end which is butt welded to the fitting, pipe or equipment.This arrangement assists flange alignment in conditions where non-alignment may cause problems. Because the flange is not in contact with line fluids, it may be made from less costly carbon steel. The stub end is made from the pipe material (illustration #304).

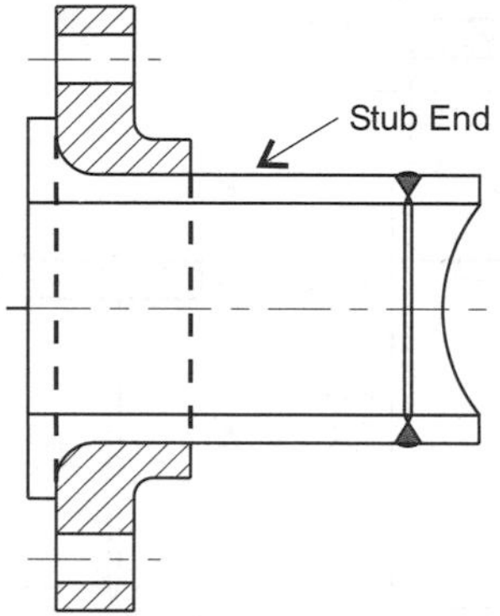
Stub End

Illustration #304 - Lap-Joint (Van Stone Flange)

Reducing Flange

This flange changes the line size without adding an extra fitting. The reducing flange changes the line size abruptly. It is not recommended where flow disturbance or turbulent conditions will cause problems (illustration #305).

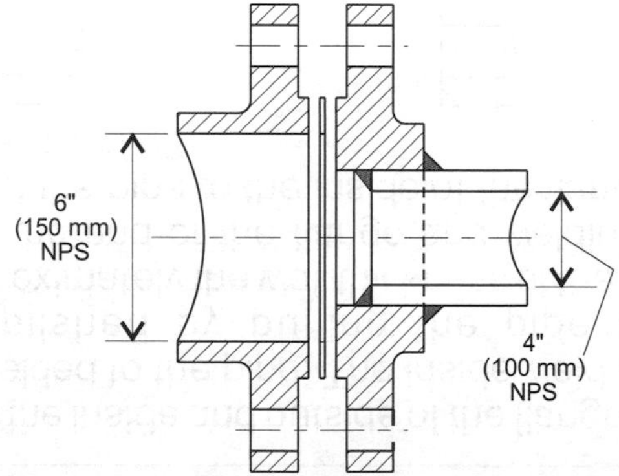
6"
(150 mm)
NPS
4"
(100 mm)
NPS

Illustration #305 - Reducing Flange

Screwed Flange

The screwed or threaded flange is often used in flanging applications where welding is not practical or desired. It is mostly used in commercial applications on low pressure and small piping (illustration #306).

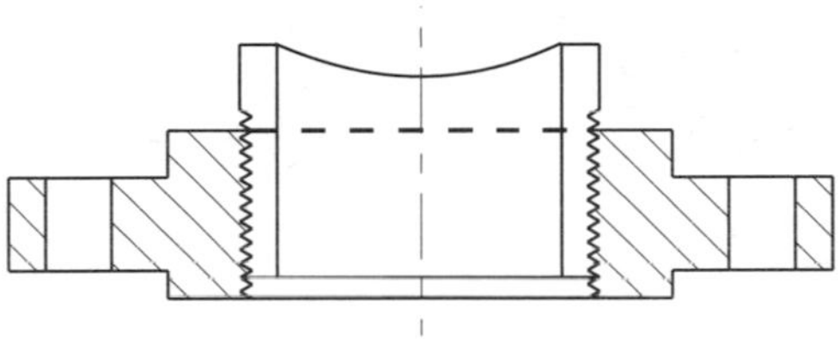

Illustration #306 - Screwed Flange

Socket Welding Flange

This flange is joined to pipe the same as socket welded fittings. It is used primarily on small piping and low pressure applications (illustration #307).

Blind Flange

The blind flange is a solid flange plate used to close-off the end of pipe, fittings, valves, and/or equipment (illustration #308).

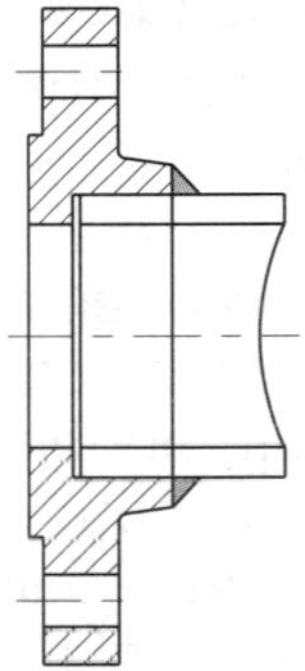

Illustration #307 - Socket Weld Flange

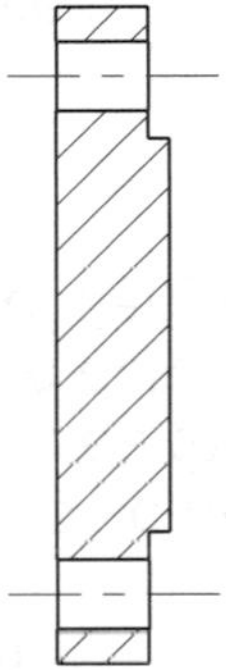

Illustration #308 - Blind Flange

Spectacle Blinds

Spectacle and line blinds are similar to a blind flange, but differ in that they fit between two flange connections. Spectacle blinds get their name from their similarity to a pair of eyeglasses or spectacles.

One side of the spectacle blind is fully closed for 100% flow shut-off, while the other side of the spectacle is open for full flow. ***With this construction, the blind can be rotated without leaving a space when it is taken out of the line. Another advantage of the spectacle construction is that it can be seen at a glance if the line is open or closed off (illustration #309).***

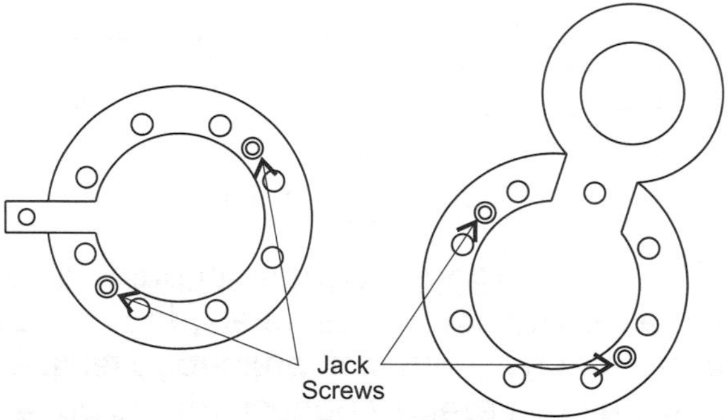
Jack
Screws

Illustration #309 - Line and Spectacle Blinds

Flange Faces

The various types of flanges are manufactured with a variety of face types. Even though there are many face types available, the most commonly used are:

- Raised face
- Flat face
- Lap joint (Van Stone flange)
- Ring joint

The flange face type should not be confused with flange "finish", which indicates the surface contact finish applied to the actual face of the flange. The major types of flange face finishes available are:

1. Smooth finish
2. Serrated finish
   a) serrated concentric grooves
   b) serrated spiral grooves

Note: Both serrated finishes have grooves 1/16 (1.6 mm) deep with 24 to 40 grooves per inch (25.4 mm). Flange face finishes other than these may be furnished as determined by end user.

Raised face:

Used in the majority of flange applications for pressures up to 900 psi (6200 Kpa). Face heights of 1/16" (1.6 mm) are used for flange classes 150, 250 and 300. Higher number flange classes use the 1/4" (6.35 mm) raised face.

ASME/ANSI Flanges

Most standard steel and alloy flanges are covered under ASME/ANSI specification B16.5 for flange pressure classes of: 150, 300, 400, 600, 900,1500, and 2500.

Cast iron flange classes and specifications are described under ASME/ANSI B16.1 standard. These flanges (cast iron) are available in classes: 25, 125, 250, and 800.

Cast iron pipe flanges are usually threaded connections; with class 25 and 125 having flat faces, and class 250 and 800 having raised faces of 1/16 inch and 1/4 inch (1.6 mm and 6.35 mm) respectively.

The American Petroleum Institute (API) also designates flange standards. Flanges manufactured to API standard are used primarily for the oil industry. They are rated for higher pressure applications and are usually used with high strength API tubular products.

Even though the dimensions of ASME/ANSI and API flanges are similar, they should not be interconnected because of the alternate pressure ratings.

Flange Markings

ASME/ANSI standards require flanges to be stamped or marked with the following information:

- Manufacturer's name or trademark.
- Nominal pipe size.
- Rating designation.
- Material designation.
- Melt code identification.
- Ring joint groove number (when applicable).

A typical example of flange marking is given in illustration #310.

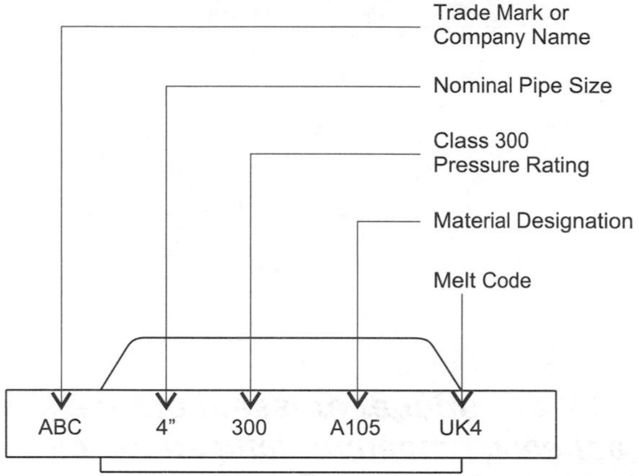

Trade Mark or Company Name
Nominal Pipe Size
Class 300 Pressure Rating
Material Designation
Melt Code
ABC
4"
300
A105
UK4

Illustration #310 - Flange Identification and Marking Example

Specific pipe flange and bolt dimensions for cast iron and steel flanges corresponding to ASME/ANSI standards are given in tables #44 and #45.

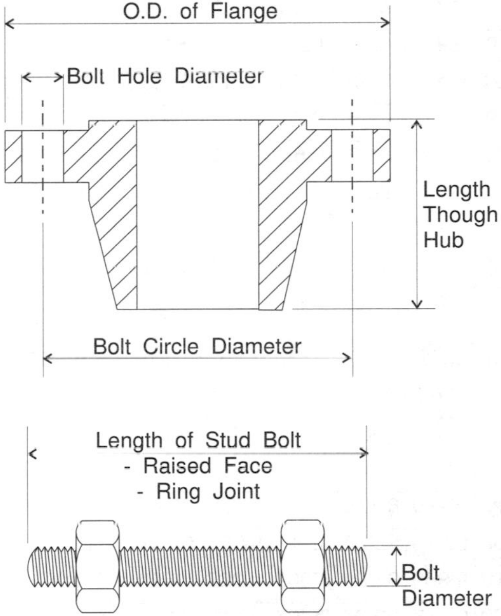
O.D. of Flange
Bolt Hole Diameter
Length
Though
Hub
Bolt Circle Diameter
Length of Stud Bolt
- Raised Face
- Ring Joint
Bolt
Diameter

Table #44 & #45 - Flange Dimension Description

Flange Dimension Notes - Tables #44 & #45

1. Dimensions based on ASME/ ANSI pipe flanges.
2. Dimensions for flange length thru hub include 0.06 in. (1.5mm) raised face for Classes 150 and 300.
3. Dimensions for flange length thru hub include 0.25 in. (6.4mm) raised face for Classes 400 and higher.
4. Threaded, Slip-on, or Socket flange styles may not be commercially available in all sizes stated.

FLANGE AND BOLT DIMENSIONS - CLASS 150 STEEL AND CLASS 125 CAST IRON																				
Nominal Pipe Size	in	1/2	3/4	1	1 1/4	1 1/2	2	2 1/2	3	4	5	6	8	10	12	14	16	18	20	24
	mm	15	20	25	32	40	50	65	80	100	125	150	200	250	300	350	400	450	500	600
O.D. Flange	in	3.50	3.88	4.25	4.62	5.00	6.00	7.00	7.50	9.00	10.00	11.00	13.50	16.00	19.00	21.00	23.50	25.00	27.50	32.00
	mm	88.9	98.6	108.	117.	127.	152.	178.	191.	228.6	254.0	279.4	342.9	406.4	482.6	533.4	596.9	635.0	698.5	812.8
Bolt Circle Diameter	in	2.38	2.75	3.12	3.50	3.88	4.75	5.50	6.00	7.50	8.50	9.50	11.75	14.25	17.00	18.75	21.25	22.75	25.00	29.50
	mm	60.5	69.9	79.3	88.9	98.6	120.	139.	152.	190.5	215.9	241.3	298.5	362.0	431.8	476.3	539.8	577.9	635.0	749.3
# of Bolts		4	4	4	4	4	4	4	4	8	8	8	8	12	12	12	16	16	20	20
Bolt Diameter	in	1/2	1/2	1/2	1/2	1/2	5/8	5/8	5/8	5/8	3/4	3/4	3/4	7/8	7/8	1	1	1 1/8	1 1/8	1 1/4
	mm	12.7	12.7	12.7	12.7	12.7	16.0	16.0	16.0	16.0	20.0	20.0	20.0	23.0	23.0	25.0	25.0	29.0	29.0	32.0
Bolt Length Raised Face	in	2.25	2.50	2.50	2.75	2.75	3.25	3.50	3.50	3.50	3.75	4.00	4.25	4.50	4.75	5.25	5.25	5.75	6.25	6.75
	mm	57.2	63.5	63.5	69.9	69.9	82.6	88.9	88.9	88.9	95.3	101.6	108.0	114.3	120.7	133.4	133.4	146.0	158.8	171.5
Bolt Length Ring Joint	in	n/a	n/a	3.00	3.25	3.25	3.75	4.00	4.00	4.00	4.25	4.50	4.75	5.00	5.25	5.75	5.75	6.25	6.75	7.25
	mm	n/a	n/a	76.2	82.6	82.6	95.3	101.	101.	101.	108.0	114.3	120.7	127.0	133.4	146.1	146.1	158.8	171.5	184.2
Bolt Hole Diameter	in	0.62	0.62	0.62	0.62	0.62	0.75	0.75	0.75	0.75	0.88	0.88	0.88	1.00	1.00	1.12	1.12	1.25	1.25	1.38
	mm	16.0	16.0	16.0	16.0	16.0	19.0	19.0	19.0	19.0	22.0	22.0	22.0	26.0	26.0	29.0	29.0	32.0	32.0	35.0
Welding Neck Length	in	1.88	2.06	2.19	2.25	2.44	2.50	2.75	2.75	3.00	3.50	3.50	4.00	4.00	4.50	5.00	5.00	5.50	5.69	6.00
	mm	47.8	52.3	55.6	57.2	62.0	63.5	69.9	69.9	76.2	88.9	88.9	101.6	101.6	114.3	127.0	127.0	139.7	144.5	152.4
Slip-on & Socket Length	in	0.62	0.62	0.69	0.81	0.88	1.00	1.12	1.19	1.31	1.44	1.56	1.75	1.94	2.19	2.25	2.50	2.69	2.88	3.25
	mm	15.8	15.8	17.5	20.6	22.4	25.4	28.5	30.2	33.3	36.6	39.6	44.5	49.3	55.6	57.2	63.5	68.3	73.2	82.6
NOTE: Shaded boxes do not show the first decimal place because of space constraints.																				

Table #44 - Flange and Bolt Dimensions (Class 150/125)

FLANGE AND BOLT DIMENSIONS - CLASS 300 STEEL OR 250 CAST IRON																				
Nominal Pipe Size	in	1/2	3/4	1	1 1/4	1 1/2	2	2 1/2	3	4	5	6	8	10	12	14	16	18	20	24
	mm	15	20	25	32	40	50	65	80	100	125	150	200	250	300	350	400	450	500	600
O.D. Flange	in	3.75	4.62	4.88	5.25	6.12	6.50	7.50	8.25	10.00	11.00	12.50	15.00	17.50	20.50	23.00	25.50	28.00	30.50	36.00
	mm	95.3	117.	124.	133.	155.	165.	190.	109.	254.0	279.4	317.5	381.0	444.5	520.7	584.2	647.7	711.2	774.7	914.4
Bolt Circle Diameter	in	2.62	3.25	3.50	3.88	4.50	5.00	5.88	6.62	7.88	9.25	10.62	13.00	15.25	17.75	20.25	22.50	24.75	27.00	32.00
	mm	66.5	82.6	88.9	98.6	114.	127.	149.	168.	200.2	235.0	269.7	330.2	387.4	450.9	514.4	571.5	628.7	685.8	812.8
# of Bolts		4	4	4	4	4	8	8	8	8	8	12	12	16	16	20	20	24	24	24
Bolt Diameter	in	1/2	5/8	5/8	5/8	3/4	5/8	3/4	3/4	3/4	3/4	3/4	7/8	1	1 1/8	1 1/8	1 1/4	1 1/4	1 1/4	1 1/2
	mm	12.7	15.9	15.9	15.9	19.1	16.0	20.0	20.0	20.0	20.0	20.0	23.0	25.0	29.0	29.0	32.0	32.0	32.0	38.0
Bolt Length Raised Face	in	2.50	3.00	3.00	3.25	3.50	3.50	4.00	4.25	4.50	4.75	4.75	5.50	6.25	6.75	7.00	7.50	7.75	8.00	9.00
	mm	63.5	76.2	76.2	82.6	88.9	90.0	101.	108.	114.3	120.7	120.7	140.0	158.8	171.5	177.8	190.5	196.9	203.2	228.6
Bolt Length Ring Joint	in	3.00	3.50	3.50	3.75	4.00	4.00	4.50	4.75	5.00	5.25	5.50	6.00	6.75	7.25	7.50	8.00	8.25	8.75	10.00
	mm	76.2	88.9	88.9	95.3	101.	101.	114.	120.	127.0	133.4	140.0	152.4	171.5	184.2	190.5	203.2	209.6	222.3	254.0
Bolt Hole Diameter	in	0.62	0.75	0.75	0.75	0.88	0.75	0.88	0.88	0.88	0.88	0.88	1.00	1.12	1.25	1.25	1.38	1.38	1.38	1.62
	mm	16.0	19.0	19.0	19.0	22.0	19.0	22.0	22.0	22.0	22.0	22.0	26.0	29.0	32.0	32.0	35.0	35.0	35.0	42.0
Welding Neck Length	in	2.06	2.25	2.44	2.56	2.69	2.75	3.00	3.12	3.38	3.88	3.88	4.38	4.62	5.12	5.62	5.75	6.25	6.38	6.62
	mm	52.3	57.2	62.0	65.0	68.3	69.9	76.2	79.3	85.9	98.6	98.6	111.3	117.4	130.1	142.8	146.1	158.8	162.1	168.2
Slip-on & Socket Length	in	0.88	1.00	1.06	1.06	1.19	1.31	1.50	1.69	1.88	2.00	2.06	2.44	2.62	2.88	3.00	3.25	3.50	3.75	4.19
	mm	22.4	25.4	27.0	27.0	30.2	33.3	38.1	43.0	47.8	50.8	52.4	62.0	66.6	73.2	76.2	82.6	88.9	95.3	106.4
NOTE: Shaded boxes do not show the first decimal place because of space constraints.																				

Table #45 - Flange and Bolt Dimensions (Class 300/250)

Flange Gaskets

Pipe flange gaskets are used to provide a leak-tight seal between two flange faces. ***In order to provide this seal, the gasket must be able to flow or form under bolt compression to fill all irregularities in the flange sealing face. The gaskets must also withstand possible high service temperatures and corrosive products while also being strong enough to prevent the system pressure from blowing it out.***

Gaskets are generally available in the following three flange face types:

- Full face gasket - covers the full face or area of the flange.
- Flat ring gasket - covers only the sealing area or raised face of the flange.
- Metallic ring gasket - designed to fit between the U-shaped machined grooves of ring type flanges.

Examples of each of these three flange styles are shown in illustration #311.

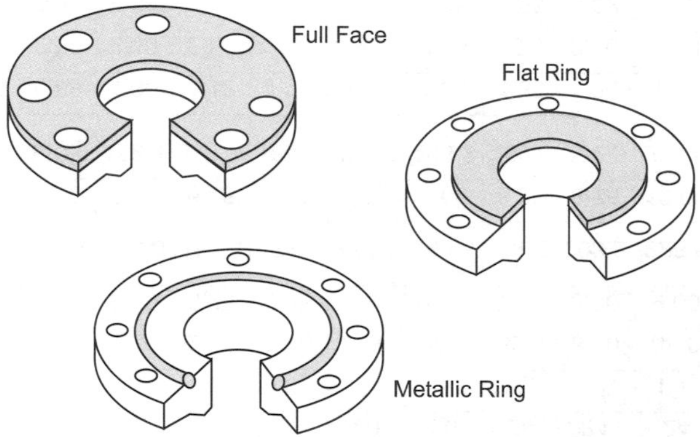
Full Face
Flat Ring
Metallic Ring

Illustration #311 - Gasket Face Types

GASKET MATERIAL SELECTION			
	MAX TEMP.		
MATERIAL	°F	°C	SERVICE PROPERTIES
Acrylic	450	(232)	Moderate heat resistance, but poor cold handling capability. Good resistance to oils, aliphatic and aromatic hydrocarbons. Poor resistance to water, alkalies and some acids.
Asbestos: Compressed asbestos and composites	750	(398)	Best general gasket material, but because of its low strength and high porosity, pure asbestos is seldom used. It is usually mixed with plastic or rubber to form compressed asbestos fibre (CAF). Large number of combinations available; properties vary widely depending on materials used with asbestos. CAUTION: See note at end of table #47.
Asbestos - TFE (Teflon)	500	(260)	Combines heat resistance and sealing properties of asbestos with the chemical inertness of Teflon.
Butyl	300	(148)	Good resistance to water, alkalies and dilute acids. Poor resistance to oils, gasoline and most solvents.
Cellulose fibre	300	(148)	Moisture and humidity changes the physical dimensions and hardness and softness of the gasket. Generally good resistance to chemicals, except strong acids.
Cork compositions surfaces	250	(121)	Conforms well to irregular flange. High resistance to oils, water, and many chemicals. Should not be used with inorganic acids, alkalies, oxidizing solutions, and live steam.
Cork Rubber	300	(148)	Good conformability and resistance to fatigue under bolting. Chemical inertness of gasket depends on rubber type used.
Neoprene	250	(121)	One of the most common gasket materials with excellent mechanical properties. It has good resistance to water, alkalies, most oil and solvents (except aromatic, chlorinated, or ketone types).
Nitrile	300	(148)	Good resistance to water, oils, gasoline, and dilute acids.
Metal: Aluminum	800	(426)	High corrosion resistance, but may be slightly attacked by strong acids and alkalies.
Copper	600	(315)	Both copper and brass offer good corrosion resistance at moderate temperatures.
Brass	500	(260)	
Inconel	2000	(1093)	Excellent heat and oxidation resistance.

Table #46 - Gasket Material Selection

GASKET MATERIAL SELECTION			
	MAX TEMP.		
MATERIAL	°F	°C	SERVICE PROPERTIES
Lead	500	(260)	Good chemical resistance and the best conformability of all metal gaskets.
Monel	1500	(815)	High corrosion resistance against most acids and alkalies. Attacked by strong hydrochloric and strong oxidizing acids.
Nickel	1400	(760)	Generally high temperature and corrosion resistance.
Stainless steel: 302 304 316 410 430	1150 1000 1000 1200 1400	(621) (537) (537) (648) (760)	Stainless steels in general are highly corrosion resistant to most chemicals. Unsatisfactory for wet chlorine gas and liquid, chlorides and some acids.
(Metal Composites)	-	-	Many metal and non-metal combinations are available; properties vary widely depending on materials used. Non-metallic material inserted with metal gaskets or metal combinations may affect the gasket's temperature limit.
Rubber natural	225	(107)	Good mechanical properties, but poor weathering and aging properties. Impervious to air and water. Fair to good resistance to acids and alkalies. Unsuitable for oils and gasoline.
Silicon	600	(315)	Good heat resistance properties, but poor resistance to high pressure steam. Fair to average resistance to water, acids and alkalies. Poor resistance to oil and solvents.
Styrene-butadiene	250	(121)	Similar to natural rubber, but better water resistance properties. Fair to good resistance to acids and alkalies. Unsuitable for oils, gasoline and solvents.
Teflon (TEF)	500	(260)	Is resistant to almost all chemicals and solvents. Good heat resistance and sealing properties at low temperatures.
Viton and Fluorel	450	(232)	Resistant to fuels, oils, lubricants and hydraulic fluids. Good resistance to ozone and weathering combined with good mechanical properties.
NOTE: Asbestos fibres are considered to be a health hazard and care must be taken when cutting or grinding asbestos gasket material. Do not cut or grind any gasket material before knowing the composition of the material. If uncertain about the gasket material to be fabricated, simply don't until all safety concerns can be accurately answered.			

Table #47 - Gasket Material Selection

Flange Bolting

There are two basic types of bolts used in making flange connections: a machine bolt that uses one nut, and the more commonly used stud bolt with two nuts. Both types are displayed in illustration #312. The most common thread classification used for flange bolts and nuts is the Unified Screw Thread Standard.

The Unified Screw Thread Standard is used in Canada, the United States, and Great Britain to classify bolts and nuts. ***Flange bolts and nuts are classified under this standard as: UNC (Unified Coarse) class 2, (medium fit) A for bolts and B for nuts.***

ASTM Material Bolt Specifications

ASME/ANSI standard B16.5 categorize ASTM flange bolting materials into the following groups:

- High Strength Bolting
- Intermediate Strength Bolting
- Low Strength Bolting
- Nickel and Special Alloy Bolting

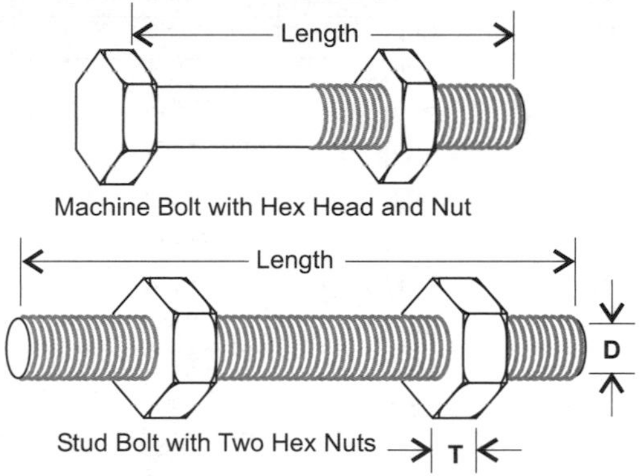
Length
Machine Bolt with Hex Head and Nut
Length
D
Stud Bolt with Two Hex Nuts
T

NOTES:

- Length of machine bolt is measured from base of bolt head to end point
- Length of stud bolt is measured without point height
- Bolt diameter "D" equals heavy hex nut thickness "T"

Illustration #312 - Machine Bolt and Stud Bolt

High Strength Bolting materials can be used in any flange jointing application when all the listed materials and gaskets are within the standard.

Flange Bolt Tightening

When tightening flange bolts, the flange faces must first align properly to provide even contact on the gasket surface. Before installing stud bolts, apply thread lubricant to each bolt. The lubricant makes tightening and future dismantling easier. Bolts should be installed hand tight and then evenly tightened in a crisscross pattern.

Note: See illustration #313 for bolt tightening sequence of flanges.

The proper wrench size for Imperial heavy hex nuts can be calculated by:

Wrench size = (1 1/2 x Bolt Diameter) + 1/8" (Imperial sizes only).

Example: Find the wrench size for a heavy hex nut used with a stud bolt diameter of 1 1/4 inches.

$$\text{Wrench size} = (1\tfrac{1}{2} \times 1\tfrac{1}{4}) + \tfrac{1}{8}$$
$$= (\tfrac{3}{2} \times \tfrac{5}{4}) + \tfrac{1}{8}$$
$$= 1\tfrac{7}{8} + \tfrac{1}{8}$$
$$= 2 \text{ inches}$$

Table #48 provides standard wrench sizes for heavy hex nuts used with stud bolts in both metric and inch sizes.

WRENCH SIZES FOR HEAVY HEX NUTS USED ON FLANGE STUD BOLTS				
Stud Size (inches)	Wrench Size (inches)		Stud Size (mm)	Wrench Size (mm)
1/2	7/8		M12	21
5/8	1 1/16		M14	24
3/4	1 1/4		M16	27
7/8	1 7/16		M20	34
1	1 5/8		M22	36
1 1/8	1 13/16		M24	41
1 1/4	2		M27	46
1 1/2	2 3/8		M30	50
1 5/8	2 9/16		M36	60
1 3/4	2 3/4		M42	70
1 7/8	2 15/16		M48	80
2	3 1/8		M56	90
2 1/4	3 1/2		M64	100
2 1/2	3 7/8		M72	110
2 3/4	4 1/4		M80	120
3	4 5/8		M90	135
3 1/2	5 3/8		M100	150

Table #48 - Wrench Sizes on Stud Bolts

Flange Tightening

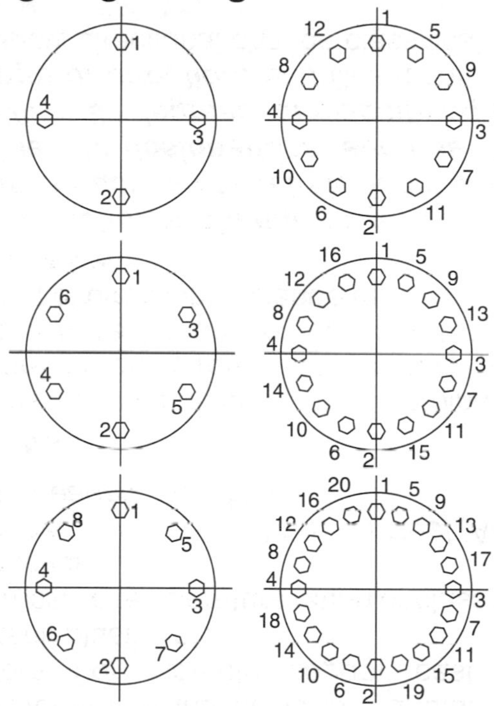

NOTE: Numbers indicate tightening sequence

Illustration #313 - Valve Flange Tightening

Pipe Fitting Types

Pipe fittings are the joining components that make possible the assembly of equipment, valves, and pipe into functioning piping systems. Fittings are manufactured to perform one or more of the following functions:

- Change direction of piping in system.
- Connect or join piping and/or equipment.
- Provide for branches, access, take-offs or auxiliary connections.
- Block or regulate flow within piping or equipment.

Fittings are specified or identified by:

Nominal pipe size or tube size that the fitting is manufactured to fit.

- Type or description of thc fitting. For example, tees, wyes, elbows, crosses, couplings, etc.
- Joining or connecting method of the fitting. For example, threaded, soldered, welded, etc.

- Material that the fitting is manufactured from. For example, copper, cast iron, steel, plastic, etc.
- Pressure temperature rating or class designation.

Example: 2" class 3000 carbon steel (ASTM 105) threaded straight tee.

Elbows

Fittings that change direction in a piping system are generally referred to as elbows. Elbows are designated or described by the amount of directional change they make in a piping system.

This directional change is given in degrees or fractions of a circle. Most elbows use degree designations, such as: 22½, 45, 60, or 90 degrees for classifying their change of direction. See illustration #314 for elbow directional change classifications.

Elbows are designated by the angle or degree of change they make relative to a circle. Angles for elbows range from 11¼ through 180 degrees.

Cast iron soil fittings on the other hand, are referred to in fractions of a circle, such as: 1/4 bend, 1/8 bend and 1/16 bend etc.

Cast iron bend designations are determined by dividing the elbow fitting angle by 360° (degrees in a circle). Cast iron designations are expressed as a fraction.

Example for cast iron:

$$\text{Bend} = \frac{\text{Elbow Fitting Angle}}{360^\circ}$$

$$\text{Bend} = \frac{45^\circ}{360^\circ} = 1/8$$

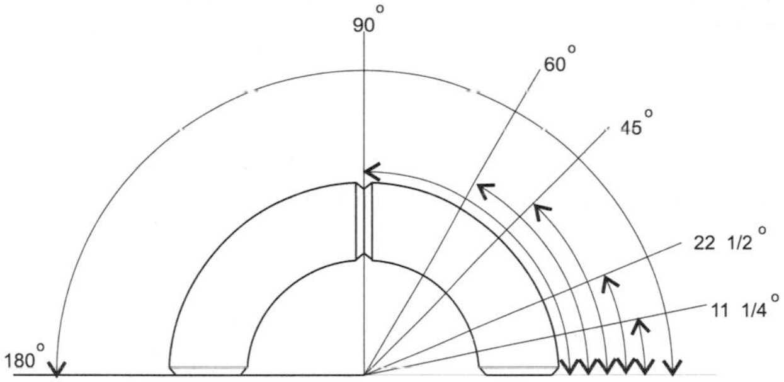
90°
60°
45°
22 1/2°
11 1/4°
180°

Illustration #314 - Elbow Fitting Angles

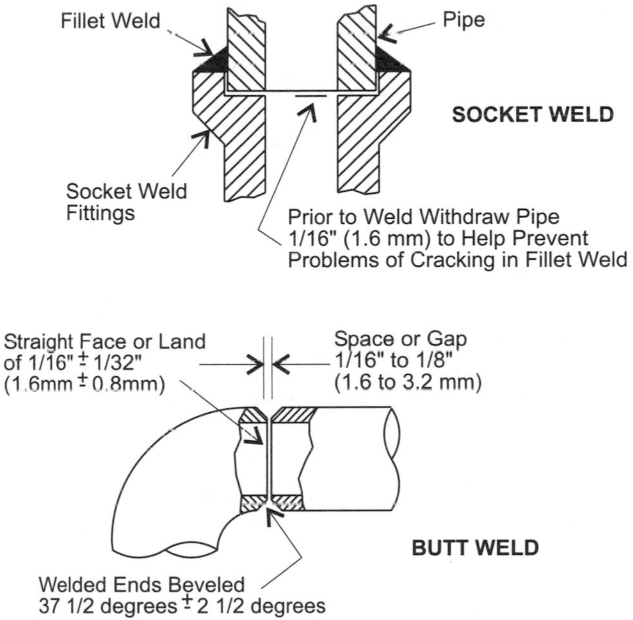
Fillet Weld
Pipe
SOCKET WELD
Socket Weld Fittings
Prior to Weld Withdraw Pipe 1/16" (1.6 mm) to Help Prevent Problems of Cracking in Fillet Weld
Straight Face or Land of 1/16" ± 1/32" (1.6mm ± 0.8mm)
Space or Gap 1/16" to 1/8" (1.6 to 3.2 mm)
BUTT WELD
Welded Ends Beveled 37 1/2 degrees ± 2 1/2 degrees

Illustration #315 - Typical Socket & Butt Weld Fittings

Welded Fittings

Fittings are available for welded joints in either socket welded style or butt welded style. Typical cross sections of both socket and butt welded joints are displayed in illustration #315.

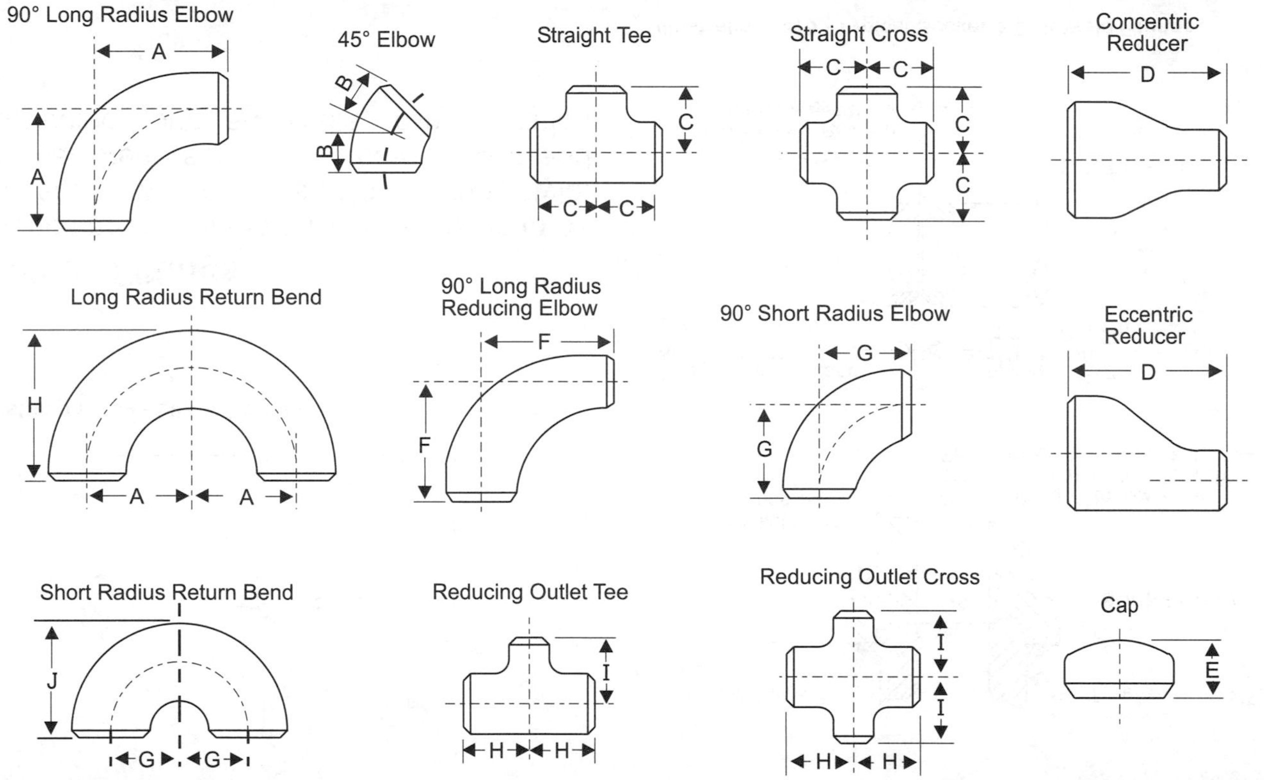
90° Long Radius Elbow
A
A
45° Elbow
B
B
Straight Tee
C
C
C
Straight Cross
C
C
C
C
Concentric
Reducer
D
Long Radius Return Bend
H
A
A
90° Long Radius
Reducing Elbow
F
F
90° Short Radius Elbow
G
G
Eccentric
Reducer
D
Short Radius Return Bend
J
G
G
Reducing Outlet Tee
I
H
H
Reducing Outlet Cross
I
I
H
H
Cap
E

Illustration #316 - Butt Weld Fittings

DIMENSIONS FOR BUTT WELD FITTING - INCHES

Nom. Pipe Size	A	B	C	D	E	F	G	H	J
1/2	1.50	0.62	1.00	-	1.00	-	-	1.88	-
3/4	1.12	0.44	1.12	1.50	1.00	-	-	1.69	-
1	1.50	0.88	1.50	2.00	1.50	-	1.00	2.19	1.62
1 1/4	1.88	1.00	1.88	2.00	1.50	-	1.25	2.75	2.06
1 1/2	2.25	1.12	2.25	2.50	1.50	-	1.50	3.25	2.44
2	3.00	1.38	2.50	3.00	1.50	3.00	2.00	4.19	3.19
2 1/2	3.75	1.75	3.00	3.50	1.50	3.75	2.50	5.19	3.94
3	4.50	2.00	3.38	3.50	2.00	4.50	3.00	6.25	4.75
3 1/2	5.25	2.25	3.75	4.00	2.50	5.25	3.50	7.25	5.50
4	6.00	2.50	4.12	4.00	2.50	6.00	4.00	8.25	6.25
5	7.50	3.12	4.88	5.00	3.00	7.50	5.00	10.31	7.75
6	9.00	3.75	5.62	5.50	3.50	9.00	6.00	12.31	9.31
8	12.00	5.00	7.00	6.00	4.00	12.00	8.00	16.31	12.31
10	15.00	6.25	8.50	7.00	5.00	15.00	10.00	20.38	15.38
12	18.00	7.50	10.00	8.00	6.00	18.00	12.00	24.38	18.38
14	21.00	8.75	11.00	13.00	6.50	21.00	14.00	28.00	21.00
16	24.00	10.00	12.00	14.00	7.00	24.00	16.00	32.00	24.00
18	27.00	11.25	13.50	15.00	8.00	27.00	18.00	36.00	27.00
20	30.00	12.50	15.00	20.00	9.00	30.00	20.00	40.00	30.00
22	33.00	13.50	16.50	20.00	10.00	-	22.00	44.00	-
24	36.00	15.00	17.00	20.00	10.50	36.00	24.00	48.00	36.00
26	39.00	16.00	19.50	24.00	10.50	-	-	-	-
28	42.00	17.25	20.50	24.00	10.50	-	-	-	-
30	45.00	18.50	22.00	24.00	10.50	-	-	-	-
32	48.00	19.75	23.50	24.00	10.50	-	-	-	-
34	51.00	21.00	25.00	24.00	10.50	-	-	-	-
36	54.00	22.25	26.50	24.00	10.50	-	-	-	-
38	57.00	23.62	28.00	24.00	12.00	-	-	-	-
40	60.00	24.88	29.50	24.00	12.00	-	-	-	-
42	63.00	26.00	30.00	24.00	12.00	-	-	-	-
44	66.00	27.38	32.00	24.00	13.50	-	-	-	-
46	69.00	28.62	33.50	28.00	13.50	-	-	-	-
48	72.00	29.88	35.00	28.00	13.50	-	-	-	-

LEGEND

A = 90° Long Radius Elbow

B = 45° Elbows

C = Tees and Crosses

D = Reducing Couplings Con/Ecc

E = Caps

F = Reducing 90° Elbows

G = Short Radius 90° Elbows

H = Long Radius Return Bends

J = Short Radius Return Bends

DIMENSIONS FOR BUTT WELD FITTING - MILLIMETRES (cont.)									
Nom. Pipe Size	A	B	C	D	E	F	G	H	J
15	38	16	25	-	25	-	-	48	-
20	29	11	29	38	25	-	-	43	-
25	38	22	38	51	38	-	25	56	41
32	48	25	48	51	38	-	32	70	52
40	57	29	57	64	38	-	38	83	62
50	76	35	64	76	38	76	51	106	81
65	95	44	76	89	38	95	64	132	100
80	114	51	86	89	51	114	76	159	121
90	133	57	95	102	64	133	89	184	140
100	152	64	105	102	64	152	102	210	159
125	190	79	124	127	76	190	127	262	197
150	229	95	143	140	89	229	152	313	237
200	305	127	178	152	102	305	203	414	313
250	381	159	216	178	127	381	254	518	391
300	457	190	254	203	152	457	305	619	467
350	533	222	279	330	165	533	356	711	533
400	610	254	305	356	178	610	406	813	610
450	686	286	343	381	203	686	457	914	686
500	762	318	381	508	229	762	508	1016	762
550	838	343	419	508	254	-	559	1118	-
600	914	381	432	508	267	914	610	1119	914
650	991	406	495	610	267	-	-	-	-
700	1067	438	521	610	267	-	-	-	-
750	1143	470	559	610	267	-	-	-	-
800	1219	502	597	610	267	-	-	-	-
850	1295	533	635	610	267	-	-	-	-
900	1372	565	673	610	267	-	-	-	-
950	1448	600	711	610	305	-	-	-	-
1000	1524	632	749	610	305	-	-	-	-
1050	1600	660	762	610	305	-	-	-	-
1100	1676	695	813	610	343	-	-	-	-
1150	1723	727	851	711	343	-	-	-	-
1200	1829	759	889	711	343	-	-	-	-

LEGEND

A = 90° Long Radius Elbow

B = 45° Elbows

C = Tees and Crosses

D = Reducing Coup

E = Caps

F = Reducing 90° Elbows

G = Short Radius 90° Elbows

H = Long Radius Return Bends

J = Short Radius Return Bends

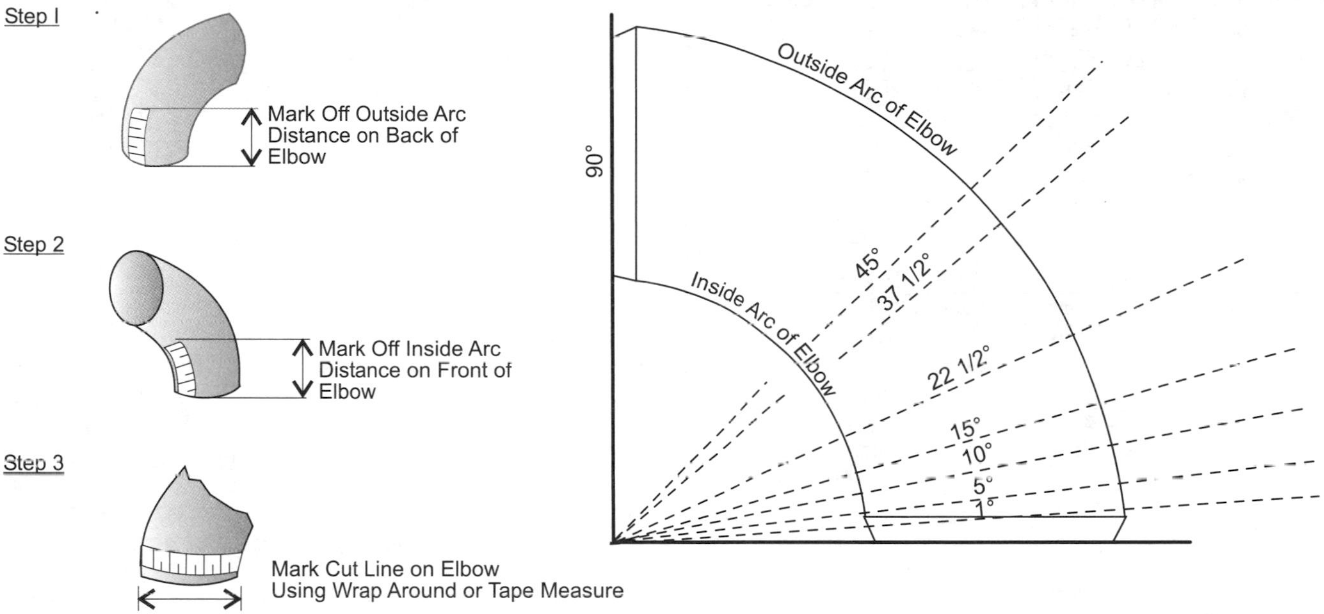
Step I
Mark Off Outside Arc
Distance on Back of
Elbow
Step 2
Mark Off Inside Arc
Distance on Front of
Elbow
Step 3
Mark Cut Line on Elbow
Using Wrap Around or Tape Measure
90°
Outside Arc of Elbow
Inside Arc of Elbow
45°
37 1/2°
22 1/2°
15°
10°
5°
1°

Illustration #317 - Cutting Odd Angle Elbows

ELBOWS FABRICATED FROM 90° L.R. ELBOWS (Inches)														
Nom. Pipe Size	Outside Arc Distance for Required Elbow Degree							Inside Arc Distance for Required Elbow Degree						
	1°	5°	10°	15°	22½°	37½°	45°	1°	5°	10°	15°	22½°	37½°	45°
2	5/64	3/8	23/32	1 3/32	1 21/32	2 3/4	3 9/32	1/32	5/32	5/16	15/32	23/32	1 3/16	1 7/16
2 1/2	3/32	7/16	29/32	1 11/32	2 1/32	3 3/8	4 1/16	3/64	3/16	13/32	19/32	29/32	1 1/2	1 13/16
3	7/64	9/16	1 1/8	1 5/8	2 15/32	4 3/32	4 29/32	3/64	1/4	1/2	23/32	1	1 13/16	2 5/32
3 1/2	1/8	5/8	1 9/32	1 29/32	2 27/32	4 3/4	5 11/16	1/16	9/32	9/16	27/32	1 9/32	2 1/8	2 9/16
4	9/64	23/32	1 7/16	2 5/32	3 1/4	5 13/32	6 15/16	1/16	5/16	21/32	31/32	1 15/32	2 7/16	2 15/16
5	3/16	29/32	1 25/32	2 11/16	4 1/32	6 23/32	8 1/16	5/64	13/32	13/16	1 1/4	1 27/32	3 3/32	3 23/32
6	7/32	1 1/16	2 5/32	3 7/32	4 27/32	8 1/16	9 21/32	3/32	1/2	1	1 1/2	2 7/32	3 23/32	4 15/32
8	9/32	1 7/16	2 27/32	4 9/32	6 13/32	10 11/16	12 13/16	1/8	11/16	1 11/32	2	3 1/32	5 1/32	6 1/32
10	11/32	1 25/32	3 9/16	5 11/32	8	13 11/32	16	5/32	27/32	1 11/16	2 17/32	3 25/32	6 5/16	7 9/16
12	7/16	2 1/8	4 1/4	6 3/8	9 9/16	15 31/32	19 5/32	7/32	1	2 1/32	3 1/16	4 9/16	7 19/32	9 1/8
14	1/2	2 7/16	4 7/8	7 5/16	11	18 5/16	22	1/4	1 7/32	2 7/16	3 21/32	5 1/2	9 5/32	11
16	9/16	2 13/16	5 19/32	8 3/8	12 9/16	20 15/16	25 1/8	9/32	1 13/32	2 13/16	4 3/16	6 9/32	10 15/32	12 5/8
18	5/8	3 1/8	6 9/32	9 7/16	14 1/8	23 9/16	28 9/32	5/16	1 9/16	3 1/8	4 23/32	7 1/16	11 25/32	14 1/8
20	11/16	3 1/2	7	10 15/32	15 23/32	26 3/16	31 13/32	11/32	1 3/4	3 1/2	5 1/4	7 27/32	13 3/32	15 11/16
22	3/4	3 27/32	7 11/16	11 17/32	17 9/32	28 13/16	34 9/16	3/8	1 29/32	3 27/32	5 3/4	8 5/8	14 3/8	17 9/32
24	27/32	4 3/16	8 3/8	12 9/16	18 27/32	31 13/32	37 11/16	13/32	2 3/32	4 3/16	6 9/32	9 7/16	15 11/16	18 27/32
26	29/32	4 17/32	9 3/32	13 5/8	20 13/32	34 1/32	40 27/32	15/32	2 9/32	4 17/32	6 13/16	10 7/32	17 1/32	20 13/32
30	1 1/32	5 1/4	10 15/32	15 3/4	23 9/16	39 1/4	47 1/8	17/32	2 5/8	5 1/4	7 5/8	11 25/32	19 5/8	23 9/16
34	1 5/32	5 29/32	11 27/32	17 13/16	26 23/32	44 17/32	53 3/8	19/32	2 31/32	5 29/32	8 29/32	13 3/8	22 9/32	26 11/16
36	1 7/32	6 1/4	12 17/32	18 7/8	28 7/32	47	56 17/32	5/8	2 13/16	6 1/4	9 7/16	14 1/8	23 5/8	28 1/4
42	1 7/16	7 5/16	14 5/8	22	32 31/32	54 31/32	65 15/16	23/32	3 21/32	7 5/16	10 19/32	16 1/2	26 3/8	32 31/32

Table #51 - Elbows Fabricated from 90 Degree L.R. Elbows (Inches)

ELBOWS FABRICATED FROM 90° L.R. ELBOWS (Millimetres)														
Nom. Pipe Size	Outside Arc Distance for Required Elbow Degree							Inside Arc Distance for Required Elbow Degree						
	1°	5°	10°	15°	22½°	37½°	45°	1°	5°	10°	15°	22½°	37½°	45°
50	1.9	9.5	18.3	27.8	42.1	69.9	83.3	0.8	4.0	7.9	11.9	18.3	30.2	36.5
65	2.4	11.1	23.0	34.1	51.6	85.7	103.2	1.2	4.8	9.5	15.1	23.0	38.1	46.0
80	2.8	14.3	28.6	41.3	62.7	104.0	124.6	1.2	6.4	12.7	18.3	27.8	46.0	54.8
90	3.2	15.9	32.5	48.4	72.2	120.7	144.5	1.6	7.1	14.3	21.4	32.5	54.0	65.1
100	3.6	18.3	36.5	54.8	82.6	137.3	164.3	1.6	7.9	16.7	24.6	37.3	61.9	74.6
125	4.8	23.0	45.2	68.3	102.4	170.7	204.8	1.9	10.3	20.6	31.8	46.8	78.6	94.5
150	5.6	27.0	54.8	81.8	123.0	204.8	245.3	2.4	12.7	25.4	38.1	56.4	94.5	113.5
200	7.1	36.5	72.2	108.7	162.7	271.5	325.4	3.2	17.5	34.1	50.8	77.0	127.8	153.2
250	8.7	45.2	90.5	135.7	203.2	338.9	406.4	4.0	21.4	42.9	64.3	96.0	160.3	192.1
300	11.1	54.0	108.0	161.9	242.9	405.6	486.6	5.6	25.4	51.6	77.8	115.9	192.9	231.8
350	12.7	61.9	123.8	185.7	279.4	465.1	558.8	6.4	31.0	61.9	92.9	139.7	232.6	279.4
400	14.3	71.4	142.1	212.7	319.1	531.8	638.2	7.1	35.7	71.4	106.4	159.5	265.9	320.7
450	15.9	79.4	159.5	239.7	358.8	598.5	718.3	7.9	39.7	79.4	119.9	179.4	299.2	358.8
500	17.5	88.9	177.8	265.9	399.3	665.2	797.7	8.7	44.5	88.9	133.4	199.2	332.6	398.5
550	19.1	97.6	195.3	292.9	438.9	731.8	877.9	9.5	48.4	97.6	146.1	219.1	365.1	438.9
600	21.4	106.4	212.7	319.1	478.6	797.7	951.3	10.3	53.2	106.4	159.5	239.7	398.5	478.6
650	23.0	115.1	231.0	346.1	518.3	864.4	1037.4	11.9	57.9	115.1	173.0	259.6	432.6	518.3
750	26.2	133.4	265.9	400.1	598.5	997.0	1197.0	13.5	66.7	133.4	200.0	299.2	498.5	598.5
850	29.4	150.0	300.8	452.4	678.7	1131.1	1355.7	15.1	75.4	150.0	226.2	339.7	565.9	601.7
900	31.0	158.8	318.3	479.4	716.8	1193.8	1435.9	15.9	71.4	158.8	239.7	358.8	600.1	717.6
1050	36.5	185.7	371.5	558.8	837.4	1396.2	1674.8	18.3	92.9	185.7	269.1	419.1	669.9	837.4

Table #52 - Elbows Fabricated from 90 Degree L.R. Elbows (Millimetres)

Pipe and Fitting Representation

Pipe and fittings are shown on drawings and blueprints as either single or double lines, see illustration #318. Because single line pipe drawings are faster to draw, most prints use this method of showing pipe and fittings. Weld joints are indicated with a dot or an X.

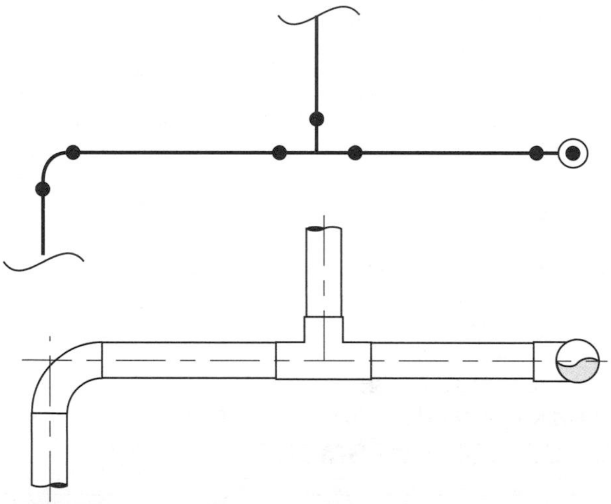

Illustration #318 - Single and Double Line Drawings

Double line pipe drawings are usually only used on pipe sizes over 12 inches (30 mm), and where it is important to show the clearance or relationship between lines and/or equipment.

Line Identification Numbers

Line identification numbers or codes are used in industry to differentiate between the various pipe runs throughout a system. The line number is typically placed beside the line or located directly in the pipe line drawing as shown in illustration #319.

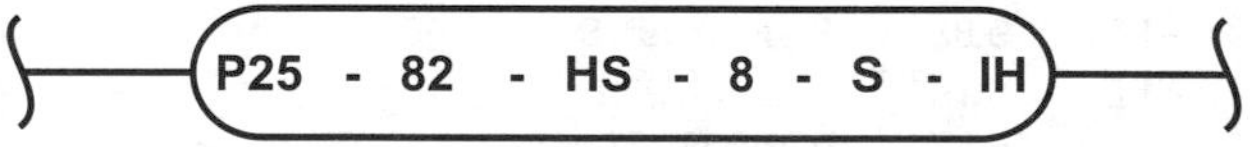
P25 - 82 - HS - 8 - S - IH

Illustration #319 - Pipe Identification Number Symbol

Even though the line identification codes are not standardized, most companies provide the same fundamental information within each line number.

Line Identification Numbers

The following gives an example of the information that may be found in a typical line number:

P25-82-HS-8-S-IH

P25 - sequential number of the line (25th line in process)

82 - denotes the area number of the line (i.e. Area 82 in plant)

HS - represents the medium of conveyed fluid (High Pressure Steam)

8 - line pipe size (8 inch/400 mm)

S - pipe material specification (Standard / Carbon Steel Pipe to API 5L Grade B or A, Flanges to ASTM A181 Grade B)

IH - insulation type (Hot Insulation)

Note: It should be noted that the line number remains with that line, except where the size changes or the line runs through a major piece of equipment. Branch lines taken off the continuous line will have different line numbers regardless of branch size. The sequence of number or letter identification for line specification are determined by the company and vary from one company to another.

Standard Piping Symbols

Standard piping symbols for fittings, valves, and line designations on drawings as a rule correspond to ANSI Z32.23 standard. Commonly used single and double line fittings and valve symbols are shown in illustrations #320 through #324. Companies often modify these symbols, but typically the variations are slight and easily recognized.

Standard Piping Symbols

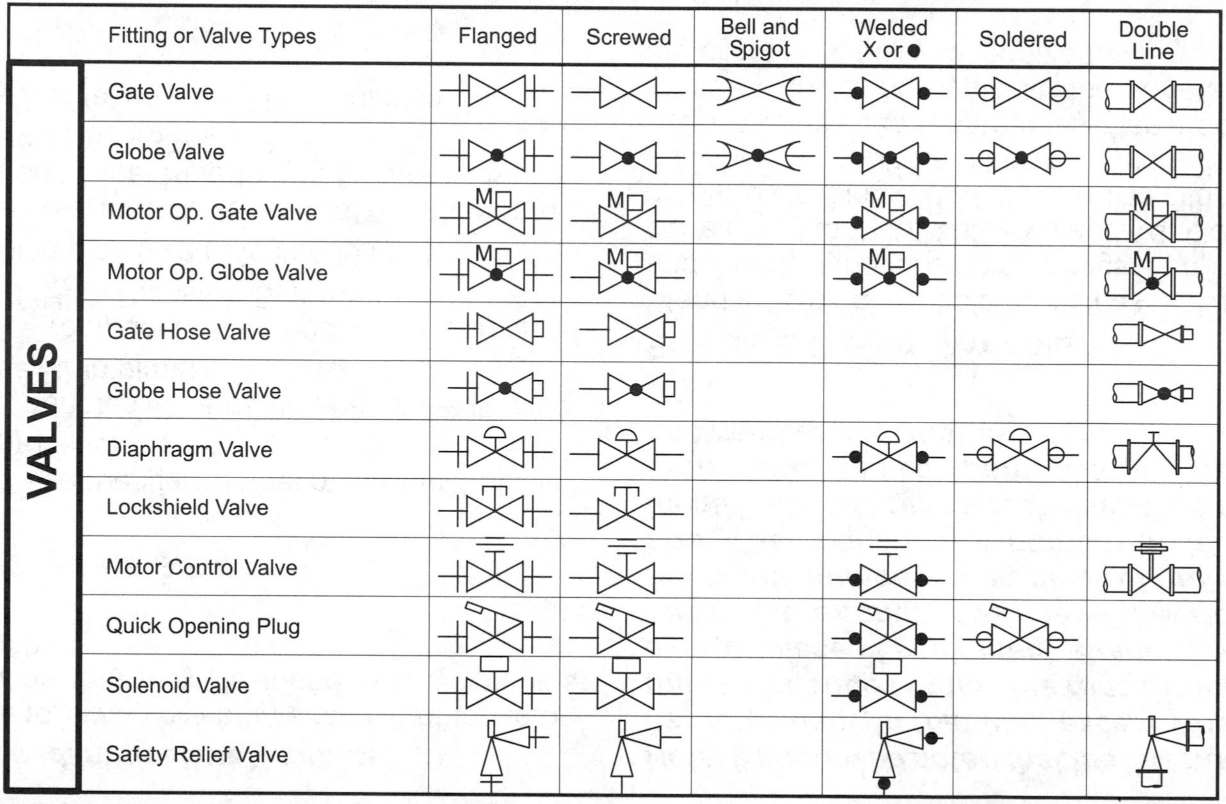

Fitting or Valve Types
Flanged
Screwed
Bell and Spigot
Welded X or ●
Soldered
Double Line
VALVES
Gate Valve
Globe Valve
Motor Op. Gate Valve
Motor Op. Globe Valve
Gate Hose Valve
Globe Hose Valve
Diaphragm Valve
Lockshield Valve
Motor Control Valve
Quick Opening Plug
Solenoid Valve
Safety Relief Valve
M

Illustration #320 - Commonly Used Fitting and Valve Symbols

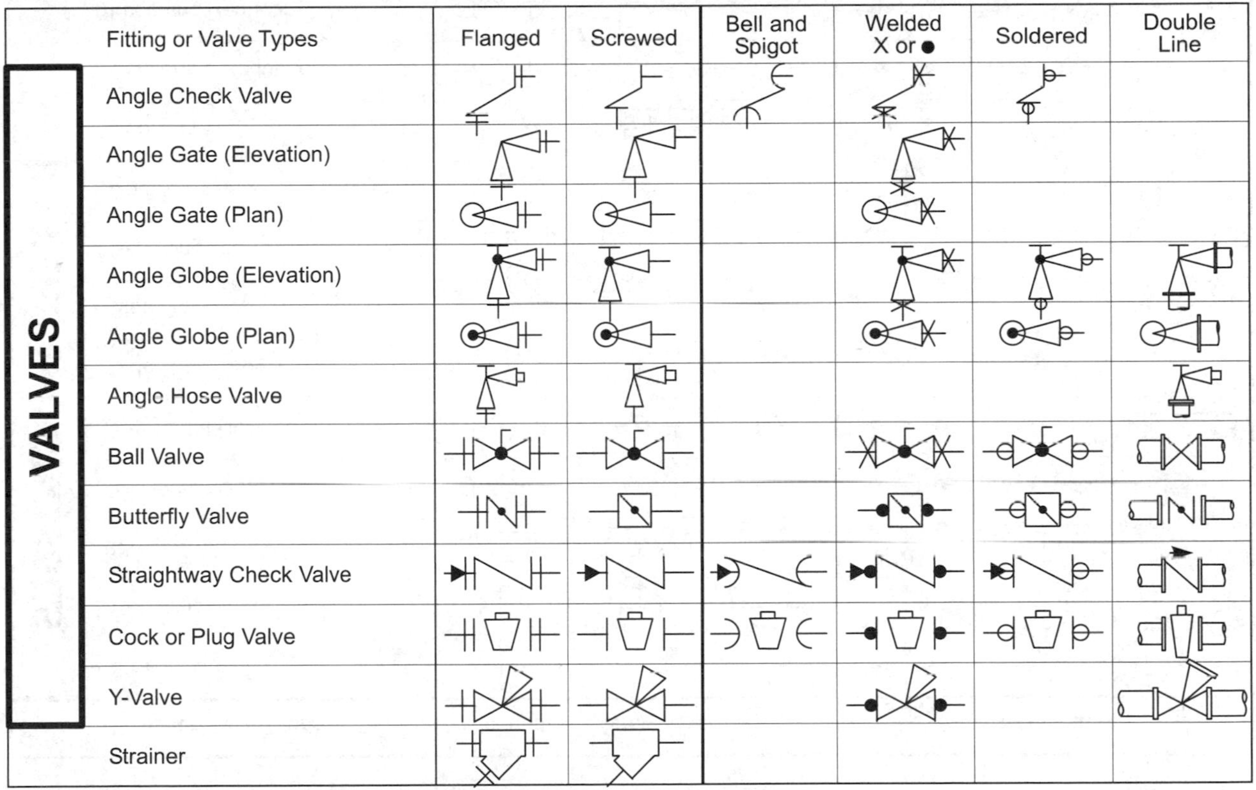
Fitting or Valve Types
Flanged
Screwed
Bell and Spigot
Welded X or ●
Soldered
Double Line
VALVES
Angle Check Valve
Angle Gate (Elevation)
Angle Gate (Plan)
Angle Globe (Elevation)
Angle Globe (Plan)
Angle Hose Valve
Ball Valve
Butterfly Valve
Straightway Check Valve
Cock or Plug Valve
Y-Valve
Strainer

Illustration #321 - Commonly Used Fitting and Valve Symbols

Standard Piping Symbols

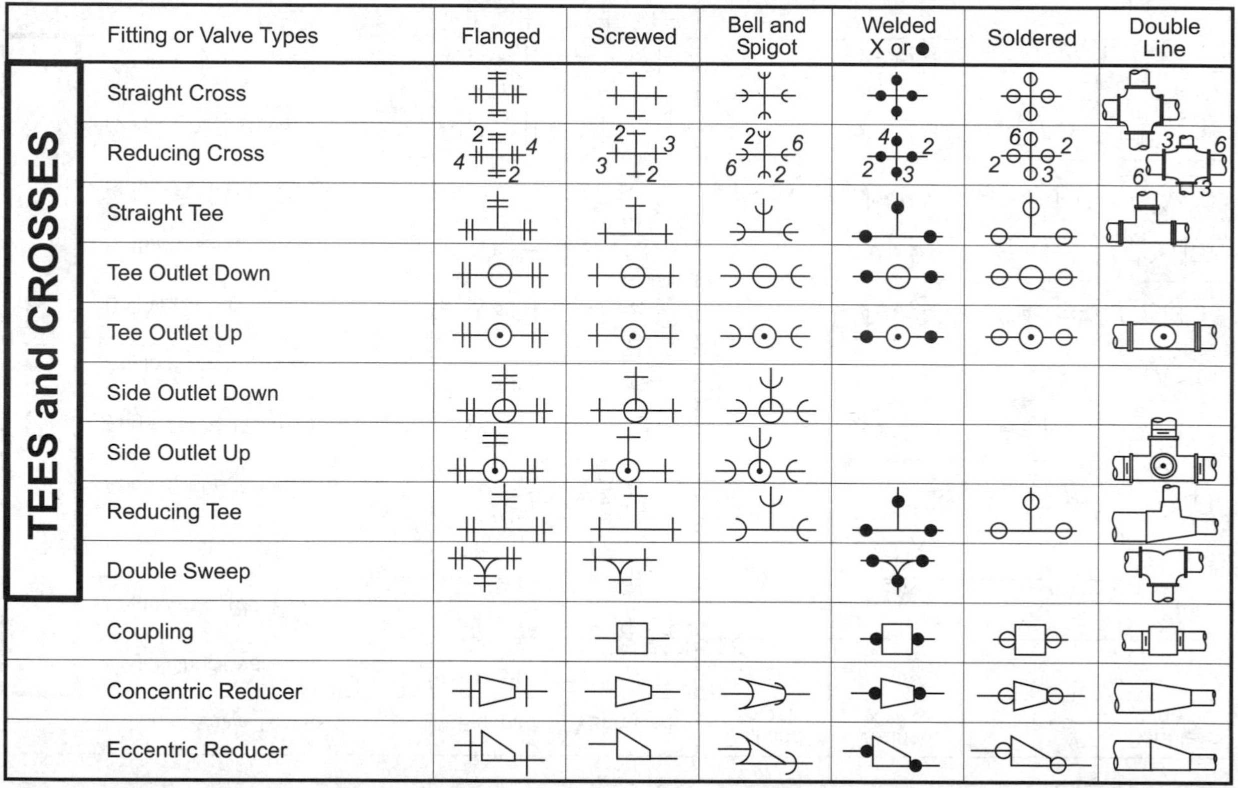
Fitting or Valve Types
Flanged
Screwed
Bell and Spigot
Welded X or ●
Soldered
Double Line
TEES and CROSSES
Straight Cross
Reducing Cross
Straight Tee
Tee Outlet Down
Tee Outlet Up
Side Outlet Down
Side Outlet Up
Reducing Tee
Double Sweep
Coupling
Concentric Reducer
Eccentric Reducer
2 4 4 2
2 3 3 2
2 6 6 2
4 2 2 3
6 2 2 3
3 6 6 3

Illustration #322 - Commonly Used Fitting and Valve Symbols

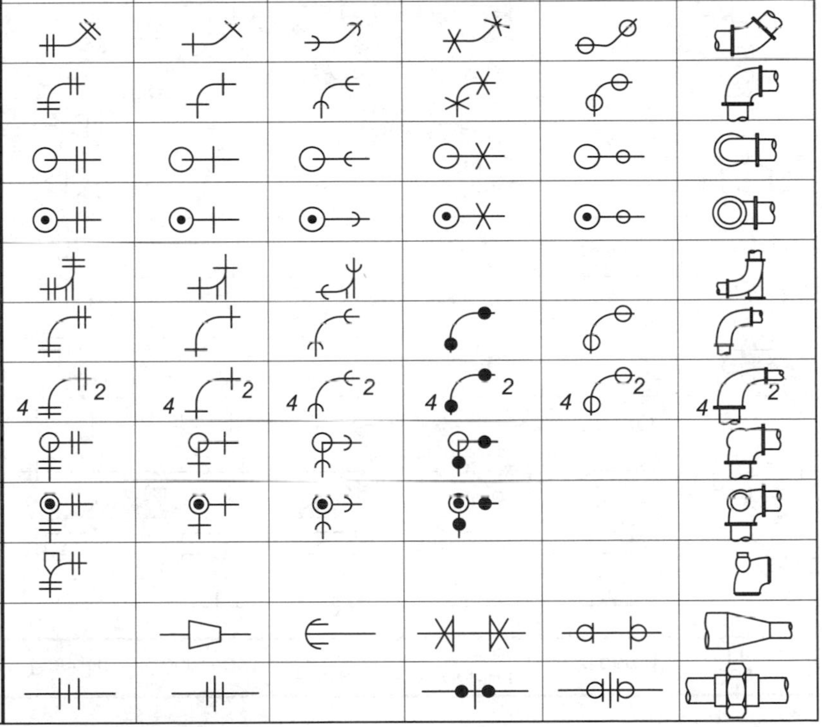

	Fitting or Valve Types	Flanged	Screwed	Bell and Spigot	Welded X or ●	Soldered	Double Line
ELBOWS	45° Elbow						
	90° Elbow						
	Elbow Turned Down						
	Elbow Turned Up						
	Base Elbow						
	Long Radius Elbow						
	Reducing Elbow	4 2	4 2	4 2	4 2	4 2	4 2
	Side Outlet (Turned Down)						
	Side Outlet (Turned Up)						
	Elbowlet						
	Bushing						
	Union						

Illustration #323 - Commonly Used Fitting and Valve Symbols

Standard Piping Symbols

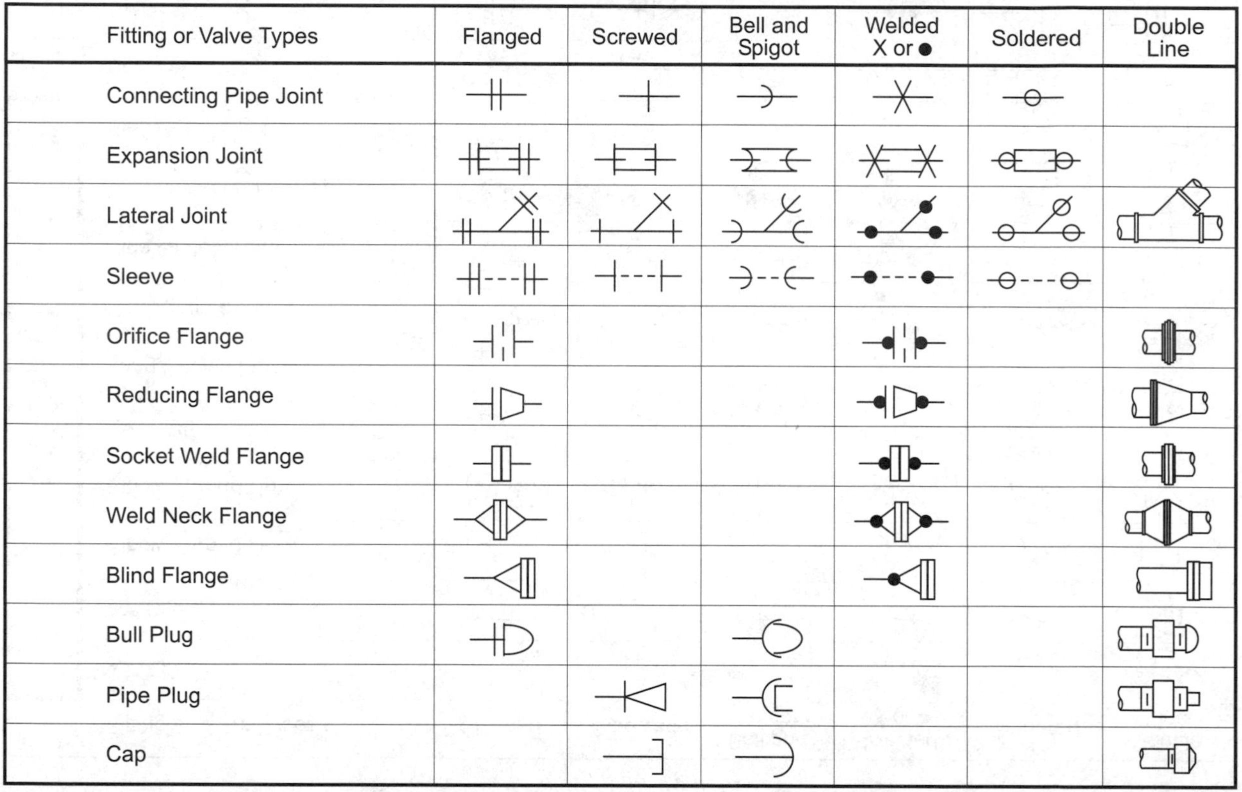
Fitting or Valve Types
Flanged
Screwed
Bell and Spigot
Welded X or ●
Soldered
Double Line
Connecting Pipe Joint
Expansion Joint
Lateral Joint
Sleeve
Orifice Flange
Reducing Flange
Socket Weld Flange
Weld Neck Flange
Blind Flange
Bull Plug
Pipe Plug
Cap

Illustration #324 - Commonly Used Fitting and Valve Symbols

Notes and Specifications

Any information that is not easily interpreted from a drawing or blueprint is usually noted for recognition. Piping notes can be classified as either general or local.

General notes, when used, apply to the entire drawing and are normally placed close to the edge of the drawing or near the title block. Local or specific notes take priority over general notes and convey precise information about one part or area of the drawing. Items such as reducer sizes and valve types are locally noted or called out by size and, in the case of valves, given a number to represent a specific type. Examples of a common local note and callout are presented in Illustration #325.

Specification or Specs, as they are often referred to, are the written guide lines or project standards to which the job is to be constructed.

Pipe material specifications deal with the requirements for pipe, valves, fittings, flanges, and gaskets which are not normally found on the piping drawing. Specifications for a particular project are found in the project standards or project specification book.

Most notes use abbreviations extensively to save time and space in preparing the drawing.

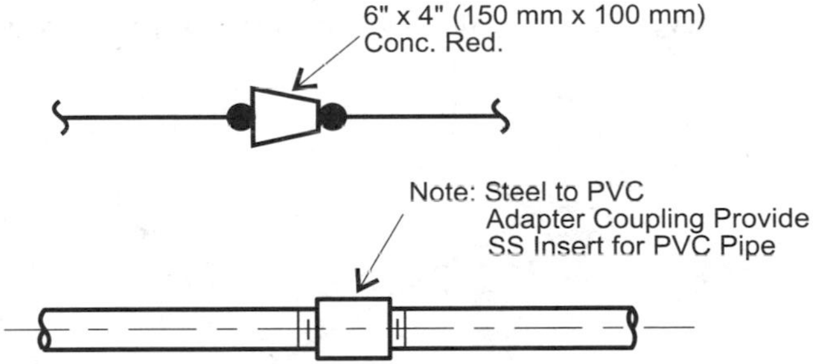
6" x 4" (150 mm x 100 mm)
Conc. Red.
Note: Steel to PVC
Adapter Coupling Provide
SS Insert for PVC Pipe

On spool sheet drawings designated callout numbers are often used for common items.

Illustration #325 - Typical Local Note and Callout Information Found on Blueprints

Isometric or Iso Drawings

The most used pictorial drawing in the piping industry is the isometric projection. The major advantage of an isometric drawing is that three sides of the object are displayed in one practical easy-to-read view. This ease of interpreting an isometric drawing as compared to an orthographic drawing is shown in illustration #326 and #327.

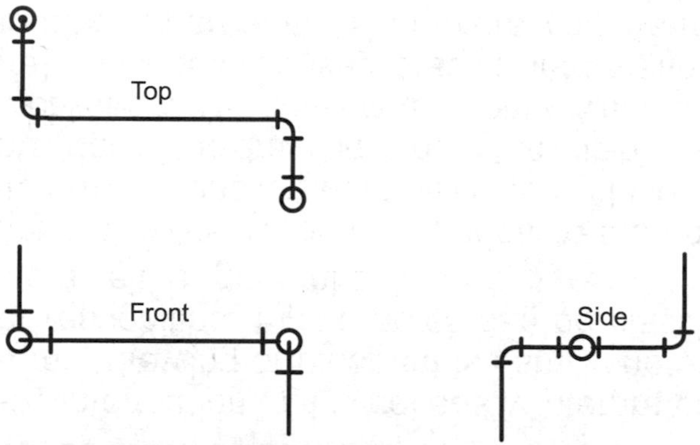
Top
Front
Side

Illustration #326 - Orthographic Piping Projection

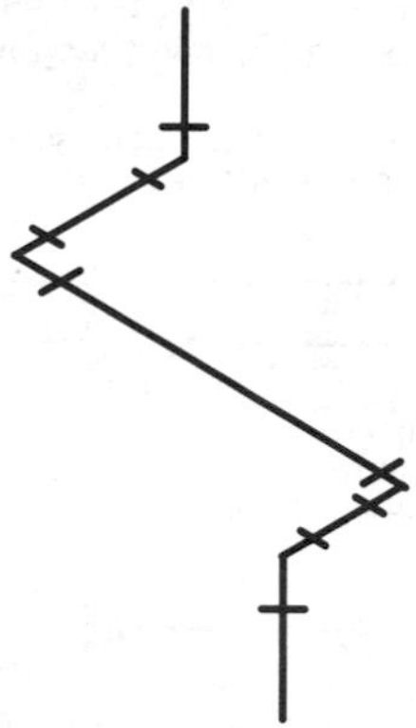

Illustration #327 - Isometric Drawing of the Same System

Some companies use isometric projection as their major piping working print, but because of the complexity involved in drawing overlapping multiple pipe runs, it is often only used for fabrications and detail piping work.

Isometric drawing construction uses three axis that are equally spaced at 120 degrees form each other. All horizontal lines are drawn at angles of 30 degrees, while all vertical lines remain vertical, see illustration #328.

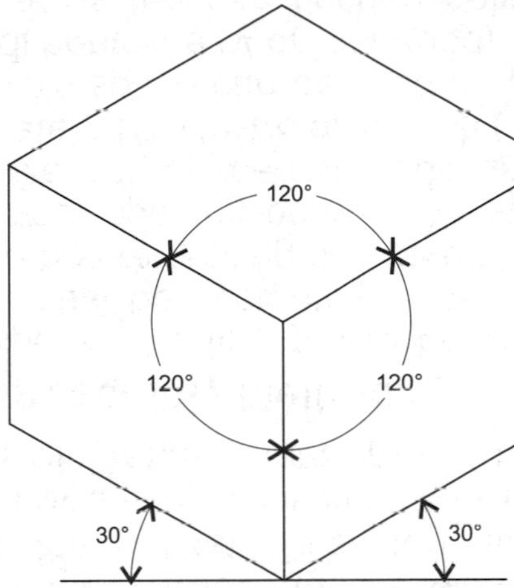
120°
120°
120°
30°
30°

Illustration #328 - Isometric Lines and Axes

Isometric or Iso Drawings

In piping systems, not all lines run at right angles to each other. When diagonal lines are needed on isometric drawings, they are shown by framing the diagonal line. The frame is represented by an isometric square or rectangle in the same plane as the offset, shown in illustration #329.

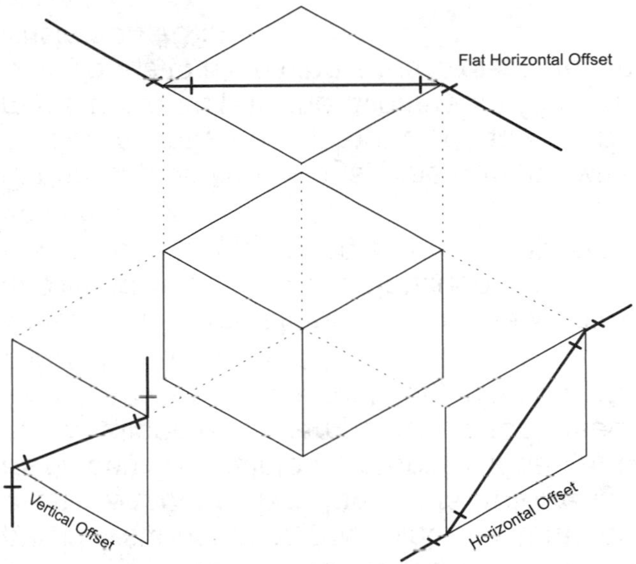
Flat Horizontal Offset
Vertical Offset
Horizontal Offset

Illustration #329 - Isometric Lines and Axes

Isometric Dimensions

Dimensions on isometric drawings are normally indicated and should not be scaled from the drawing.

When drawing isometric piping, the tendency is to give priority to indicating and positioning fittings and valves for clarity rather than to scale. The dimensions given are center-to-center for most fittings and face-to-face for flanges and valves.

Hash marks or parallel extension lines used inside dimension lines on flanges and valves indicate that the face-to-face dimension includes the gasket dimension. Illustration #330 shows a typical isometric drawing and the basic information that may be found on it.

Joint Assembly Methods

The pipe and/or fitting(s) to be welded together must be accurately assembled and gapped before tacking can take place. Gap or the root opening between the two ends must be evenly spaced with a distance of approximately 1/16 to 1/8 of an inch (1.6 to 3.2 mm). This space can be fixed by placing a piece of bent wire (V or U shaped) the same diameter as the gap needed between the ends to be joined.

Note: Joint preparation should include cleaning joint ends of any substance such as oil, grease, rust, paint, or scale that may interfere with the welding process.

Not only must the gap between the beveled ends be maintained, but both the inside and outside surfaces of the joint must match evenly without high or low spots (referred to as hi-low). To maintain proper joint gap and hi-low alignment, clamps are often used. Two types of pipe and fitting clamps are shown in illustration #331.

Proper hi-low and alignment on smaller pipe and fitting sizes can be maintained simply by the use of a piece of angle iron, see illustration #332.

On larger pipe and fittings, pipe with thin wall or pipe slightly out of round, dogs can be made up to help in the alignment of hi-low. Using dogs to align pipe ends is displayed in illustration #333.

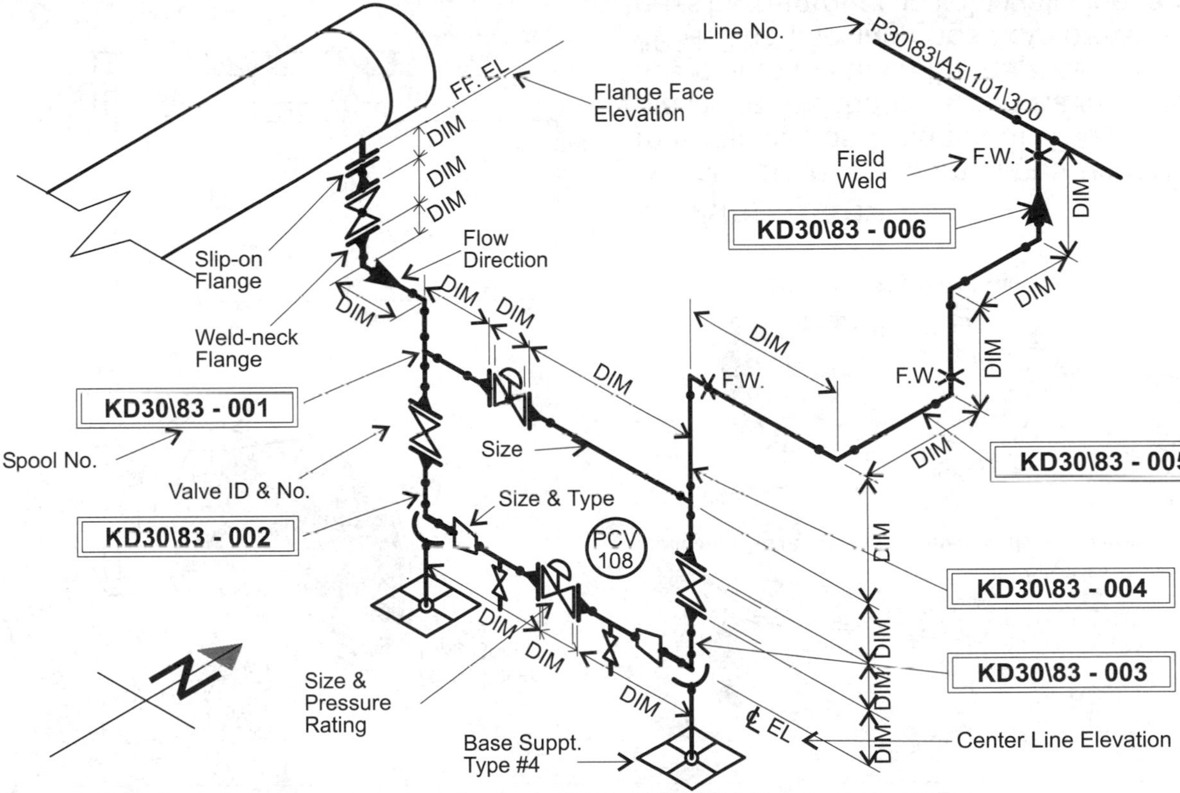
Line No.
P30\83\A5\101\300
FF. EL
Flange Face Elevation
DIM
Field Weld
F.W.
KD30\83 - 006
Slip-on Flange
Flow Direction
Weld-neck Flange
KD30\83 - 001
Spool No.
Valve ID & No.
Size
Size & Type
PCV 108
KD30\83 - 002
KD30\83 - 005
KD30\83 - 004
KD30\83 - 003
Size & Pressure Rating
Base Suppt. Type #4
℄ EL
Center Line Elevation
N

Illustration #330 - Typical Isometric Drawing

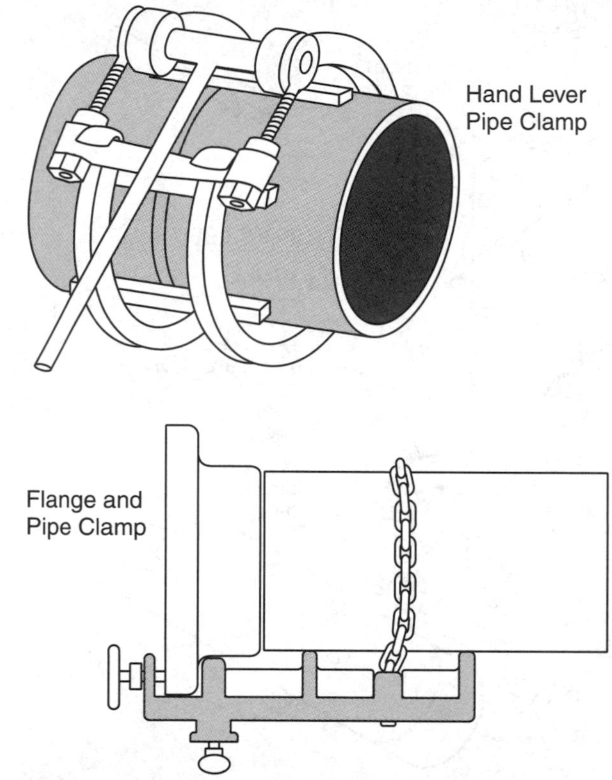
Hand Lever
Pipe Clamp
Flange and
Pipe Clamp

Illustration #331 - Pipe and Fitting Alignment Clamps

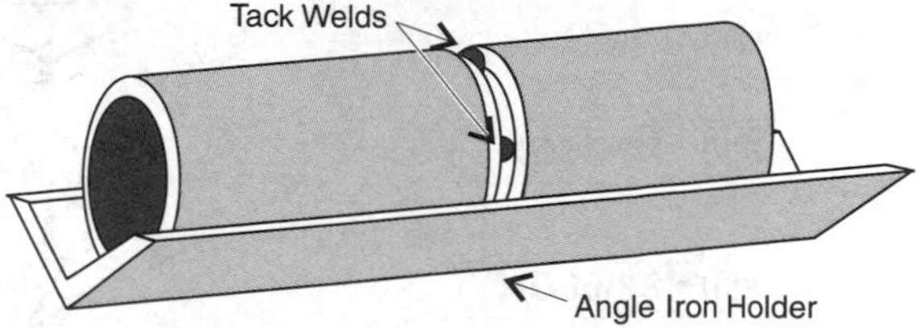
Tack Welds
Angle Iron Holder

Illustration #332 - Pipe Alignment with Angle Iron

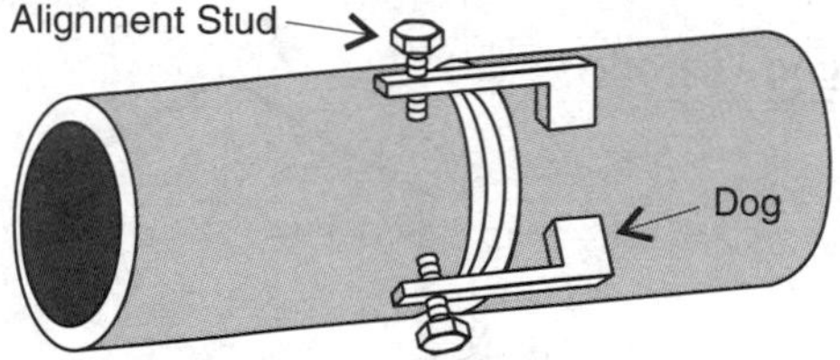
Alignment Stud
Dog

Illustration #333 - Pipe Alignment with Fabricated Dogs

Backing Rings

Backing rings are sometimes used to help maintain gap and alignment. These rings are placed inside the pipe and have nodules in the joint to maintain the gap, see illustration #334. The backing rings help prevent root-pass burn-through in light wall pipe, and prevent slag or spatter from entering the pipe.

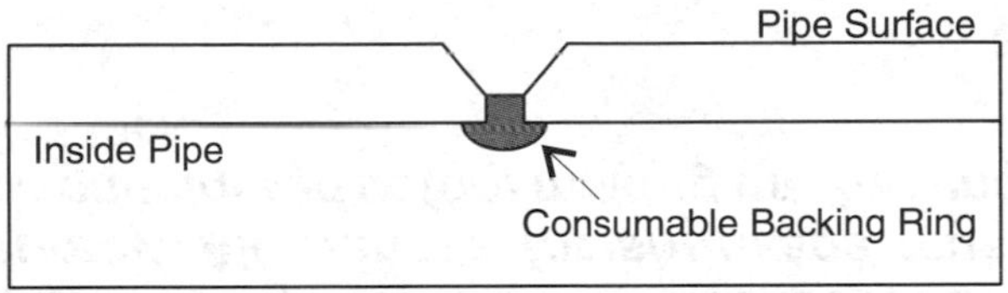
Pipe Surface
Inside Pipe
Consumable Backing Ring

Illustration #334 - Consumable Backing Rings

This ring becomes part of the piping system and may cause flow restriction. Some backing rings are described as consumable and are designed to melt under welding heat. This type of ring is typically used with the gas tungsten arc welding (GTAW) process.

Tacking the Joint

After the pipe and/or fitting(s) are aligned and properly gapped, four tack welds should be evenly spaced around the joint. The tacks maintain the spacing and alignment during the welding of the joint. The length of the tack weld should be approximately three times the pipe wall thickness.

When using a spacer wire, the wire should be removed after the first tack is welded.

The second tack weld is made on the opposite side from the first, 180 degrees opposite.

The third tack is made 90 degrees from either the first or second tack. Adjust the gap until the openings are equalized, or if one side of the root opening is slightly wider, then the third tack weld should be placed there. Any shrinkage in the third tack weld will help to even out the root opening space. The fourth tack weld is placed 180 degrees from the third. Common tack welding locations for pipe and fittings are outlined in illustration #335 & #336.

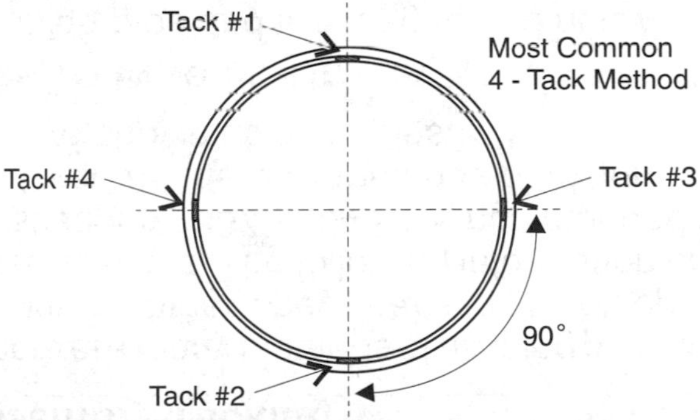
Tack #1
Most Common
4 - Tack Method
Tack #4
Tack #3
90°
Tack #2

Illustration #335 - Four Weld Tacks

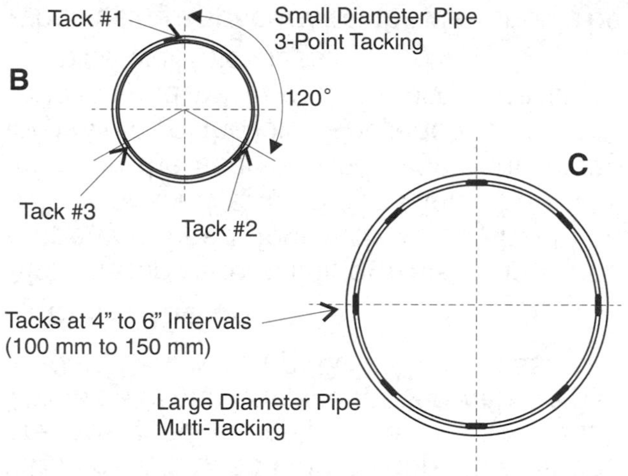
Tack #1
Small Diameter Pipe
3-Point Tacking
B
120°
Tack #3
Tack #2
C
Tacks at 4" to 6" Intervals
(100 mm to 150 mm)
Large Diameter Pipe
Multi-Tacking

Illustration #336 - Three & Multiple Tack Welds

Note: After tacking, the alignment and gap spacing should be re-checked for accuracy. Allowances for shrinkage must be considered before making the 2nd and 3rd tack.

There are many methods of aligning pipe and fittings to other spool parts or to blueprint specifications. The following information and illustrations #337 - #343 are not intended to be taken as the only methods of alignment, but are shown as examples.

Tee To Pipe Fit-Up

1. Align pipe and tee for gap and hi-low.
2. Tack on top.
3. Again align, then open up bottom slightly to allow for shrinkage.
4. Tack on bottom.
5. Check gap on each side, tack widest side first, then opposite side.

Two methods of checking the alignment are shown in illustration #337, one with two squares and the other by a square and tape measure.

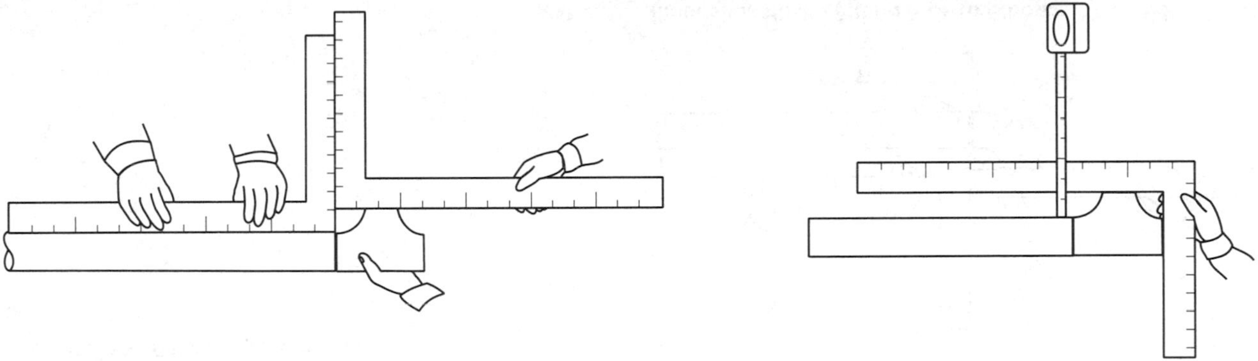

Illustration #337 - Fitting Pipe to Tee

Two Square Method of Pipe Alignment

1. Butt joint together with proper gap.
2. Align for straightness and hi-low at the joint.
3. Tack on one side.
4. On the side opposite the tack, again align pipe for straightness, then open the joint slightly to allow for shrinkage, then tack.
5. Roll pipe one quarter turn, check for straightness, open one side slightly and tack.
6. Tack opposite side.
7. Tacks should not be over 3/4 (19 mm) of an inch long.

Note: Two squares can be used to check pipe for alignment, see illustration #338.

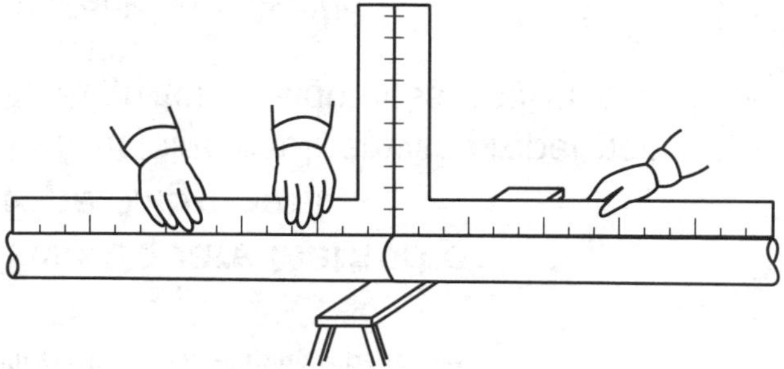

Illustration #338 - Fitting Pipe Sections

90° Elbow Fit-Up

1. Align pipe and elbow for gap and hi-low.
2. Tack on top.
3. Again align, then open up bottom slightly to allow for shrinkage.
4. Tack bottom.
5. Check gap on each side, tack widest side first, then opposite side.

Note: Two squares or a level can be used to check squareness, see illustration #339.

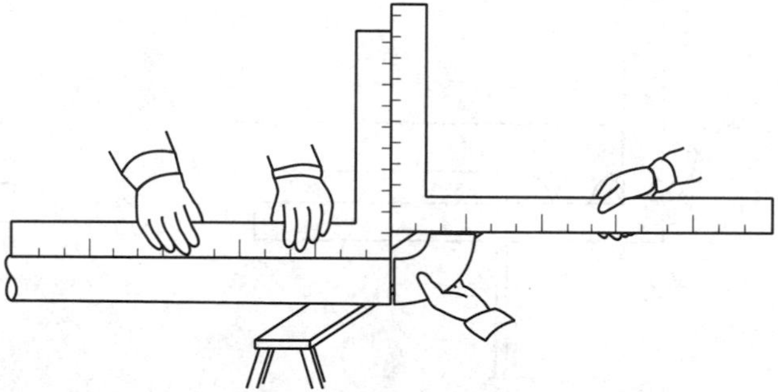

Illustration #339 - Fitting Pipe to Elbow

45° Elbow Fit-Up

The fit-up procedure for a 45° elbow is similar to that of a 90° elbow. Shown in illustration #340 are two methods of checking the alignment, one by squares and the other by spirit level.

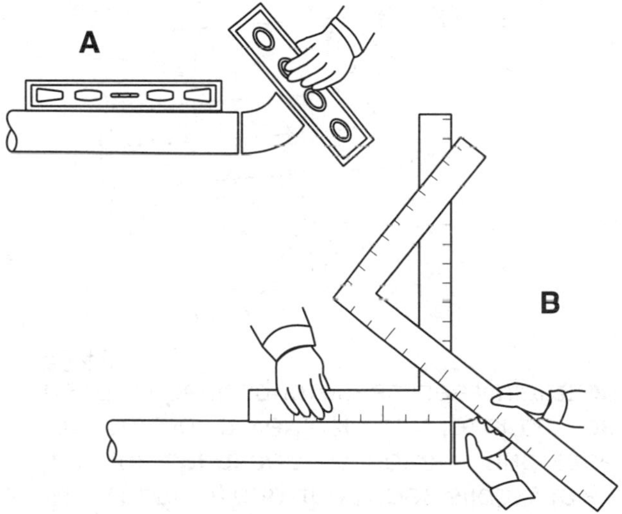
A
B

Illustration #340 - Fitting Pipe to 45 Degree Elbow

Pipe To Flange Fit-Up

1. Butt up flange to pipe. Three things have to be watched at the same time, that is gap, hi-low and level of holes (two-holing the flange), see illustration #341.
2. Tack on top.

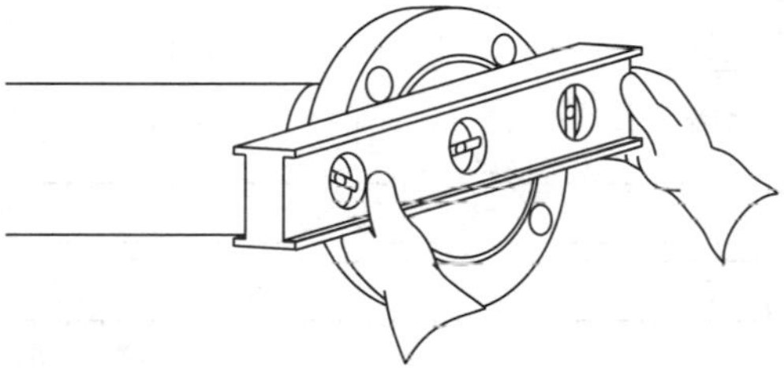

Illustration #341 - Two-Holing Flange

3. Align bottom, gap, then open slightly to allow for shrinkage. A square and tape measure or a vertical spirit level can be used to check squareness, see illustration #342.

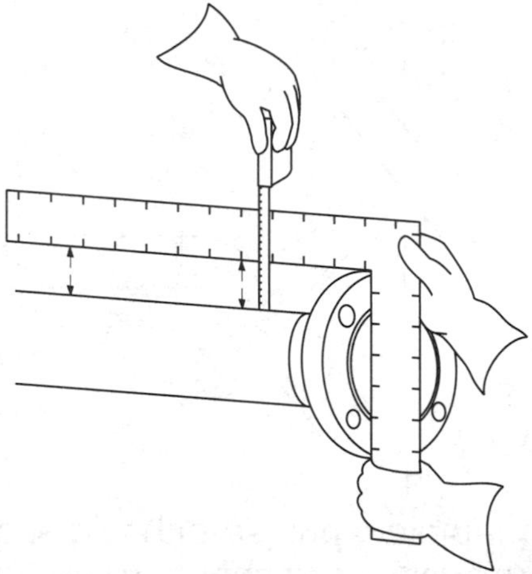

Illustration #342 - Check Alignment of Pipe to Flange

4. Tack bottom.
5. Using a square on the sides, check gap and squareness, then tack both sides.

Small diameter Pipe Jig

A jig made of channel is helpful in aligning small diameter pipe and elbows. Layout a 90" notch on both sides of a channel and cut out to form a "V". Heat, bend to a 90° angle, and weld. See illustration #343.

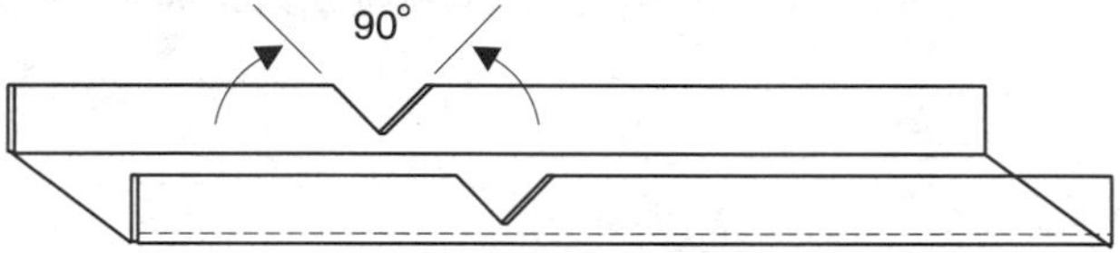
90°

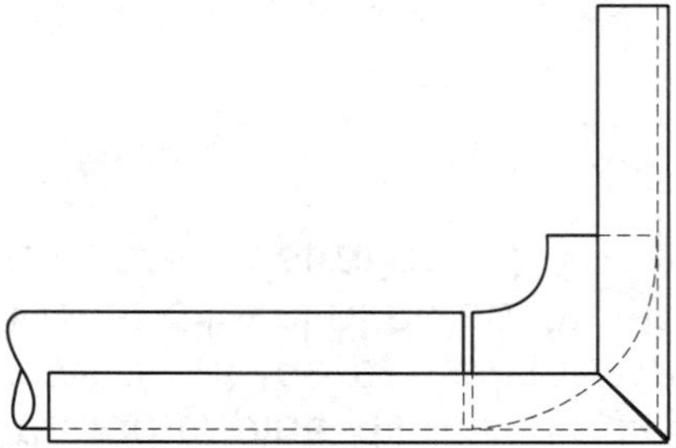

Illustration #343 - Jig for Aligning Elbows

SECTION NINE QUESTIONS
Piping

1. *Determine if the following statement is true or false. Of the three usual pipe grades, A, B, C, grade C is the most commonly used.*
   - ❒ true ❒ false

2. *Which of the following applies to the correct sizing of pipe for any given pipe size?*
   - ❒ O.D. same – I.D. varies
   - ❒ I.D. same – O. D. varies
   - ❒ both may vary
   - ❒ both remain constant

3. *The term "schedule" when referring to pipe means:*
   - ❒ outside diameter
   - ❒ inside diameter
   - ❒ nominal pipe size
   - ❒ wall thickness

4. *An NPS 14 inch pipe has an actual outside diameter of how many inches?*
   - ❒ 14 inches
   - ❒ 14.375 inches
   - ❒ 14.5 inches
   - ❒ depends on schedule

5. *When measuring a 3 inch standard wall pipe, it would measure 3 inches at:*
   - ❒ outside diameter
   - ❒ inside diameter
   - ❒ mean diameter
   - ❒ nominal diameter

6. *Determine if the following statement is true or false. For all pipe sizes up to 10 inches, standard wall pipe has the same wall thickness as schedule 40.*
   - ❒ true ❒ false

7. *Determine if the following statement is true or false. For all pipe sizes up to 20 inches, extra strong pipe has the same wall thickness as schedule 80.*
   - ❒ true ❒ false

8. *The flange type that butt welds to pipe end is called a:*
   - ❒ slip-on flange
   - ❒ butt weld flange
   - ❒ weld neck flange
   - ❒ raised face flange

9. *The flange type that has a fillet weld to a pipe end is called a:*
   - ❒ weld neck flange
   - ❒ slip-on flange
   - ❒ fillet weld flange
   - ❒ raised face flange

10. *What is an advantage of a spectacle blind?*
   - ❒ closes or opens line flow
   - ❒ can be rotated without leaving space
   - ❒ easy to see if line is open or closed
   - ❒ all of the above

11. *Determine if the following statement is true or false. All manufactured flange faces use a typical serrated concentric circle groove finish.*
   - ❒ true ❒ false

12. *What is the nominal pressure rating for a weld-neck flange stamped with the following: 3", 150, A105.*
   - ❒ 3 lbs
   - ❒ 105 lbs
   - ❒ 150 lbs
   - ❒ 300 lbs

13. *What type of gasket will cover the entire flange area with holes punched out for the bolt holes?*
   - ❒ flat ring
   - ❒ full face
   - ❒ metallic ring
   - ❒ all of the above

14. *Selecting the correct wrench size for any given hex head nut (not metric sizes) can be found by using:*
   - ❒ wrench size = 1 1/2 x bolt diameter + 1/8
   - ❒ wrench size = 1 1/2 x bolt diameter + 1/2
   - ❒ wrench size = 2 x bolt diameter + 1/2
   - ❒ wrench size = 2 x bolt diameter + 1/8

15. *Manufactured pipe elbows are available with what degree of turn?*

❒ 90
❒ 45
❒ both a and b
❒ increments of every 5 degrees from 0 to 90

16. *Determine if the following statement is true or false. A fabricated elbow can only be cut in 10 degree increments.*

❒ true ❒ false

17. *What would several dots on a single line piping print indicate?*

❒ flange face to center of fitting
❒ flange face to face
❒ location of welded joints
❒ location of threaded joint

18. *Determine if the following statement is true or false. It is more difficult to interpret a single line isometric than an orthographic projection drawing.*

❒ true ❒ false

19. *Determine if the following statement is true or false. Missing dimensions can be easily and accurately measured from an isometric pipe drawing.*

❒ true ❒ false

20. *Determine if the following statement is true or false. Dimensions between most fittings are shown as "center-to-center".*

❒ true ❒ false

21. *Dimensions between most flanges are shown as:*

❒ center-to-center
❒ face-to-face
❒ I.D. to I.D.
❒ O.D. to O.D.

22. *Determine if the following statement is true or false. When fitting two pipe sections together, it is always best to use a back-up ring as they never cause any flow restriction.*

❒ true ❒ false

23. *Which of the following is a primary consideration when fitting a flange to a pipe in that is non-moveable.*
   - ❐ two-holing flange
   - ❐ pipe to flange hi-low
   - ❐ pipe to flange gap
   - ❐ all of above

SECTION TEN

STRUCTURAL STEEL

Structural Shapes

Structural steel shapes come from the manufacturer's mill in a multitude of sizes, weights and shapes.

The nomenclature of some of the more common shapes are indicated in illustration #344.

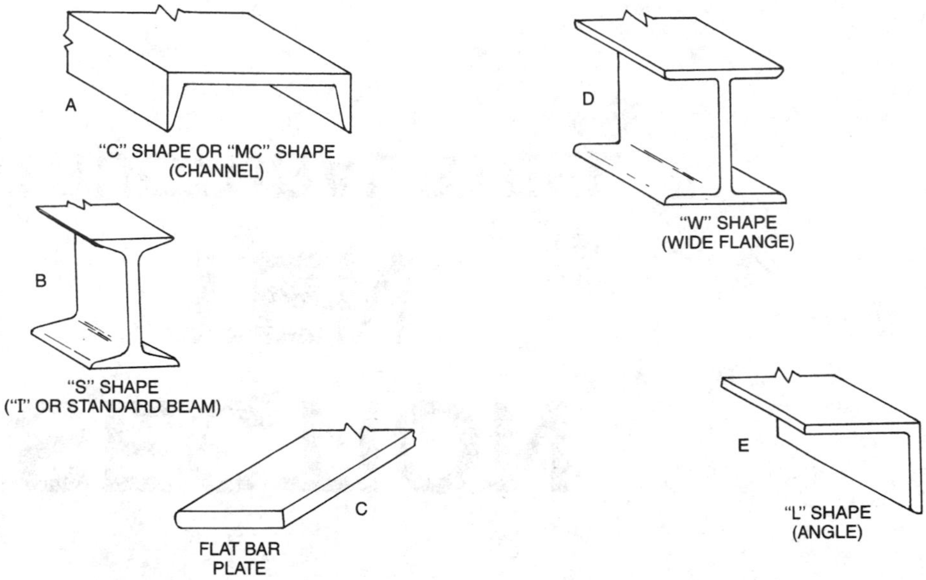
A
"C" SHAPE OR "MC" SHAPE
(CHANNEL)
D
"W" SHAPE
(WIDE FLANGE)
B
"S" SHAPE
("I" OR STANDARD BEAM)
C
FLAT BAR
PLATE
E
"L" SHAPE
(ANGLE)

Illustration #344 - Structural Shapes

Structural Shapes

In the 1970's the designated names of structural steel shapes were changed. However, habits are hard to change and the old names are still used. The new names can be somewhat confusing; for example, columns, wide flange and beams, vs. the new designations of W shape for columns, S shape for beams and M shape for miscellaneous beams and columns.

W columns and W beams are nominal sizes only, not exact measurement. W columns have equal flange and web thickness, W beams unequal flange and web thickness.

M shape is nominal depth. S beam is exact depth and has a tapered flange.

Tees designated as ST, WT and MT are made by cutting, S, W and M shapes in half.

The comparison between the old and new designations are shown on table #53.

OLD NAME	NEW NAME	OLD DESIGNATION	NEW DESIGNATION
Wide flange	W Shape	24 WF 76	W 24 x 76
Light beam	W Shape	14 B 26	W 14 x 26
Standard beam	S Shape	12 I 35.0	S 12 x 35.0
Miscellaneous column	M Shape	4 M 13	M 4 x 13
Junior beam	M Shape	10 Jr. 9.0	M 10 x 9
Standard channel	C Shape	12 [20.7]	C 12 x 20.7
Miscellaneous channel	MC Shape	18 [42.7 or 18 x 4 [42.7	MC 18 x 42.7
Equal leg angle	L Shape	L 6 x 6 x 1 or L 6 x 6 x 1	L 6 x 6 x 1
Unequal leg angle	L Shape	L 8 x 6 x 1 or L 8 x 6 x 1	L 8 x 6 x 1
Bearing pile	HP Shape	12 BP 53	HP 12 x 53
Structural tee cut from wide flange	WT Shape	ST 12 WF 38	WT 12 x 38
Structural tee cut from standard beam	ST Shape	ST 6117.5	ST 6 x 17.5
Structural tee cut from miscellaneous beam	MT Shape	ST 3 M 10	MT 3 x 10
Welded wide flange	Welded Wide Flange	27 WWF 77	WWF 27 x 77

Table #53 - Structural Shape Nomenclature

Dimensions of Shapes

There is a definite sequence to the method used to indicate the type, depth, weight and length of the various shapes. For beams and columns (W, S, M shapes) the first letter is the symbol, followed by the depth in inches, the weight per foot in pounds, finally the overall length, (or depth in millimeters, weight per meter in kilograms and length in millimeters).

Eg: W 14 x 26 x 14'3"

(W 360 x 39 x 4343)

Channel (C shape) will have the symbol, the width, the weight, followed by the length.

Eg: C 12 x 20.7 x 8'9"

(C 310 x 31 x2667)

Structural Symbols

The symbols used to indicate the various types of structural shapes are indicated in illustration #345.

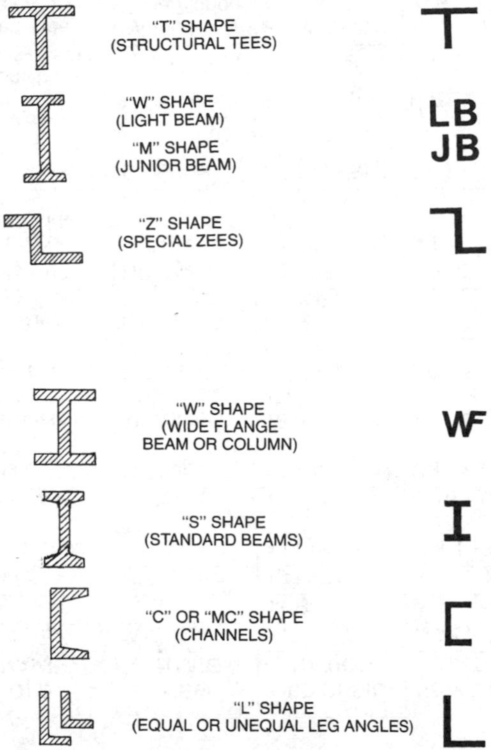
"T" SHAPE
(STRUCTURAL TEES)
T
"W" SHAPE
(LIGHT BEAM)
LB
"M" SHAPE
(JUNIOR BEAM)
JB
"Z" SHAPE
(SPECIAL ZEES)
"W" SHAPE
(WIDE FLANGE
BEAM OR COLUMN)
WF
"S" SHAPE
(STANDARD BEAMS)
I
"C" OR "MC" SHAPE
(CHANNELS)
"L" SHAPE
(EQUAL OR UNEQUAL LEG ANGLES)
L

Illustration #345 - Structural Symbols

Structural Members

Prefabricated members which are used in various types of construction but cannot be obtained from a steel mill are indicated in illustration #346.

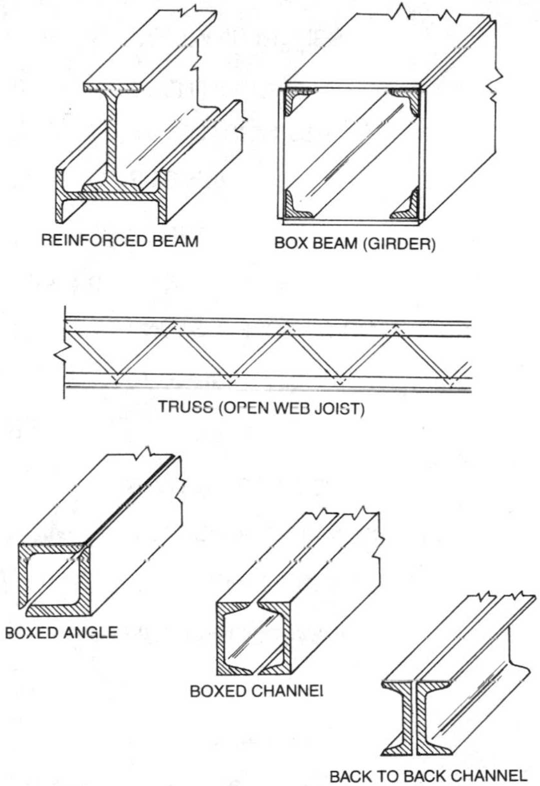
REINFORCED BEAM
BOX BEAM (GIRDER)
TRUSS (OPEN WEB JOIST)
BOXED ANGLE
BOXED CHANNEl
BACK TO BACK CHANNEL

Illustration #346 - Fabricated Structural Members

Common Structural Symbols

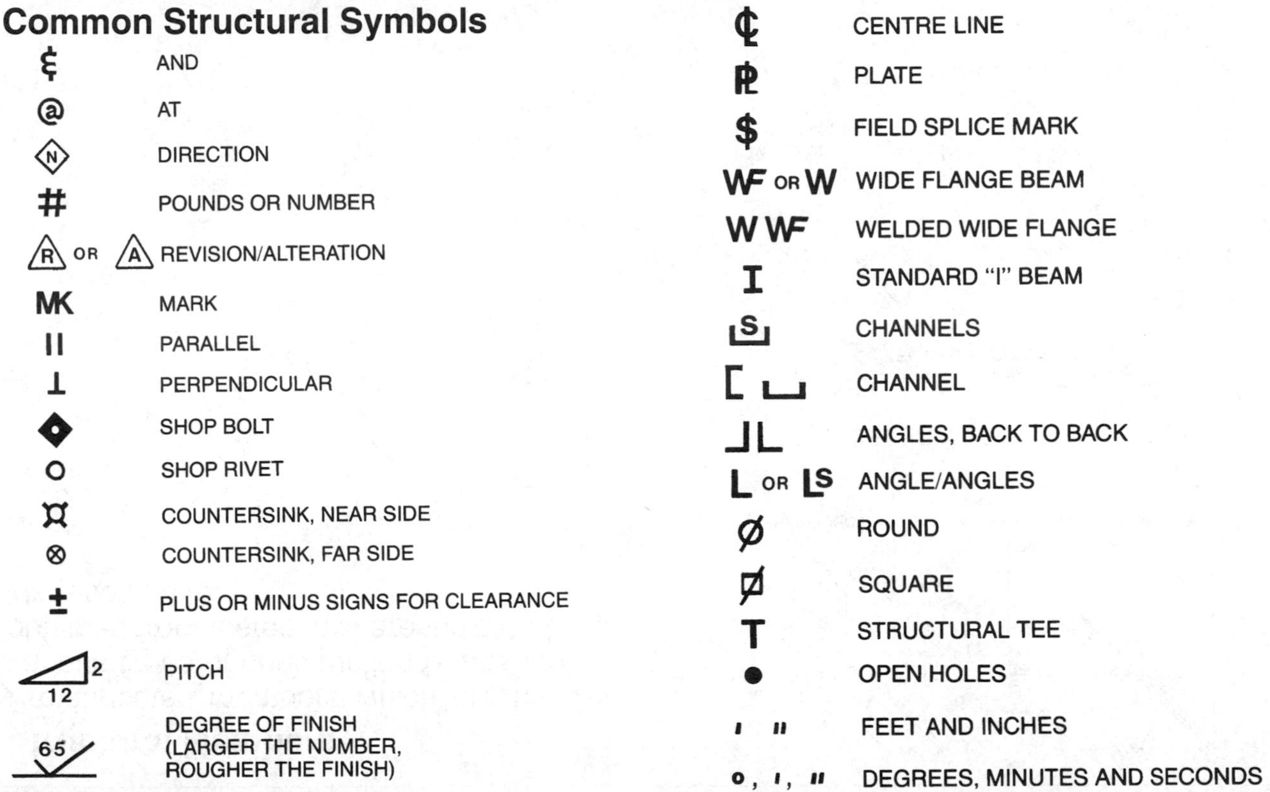

Symbol	Meaning
¢	AND
@	AT
◇N	DIRECTION
#	POUNDS OR NUMBER
R or A	REVISION/ALTERATION
MK	MARK
‖	PARALLEL
⊥	PERPENDICULAR
◆	SHOP BOLT
O	SHOP RIVET
¤	COUNTERSINK, NEAR SIDE
⊗	COUNTERSINK, FAR SIDE
±	PLUS OR MINUS SIGNS FOR CLEARANCE

PITCH

DEGREE OF FINISH (LARGER THE NUMBER, ROUGHER THE FINISH)

Symbol	Meaning
₵	CENTRE LINE
℞	PLATE
$	FIELD SPLICE MARK
WF or W	WIDE FLANGE BEAM
W WF	WELDED WIDE FLANGE
I	STANDARD "I" BEAM
⌊S⌋	CHANNELS
[⌞	CHANNEL
⌐L	ANGLES, BACK TO BACK
L or LS	ANGLE/ANGLES
∅	ROUND
⊘	SQUARE
T	STRUCTURAL TEE
●	OPEN HOLES
' "	FEET AND INCHES
°, ', "	DEGREES, MINUTES AND SECONDS

Illustration #347 - Structural Symbols

Building Nomenclature

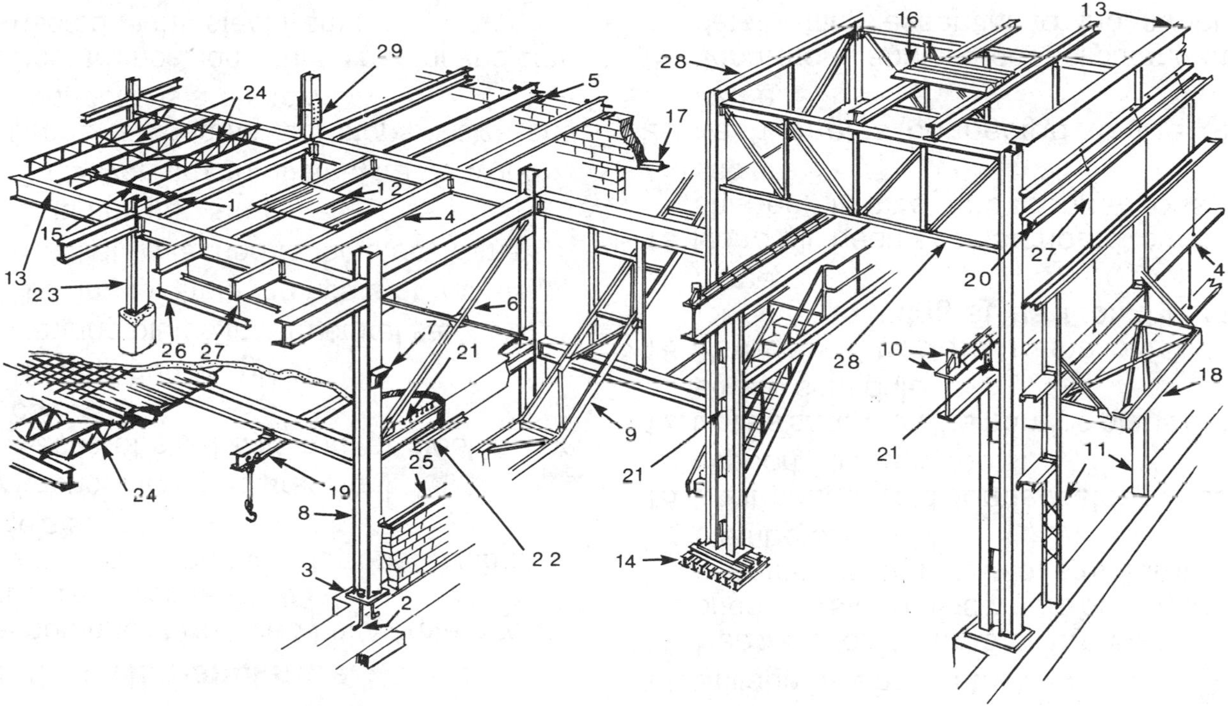
29
24
5
17
28
16
13
12
1
4
15
13
23
6
26
27
7
21
20
27
4
28
10
18
21
9
21
11
24
25
19
8
22
14
3
2

Illustration #348 - Building Nomenclature

Building Nomenclature

The nomenclature listed below refers to the numbers in illustration #348.

1. Anchors or hangers for open web steel joists.
2. Anchors for structural steel.
3. Bases of steel and iron for steel or iron columns.
4. Beams, purlins, girts.
5. Bearing plates for structural steel.
6. Bracing for steel members or frames.
7. Brackets attached to the steel frame.
8. Columns and struts.
9. Conveyor structural steel frame work.
10. Crane rail beams and stops if size and connections are shown.
11. Door frames constituting part of and connected to the steel frame.
12. Floor and roof plates (raised pattern or plain), grating, connecting to steel frame.
13. Girders.
14. Grillage beams of steel.
15. Headers or trimmers for support of openweb steel joists where such headers or trimmers frame into structural steel members.
16. Light-gauge cold formed steel used to support floor and roofs.
17. Lintels shown on the framing plans or otherwise scheduled.
18. Marquees (structural frame only) when forming an integral part of the steel frame.
19. Monorail beams of standard structural shapes, if size and connections are shown.
20. Sash angles connected to the steel frame.
21. Separators, angles, tees, clips and other detail fitting essential to the structural steel frame.
22. Shelf angles.
23. Steel core for composite columns.

24. Steel joists (standardized trusses) openweb steel joists, bracing, and accessories when supplied with steel joists.
25. Steel window sills attached to the steel frame and forming part thereof.
26. Suspended ceiling supports of structural steel shapes 3 inches or greater in depth.
27. Ties, hangers and sag rods forming part of the structural frame.
28. Trusses and brace frames.
29. Rivets and bolts.

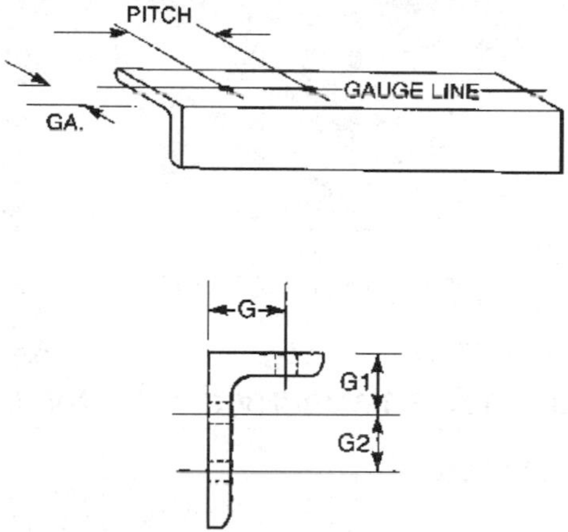
PITCH
GAUGE LINE
GA.
G
G1
G2

Illustration #349 - Gauge and Pitch Lines

Gauge Lines

When bolt holes in structural members are laid out, they are on gauge lines. Gauge is the distance from the line to the heel of an angle, channel or from the centerline of a beam web. The holes are spaced parallel to the length of the member. The pitch is the hole spacing on the gauge line. See tables #54 and #55 for standard gauges.

STANDARD GAUGES FOR ANGLES														
LEG	8	7	6	5	4	$3\frac{1}{2}$	3	$2\frac{1}{2}$	2	$1\frac{3}{4}$	$1\frac{1}{2}$	$1\frac{3}{8}$	$1\frac{1}{4}$	1
G	$4\frac{1}{2}$	4	$3\frac{1}{2}$	3	$2\frac{1}{2}$	$2\frac{1}{4}$	$1\frac{3}{4}$	$1\frac{3}{8}$	$1\frac{1}{8}$	1	$\frac{7}{8}$	$\frac{7}{8}$	$\frac{3}{4}$	$\frac{5}{8}$
G1	3	$2\frac{1}{2}$	$2\frac{1}{4}$	2										
G2	3	3	$2\frac{1}{2}$	$1\frac{3}{4}$										

Table #54 - Gauges for Angles

Standard Gauges

STANDARD I-BEAM FLANGE GAUGES

Depth Weight	Flange Width	Gauge
6" I @ 12.5#	3 3/8"	2"
8" I @ 18.4#	4"	2 1/4"
10" I @ 25.4#	4 5/8"	2 3/4"
12" I @ 31.8#	5"	3"
15" I @ 42.9#	5 1/2"	3 1/2"
18" I @ 54.7#	6"	3 1/2"

STANDARD WF BEAM FLANGE GAUGES

Depth Weight	Flange Width	Gauge
6" I @ 12#	5"	2 1/4"
8" I @ 17#	5 1/4"	2 3/4"
10" I @ 21#	5 3/4"	2 3/4"
12" I @ 27#	6 1/2"	3 1/2"
15" I @ 30#	6 3/4"	3 1/2"
18" I @ 36#	7"	3 1/2"

STANDARD BEAM WEB GAUGES

Beam Depth	Gauge	Clip Length
6"	Center Line	3"
8"	2 1/2" - 3" - 2 1/2"	5 1/2"
10"	3" - 4" - 3"	7"
12"	3" - 3" - 3" - 3"	9"
14"	4" - 3" - 3" - 4"	9"
16"	3 1/2" - 3" - 3" - 3" - 3 1/2"	12"

STANDARD CHANNEL FLANGE GAUGES

Size	Flange	Gauge
4" @ 5.4#	1 5/8"	1"
5" @ 6.7#	1 3/4"	1 1/8"
6" @ 8.2#	1 7/8"	1 1/8"
7" @ 9.8#	2 1/8"	1 1/4"
8" @ 11.5#	2 1/4"	1 3/8"
9" @ 13.4#	2 3/8"	1 3/8"
10" @ 15.3#	2 5/8"	1 1/2"
12" @ 20.7#	3"	1 3/4"
15" @ 33.9#	3 3/8"	2"

STANDARD CHANNEL WEB GAUGES

Size	Gauge	Clip Length
4"	Center Line	2"
5"	Center Line	2 1/2"
6"	1 3/4" - 2 1/2" - 1 3/4"	4 1/2"
7"	2" - 3" - 2"	5"
8"	2 1/4" - 3 1/2" - 2 1/4"	6"
9"	2 1/2" - 4" - 2 1/2"	6 1/2"
10"	2 1/2" - 5" - 2 1/2"	7 1/2"
12"	3" - 3" - 3" - 3"	9"
15"	3" - 3" - 3" - 3" - 3"	12"

Table #55 - Standard Gauges

Beam Gauges and Connections

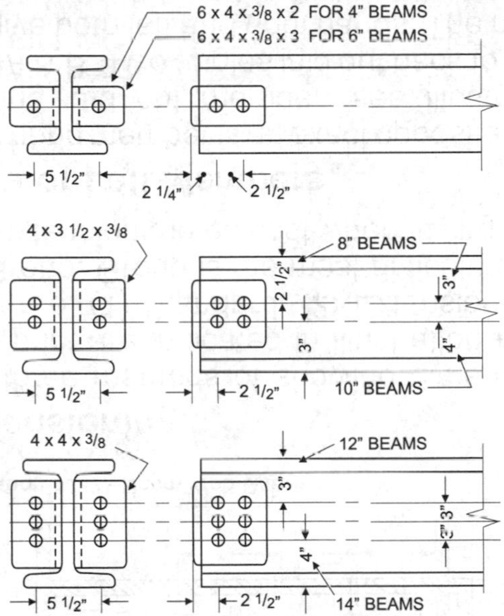
6 x 4 x 3/8 x 2 FOR 4" BEAMS
6 x 4 x 3/8 x 3 FOR 6" BEAMS
5 1/2"
2 1/4"
2 1/2"
4 x 3 1/2 x 3/8
8" BEAMS
2 1/2"
3"
3"
4"
5 1/2"
2 1/2"
10" BEAMS
4 x 4 x 3/8
12" BEAMS
3"
3"
3"
4"
5 1/2"
2 1/2"
14" BEAMS

Illustration #350 - Beam Gauges and Connections

Beam Board

The use of a beam board makes the layout of dimension lines on a beam web much easier. The board can slide on top of a measuring tape and the dimension lines are marked with a soapstone, flange to flange, see illustration #351.

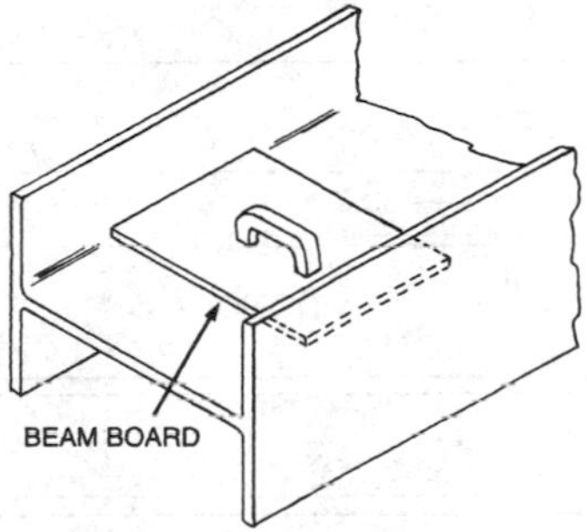
BEAM BOARD

Illustration #351 - Beam Board

Beam Web Gauge

A beam web gauge simplifies the gauging of holes in a web after the beam board has been used to mark the dimension lines. The gauge distances of the web holes are marked on the beam web gauge and then transferred to the dimension line, see illustration #352.

Beam Web Gauge

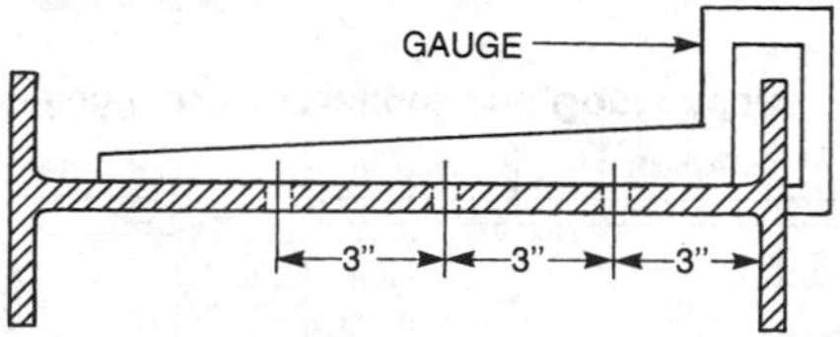
GAUGE
3"
3"
3"

Illustration #352 - Beam Web Gauge

Dimensioning

The three methods of showing dimensions on a print are indicated in illustration #353. They are, (1) Standard, (2) Extension, and (3) Group. Group is the most difficult to use and extension the easiest when laying out.

Right or Left Members

A left hand member is an exact opposite to an existing laid out member, see illustration #354A & B. Two angles laid out back to back will give both left and right hands. The member must be symmetrical about the centerline. A few general rules are:

1. Symmetrically dimensioned angles can be left or right.
2. Plates with cut outs and holes can be reversed for the opposite hand.
3. Channels laid out with the web centerline as the gauge can be used for right or left. Watch for any copes.

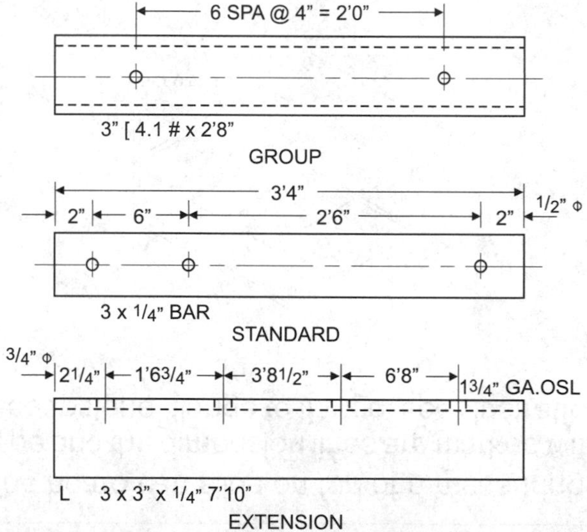
6 SPA @ 4" = 2'0"
3" [4.1 # x 2'8"
GROUP
3'4"
2"
6"
2'6"
2"
1/2" ϕ
3 x 1/4" BAR
STANDARD
3/4" ϕ
21/4"
1'63/4"
3'81/2"
6'8"
13/4" GA.OSL
L 3 x 3" x 1/4" 7'10"
EXTENSION

Illustration #353 - Dimensioning Methods

Right and Left Members

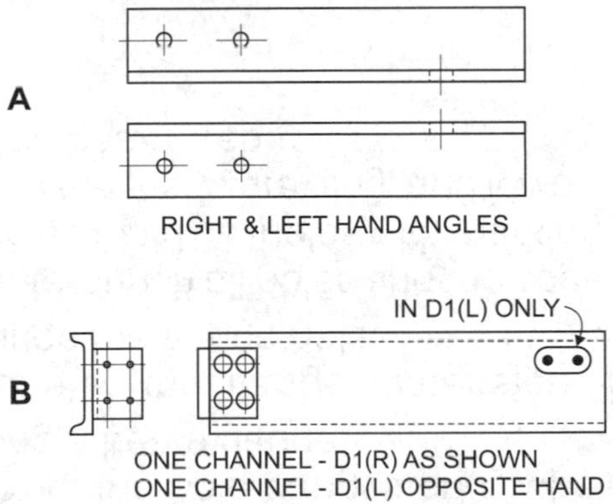
A
RIGHT & LEFT HAND ANGLES
B
IN D1(L) ONLY
ONE CHANNEL - D1(R) AS SHOWN
ONE CHANNEL - D1(L) OPPOSITE HAND

Illustration #354 - Right and Left Hand Angles/Channel

Right and Left Skew

A structural section with an oblique member is a skew. The left and right is indicated below in illustration #355.

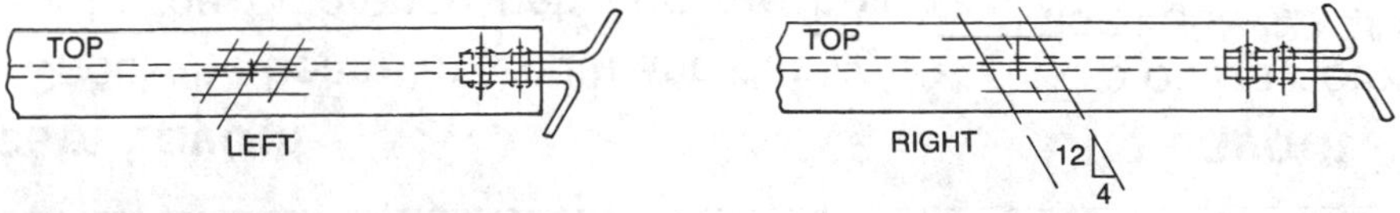
TOP
LEFT
TOP
RIGHT
12
4

Illustration #355 - Right and Left Skew

Coping

To cope means shaping or cutting the end of a structural member to fit into another structural member, see illustration #356 and illustration #357.

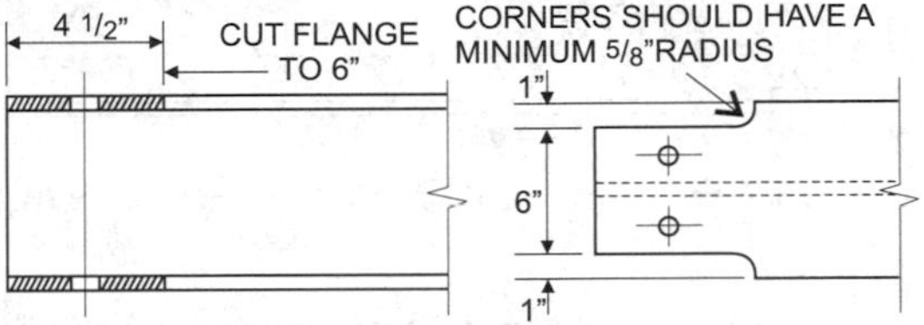
4 1/2"
CUT FLANGE TO 6"
CORNERS SHOULD HAVE A MINIMUM 5/8"RADIUS
1"
6"
1"

Illustration #356 - Coping a Beam

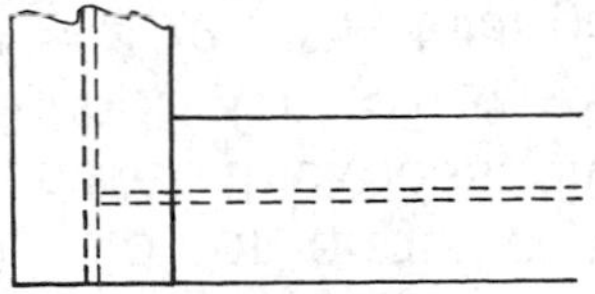

Illustration #357 - Two Beams Fitted Together

Beam Layout

- Check the beam for length and depth.
- Note the difference between the beam length and the overall length.
- Clamp the tape on the end of the beam at the 1/4" mark (for clip clearance).
- Draw all web lines at the required dimension using a beam board.
- Layout the hole gauges and cope depth using a beam gauge.
- Transfer the flange dimension lines. Gauge the flange holes.
- Centerpunch all holes and the cope lines. Circle all laid out holes with marking paint. Paint the mark, drawing, and job numbers in the beam web.

Clip Layout

The beam note concerning clips on illustration #358, 2 - 4" x 4" x 3/8" L^s x 5 1/2", indicates two back to back angles on the beam web. The 5 1/2 inch gauge straddles the web centerline. The rule for angle clip gauge is: Gauge, minus web thickness, divide by two, minus 1/16 inches. Or, (5 1/2" – 3/8") ÷ 2 = 2 9/16" - 1/16" = 2 1/2". The total gauge is 5 1/2 inches, the web thickness is 3/8 inches. The gauge of each angle is 2 1/2 inches.

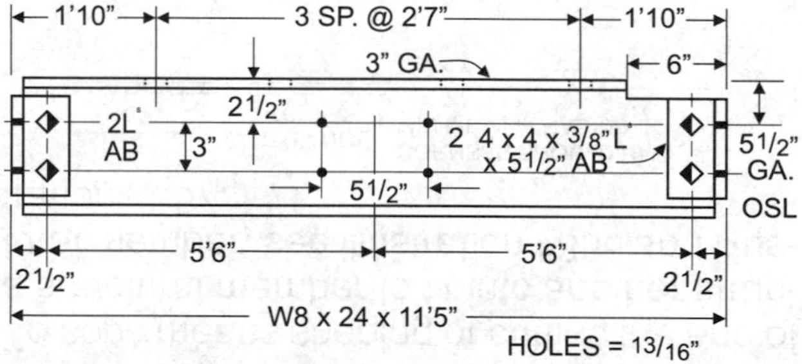
1'10"
3 SP. @ 2'7"
1'10"
3" GA.
6"
2 1/2"
2L
AB
3"
2 4 x 4 x 3/8" L
x 5 1/2" AB
5 1/2"
GA.
OSL
5 1/2"
5'6"
5'6"
2 1/2"
2 1/2"
W8 x 24 x 11'5"
HOLES = 13/16"

Illustration #358 - Beam Layout

Miter Joint Development

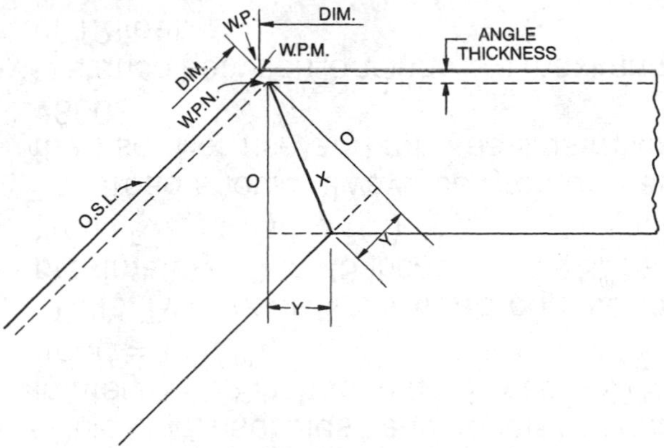
W.P.
DIM.
W.P.M.
ANGLE THICKNESS
DIM.
W.P.N.
O
O
X
O.S.L.
Y
Y

Illustration #359 - Miter Joint Layout

To layout a template for an angle iron miter joint with an inward bend, without entirely cutting the angle, proceed as follows:

1) Layout the joint, full size with the legs at the correct angle.
2) From work point M, (W.P.M.) bisect the angle with line X; (the eventual cut line).
3) As the actual cut is only to the inside of the outstanding leg, establish W.P.N.
4) From W.P.N. draw lines squaring off both sides of the joint, (2 lines marked O).
5) The two sections, indicated by lines X-O-Y are the pieces required to be cut off, with the two legs then pulled together on line X.

SAFE EDGE DISTANCES FOR HOLES IN STRUCTURALS	
Hole Size	**Edge Distance**
9/32"	3/8"
11/32"	1/2"
7/16"	5/8"
9/16"	7/8"
11/16"	1 1/8"
13/16"	1 1/4"
15/16"	1 1/2"
1 1/16"	1 3/4"

Table #56 - Structural Edge Distances

Stairways

Stairways come in a wide variety of types, including those for commercial buildings, industrial plants, hanging, free standing and spiral. Several common points for most stair types are:

- Width - usually 2 feet 6 inches or more.
- Rise and Run

  - Rule One: riser plus tread equals approximately $17^1/_2$ inches (e.g.- 8" rise + $9^1/_2$" tread = $17^1/_2$")

  - Rule Two: riser times tread equals approximately 70 to 75 inches (e.g.- 8" rise times $9^1/_2$" tread = 76").

  The tread should always be greater than the rise. For rise and run see illustration #360.
- Distance between landings is a maximum of 12 feet.
- Landings are a minimum length of 3 feet. Stairway headroom clearance is a minimum 7 feet 6 inches.
- Landing headroom clearance is a minimum of 7 feet.
- Wall to handrail clearance is a minimum of 3 inches.
- Stringers are normally C8 x 11.5 or C10 x 15.3, toe out, (C = Channel).

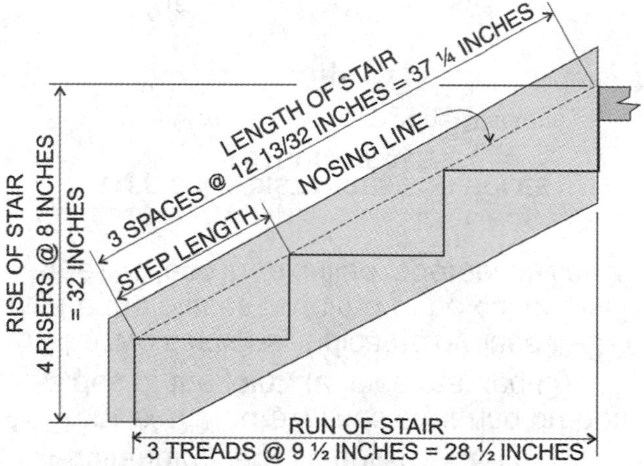
LENGTH OF STAIR
3 SPACES @ 12 13/32 INCHES = 37 ¼ INCHES
STEP LENGTH
NOSING LINE
RISE OF STAIR
4 RISERS @ 8 INCHES
= 32 INCHES
RUN OF STAIR
3 TREADS @ 9 ½ INCHES = 28 ½ INCHES

Illustration #360 - Stair Rise and Run

Stair Stringer Development

1. Draw a full length nosing line, x, see illustration #361.
2. Layout stair length on nosing line.
3. Divide the stair length into the required number of steps.
4. Layout the full lines for risers and treads.
5. Check the lengths, number of steps, rise & tread lengths etc.
6. Centerpunch all cuts and holes and mark with paint.

STANDARD GAUGES	
Steel Sheets	U.S. Standard
Steel Plates	Birmingham
Steel Wire	Washburn & Moen
Copper Wire	Brown & Sharpe

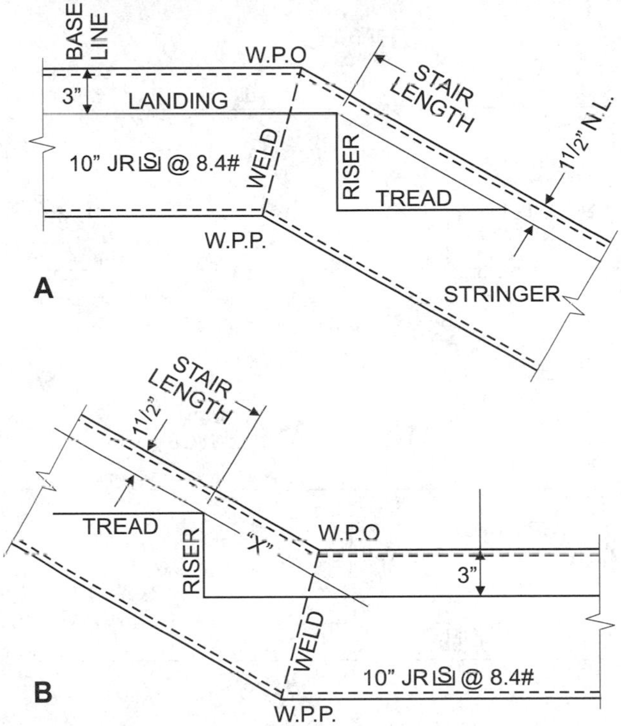
BASE LINE
W.P.O
STAIR LENGTH
3"
LANDING
11/2" N.L.
10" JR S @ 8.4#
WELD
RISER
TREAD
W.P.P.
A
STRINGER
STAIR LENGTH
11/2"
TREAD
RISER
"X"
W.P.O
3"
WELD
10" JR S @ 8.4#
B
W.P.P.

Illustration #361 - Stair Stringer Layout

Stair Stringer Development

Stringer Landing Miter Cuts

1. Establish Work Point O (W.P.O.), see illustration #362A & B, at the top of the stair stringer.
2. From W.P.O. measure 10 inches, (stringer depth) parallel to the riser line.
3. Draw a line on this 10 inch measurement parallel to the tread down to the bottom of the stringer. This establishes point P.
4. Join points O and P. This is the stringer bevel cut line.
5. Use a bevel square to mark the same angle cut line, in reverse, on the top landing stringer.
6. The identical procedure will be used to layout the cut lines for the bottom landing stringer and the bottom of the stair stringer.

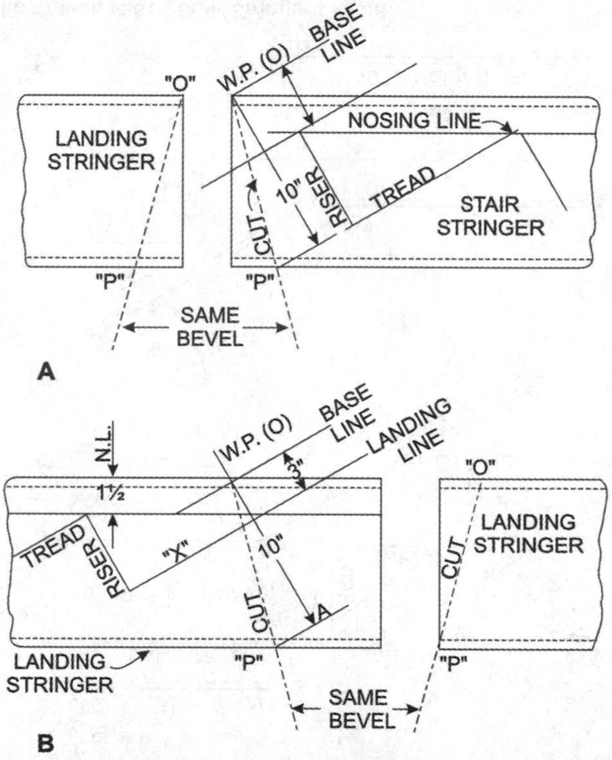
"O"
W.P. (O)
BASE LINE
LANDING STRINGER
NOSING LINE
10"
RISER
TREAD
CUT
STAIR STRINGER
"P"
"P"
SAME BEVEL
A
N.L.
1½
W.P. (O)
BASE LINE
3"
LANDING LINE
"O"
TREAD
RISER
"X"
10"
CUT
A
LANDING STRINGER
CUT
LANDING STRINGER
"P"
"P"
SAME BEVEL
B

Illustration #362 - Top and Bottom Landing Miters

Ladders

The two basic types of ladders are front approach and side approach. These are indicated in the following diagram. With a few job to job variations, the following are common features of most ladders;

- Rungs - made of round bar 16 inches inside measurement, welded to stringers. Should be a minimum of 7 inches from wall for front approach and 15 inches centerline of ladder for side approach. Rungs should be 12 inches apart.
- Clips or brackets are welded or bolted to stringers and usually spaced 8 feet to 10 feet apart.
- Safety hoops - made of $1^1/_2 \times {}^1/_4$ or $2 \times {}^1/_4$ flat bar. Bottom hoop should be 8 feet above ground or platform level. Inside radius of hoop should be a minimum of 13 inches.

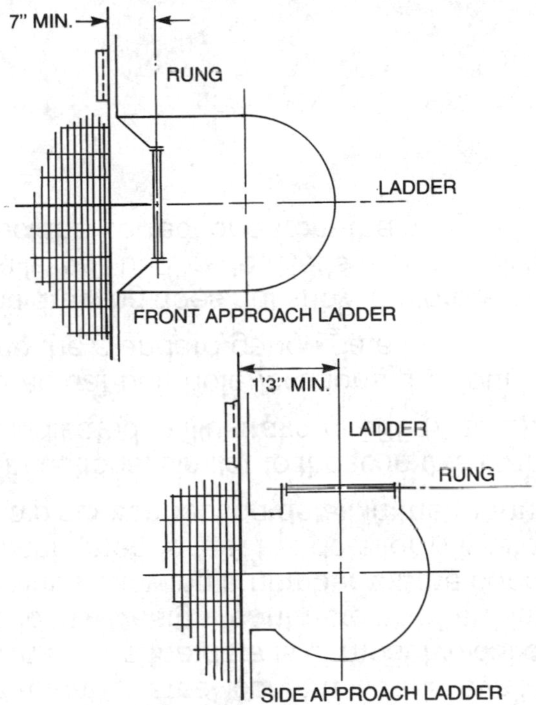
7" MIN.
RUNG
LADDER
FRONT APPROACH LADDER
1'3" MIN.
LADDER
RUNG
SIDE APPROACH LADDER

Illustration #363 - Typical Ladder Approach

Handrails

Typical handrail components are post, top rail, mid rail and toe or kick plate. The post and rails are usually $2^1/2$ x $2^1/2$ x $^1/4$ angle or 2 inch pipe. A typical handrail assembly is indicated below in illustration #364.

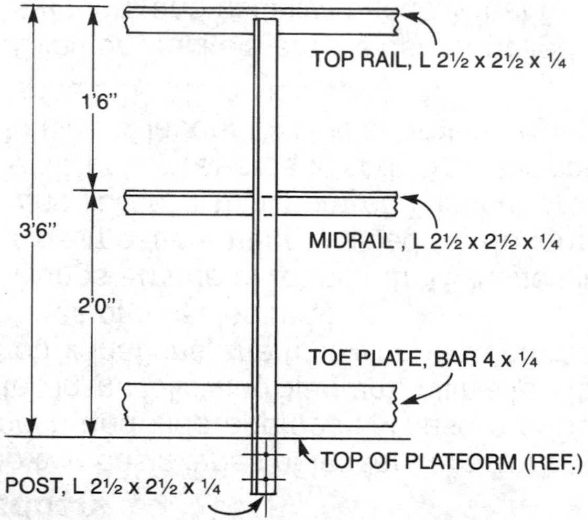
TOP RAIL, L 2½ x 2½ x ¼
1'6"
3'6"
MIDRAIL , L 2½ x 2½ x ¼
2'0"
TOE PLATE, BAR 4 x ¼
TOP OF PLATFORM (REF.)
POST, L 2½ x 2½ x ¼

Illustration #364 - Typical Handrail

Structural Connections

A manual of steel construction is available which shows the details of most typical connections. Design contractors often issue drawings showing a number for the connection, this means that the detailer will refer to the typical connection detail in the manual.

Connections, similar to those in this manual are indicated in illustration #365 (A to L).

The actual bolt hole locations are found by using the standard gauge data.

If the drawing does not show the proper joint detail it will be the detailer's responsibility to select the correct one from the manual.

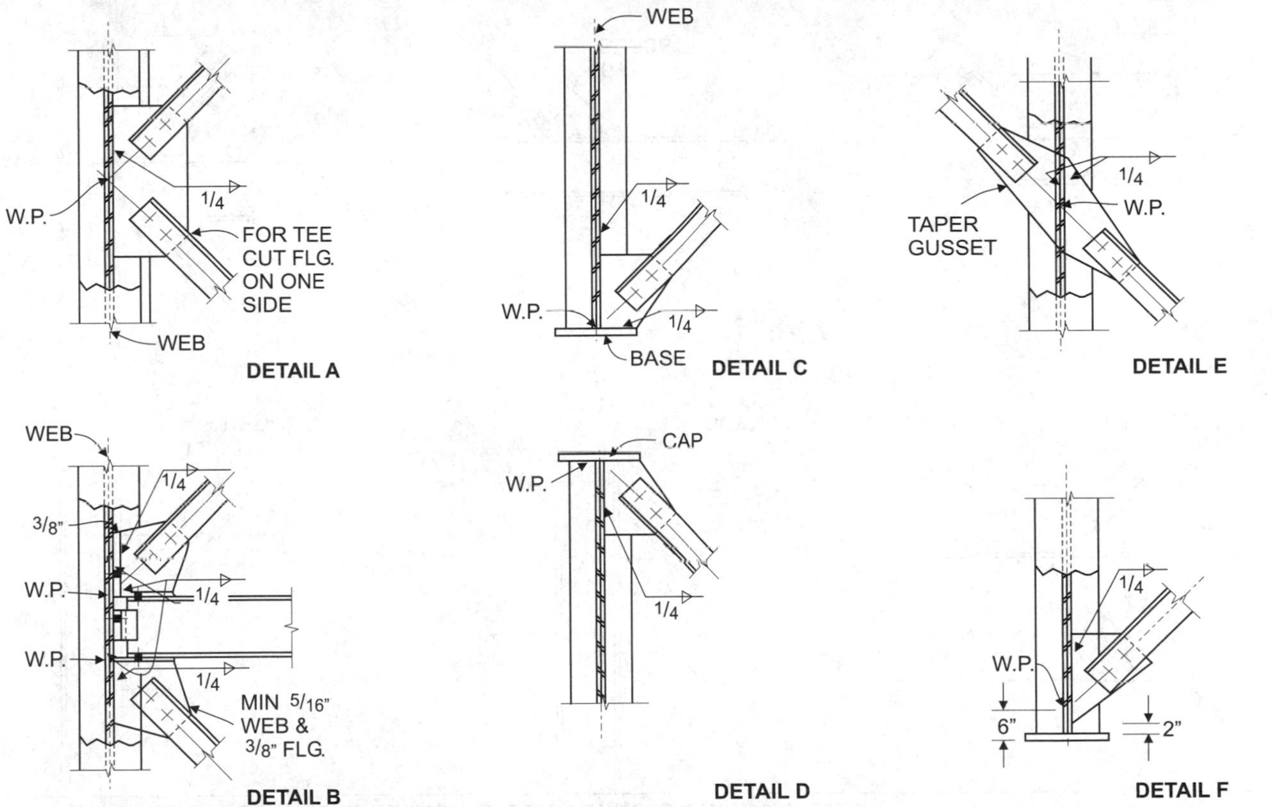
WEB
W.P.
1/4
FOR TEE
CUT FLG.
ON ONE
SIDE
WEB
DETAIL A
WEB
1/4
W.P.
1/4
BASE
DETAIL C
1/4
TAPER
GUSSET
W.P.
DETAIL E
WEB
1/4
3/8"
W.P.
1/4
W.P.
1/4
MIN 5/16"
WEB &
3/8" FLG.
DETAIL B
CAP
W.P.
1/4
DETAIL D
1/4
W.P.
6"
2"
DETAIL F

Illustration #365 - Bolted Structural Connections

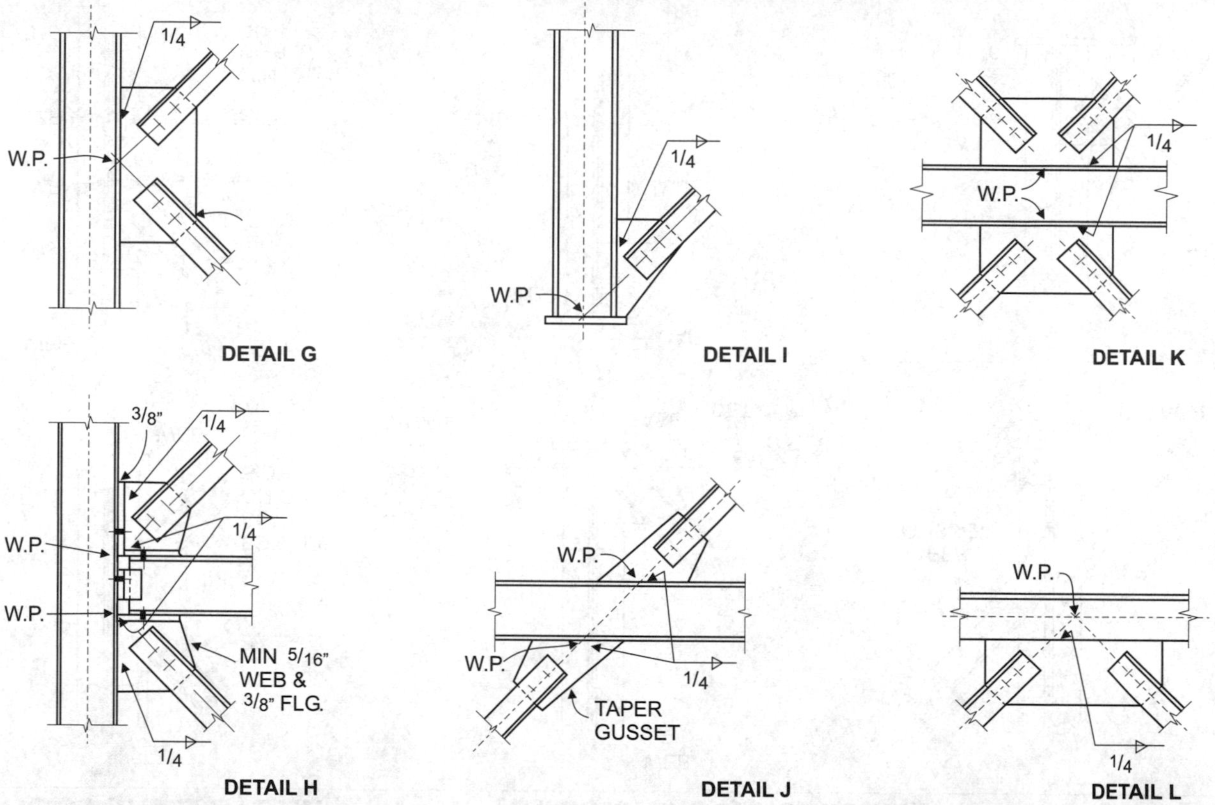
1/4
W.P.
DETAIL G
1/4
W.P.
DETAIL I
1/4
W.P.
DETAIL K
3/8"
1/4
1/4
W.P.
W.P.
MIN 5/16"
WEB &
3/8" FLG.
1/4
DETAIL H
W.P.
W.P.
1/4
TAPER
GUSSET
DETAIL J
W.P.
1/4
DETAIL L

Illustration #366 - Bolted Structural Connections

SECTION TEN QUESTIONS
Structural Steel

1. *The term "channel" would refer to which shape designation?*
   - ❒ C shape
   - ❒ MC shape
   - ❒ S shape
   - ❒ W shape

2. *Which one of these structural shapes is designated in exact dimensions? (depth of member)*
   - ❒ W shape
   - ❒ M shape
   - ❒ WM shape
   - ❒ S shape

3. *Determine if the following statement is true or false. A W14 x 26 x 14'3" would have a depth of 26 inches and weight of 14 lbs per foot.*
   ❒ true ❒ false

4. *Referring to question number 3, what would be the total weight of the beam?*
   - ❒ 26 lbs
   - ❒ 199.5 lbs
   - ❒ 364 lbs
   - ❒ 370.5 lbs

5. *Referring to illustration #348 on page 351, item number 8 is called:*
   - ❒ column
   - ❒ beam
   - ❒ girder
   - ❒ truss

6. *Item number 3 on page 351 is called a:*
   - ❒ footer
   - ❒ header
   - ❒ truss
   - ❒ base plate

7. *A layout line measured from the heel of an angle iron to the centerline of a hole is called a:*
   - ❒ pitch line
   - ❒ gauge line
   - ❒ layout line
   - ❒ reference line

8. *What is the hole spacing called along the line referred to in question 7?*
   - ❒ pitch
   - ❒ gauge
   - ❒ layout
   - ❒ reference

9. *What can be used to make the layout of dimension lines easier when laying out the web of a beam?*
   - ❒ beam web gauge
   - ❒ 2 foot steel square
   - ❒ chalkline
   - ❒ beam board

10. *What item simplifies the gauging of holes in the web of a beam after dimension lines have been layed out?*
    - ❒ beam web gauge
    - ❒ 2 foot steel square
    - ❒ chalkline
    - ❒ beam board

11. *Which method of showing dimensions on a structural print is the easiest to use when laying out?*
    - ❒ extension
    - ❒ group
    - ❒ standard
    - ❒ modified

12. *Two pieces of angle (L shapes) layed out back-to-back would result in what type of components?*
    - ❒ identical
    - ❒ right and left hand
    - ❒ skewed
    - ❒ none of the above

13. *The term most commonly used to shape or cut the end of a structural member to fit into another one is called:*
- ❐ shearing
- ❐ skewing
- ❐ coping
- ❐ gauging

14. *A tape measure is clamped to a structural member starting at the 1/4 inch mark when beginning to lay out the member. What is the reason for not starting at the end of the tape?*
- ❐ ± minus tolerance
- ❐ clip clearance
- ❐ beam was cut too short
- ❐ gauge tolerance

15. *When laying out a stairway, to maintain comfortable steps and stair angle, the riser plus the tread dimensions should add up to approximately:*
- ❐ 17 1/2 inches
- ❐ 70 inches
- ❐ 75 inches
- ❐ 76 inches

16. *For a stairway, the riser times the tread should multiply out to approximately:*
- ❐ 17 1/2 inches
- ❐ 70 inches
- ❐ 76 inches
- ❐ none of the above

17. *Determine if the following statement is true or false. On a stairway the rise is always greater than the run.*

❐ true ❐ false

18. *Determine if the following statement is true or false. Stringers for steel stair construction are normally made from C-8 or C-10 channel.*

❐ true ❐ false

19. *The recommended vertical distance between ladder rungs is:*
- ❐ 16 inches
- ❐ 7 inches
- ❐ 1 foot
- ❐ 15 inches

20. *What is the typical distance from the top of the top rail to the top of platform?*
- ☐ 12 inches
- ☐ 20 inches
- ☐ 36 inches
- ☐ 42 inches

SECTION ELEVEN

CONCRETE REINFORCING

Concrete Reinforcing

Concrete is extremely strong, however, it can move under load. To provide extra strength, the concrete is poured around some type of steel reinforcing bar system. The rebar size and type must be engineered to match the use and load on the concrete.

There are several different kinds of steel rebar that can be used depending on the end use and the environmental conditions. These range from the basic "black" steel commonly used in most structures, to epoxy coated rebar for wet conditions, to non-magnetic stainless steel rebar used in hospital or lab MRI rooms.

Some of the advantages and disadvantages include:

"Black" Steel:

- Cheapest and most common
- Excellent when moisture free
- Will rust in moist conditions such as bridge decks, parking structures and marine applications.

Epoxy Coated:

- Does not bond well to concrete
- Easily damaged which could intensify corrosion
- Excellent for submerged conditions
- Expensive to produce

Stainless Steel:

- Corrosion resistant
- Will withstand handling abuse
- Magnetic or non-magnetic
- Most expensive

Fiber-Reinforced Polymer (FRP) types of non-steel rebar have been developed in recent years. The three types are glass fiber (GFRP), carbon fiber (CFRP), and aramid fiber (a type of nylon similar to kevlar) (AFRP). Three general advantages over the standard "black" steel rebar include:

- Higher tensile strength
- 4-6 times lighter
- Non-corrosive

Of the three types, carbon (CRP) has the highest tensile strength and glass (GFRP) the lowest, and carbon the shortest elongation and glass the longest. Glass is transparent to radio frequencies and magnetic fields. The elasticity of carbon is close to that of steel.

Due to the fact that the vast majority of rebar used for construction is made of steel, that is the type mentioned in the following pages.

Reinforcing Bar Sizing

The steel used for concrete reinforcing is manufactured under specification, much as any other type of steel product.

The most common type of rebar steel is the deformed round type, although the steel could be square or plain. The deformed is preferred due to a higher bond between concrete and steel.

The American Society for Testing Materials (ASTM) has established a standard for designation of bar sizes. The number of each bar corresponds to the number of eighths in the bar diameter.

Eg. #4 = $^4/_8$ or $^1/_2$ inch

#7 = $^7/_8$ or $^7/_8$ inch.

Metric bar is designated in graduations of 5 millimeters in a range from 10 to 55. Although the numbering and color code systems are the same as Imperial, there is little similarity in the sizes.

BAR SIZES	WEIGHT	NOMINAL DIMENSIONS	
NUMBERS	POUNDS PER FOOT	DIAMETER INCHES	CROSS SECTIONAL AREA - SQ. INCHES
2	.167	.250	.05
3	.376	.375	.11
4	.668	.500	.20
5	1.043	.625	.31
6	1.502	.750	.44
7	2.044	.875	.60
8	2.670	1.000	.79
9	3.400	1.128	1.00
10	4.303	1.270	1.27
11	5.313	1.410	1.56

Table #57 - Standard A305 Reinforcing Bars

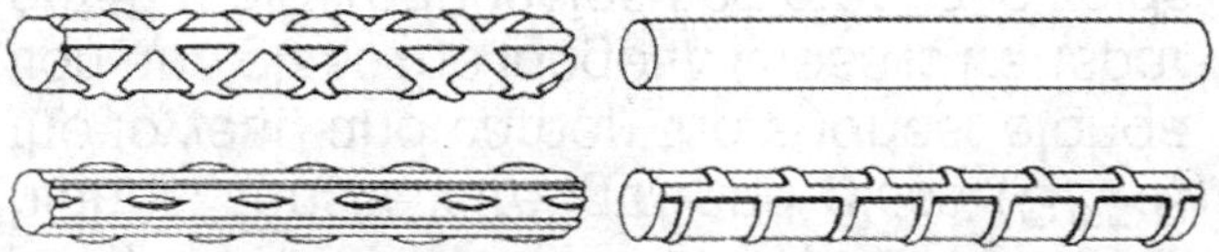

Illustration #367 - Types of Reinforcing Bar

Bar Weight

Bar weights per linear foot are shown in Table #57. If the weight of a bar is needed and the chart is not available, a simple formula can be used to establish the close approximate weight. Bar number squared ÷ 24 = weight per foot.

Eg. #4 bar

$$\frac{4x4}{24} = \frac{16}{24} = .666\ lbs.per\ ft.$$

(Chart = .668 lbs. per ft.)

Eg. #7 bar

$$\frac{7x7}{24} = \frac{49}{24} = 2.042\ lbs.per\ ft.$$

(Chart = 2.044 lbs. per ft.)

COLOR MARKING CHART	
1. White	6. Light Green
2. Red	7. Orange
3. Dark Green	8. Light Blue
4. Yellow	9. Brown
5. Dark Blue	10. Pink

Table #58 - Color Marking Chart

COMPARISON OF IMPERIAL & METRIC SIZES						
IMPERIAL BAR			METRIC BAR			METRIC BAR IS
SIZE	AREA in^2	AREA mm^2	DESIG.	AREA in^2	AREA mm^2	
#3	.11	71	10M	.16	100	45% L
#4	.20	129	10M	.16	100	20% S
#4	.20	129	15M	.31	200	55% L
#5	.31	200	15M	.31	200	SAME
#6	.44	284	20M	.47	300	6.8% L
#7	.60	387	20M	.47	300	22% S
#7	.60	387	25M	.78	500	30% L
#8	.79	510	25M	.78	500	1.3% S
#9	1.00	645	30M	1.09	700	9% L
#10	1.27	819	30M	1.09	700	14% S
#10	1.27	819	35M	1.55	1000	22% L
#11	1.56	1006	35M	1.55	1000	0.6% S
#14	2.25	1452	45M	2.33	1500	3.5% L
#18	4.00	2581	55M	3.88	2500	3.0% S

Table #59 - Metric Comparison

Bar Size	Approximate Diameter mm	Bar Size	Approximate Diameter mm
10M	13	30M	33
15M	18	35M	39
20M	22	45M	48
25M	28	55M	62

Table #60 - Metric Diameter

Metric Comparison

WEIGHT OF IMPERIAL AND METRIC REINFORCING BARS				
IMPERIAL WEIGHT				
BAR SIZE	lb/ft	lb/m	kg/m	kg/ft
#3	0.376	1.234	0.560	0.171
#4	0.668	2.192	0.994	0.303
#5	1.043	3.422	1.552	0.473
#6	1.502	4.928	2.235	0.681
#7	2.044	6.706	3.042	0.927
#8	2.670	8.760	3.973	1.211
#9	3.400	11.155	5.060	1.542
#10	4.303	14.117	6.404	1.952
#11	5.313	17.431	7.907	2.410
#14	7.650	25.098	11.384	3.470
#18	13.600	44.619	20.239	6.169
METRIC MASS				
BAR DESIG.	kg/m	lb/m	lb/ft	kg/ft
10M	0.785	1.731	0.528	0.239
15M	1.570	3.461	1.055	0.479
20M	2.355	5.192	1.583	0.718
25M	3.925	8.653	2.638	1.196
30M	5.495	12.114	3.693	1.675
35M	7.850	17.306	5.275	2.393
45M	11.775	25.959	7.912	3.589
55M	19.625	43.265	13.188	5.982

Table #61 - Weight of Reinforcing Bars

Rebar General Guidelines

Various organizations have established standards and specifications for rebar and its fabrication and placement. A few of the more standard guidelines are listed below.

- No splices of reinforcing bars shall be made without prior approval of the architect or engineer except when shown on the plans.
- All bars should be free from scale, grease, loose rust, or any substance that will destroy the bond.
- When permitted, all column bars shall be spliced a minimum of 20 bar diameters and not less than 12 inches (305 mm).
- When permitted, all bars in slabs, walls, and footers shall be spliced a minimum of 24 bar diameters and not less than 12 inches (305 mm).
- All laps or splices should be staggered when possible.

General Guidelines

- The minimum clear spacing between any two parallel reinforcing bars (except column bars) shall be at least one bar diameter and not less than one inch (25 mm).
- The minimum clear spacing between two column reinforcing bars shall be at least 1 1/2 bar diameters and not less than 1 1/2 inches (38 mm).
- Unless otherwise specified, bottom bars in slabs, beams, or joists should extend at least 6 inches (152 mm) into the support. This applies to the standard A305 (deformed) bar. If any other type of bar is used it must extend at least 10 bar diameters and terminate in a hook.
- Two, #4 bars in the top of the wall footings under any door or opening. The bars should be at least 4 feet (1 219 mm) longer than the opening.
- Unless otherwise specified, reinforce all walls with #4 bars horizontally and vertically, at 12 inch (305 mm) centers.
- Unless otherwise specified, all column bars should have 3 inches (76 mm) clearance at the top.
- Mesh (welded wire fabric) must have one full mesh end lap and one full mesh edge lap and be wired together. The mesh must extend into any supporting beam or wall for anchorage.
- When not noted on the plans, the short bars of a two-way slab may be placed in the bottom layer.
- Two, #3 bars should be provided for the tops of all stirrups in beams.
- The length of all deformed dowels in walls, unless otherwise specified, shall be 48 bar diameters, but less than 24 inches (610 mm).
- All hooks on stirrups or column ties are to be not less than 2 inches (51 mm).

- The outside diameter of a hook shall be from 8 to 10 bar diameters, unless otherwise specified.
- The straight end beyond the hook of a hook bar shall be approximately 4 bar diameters.
- A length of approximately 15 bar diameters should be allowed for the bending of a hook.
- When bending truss rods, a pin of not less than 6 diameters should be used for bars up to #8; a pin of not less than 8 diameters should be used for bars over #8.
- When bending stirrups or ties from 90 degrees to 135 degrees, a pin of not less than 2 bar diameters should be used; when bending stirrups or ties over 135 degrees, a pin of not less than 3 bar diameters should be used.

Cut Length Tolerances

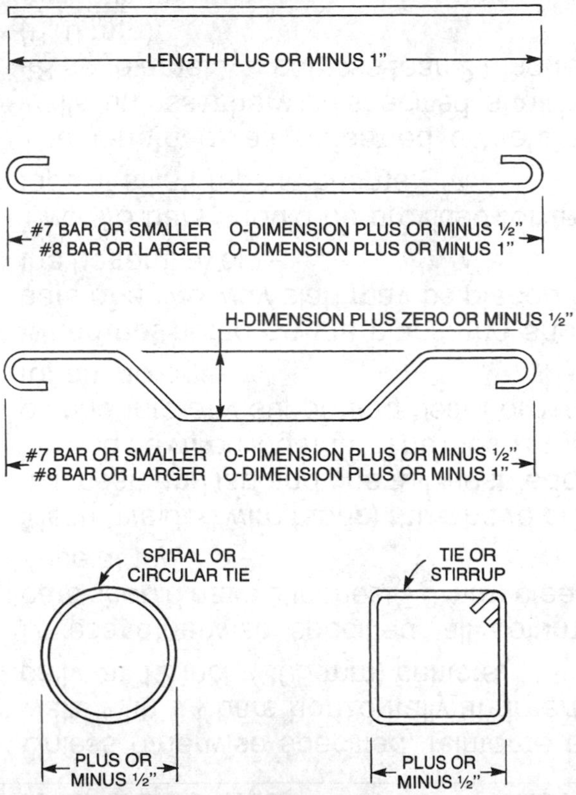
LENGTH PLUS OR MINUS 1"
#7 BAR OR SMALLER O-DIMENSION PLUS OR MINUS ½"
#8 BAR OR LARGER O-DIMENSION PLUS OR MINUS 1"
H-DIMENSION PLUS ZERO OR MINUS ½"
#7 BAR OR SMALLER O-DIMENSION PLUS OR MINUS ½"
#8 BAR OR LARGER O-DIMENSION PLUS OR MINUS 1"
SPIRAL OR CIRCULAR TIE
TIE OR STIRRUP
PLUS OR MINUS ½"
PLUS OR MINUS ½"

Illustration #368 - Cut Length Tolerances

Rebar Fabrication

The following are a few general suggestions for proper makeup of rebar shapes.

- Bar over $^3/_8$ inches (10 mm) should be machine bent where possible.
- Cold bend bar up to $1^1/_8$ inches (29 mm). Bends, except for hooks, should have a bend diameter of 6 bar diameters for sizes under 1 inch (25 mm). Sizes over this are bent to 8 diameters.
- Ninety degree hooks are bent to at least 4 bar diameters.
- Ninety degree hooks should also have an extension of 12 bar diameters.

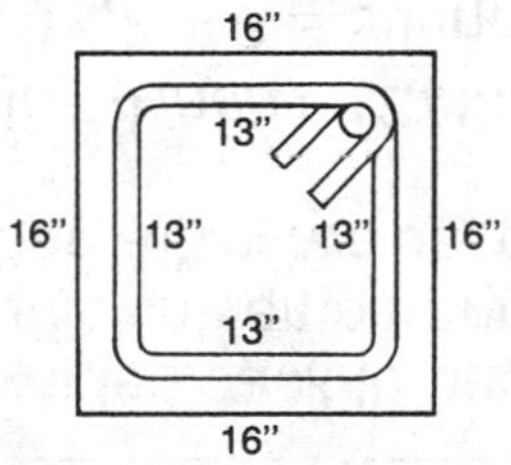
16"
13"
16"
13"
13"
16"
13"
16"

Illustration #369 - Column Tie

Column Ties

A column tie should have a specified amount of clearance. This is normally $1^1/_2$ inches unless otherwise specified. A 16 inch by 16 inch finished column would therefore have a column tie with outside measurements of 13 inches by 13 inches, see illustration #369.

If the rodman must make up such a tie in the field he must first calculate approximately how much bar he will require.

1. $1^1/_2$ inches of clearance means that the perimeter of the tie will be 12 inches less than the column perimeter.
2. Adds 6 inches to the tie perimeter to find the length of rod required.

Eg. 16 inch column

1. column perimeter = 64 inches.
2. column tie perimeter = 64 - 12 = 52 inches.
3. rod required, 52 + 6 = 58 inches.

Two angles welded back to back on a plate will make a sufficient temporary vice for field bending of rebar. Allow two bar diameters for each bend.

Eg: Column tie *14 inch x 12 inch of #3 bar*

1. bar length = 52 + 6 = 58 inches.
2. layout as follows:
   A. 5 inches = hook
   B. $12^1/_2$ = $1^1/_2$ less than 14 inches
   C. $11^1/_4$ = $^3/_4$ less than 12 inches
   D. $13^1/_4$ = $^3/_4$ less than 14 inches
   E. $11^1/_4$ = $^3/_4$ less than 12 inches
3. rod layout marking:

5"	$12^1/_2$"	$11^1/_4$"	$13^1/_4$"	$4^3/_4$"

4. Place the bar in the vice on the 5 inch mark with the remainder protruding, then bend with a piece of pipe pushed over the bar and up against the vice.

Bar Hooks

A bar hook requires an additional 12 diameters added to the out to out measurement for field fabrications, see illustration #370.

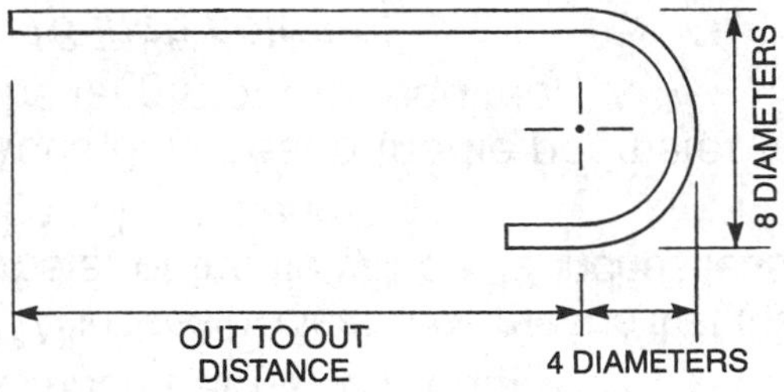
8 DIAMETERS
OUT TO OUT DISTANCE
4 DIAMETERS

Illustration #370 - Bar Hook

Eg: A single #5 bar hook with an out to out measurement of 4 feet would require 4 feet $7^1/_2$ inches of bar.

The radius of 4 diameters, which is $2^1/_2$ inches, is subtracted from the 4 foot length. This means a mark at 3 feet $9^1/_2$ inches. The bar is placed in a vice at this mark and is then bent.

To mark a bar for a 180 degree hook the mark back distances will be from the out to out distance.

#3 = 1 1/2 inches	#4 = 2 inches
#5 = 2 1/2 inches	#6 = 3 inches
#7 = 3 1/2 inches	#8 = 4 inches

The easiest way to layout a double hook is to mark the center of the bar and then proceed out each way, as with a single. The difference will be in the initial bar length which means 24 bar diameters are added, not 12.

Bar Splicing

A minimum standard for splicing of deformed rebar has been established. The minimum splice for columns is 20 bar diameters, or a 12 inch minimum. For slabs, footings and walls the minimum is 24 bar diameters, or a minimum of 12 inches.

Another method to establish the proper splice is through the use of bar numbers. Column splices can be found by multiplying the bar number by $2^1/_2$ (Imperial only).

Eg: #6 bar

= 6 x $2^1/_2$ = 15 inches

For splices other than columns the multiplier is 3.

Eg: #7 bar

= 7 x 3 = 21 inches

BAR SIZE	MINIMUM SPLICE FOR DEFORMED COLUMN BARS (in)	MINIMUM SPLICE FOR DEFORMED BARS OTHER THAN COLUMNS (in)
#3	7 1/2	9
#4	10	12
#5	12 1/2	15
#6	15	18
#7	17 1/2	21
#8	20	24
#9	22 1/2	27
#10	25	30

Table #62 - Minimum Splice Standards

Minimum Concrete Protection

A minimum amount of coverage is required for rebar embedded in concrete. The suggested minimums are listed below. Also see illustration #371.

1. $1^1/_2$ inches (40 mm) over steel in columns
2. $1^1/_2$ inches (40 mm) on sides and bottom of girders
3. $^3/_4$ inches (20 mm) on sides and bottom of joists
4. $^3/_4$ inches (20 mm) for slabs not exposed to ground
5. 2 inches (50 mm) when exposed to ground
6. 3 inches (75 mm) on bottom of footings

Accessories

Reinforcing bars must be spaced correctly and held in the proper position during the concrete pour. The following standard accessories are manufactured to maintain the proper clearance. See illustration #372.

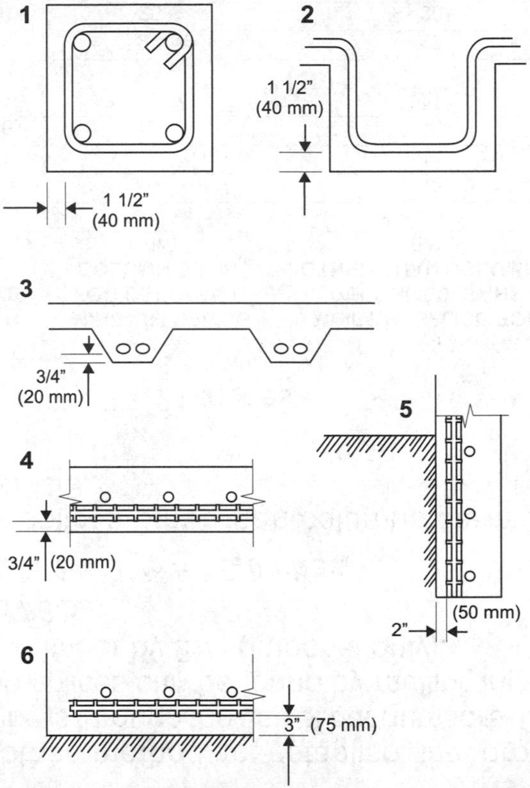
1
2
1 1/2" (40 mm)
1 1/2" (40 mm)
3
3/4" (20 mm)
4
3/4" (20 mm)
5
2" (50 mm)
6
3" (75 mm)

Illustration #371 - Concrete Protection

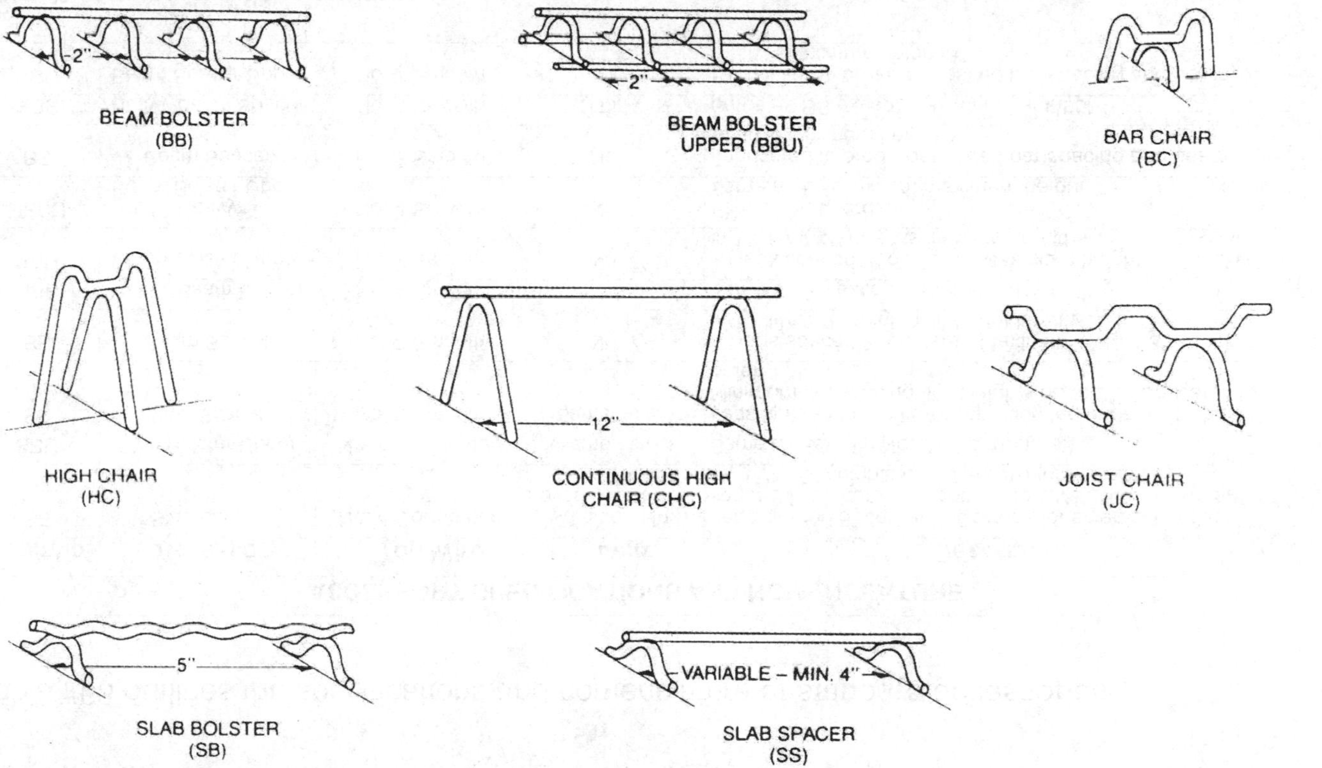
2"
BEAM BOLSTER
(BB)
2"
BEAM BOLSTER
UPPER (BBU)
BAR CHAIR
(BC)
HIGH CHAIR
(HC)
12"
CONTINUOUS HIGH
CHAIR (CHC)
JOIST CHAIR
(JC)
5"
SLAB BOLSTER
(SB)
VARIABLE – MIN. 4"
SLAB SPACER
(SS)

Illustration #372 - Accessories

Table #63 outlines the specifications and nomenclature of standard accessories.

ACCESSORY SPECIFICATIONS AND NOMENCLATURE				
Symbol	**Accessory**	**Top Wire**	**Legs**	**Description**
SB	Slab Bolster	No. 4 Corrugated	3/4" high - No. 7 over 3/4" - No. 5	Legs spaced 5" centers - Corrugations vertical or flat spaced 1" centers - Heights up to 1 1/2". Stocked in 3/4", 1", 1 1/2", 2" heights and 5 and 10 foot lengths.
SBU	Slab Bolster Upper	No. 4 Corrugated	Same as SB	Same as SB with No. 7 wire runners.
SS	Slab Spacer	No. 5 Smooth	Same as SB	Legs spaced to provide supporting leg under each bar. Minimum leg spacing 4" - Heights up to 2". Fabricated to order.
BB	Beam Bolster	No. 7 Smooth	No. 7	All legs spaced 2" centers - Maximum height 3". Stocked in 1", 1 1/2", 2" heights, in 5 foot lengths.
HBB	Heavy Beam Bolster	No. 4 Smooth	No. 4	Same as BB except maximum height 5'.
BBU	Beam Bolster Upper	No. 7 Smooth	No. 7	All legs spaced 2" centers - Maximum height 3". Stocked in 1", 1 1/2", 2" heights, in 5 foot lengths.
HBBU	Heavy Beam Bolster Upper	No. 4 Smooth	No. 4	Fabricated to order. Same as BBU except maximum height 3".
BS	Beam Spacer	No. 7 Smooth	No. 7	Fabricated to order for desired bar spacing and beam width - Maximum height 3".
HBS	Heavy Beam Spacer	No. 4 Smooth	No. 4	Same as BS except maximum height 5".
BSU	Beam Spacer Upper	No. 7 Smooth	No. 7	Fabricated to order for desired bar spacing and beam width - Maximum height 3".

Table #63 - Accessories and Nomenclature

ACCESSORY SPECIFICATIONS AND NOMENCLATURE				
Symbol	**Accessory**	**Top Wire**	**Legs**	**Description**
HBSU	Heavy Beam Spacer Upper	No. 4 Smooth	No. 4	Same as BSU except maximum height 5".
JC	Joist Chair	No. 8	No. 8	Made and stocked only in 4, 5, 6 inch widths and 3/4", 1", 1 1/2" heights.
BC	Bar Chair	No. 8	No. 8	Made and stocked only in 3/4" , 1", 1 1/2" and 2" heights.
HC	Individual High Chairs	No. 5	No. 5	For heights 2" to 4". Over 4" to 6" No. 4 wire over: 6" to 9" No. 2 wire: over 9" No. 0 wire. Stocked in 1/4" increments from 2" to 6".
CHC	Continuous High Chairs	No. 2	Same as for HC	Legs 12" on centers. Over 6" high top wire is No. 0. Fabricated to order.
HCHC	Heavy Continuous High Chairs	Same as CHC	Same as CHC	Legs 8" on centers. Over 6" top wire is No. 0. Fabricated to order.
CHCU	Continuous High Chair Upper	Same as CHC	Same as CHC	Same as CHC with No. 5 wire runners.
SSI	Snap-In Slab Spacer	No. 5 Smooth	No. 7 Special	For 3/8", 1/2", 5/8" and 3/4" bars. Heights 1/2", 3/4", 1". Fabricated to order. Preferably not over 5 ft lengths.
SBP	Slab Bolster with Plate	Same as SB	Same as SB	Plate is 20 gauge, 2 3/4" wide. Plate also applied to SS, BB, HBB, BS and HBS. Fabricated to order.
SHC	Special High Chair	Same as HC	Same as HC	Cross wires of No. 0 gauge. Fabricated to order.
CSBC	Combination SB and HC	Same as SB	Same as HC and SB	High and low legs 12" on center, alternating. Fabricated to order.

Table #64 - Accessories and Nomenclature

Wire Ties

For ease of handling, the rodman should have approximately 20 strands of wire coiled at a diameter of 18 inches. The coil is placed over the head and under the arm with the wire end coming out on the left side for a right handed person.

The roll is shifted as the wire is used.

Illustration #373 shows several of the more common types of ties.

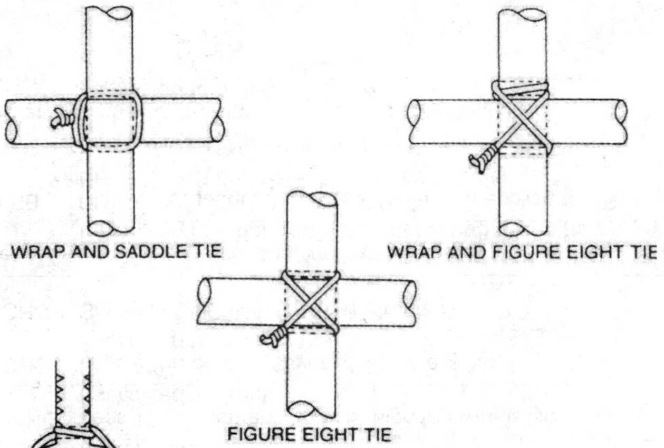
WRAP AND SADDLE TIE
WRAP AND FIGURE EIGHT TIE
FIGURE EIGHT TIE

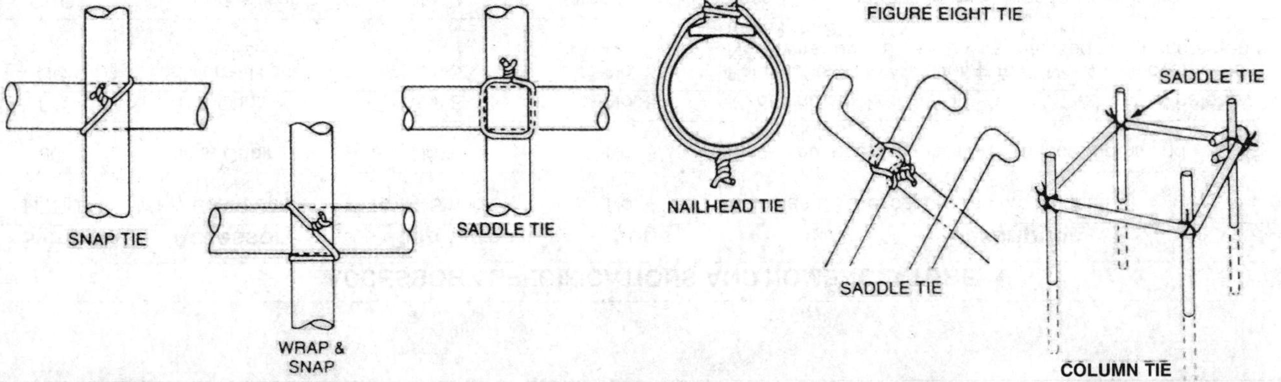
SNAP TIE
WRAP &
SNAP
SADDLE TIE
NAILHEAD TIE
SADDLE TIE
SADDLE TIE
COLUMN TIE

Illustration #373 - Wire Ties

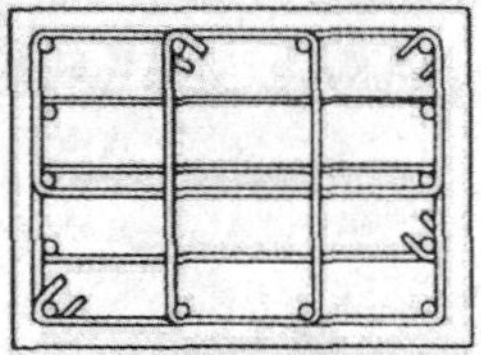

COLUMN STEEL
ARRANGED FOR
BENDING & DIRECT STRESS

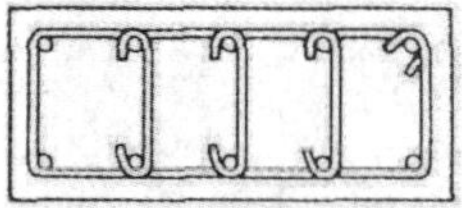

ALTERNATE METHOD
OF TIE ARRANGEMENT
FOR ELONGATED COLUMNS

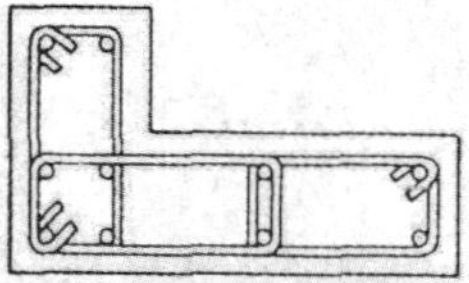

TYPICAL ARRANGEMENT
OF CORNER COLUMNS

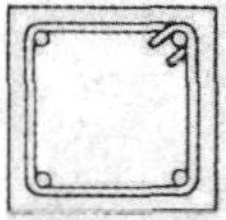

4-BARS
SINGLE TIES

6-BARS
2-TIES PER SET

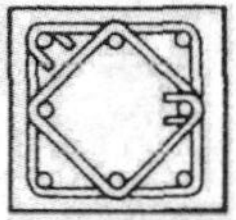

8-BARS
2-TIES PER SET

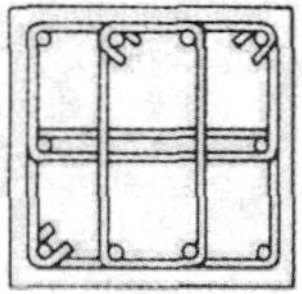

10-BARS
3-TIES PER SET

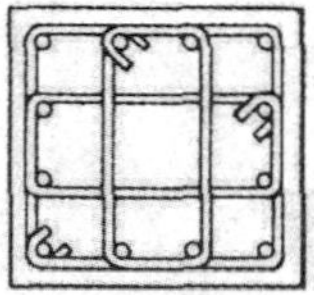

12-BARS
3-TIES PER SET

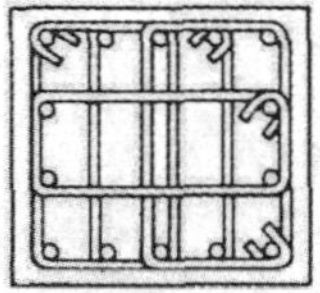

14-BARS
4-TIES PER SET

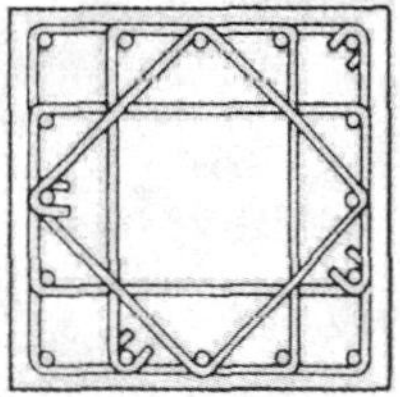

16-BARS
4-TIES PER SET

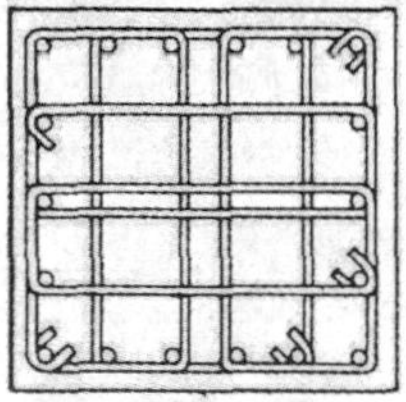

18-BARS
5-TIES PER SET

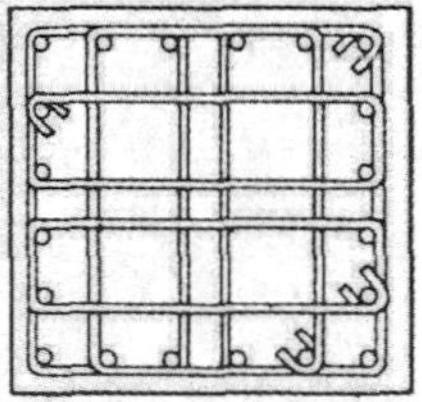

20-BARS
5-TIES PER SET

Illustration #374 - Standard Column Ties

SECTION ELEVEN QUESTIONS

Concrete Reinforcing

1. *Several disadvantages of "black" steel reinforcing bar compared to epoxy coated bar are:*
   - ❒ more expensive
   - ❒ does not bond well to concrete
   - ❒ good in a wet environment
   - ❒ none of the above

2. *The best type of rebar used to build an MRI room is:*
   - ❒ epoxy coated
   - ❒ "black" steel
   - ❒ magnetic stainless steel
   - ❒ non-magnetic stainless steel

3. *Which of the following is NOT a type of material used to manufacture rebar?*
   - ❒ glass fiber
   - ❒ carbon fiber
   - ❒ aramid fiber
   - ❒ manila fiber

4. *Determine if the following statement is true or false. The primary disadvantage of the rebar types mentioned in question 3 is that all have less tensile strength than the standard "black" steel rebar.*
   - ❒ true
   - ❒ false

5. *The preferred rebar for concrete due to the higher bonding factor is:*
   - ❒ square bar
   - ❒ flat bar
   - ❒ round bar
   - ❒ deformed round bar

6. *The ASTM method for designating bar sizing is to use what fraction of an inch?*
   - ❒ 1/16 of an inch
   - ❒ 1/8 of an inch
   - ❒ 1/4 of an inch
   - ❒ 1/2 of an inch

7. *What size is a #5 rebar?*
- ❐ 5/16 inches
- ❐ 5/8 inches
- ❐ 1 1/4 inches
- ❐ 2 1/2 inches

8. *Determine if the following statement is true or false. Metric rebar sizes are in 5 mm graduations ranging from 10 mm to 55 mm.*

❐ true ❐ false

9. *The basic formula to find the approximate weight of rebar is:*
- ❐ bar number, divided by 12
- ❐ bar number, divided by 24
- ❐ bar number squared, divided by 12
- ❐ bar number squared, divided by 24

10. *Use the question 9 method to find the weight of 200 feet of number 4 rebar.*
- ❐ 66.67 pounds
- ❐ 33.33 pounds
- ❐ 266.67 pounds
- ❐ 133.33 pounds

11. *Determine if the following statement is true or false. Scale, grease, and rust will destroy the bond between rebar and concrete.*

❐ true ❐ false

12. *Determine if the following statement is true or false. When splicing or overlapping rebar, the splice or overlap distance is the same for columns and floor slabs.*

❐ true ❐ false

13. *What is the minimum clear spacing between any two parallel column reinforcing bars?*
- ❐ 1 bar diameter or 1 inch
- ❐ 1 1/2 diameters or 1 1/2 inches
- ❐ 2 diameters or 2 inches
- ❐ none of the above

14. *Determine if the following statement is true or false. When overlapping mesh (welded wire fabric) on the ends or edges, the overlap must be a minimum of 3 full mesh squares.*

❐ true ❐ false

15. *A bend (not a hook) must be made in a number 6 rebar. To maintain the proper bend diameter, multiply the bar diameter times:*

- ❒ 4 bar diameters
- ❒ 6 bar diameters
- ❒ 8 bar diameters
- ❒ 10 bar diameters

16. *Unless otherwise specified, the normal amount of clearance required for a column tie is:*

- ❒ 4 inches
- ❒ 3 inches
- ❒ 1 1/2 inches
- ❒ 2 inches

17. *Using the minimum required clearance for column ties from question 16, calculate the amount of rebar needed to make 10 ties for a 20 inch square column:*

- ❒ 80 inches
- ❒ 74 inches
- ❒ 680 inches
- ❒ 740 inches

18. *What is the suggested minimum amount of coverage required for protection of rebar in a slab exposed to the ground?*

- ❒ 3 inches
- ❒ 2 inches
- ❒ 1 1/2 inches
- ❒ 3/4 inch

19. *The simplest method of tying 2 pieces of crossed rebar would be a:*

- ❒ snap tie
- ❒ wrap and snap
- ❒ figure eight tie
- ❒ nail head tie

SECTION TWELVE

WELDING

Introduction to Welding

This section will include information on:

Welder Performance Qualification
Welding Definitions
General Welding Safety
Fire Prevention
Oxy-Acetylene Equipment
Cutting and Brazing
Basic Welding Electricity
Welding Machines, Polarity
Welding Electrodes
Weld Joint Types and Weld Symbols
Various Types of Welding Technique
Weld Procedures
Welding Pre-heat and Distortion
Window and Mirror Welds
Pipe Purging for Welding
Preparation of Pipe Test Coupons
Plasma and Carbon-arc Cutting.

The intention of this section is to present, in a concise manner, certain fundamental facts about the welding trade and to provide knowledge which will enable tradespersons to make better use of the welding processes.

Welding is a very complex topic and cannot be completely covered in the Metal Trades Handbook and/or Training Manual. Further study of recognized reference material is recommended.

Welding may be loosely defined as a method of joining metals by the melting together of filler metal and base metal, or of base metal only. This is known as fusion welding. There are other welding methods in addition to fusion welding. These include pressure welding, and explosion welding. This section will only discuss processes that are used in fusion welding.

Welder Performance Qualifications

Any production welding for any employer will have to be backed up with some type of qualification. Qualified welders are welders who have passed a performance test that shows their ability to deposit sound weld metal. A performance test can be as simple as a single pass fillet weld on a T joint, or a complicated multi process groove weld on a pipe.

Qualification tests may be conducted with or without backing material on any type of base metal including non-ferrous base metals. A welder may be tested using any process that is detailed in the company or project welding specifications.

As there are many different fabrication and construction codes, the specific code must be referenced when taking or administering a welding test.

The majority of welder performance tests are to ASME Section IX. In Canada some tests conform to CSA W47.1, also known as the CWB test.

Performance testing certifications, or weld tickets, always expire on a pre-determined date, for example two years after the date of issue. However tickets can be withdrawn at any time if there is justification to do so.

Be sure that the referencing code is followed before, during, and after welding.

Determine what the inspector wants before starting a performance test. Ask the inspector questions such as:

- The welding process to be used. It may even be a combination of processes such as GTAW root, and SMAW fill and cap.
- Type of filler metal to be used
- How long are the tacks allowed to be?

- The amount of penetration allowed or required.
- Number of passes.
- What type of pass, whether weave bead, or stringer beads.
- Position of test.
- Progression of welding, up hand or down hand.
- Length of time allowed for the test.
- Pipe test coupons.
- Location of weld test facility.
- What type of welding ticket will be issued.
- How long the welding ticket is good for.

For information on the preparation of Pipe Test Coupons see page #505

Non-destructive testing of welds is a standard and normal procedure. For information on the types of NDT see Section Fourteen.

Codes and Welder Certification

Several industry and government agencies issue specifications governing specific welded products or areas of application. The specifications may require qualification of electrodes, testing of welding procedures, testing of completed welds, and the certification of welders through performance tests.

Due to the many variables in the design, fabrication, welding techniques and erection that affect the results, the serviceability of the product or structure is the responsibility of the designer. The designer or builder must know the code requirements before starting the job.

All welders who work on jobs that are covered by codes may be required to take a qualification test under the code.

Welders certified to one construction code are not necessarily qualified to work under a different construction code. Sometimes operator testing qualifies a welder for only one job. If processes or procedures are altered, retesting is often required. Certification for one employer does not necessarily allow a welder to work for another employer. Periodic retesting is sometimes required. In summary, "certification" must conform to the specific requirements of the situation.

Pipelines

American Petroleum Institute, also known as API, 1801 K Street, Washington, D.C. 20006. This association of the petroleum industry publishes various standards involved with welding of cross country pipelines. In Canada contact the appropriate Provincial Government department.

Pressure Vessels & Piping

American Society of Mechanical Engineers (ASME), is an engineering society which publishes standards for welding on pressure vessels and piping. Section IX is the welding and brazing qualification section of this boiler and pressure vessel code. In the U.S. contact the American Society of Mechanical Engineers, 345 East 47th Street, New York, New York 10017.

In Canada contact the appropriate jurisdictional authority that administers the codes for the respective government.

AWS American Welding Society is a non-profit technical society founded for the purpose of advancing the art and science of welding. In the U.S. contact the American Welding Society, 2501 N.W. 7th Street, Miami, Florida 33125.

Canadian Welding Bureau (CWB) is a division of the Canadian Standards Association and its purpose is to provide the necessary codes and standards covering all phases of welding.

In Canada contact the Canadian Welding Bureau, 7250 W. Credit Ave., Mississauga, L5N 5N1, phone:(416) 5421312..

A number of the codes and standards, such as the boiler and pressure vessel code, were originally written in the United States. These various codes and standards were adopted by Canada for use in manufacturing plants, pressure vessel manufactures, and industry.

The following table lists some of the organizations that may influence the work of welder.

Organizations Affecting the Welding Trade		
Organization	**Acronym**	**What the organization covers**
American Iron and Steel Institute	AISI	Develops specifications for iron and steel products
American Petroleum Institute	API	An association that acts on behalf of the petroleum industry
American Society of Mechanical Engineers	ASME	Responsible for more than 600 standards including the boiler and pressure vessel code, and the pressure piping code.
American Society for Testing and Materials	ASTM	Publishes standards for test methods, specifications, practices, guides, classifications, and terminology.
American Welding Society	AWS	Produces specifications for filler metals, welding symbols, welding inspection, and safety.
Canadian Institute of Steel Construction	CISC	Developed a code and standard practices for the construction of buildings
Canadian Standards Association	CSA	Produces standards and specification in many areas including electrical, electronics, construction, quality management systems, and health and safety .
National Board of Boiler and Pressure Vessel Inspectors	NBBPVI	Ensures that the ASME boiler and pressure vessel code is followed.
National Electrical Manufacturers Association	NEMA	Represents manufacturers of welding related equipment.
Society of Automotive Engineers	SAE	Publishes welding standards for the automotive and aerospace industries.

Table #65 - Organizations Affecting the Welding Trade

Glossary of Welding Definitions

AC: alternating current.

ASME: the American Society of Mechanical Engineers. Section IX of the Boiler and Pressure Code provides for qualification tests of procedures and personnel for welding under that code.

AWS: the American Welding Society is an organization devoted to promoting welding.

Backfire: a situation where the oxy-fuel flame momentarily goes out, then re-establishes itself inside the cutting or welding tip; also present are wisps of smoke, and popping sounds.

Backing Ring or Backing Bar: used to support and retain molten weld metal. It may be in the form of a ring or a bar. The backing may or may not become part of the weld nugget.

Base Metal or Parent Metal: the metal or material to be welded, brazed, soldered or cut.

Bevel: the angle shape at the edge of a plate.

Bevel Angle: the angle formed between the prepared edge of a member and a plane perpendicular to the surface of the member. A typical bevel angle is 30°.

Brazing: a welding procedure that uses copper, zinc and other alloys as filler metal, for example a copper and zinc (Cu-Zn) brazing rod. The process is usually done above 840°F (450°C). It uses capillary action to evenly distribute the filler metal around the joint area.

Braze Welding: this is done at a higher temperature than brazing. Usually the temperature is above 1650°F (900°C). The process would use the same alloyed filler metals but does not use capillary action to allow the filler metal to flow around the joint area.

Glossary of Welding Definitions

Burnback: a situation when the combustion process takes place in the tip or mixing chamber and black smoke, sparks, and a screeching sound emits from the tip.

Butt Joint: one of the basic welding joints when two members are joined and aligned in approximately the same plane.

CAC-A: carbon arc cutting with compressed air.

Capillary Action: the surface tension between the filler metal and the surface of the base metal. Capillary action allows the solder or brazing material to flow through the tightly fitted joint, and become evenly distributed at the joint area.

CSA: the Canadian Standards Association.

Current: the flow of electrons from the negative terminal to the positive terminal, and is measured in amperes.

DCRP: direct current reverse polarity, or electrode positive, sometimes referred to as DCEP.

DCSP: direct current straight polarity, or electrode negative, sometimes referred to as DCEN.

Distortion: during the welding process, the base and the weld metal go through heating and cooling cycles, creating non-uniform expansion and contraction. The result is a weldment that has been pulled out of shape.

Ductility: the ability of a material to bend or permanently deform without breaking.

Glossary of Welding Definitions

Effective Throat: the minimum distance between the root of a weld and the face of the fillet, not including any reinforcement. Effective throat is usually a concern to the engineers when determining weld strength.

EGW: electrogas welding.

Elasticity: the ability of a material to be put under load and return to its original shape when the load is released.

EMF: electromotive force. EMF is another name for voltage, and is the pressure that causes electrons to flow in a circuit.

FCAW: flux cored arc welding.

Ferrous: any metal where iron is by far the major ingredient, such as carbon steel or stainless steel.

Flashback: a situation whereby the oxy-fuel flame burns back all the way to the regulators attached to the cylinders, which can lead to an explosion. Improperly setting up, lighting, or shutting down an oxy-acetylene cutting or welding outfit may cause flashbacks.

GMAW: gas metal arc welding.

GTAW: gas tungsten arc welding.

Hardness: the ability of a material to resist indentation or penetration.

HAZ: heat affected zone is an area directly adjacent to the weld nugget.

Included Angle or Groove Angle: the total included angle of the groove in a butt joint An included angle is made up of 2 bevel angles. A typical groove angle is 60°.

Glossary of Welding Definitions

Incomplete Fusion: is a weld defect whereby fusion between the weld beads and/or parent metal is prevented by poor welding rod manipulation and/or welding parameters.

Incomplete Joint Penetration: a weld defect whereby the root bead does not penetrate through the entire thickness of the base metal and protrude out the root side.

Infusorial Earth: a deposit of fine, usually white, siliceous material composed mainly of the shells of the microscopic plants called diatoms.

Joint Penetration: the amount that the first pass, or root bead, penetrates into the base/parent metal. This is how the welder achieves a root profile and complete fusion. The penetration will be detailed in the welding symbol.

Joint Preparation: is the amount of plate that is removed by the bevel in order to leave behind a land. In the case of GTAW and GMAW, the bevel usually leaves a knife-edge. The welding symbol is a good place to reference the dimensions for joint preparation, such as a J, U, or V, groove preparation.

Kerf: the width of the cut, after a cutting process.

Low Temperature Brazing, or Soldering: this process is basically the same as brazing, but is done at a lower temperature of 400°F (200°C) and above. Soldering also relies on capillary action.

Nonferrous: a metal such as aluminium or brass that contains no appreciable amount of iron.

Glossary of Welding Definitions

Notch Effect: any place around a weld, or the parent metal, where a point of weakness has been created. This can be from the manufacturing process, or a situation such as an over weld, under weld, or an arc strike.

OAC: oxy-acetylene cutting.

OFC: oxy-fuel cutting.

OAW: oxy-acetylene welding.

PAC: plasma arc cutting.

PAW: plasma arc welding.

Plasma Gas (Ionized Gas): a process whereby one or more electron is stripped from the atom of an inert gas through the application of heat from the arc. This makes the plasma gas electrically conductive. Plasma is used in PAC/PAW, and ionized in GTAW, and GMAW.

Pre-heat: the application of heat prior to welding, brazing, and/or cutting, usually specific to a welding procedure.

RSW: resistance spot welding.

PWHT: post weld heat treatment.

Root Face or Land: the portion of the joint where the members are closest to each other. The root land is specific to each weld and will be detailed in the welding symbol.

Root Opening or Root Gap: is the separation at the root of the joint between the pieces of base metal. The root gap will be detailed in the welding symbol.

Glossary of Welding Definitions

SAW: submerged arc welding.

SMAW: shielded metal arc welding.

SW: spot welding.

TB: torch brazing.

Tensile Strength: the ultimate strength that a material can withstand. When the ultimate tensile strength (UTS) is exceeded the material will pull apart or fail.

Toughness: the ability of a material to resist repeated blows.

UV Rays: ultra violet rays from the high end of the visible light spectrum.

Voltage: the electrical force that will cause current to flow.

Weld Reinforcement: weld metal quantity required to fill the joint plus build up on the root side, and build up on the cap side. On a fillet weld it is the extra filler metal above and beyond the effective throat.

Welding Sequence: is the order in which the beads of a multi-pass weld are deposited, or the method of spreading the stresses around a component. A welding sequence will be laid out in a weld procedure.

Weld Size: the penetration achieved in a groove weld, the leg length in a fillet weld, and the area of fusion in a spot weld. Weld sizes are detailed on blue prints and welding symbols.

Yield Strength: the amount of force required to permanently deform a material.

General Welding Safety

Welding presents many hazards, however a welder is able to use safety equipment to reduce exposure to hazards in the industry. These include ear, eye, skin, and breathing protection. A welder should always take advantage of this personal protective equipment. There are also procedures that have been developed to allow the welder to work in a safe environment. Some of the hazards that a welder will encounter are:

- Contact burns from hot metal, slag, sparks, and flames.
- Eye injuries from harmful infrared and ultra violet (UV) rays, or from flying metal particles.
- Explosions due to improper handling of compressed gas cylinders, gases, and welding equipment.
- Explosions within enclosed objects or vessels that contain flammable materials. ***(These are extremely dangerous and life threatening)***
- Explosions due to the improper handling of welding equipment.
- Fires caused by flying sparks, slag and hot metal.
- Harmful or poisonous gases encountered from welding some metals, or cladded metals.
- Harmful or poisonous gases created when UV rays react with cleaners, and degreasers.
- Crushing injuries from the misuse of tools and equipment.

Clothing

The best possible clothing material for welding is tanned leather. However clothing made of leather is expensive, hot and heavy.

Cotton denims are the most popular. Denim is inexpensive and sheds sparks reasonably well.

A welder's clothing should conform to the following:

- Pants should not have cuffs.
- Shirt pockets should have flaps, or be removed.
- Shirts should have the top button done up to prevent burns to the lower neck.
- Steel toed boots, not shoes, should be worn, and laced up to the top.
- A cap or beanie should be worn to protect the head and hair.
- Gauntlet type gloves should be worn.

Do not wear light or frayed cotton or flannelette clothing as these materials tend to catch fire easily and quickly.

Do not wear oily clothing or clothing made from synthetic fibers, such as nylon, or rayon.

Along with the above, other basic PPE equipment (personal protective equipment) such as industry and government approved eye, hearing and head protection must be worn.

Welding Lenses, Standard, and Auto Darkening

The welder needs protection against visible light, UV rays, infra red rays, flying metal particles, sparks and slag. A good pair of approved safety glasses worn at all times will offer protection from some of these hazards, however safety glasses will not protect the worker from UV or infrared rays.

Proper filter lenses must be worn during welding and cutting operations, or permanent eye damage will result!

Eye Damage from UV Rays, and Infrared Rays

Two of the most common types of eye damage are arc flash, and cataracts; they are characterized by the following:

- Arc flash is a term used to describe eye damage caused by UV rays from the welding arc. The arc sun burns the surface of the eyeballs and creates small water blisters. This condition is described as having sand in the eyes. The result is that the eyelids flutter and tears are profuse.
- Cataracts are formed on the retina as a result of damage from infrared rays. This is the result of not using the correct filter lenses when performing OAC, and OAW operations.

The following medical aids will help the welder deal with an arc flash, however a doctor's prescription is recommended.

1% Pontocain drops, 2% Butyn drops,
1% Holocaine.

Do not use these medical aids for over 12 hours as they may hide a much more serious problem, such as a foreign object embedded in the eyeball.

NOTE: A person should not work if their eyes are medicated. If the eyes are not noticeably better after 12 hours, see a doctor.

Filter lenses are available in three basic colors: amber, green and cobalt blue. The shade of the lens is indicated by numbers, and the greater the number the darker the shade.

There are also many different types of photoelectric lenses, or speed glass, available in a variety of helmet configurations. Auto darkening helmets may have a variety of settings, which may include filter selection, sensitivity, delay time, and grinding settings. These auto shields can be very expensive; therefore research is necessary before purchasing.

The filter lens must eliminate glare but still allow the welding process details to be viewed clearly. In order to view the welding process clearly the welder must select the correct filter shade, or lens number.

A good rule of thumb when selecting a filter lens is to follow this procedure:

1. Arc weld or oxy-fuel cut for a few minutes.
2. Lift the welding helmet or cutting goggles.
3. Close eyes.
4. If light spots are seen a darker lens is needed.
5. If dark spots are seen a lighter shade is needed.

Filter Lens Selection Guide

Lens #	Application
Shade# 4	General Oxy Fuel Cutting, and Oxy Fuel Welding. Plasma Arc Cutting
Shade# 5	
Shade# 6	
Shade #7, 8	Heavy Oxy Fuel Cutting, Oxy Fuel Welding, and Plasma Arc Cutting.
Shade# 9	Light Arc Welding
Shade #10	General Arc Welding
Shade # 11	General GTAW, GMAW, or FCAW
Shade #12	High Amperage GTAW, GMAW, FCAW, and Air Arc Gouging

Table #66 - Selection of Welding Filter Lenses

To protect the filter lens from sparks, and spatter build-up, the filter lens should have a clear glass in front and one behind, see illustration #375. In addition there should be an approved, impact resistant, plastic lens placed in the helmet. The clear plastic lens provides extra protection when power brushing, chipping, and grinding. A glass lens should never be used as it could shatter.

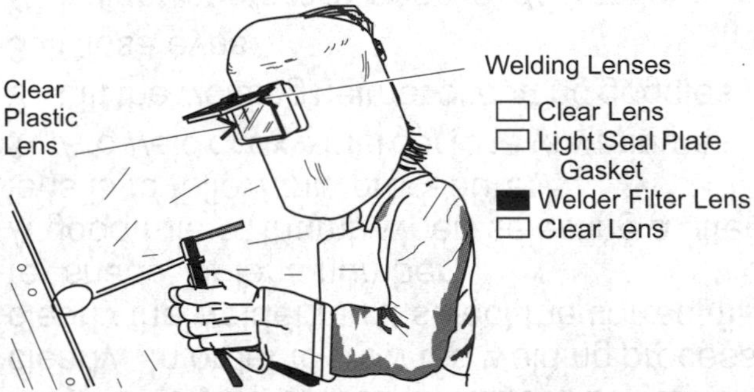
Clear
Plastic
Lens
Welding Lenses
Clear Lens
Light Seal Plate Gasket
Welder Filter Lens
Clear Lens

Illustration #375 - Welding Lenses

Ventilation

Welders should always have good ventilation. Welding shops should have at least four air changes per hour. Screens should be arranged so they do not restrict ventilation. When welding on nonferrous or galvanized metals, extra ventilation will be required. Even with good ventilation it is recommended that the welder use an approved half mask respirator that provides protection against welding fumes and airborne particles.

Respirators cannot protect against atmosphere deficiencies, such as poisons, gases, and low or high oxygen levels. Precautions must be taken into account when welding with processes using shielding gases.

Argon is heavier than air. Therefore it will sink to the bottom of a confined area and displace breathing air causing the welder to suffocate.

CO_2 reacts with UV rays producing CO, or carbon monoxide, and ozone is also formed in any welding process.

These are very harmful and unfortunately there is no respirator available that can protect against these types of hazards.

Cadmium and lead fumes are highly toxic. The welder must be provided with an approved airline respirator for use with these fumes.

Exposure to zinc fumes from galvanized steel may result in metal fume fever, commonly referred to as zinc chills. Zinc chills are self-eliminating, without any known chronic complications or after effects.

Prevention of Fires and Explosions

Fires and explosions in the welding work place are a major issue and must be dealt with through a proactive approach. Plan ahead, examine the welding environment, and anticipate the results of welding actions. Consider the following:

- Positively ensure there are no combustibles in the area. Combustibles may include: paper, cardboard, wood, or rags. Always remove any petroleum products such as oil, grease, and fuels.
- Make sure that sparks, either from welding or grinding, are showered in a safe direction away from people, supplies, and equipment.
- Approved and inspected fire extinguishers should always be located very close to the general work area. Only qualified personnel should inspect fire extinguishers, and the dated punch cards indicating the last inspection should be kept up to date.

- Be considerate if working near or around other personal. Locate screens to protect others against harmful rays, and flying particles.
- Keep work areas as neat as possible. Remove garbage and route hoses and cables in a safe manner.
- It is a common and often mandatory practice to have properly trained fire watch individuals located in the areas during welding operations. To reduce the chance of fire starting after the job is complete, inspect the work site before leaving.
- Always check to make sure there are no flammable vapors or fumes present in your work area. It is a good idea to check several times a day for fumes or vapours.
- Never weld on anything that has held a flammable substance, such as a fuel tank or chemical container.
- If unsure about the safety of a welding operation consult with a qualified safety person before beginning work.

Oxy-Acetylene Cutting, Welding, and Brazing

Oxygen Gas

Oxygen is a colorless, odorless, tasteless gas at room temperature. It is slightly heavier than air, and while not flammable, it must be considered dangerous. Oxygen (O_2) combines readily, and in some cases very violently, with many other elements.

In Canada the oxygen compressed gas cylinders will display the Workplace Hazardous Material Information System (WHMIS) symbol for oxidizing, and compressed gas. In the United States the oxygen compressed gas cylinders will display the Hazardous Product Warning Labels for oxidizing and compressed gas.

Oxygen is the element in air that supports life and combustion. In general, materials that burn in air will burn much more violently in oxygen.

Some materials, not considered combustible in air, will burn readily in oxygen. Oxygen for the purpose of cutting and welding has to be 99.5% pure.

The air liquefaction process is used to manufacture welding grade oxygen. This process super cools atmospheric air to -350°F (-194°C), and the oxygen is then boiled off and collected.

At room temperature oil and grease are not considered highly flammable, but if either element is brought in contact with pure oxygen under high pressure or friction an explosion may occur.

Remember the following when handling welding grade oxygen:

- Keep oxy-fuel equipment away from oil and grease.
- Never oil regulators or torch parts.
- Never use oxygen to blow off clothes.

Acetylene Gas

Acetylene gas (C_2H_2) is created when calcium carbide is combined with water in an acetylene generator. Acetylene gas is colorless, but fortunately has a strong pungent odor. As little as 1% in the air is quite noticeable to the average person's sense of smell and 2.5% to 80% in the air is explosive.

Acetylene gas is heavier than air, and will settle in low areas. It is a good safe work practice to never leave a cutting or welding torch in a confined space. Use the torch then take it out. In Canada the Workplace Hazardous Material Information System (WHMIS) symbol for acetylene gas is the label for Flammable Compressed Gas. In the United States the Hazardous Product Warning Label for acetylene is Flammable Gas.

It is advisable to treat mixtures of air or oxygen and acetylene as explosive. If the smell of acetylene is noticeable take no chances, extinguish all open flames and ventilate the room.

Oxygen Cylinders

An oxygen cylinder is a pressure vessel and must be handled with care and attention. A full oxygen cylinder can have as much as 2200 PSI (15,166 kPa) at room temperature. If the cylinder is left out in the sun pressures can reach 2600 PSI (17,900 kPa). For this reason high pressure gas cylinders must always have the cap attached when not in use. When in use these cylinders must be tied off securely.

The top of the cylinder is hemispherical and the valve hole is reinforced with extra metal. Oxygen cylinders come in a variety of sizes. Oxygen can also be stored in a liquid form in a cryogenic tank. This type of containment vessel relies on very low temperatures to store high volumes at low pressures.

Do not attempt any repairs to an oxygen cylinder. If a cylinder leaks, remove it from any building, place it in the open, then tag it indicating the type of fault and notify the supplier.

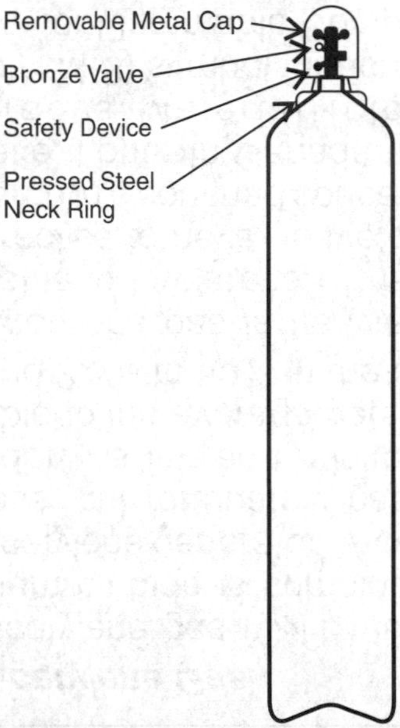
Removable Metal Cap
Bronze Valve
Safety Device
Pressed Steel Neck Ring
Illustration #376 - Oxygen Cylinder

The oxygen cylinder is protected from extreme pressure caused by heat with the use of a metal rupture disc.

This allows the slow, controlled escape of gas. The rupture disc is located in the valve, opposite the threads.

Some of the features of an oxygen cylinder are:

- All oxygen connections have right hand threads. Hoses are color-coded green.
- Oxygen cylinder valves should be opened fully while in use.
- Oxygen cylinders have no fixed draw off limit

Never rely on the color of a gas cylinder to determine the contents, always read the identification label to identify the type of gas.

Oxygen Manifold Systems

An oxygen manifold system draws oxygen from a number of cylinders concentrated in one location and delivers it to the work area. This system is used when large volumes of oxygen are needed, such as in a large fabrication shop. It reduces cylinder handling costs and also provides greater control over oxygen supply.

- Use only manifold systems obtained from reliable manufacturers.
- Only connect cylinders of equal pressure to a manifold system.
- When assembling the components use a thread sealer.
- Always check for leaks with a leak detection solution.
- Leaks in hoses should be repaired with proper tools and parts.
- Regulators and gauges should only be repaired by certified people.

Acetylene Cylinders

Acetylene is an unstable compound, therefore acetylene gas is not safely compressed beyond 15 PSI (103 kPa), especially in large volumes such as cylinders, pipelines and generators.

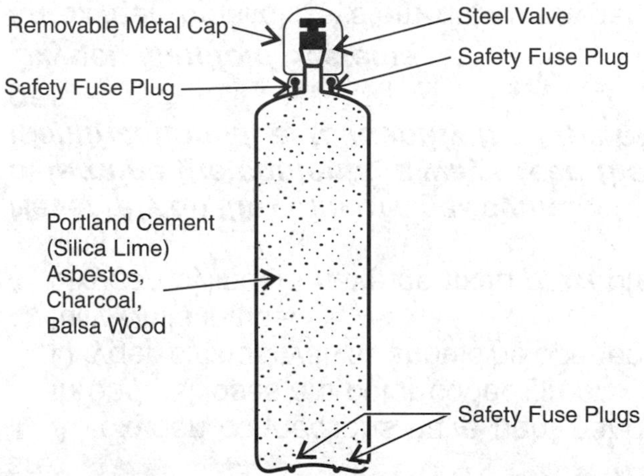
Removable Metal Cap
Steel Valve
Safety Fuse Plug
Safety Fuse Plug
Portland Cement (Silica Lime) Asbestos, Charcoal, Balsa Wood
Safety Fuse Plugs

Illustration #377 - Acetylene Cylinder

At 28 PSI (193 kPa) or greater acetylene will break down and self-ignite, or spontaneously combust. This is why acetylene regulators have a red line at 15 PSI (103 kPa), and why acetylene is always stored with stabilizing compounds.

The inside of an acetylene cylinder is not empty like an oxygen cylinder, but instead is filled with a porous material that is used to absorb acetylene. In older acetylene cylinders the porous material mainly used was shredded asbestos. Newer cylinders contain portland cement (silica lime) to which some suppliers add asbestos, charcoal and balsa wood, to provide a light weight filler with high porosity.

Acetone is also used to stabilize the acetylene by being pumped into the cylinder until 40% of the volumetric capacity is reached. Acetone absorbs acetylene by taking it into solution. This provides a safe medium for the acetylene to be stored at pressures of 250 PSI (1,723 kPa).

Because of the presence of a required amount of acetone, acetylene cylinders are weighed before being filled, then filled and weighed again. Acetylene is sold by weight.

Acetone can only give up the acetylene at a maximum volumetric rate. The maximum draw-off rate by which acetylene may be separated from acetone is 1/7 the volume of the cylinder per hour.

Safety codes call for a minimum of one fusible plug on each end of the cylinder, with one at the bottom, and one at the top near the valve. These plugs melt out in case of fire, and allow a slow controlled escape of gas, rather than a violent explosion. The fusible plugs have a melting point of about 212°F (100°C),

Some of the features of an acetylene cylinder are:

- They must be used in the vertical position to prevent acetone from being drawn off.
- Store cylinders in a cool place.
- Never attempt to transfer acetylene from one cylinder to another.
- Never attempt to interchange equipment from one type of fuel gas to another type.
- Key-type acetylene valves should be opened only one and one half turns.
- Hand wheel type valves should be opened $1^1/_2$ to 2 turns, or enough to provide sufficient flow.
- All acetylene connections have left hand threads with a groove in the nut. Hoses are color-coded red.
- Never use fittings made from copper or red brass.
- Use an approved leak detection fluid to test for leaks.

Never rely on the color of a gas cylinder to determine the contents, always read the identification label to identify the type of gas.

Acetylene Manifold Systems

In order to prevent acetone from being drawn off a single cylinder of gas, acetylene gas manifolds are used when large volumes are required. Manifold systems draw acetylene from a number of cylinders located away from the work area, usually in an acetylene storeroom. Acetylene manifold systems reduce cylinder-handling costs and provide greater control over gas supply.

When constructing a manifold system do not use copper or red brass pipes or fittings. A residue is formed when acetylene comes in contact with copper (copper is used in red brass). This residue is very unstable, and heats up enough to cause acetylene to ignite.

Yellow brass fittings, stainless steel tubing, and carbon steel piping are good materials for an acetylene gas manifold.

- Use only manifold systems obtained from reliable manufacturers.
- Only connect cylinders of equal pressure to a manifold system.
- Never use copper or red brass pipes and fittings,
- Use only yellow brass.
- When assembling the components use a thread sealer approved for acetylene gas,
- Always checks for leaks with a leak detection solution.
- If leaks are found in hoses they should be repaired with proper tools and parts.
- Regulators, and gauges should be repaired by certified people.

Oxy-acetylene Welding and Cutting Equipment (illustration #378)

A typical oxy-acetylene outfit consists of:

1. Oxygen regulator.
2. Acetylene regulator.
3. Oxygen and acetylene hose.
4. Torch body, or torch barrel.
5. Cutting attachment or cutting torch.
6. Welding tips.
7. Cutting and welding goggles.
8. Tip cleaners and strikers

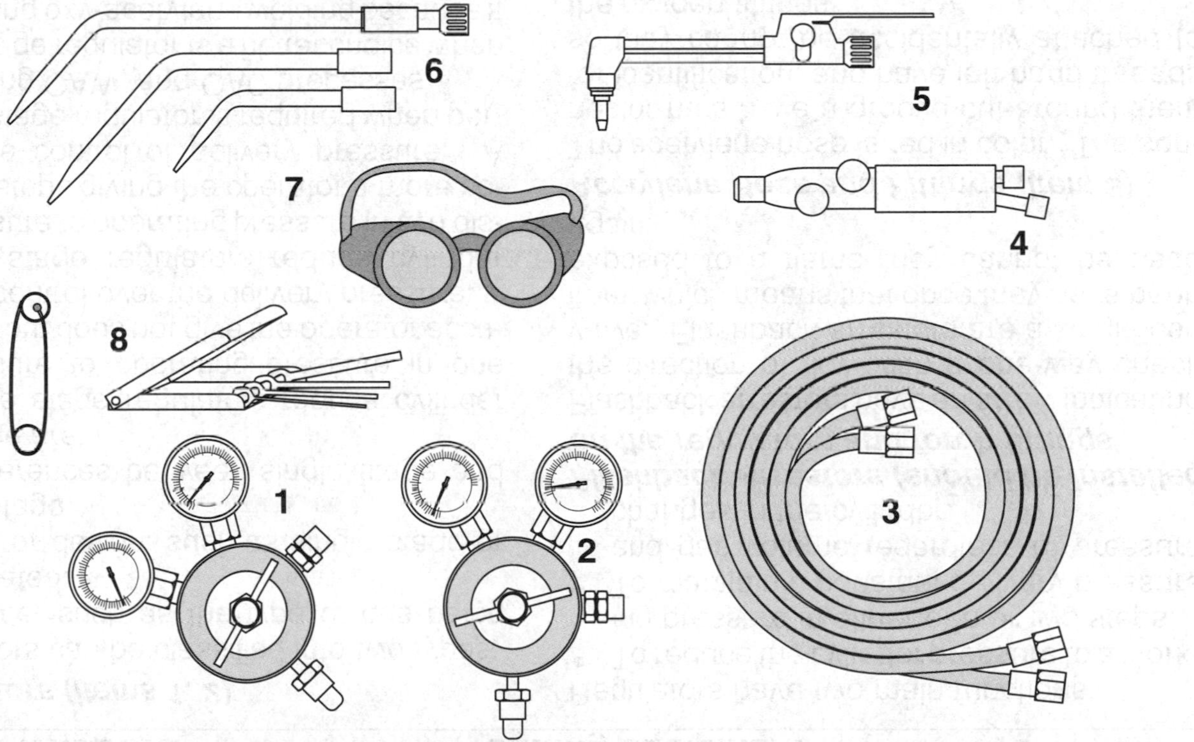
6
5
7
4
8
1
2
3

Illustration #378 - Oxyacetylene Welding and Cutting Equipment

Regulators (items 1, 2)

Regulators can be classified into two types:

- Service, such as the type of gas being regulated.
- Type or design, such as single stage or two stage.

The differences between single stage and two stage are:

- Single stage regulators reduce cylinder pressure to operating pressure in one step, but does not give the operator accurate control over the delivery pressure.
- Two stage regulators reduce cylinder pressure to operating pressure in two distinct steps giving the operator a more accurate control of delivery pressure. A two-stage regulator is required when performing OAW, and OAC processes.

A two stage regulator is a better choice when performing oxy-acetylene welding because it provides a uniform pressure regardless of the contents of the cylinders.

Regulators have two main functions:

- To reduce the cylinder pressure to a working pressure in either one or two steps.
- To maintain a constant delivery pressure and gas volume regardless of pressure changes in the cylinder.

Flashback Arrestors (should be installed on the regulators and torch fittings

Flashback arrestors have an arrow indicating the direction of flow with a one-way check valve. Flashback arrestors are a single use item, which means that once they have been exposed to a flame they cannot be used again.

Acetylene Hose and Fittings (item 3)

The acetylene hose is red in color. The connector nuts have a groove cut around them for identification, and have left hand threads so they cannot be accidentally attached to the oxygen fittings.

Oxygen Hose and Fittings (item 3)

The oxygen hose is green in color. The hose connector for oxygen is similar to acetylene except the oxygen connector has right hand threads and no groove around the nut.

Torch Body or Torch Barrel (item 4)

The torch body, or barrel, is the location where the oxygen and acetylene come together. In other words this is where oxygen and acetylene are mixed. Another name for the torch body is a mixing chamber. There are two varieties of torch bodies, one is called the combination torch and the other is a heavy-duty torch.

Cutting Attachment or Torch (item 5)

A cutting attachment or cutting torch can only be used with the combination torch. It attaches to the combination torch body. When an operator depresses the oxygen lever, oxygen is introduced into the pre-heat flame to facilitate the cutting process.

Cutting tips are specific to the type of fuel gas used and the intended use. A welder may have many types of tips, such as tips for cutting through steel plate, cutting bolt heads flush with the plate surface, and flame gouging. Cutting tips are manufactured out of copper alloys and their design, shape, and appearance will vary according to their purpose.

Welding Tips (item 6)

Welding tips usually follow a standard pattern. They are manufactured out of copper alloys, and their design, shape, and appearance may vary according to application.

Cutting and Welding Goggles (item 7)

Cutting and welding goggles must be worn to protect the operator from the harmful effects of infrared rays, UV rays, and sparks. The cutting and welding goggles should be worn over an operator's safety glasses.

Tip Cleaners, Strikers, and Other Accessories (item 8)

Tip cleaners, strikers, wrenches, and bottle carts are just some of the accessories needed to setup and maintain oxy-acetylene equipment.

Setting Up Oxy-acetylene Equipment

The following setup procedure is for equipment that is completely dismantled. All these steps are not necessary if only one part is being changed.

1. Clean your work area and read the instructions that come with the equipment. Examine all the components for defects.
2. Stand the cylinders vertically and secure them in a bottle cart, or tie them off in a secure location.
3. Uncap the cylinders.
4. Quickly open and close the cylinder valves to remove dust and dirt from the valves.
5. Attach the acetylene regulator to the cylinder valves. Flat-faced fittings of the type found on some acetylene regulator stems must have a fiber washer between the stem and the cylinder valve. Most acetylene regulators have a bull nose fitting and do not require a fiber washer between the stem and the cylinder valve.

6 Attach the oxygen regulator. It is equipped with a smaller diameter bull nose fitting. It is virtually impossible to mixed up the two regulators.

7. Attach the appropriate flash back arrestor/flow valve to each end of the regulators.
8. Attach the hoses to the regulators and tighten the connections.
9. Release the spring pressure on the regulator adjusting screws by turning anti-clockwise until they turn freely.

10. Open cylinder valves slowly, allowing a slow build up of pressure within the regulators. Always stand off to the side of the regulators when opening the cylinders.
11. Increase the working pressure on the regulators, one at a time, to purge the hoses and remove dust, dirt, and talcum powder before attaching the torch. After purging the hoses close the cylinders.
12. Attach the torch side flash back arrestor/flow valve.
13. Attach torch, mixer, tip, and tighten firmly.
14. Adjust the working pressure for both oxygen and acetylene.
15. Check connection for leaks, use an approved leak detection solution on all connections, and inspect for bubbles.
16. A quick way to ascertain whether or not there is a leak in the equipment is to close the cylinder valves and watch if the needle on the high side of the regulator falls to zero. If the needle on the high side falls to zero use an approved leak detector to detect the location of the leak.
17. If unsure about setting up oxy-acetylene equipment, ask a supervisor, or an experienced co-worker.
18. Inspect the oxy-acetylene equipment on a regular basis.

Lighting a Cutting Torch

1. After setting up the oxy-acetylene equipment review the size of the cutting tips. If using a #0, or a #1 cutting tip, pre-set the oxygen regulator at about 30 PSI, and the acetylene regulator between 3 PSI and 5 PSI.
2. If the torch is a combination type, open the torch handle oxygen needle valve fully, and leave the oxygen valve, located on the cutting attachment, closed (delete this step if using a heavy-duty cutting torch).

3. Open the acetylene needle valve about one half turn and light the torch, using a flint striker. ***DO NOT USE A LIGHTER OR MATCH***. Increase acetylene flow to take away the heavy smoke. This is referred to as just above the smoke zone. Do not take away all the smoke as the pre-heat flame will be too hot.
4. Add oxygen to the pre-heat flame by slowly opening the oxygen regulator adjusting screw to eliminate the outer feather. Once the outer feather has been eliminated and only the distinct pre-heat flame remains, a neutral flame has been achieved.
5. Depress the cutting oxygen lever, and if the outer feather reappears, readjust to a neutral flame with the lever still depressed.
6. Before beginning the cut, ensure that the cutting jet is perfectly straight. If not, clean the tip with the correct sized tip cleaner.
7. If unsure about any of the steps ask a supervisor or an experienced co-worker.

Shutting Down Oxy-acetylene Equipment

Close the acetylene torch valve, then the oxygen torch valve when cutting or welding is stopped.

When there is no further welding or cutting for a considerable length of time the following steps must be followed:

1. Close the acetylene and oxygen cylinder valves.
2. Open the torch oxygen valve to release all the pressure from the hose and regulator.
3. Turn out the pressure adjusting screws of the oxygen regulator.
4. Close the torch oxygen valve.
5. Open the torch acetylene valve to release all the pressure from the hose and regulator.

6. Turn out the pressure adjusting screw of the acetylene regulator.
7. Close the torch acetylene valve.
8. For emergency shut down of oxy-acetylene equipment in the event of a hose rupture and fire, first close the oxygen cylinder valve, and then close the acetylene cylinder valve. The next step is to use a fire extinguisher to put out the fire at the hoses.
9. Ask a supervisor if unsure about the correct emergency procedure.

Oxy-acetylene Flames for Use in Cutting and Welding.

Carbonizing/Reducing Flames - A carbonizing flame is rich in acetylene. It introduces carbon into the weld, and may be readily recognized by the feathery edge of the white cone. Some metals are welded with a carbonizing flame as it adds carbon to the weld area. See illustration #379.

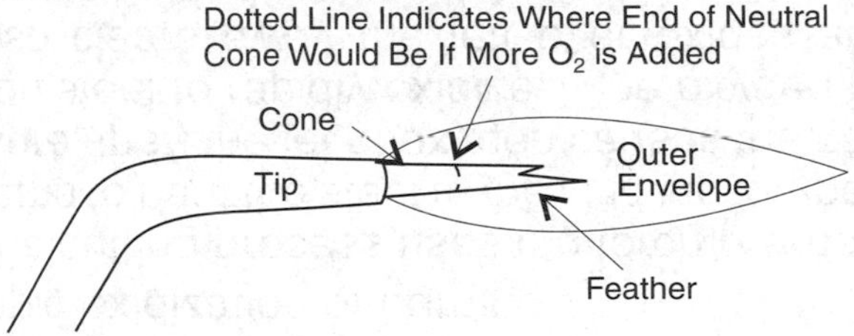
Dotted Line Indicates Where End of Neutral Cone Would Be If More O_2 is Added
Cone
Tip
Outer Envelope
Feather

Illustration #379 Carbonizing Flame

Neutral Flame - A neutral flame is produced by burning the correct mixture of oxygen and acetylene to produce a clear well-defined white cone in the flame. Welds made with a neutral flame should be free of burned metal or hard-spots and be thoroughly fused. See Illustration #380.

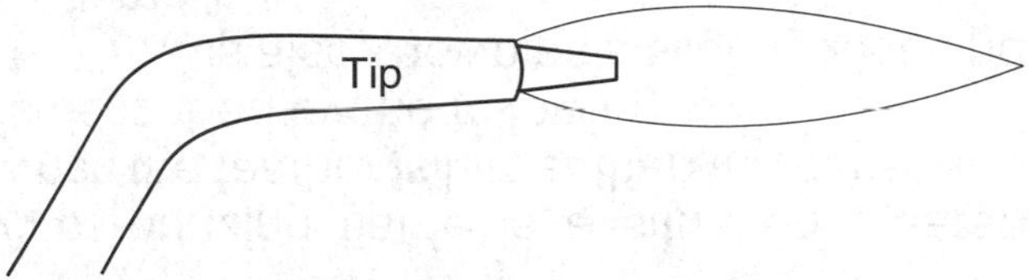
Tip

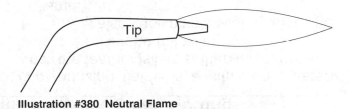

Illustration #380 Neutral Flame

Oxidizing Flame - An oxidizing flame has a shorter envelope and the small pointed white cone identifies the oxidizing flame with its excess of oxygen. This flame causes an oxidizing or burning of the weld metal. See illustration #381.

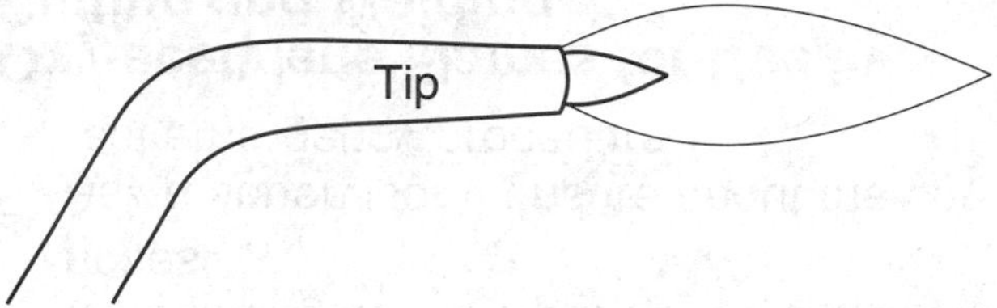
Tip

Illustration #381 Oxidizing Flame

The flames used for fusion welding and brazing are classified by the size of the cone in relation to the feather. A 1X flame is the same as a neutral flame, or in other words the cone is 1 times the size of the feather.

A carburizing flame is a situation created when the feather is larger than the cone, and is described by the following:

- $1\frac{1}{8}$ X is also known as a slightly reducing flame.
- 2X, 3X, etc., flames are also called reducing flames.

Oxy-acetylene Cutting

Under the right conditions, iron or carbon steels will progressively burn. Burning is a term used when steel is heated to the kindling temperature of approximately 5800°F (3,200°C), and exposed to pure oxygen. Steel will undergo a chemical reaction called rapid oxidization or burning.

The cutting process uses the torch pre-heat flame to heat the steel to the kindling temperature, then the jet of oxygen causes the carbon steel to rapidly oxidize. The oxygen jet also clears away the left over oxides and leaves behind a clean cut (kerf) line.

Combination Welding and Cutting Torches

The combination torch is the most popular torch as it offers the operator the ability to change from welding to cutting. The wide selection of welding tips and cutting attachments make it possible for a welder to be flexible and complete a wide range of tasks. When operating the combination torch using the cutting attachment, it is necessary to have the torch handle oxygen needle valve fully open to allow a full flow of oxygen to the cutting jet. Pre-heat oxygen is controlled by the oxygen needle valve on the cutting attachment.

See illustration #382 for a combination torch example.

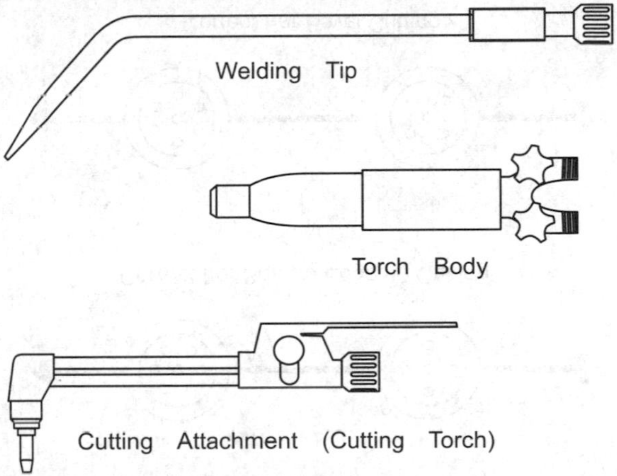
Welding Tip
Torch Body
Cutting Attachment (Cutting Torch)

Illustration #382 - Combination Torch

Heavy-Duty Hand Cutting Torch

The heavy-duty hand cutting torch is designed for cutting purposes only and is generally heavier and longer than combination torches. This torch is more rugged and generally considered better where only cutting is required. See illustration #383.

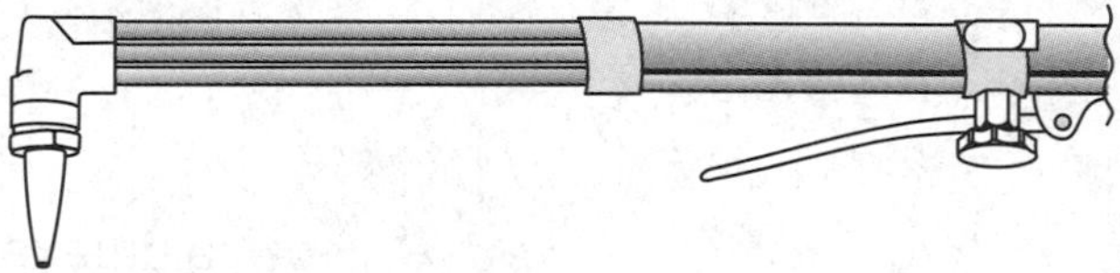

Illustration #383 Heavy Duty Hand Torch

Tip Selection

When selecting a cutting tip there are several things to consider such as, type of cut, thickness of plate, and type of fuel gas. There are tips made for gouging, cutting bolt heads flush at the surface, and heating. Also consider the following when selecting a tip:

- The larger the tip number the larger the tip (oxygen jet orifice).
- Each manufacturer uses different size holes to correspond with the numbers.
- Generally the thicker the material being cut the larger the oxygen jet orifice required.
- Not all tips will fit into all the different types of torches.
- The type of tip is related to the type of fuel gas being used. An acetylene tip cannot be used with propane gas.

Oxy-acetylene Cutting Pre-heat Hole Alignment

The correct pre-heat hole alignment is indicated in illustration #384.

Correct For Square Edge 90 Cutting

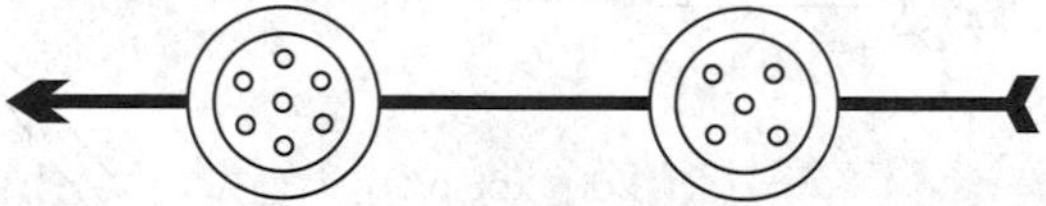

Correct For Bevel Cutting

Illustration #384 Pre-heat Hole Alignment

Starting a Cut

Heat the starting point to a bright red using a neutral flame. Depress the cutting lever slowly until the cut has been established. Move the torch along the cut at a speed to give the quality of cut required. Consider these following points when making a cut:

- Always cut with a neutral flame.
- When pressing the oxygen lever lift the torch slightly, this will reduce the amount of spatter on the tip.
- The pre-heat flames should never come in contact with the work piece.
- It is best to cut left to right, or right to left, as opposed to away or toward yourself.
- Always be as steady as possible. Be in a position to be supported through the entire cut.
- Always maintain the torch perpendicular to the work.
- If the cut (kerf) lines are curved the cut speed may be too fast.
- If the torch is backfiring the flow of gas maybe too low. Increase the regulator settings or reduce the cutting tip size.
- Always start the cut on a sharp edge such as the edge of a plate, a drilled hole, an arc bead or chisel mark, as in illustration #385.

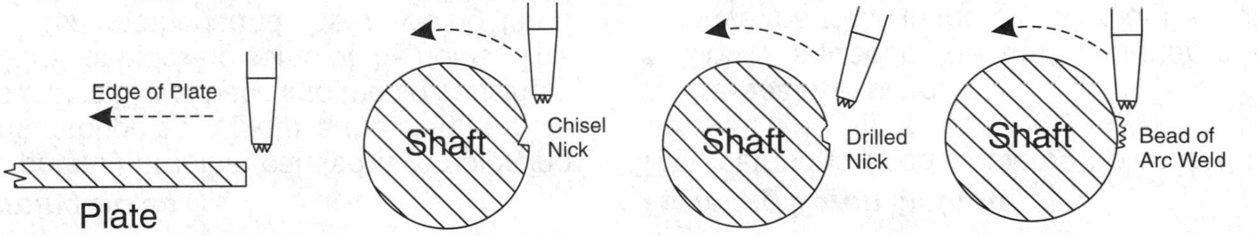
Edge of Plate
Plate
Shaft
Chisel
Nick
Shaft
Drilled
Nick
Shaft
Bead of
Arc Weld

Illustration #385 - Starting a Cut

Piercing Holes

The primary problem caused when piercing holes through solid plate is the slag and oxides that is blown back into the tip causing a backfire, or blocking some of the holes. The still torch method and the traveling torch method are two ways of piercing a hole through plate. These methods should help to avoid some problems.

Still Torch Method

This method is used to pierce holes in heavy plate.

- Pre-heat the general cut area, or the start of the cut.
- Slowly squeeze the oxygen lever and raise the torches upward. This allows the slag to blow clear of the tip.
- Lower the torch so the pre-heat holes are still slightly above the surface, and continue the cut.

Traveling Torch Method

This method is used to pierce holes in thin material.

- Pre-heat the plate.
- Slowly squeeze the cutting lever and move the torch in the direction of the cut. This allows the slag to blow out behind the tip.

Torch Inclination

Whenever a cutting torch is being used, the tip is normally perpendicular to the surface.

However a general rule of thumb is that the thinner the material being cut the more torch inclination used.

Do not use any torch inclination when shape cutting. See illustration #386.

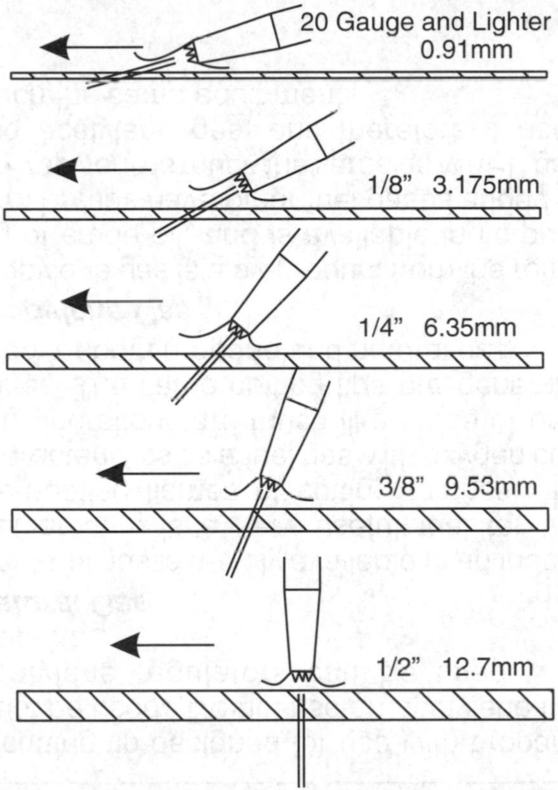
20 Gauge and Lighter
0.91mm
1/8" 3.175mm
1/4" 6.35mm
3/8" 9.53mm
1/2" 12.7mm

Illustration #386 Torch Inclination

Alternate Fuel Gases for Use With Cutting, Welding and Heating.

Methyl-acetylene Propadiene Stabilized (MPS) or, Mapp Gas.

Mapp gas is stabilized. Methyl-acetylene Propadiene is a stable compound, so there is no need for the same storage criteria as with acetylene gas. Mapp gas cylinders are simple in design, much the same as those used for propane. Equipment such as regulators, torches etc., that are used for acetylene can be used for Mapp gas.

Propane Gas

Propane is used regularly with oxygen cutting in a number of plants because of its availability, lower cost and ease of use. Propane is also a good choice for pre-heating. It has a lower temperature than acetylene gas, but a higher BTU rating. A higher BTU rating means that the volume of heat is greater and this heats up components faster.

A cutting tip designed for use with propane must be used. Do not use an acetylene tip. Acetylene regulators can be used with propane.

Natural Gas

If natural gas is readily available in an industrial area, it is a very useful fuel for the pre-heating flames of cutting torches. Its characteristics as a fuel gas with oxygen cutting operations are much like those of propane. The same cutting tips are generally used for both propane and natural gas.

Propylene Gas

Propylene gas is a by-product from the refining of crude oil, and is available in its pure form or may have other fuel gases added to it. Propylene is much the same as MAPP gas and acetylene gas, and therefore it uses much the same equipment.

There are a number of fuel gases to choose from when performing OAC and OAW, and each one of these gases has its own unique characteristics in relation to flame temperature and heat energy. Temperature is an arbitrary number used to identify the flame, in much the same way that room temperature is identified. The energy in the flame is independent of temperature and therefore a flame may have a high temperature even though it has a low level of energy.

Flame energy is expressed in British Thermal Units (BTU) or mega joules per cubic metre MJ/m^3. Acetylene gas has a high flame temperature but low energy. Propane gas has a low flame temperature, and high energy. Therefore acetylene is the best choice gas for cutting and welding while propane gas is the best choice for heating.

Fuel Gases

Fuel Gas	Energy in MJ/m^3	Energy in BTU	Flame Temp neutral
Acetylene	55	1470	3090°C 5600°F
MAPP	91	2460	2871°C 5200°F
Propane	92.5	2498	2526°C 4580°F
Natural Gas	37	1000	2538°C 4600°F
Propylene	89	2400	2871°C 5200°F

Table #67 - Fuel Gases

Oxy-acetylene Welding

Oxy-acetylene welding may be used to produce satisfactory welds on ferrous materials, with groove and fillet weld types of joint.

The OAW procedure is slow and therefore puts a tremendous amount of heat into the base metal. OAW is not recommended for alloy steels because the mechanical properties of the parent material will be changed unless an approved pre-weld heat treatment procedure is followed. The majority of OAW is done using a neutral flame, however higher strength filler metals, such as R65, use a slightly carbonizing flame in order to maintain the tensile strength.

Balancing a Welding or Brazing torch

The purpose of balancing a welding or brazing torch is to establish the maximum gas flow settings used for a particular welding or brazing tip. This compensates for normal regulator inaccuracies by setting the regulators under actual working pressure. A welding torch should be balanced every time a tip is selected and the regulator pressure must be adjusted accordingly. This balancing process is used for both oxy-acetylene welding and brazing.

Balancing Steps

1. Slowly open the oxygen cylinder valve until fully open to allow a controlled build up of pressure within the regulator. Always stand off to the side of the regulator when opening the cylinder.
2. Slowly open the acetylene cylinder valve about one and one half turns to allow a controlled build up of pressure within the regulator. Always stand off to the side of the regulator when opening the cylinder.
3. Turn the acetylene regulator adjusting screw clockwise until fuel starts to flow.
4. Open the torch acetylene needle valve about one half turn and light the torch, using a flint striker. ***DO NOT use a lighter or match.*** Fully open the torch acetylene needle valve.
5. Turn the acetylene regulator adjusting screw clockwise until the flame just leaves the tip end.
6. Adjust the gas flow with the acetylene torch valve until the flame is back to the tip end and it does not smoke.
7. Fully open the torch oxygen needle valve.
8. Slowly turn the oxygen regulator adjusting screw clockwise until a neutral flame is obtained.
9. Open the acetylene torch valve slightly and turn the oxygen regulator valve clockwise to again obtain a neutral flame.
10. Repeat step #9 until the torch acetylene needle valve is fully open and there is a bright neutral flame.
11. If unsure about any of the steps ask a supervisor or an experienced co-worker.

The following is a general procedure for use on single pass fillet welds using OAW:

- As with other welding, mechanically clean the surface before welding.
- Tack-up the joint.
- At the beginning of the joint bring the base metal up to temperature using the feather of the flame, not the cone.
- Once the base material is up to temperature and a puddle is formed, then start adding the filler metal using the dip technique.
- Fill the crater at the end of the joint.
- On light gauge material, such as 10 gauge or lighter, it may be advantageous to use smaller diameter filler wire such as 3/32-inch or less.

The following is a general procedure for use on single pass groove welds, on light gauge material about 10 gauge:

- Tack-up the joint, using a 5/32-inch gap between the components.
- After tacking, the gap should be about 1/8-inch.
- The parent material must be brought up to welding temperature using the feather, not the cone of the flame.
- Start adding the filler metal to the joint.
- It is important to note that a keyhole must always be maintained or proper penetration will not be achieved.
- Fill the crater at the end of the joint .
- When performing groove welds on lighter gauge material the welder may have better results using smaller diameter filler wire, such as 3/32-inch or less.

Oxy-Acetylene Welding Procedures						
Fusion Welding				Brazing		
Base Metal	Filler Metal	Flame	Flux	Filler Metal	Flame	Flux
Carbon Steel	L. A. Superweld	SR	None	Altem Super Bronze	N-SO	None
				Brasteel	N-SR	None
				Nickel Silver (Anaconda 828)	N-SO	Brazewell & Copox
	"HERCULES" Iron	N	None	All Easy Flo	N-SR	Handy Flux
Wrought Iron	L.A. Superweld	N	None			
Grey Cast Iron	"FUSE-WELL" Cast Iron # 11	N	Hematox	Allem Super Bronze	N-SO	None
	Moly-Nickel- Cast Iron #14	N	Hematox	Nickel Silver (Anaconda 828)	N-SO	Brazewell & Copox
Aluminum 6063,6061	AA 4043 Aluminum	SR	Albex	AA 4047 Aluminum Brazing Wire	SR	Aluminum Brazing Flux
Aluminum 5052	AA 5356 Aluminum	SR	Albex			
Electrolytic Copper	Lo-Melt" Copper	N	None	Allem Super Bronze	N-SO	None
				All Easy Flos & Sit Flos	N-SR	Handy Flux
Silicon Bronze (Everdur 1010)	Everdur 1010	SO	Copox	Allem Super Bronze	N-SO	None
				Lo-Melt Copper	N-SR	None
				All Easy Flos & SO Flos	N-SR	Handy Flux
Lead	Strips of Base Metal	N				
Yellow Brass				Lo-Melt Copper	N-SR	None
Red Brass-Bronze	Altem Super Bronze	O	None	All Easy Flos & Sit Flos	N-SR	Handy Flux
"N" - Neutral "SO" - Slightly Oxydizing "SR" - Slightly Reducing "O" - Oxydizing "R" - Reducing						

Table #68 Oxyacetylene Welding and Brazing Procedures for Ferrous and Non-Ferrous Materials.

Low Temperature Brazing or Soldering

This brazing procedure, commonly referred to as soldering, is used for joining pipe and tubing, usually copper tubing. It creates joints that are strong, permanently free from leaks, and maintenance free.

The following is a general procedure for low temperature brazing:

- Remove burrs with a reamer after cutting the tube to length.
- Clean fittings, sockets, and tube ends with a solvent and emery cloth to remove foreign material and oxides. Do not touch the surfaces after cleaning. See illustration #387 for cleaning procedures.

After cleaning, apply the flux to each joint surface. Assemble the tube into the fitting after fluxing. Where possible, turn the fittings to spread the flux uniformly, as in illustration #388.

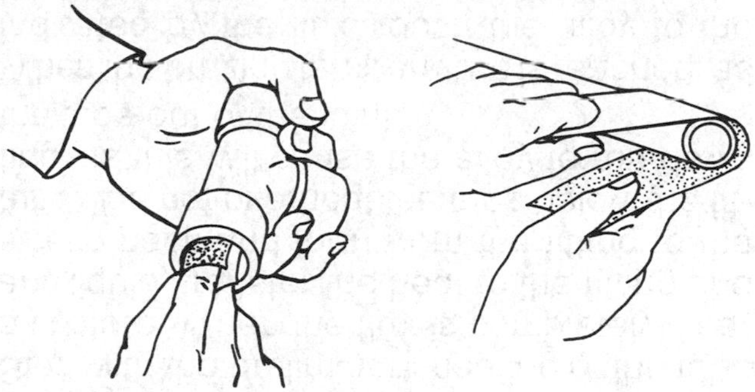

Illustration #387 Cleaning Tube

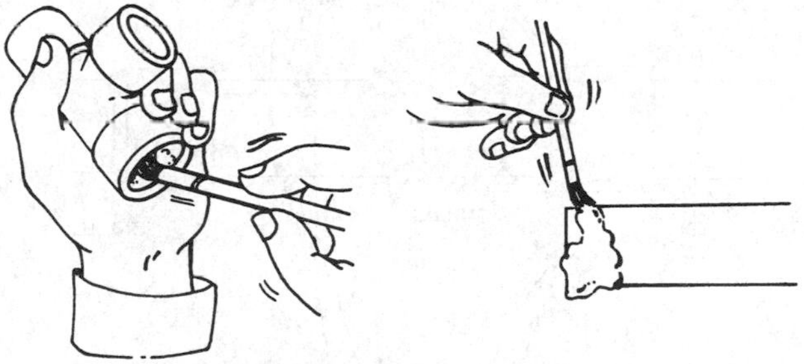

Illustration #388 - Applying Flux

- Use an oxy-acetylene tip of sufficient size (#0, or #1) to permit even heating. Use a slightly reducing, or carburizing flame such as a 1 1/8X.
- Start heating the tube about 1 inch (25mm) away from the end of the fitting. Heat evenly all around to get uniform expansion. When the flux on the tube has melted to clear liquid, transfer the heat to the fitting. The fitting and tube should be heated equally before applying the solder.
- When the flux is a clear liquid on both the fitting and the tube, pull the flame back slightly and apply the solder firmly against the tube at the junction between the tube and fitting. With proper heating and capillary action, the alloy will flow freely into the joint. See illustration #389.

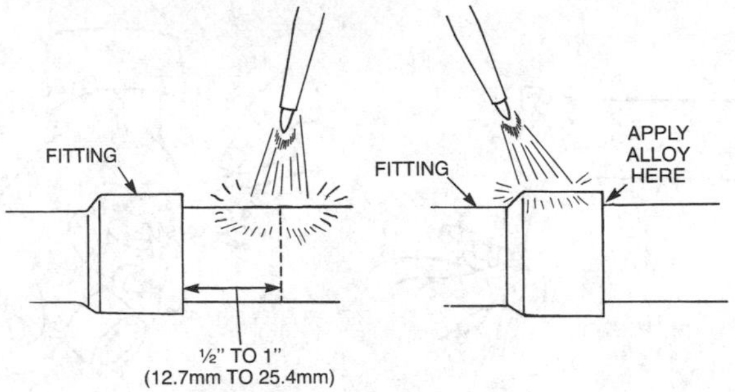
FITTING
FITTING
APPLY ALLOY HERE
½" TO 1" (12.7mm TO 25.4mm)

Illustration #389 - Applying Heat

Soldering Vertical Up-Hand Joints

Start with the preliminary heating of the tube as before. When the flux is completely clear and liquid, transfer the heat to the fitting and sweep back and forth from the fitting to the tube. Do not overheat the tube below the fitting, as this will cause the alloy to run down the tube out of the joint.

When the brazing temperature is reached, as indicated by the flux, touch the alloy to the joint with the heat aimed on the wall of the fitting to pull the alloy up into the entire joint area.

Cleaning the Remaining Brazing Flux

Immediately after the brazing alloy has set, apply a wet brush or swab to the joint to wash off the flux. The flux can be removed from the inside of the tube by flushing with water. See illustration #390.

All flux must be removed for inspection and pressure testing.

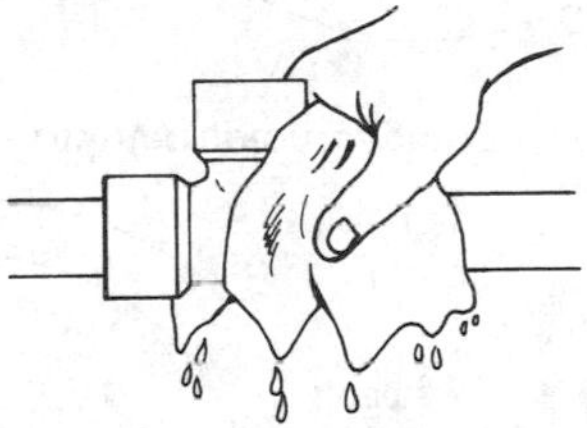

Illustration #390 - Cleaning Brazing Flux

Disassembly of a Soldered Joint

Reflux the joint area. Heat the joint uniformly to slightly above the melting point of the alloy. The tube can then be easily removed from the fitting. To reuse the tubing and fittings follow the instructions given for new material.

Basic Welding Electricity

One of the basic principles of electricity is that electrical currents flow in loops or circuits. The electron theory states that electrons flow from the negative terminal to the positive terminal in the electrical circuit.

The electrons that are flowing in a circuit are related to the flow of current, and are measured in amperes. The voltage is the force, or pressure that causes the current to flow. Voltage is sometimes called EMF, which means electromotive force. See illustration #391.

To shut off the flow of electrons in an electrical circuit, the circuit has to be broken and an air gap created. See illustration #392.

If the EMF is strong enough, or the voltage is high enough, electrons will be forced across the gap and the current, or electrons, will continue to flow along the circuit to the positive terminal. See illustration #393.

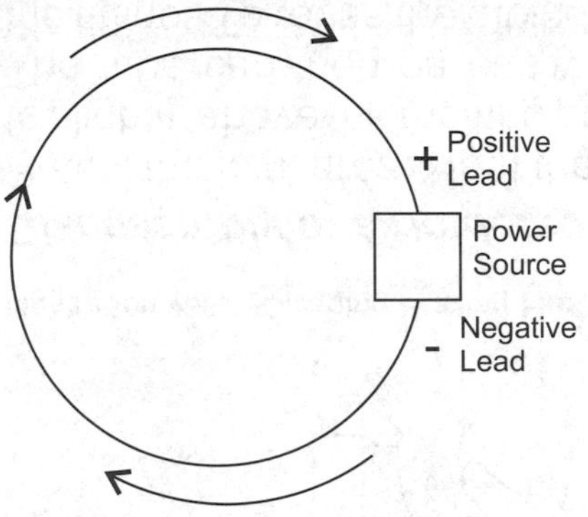
+ Positive Lead
Power Source
- Negative Lead

Illustration #391 - Uninterrupted Circuit

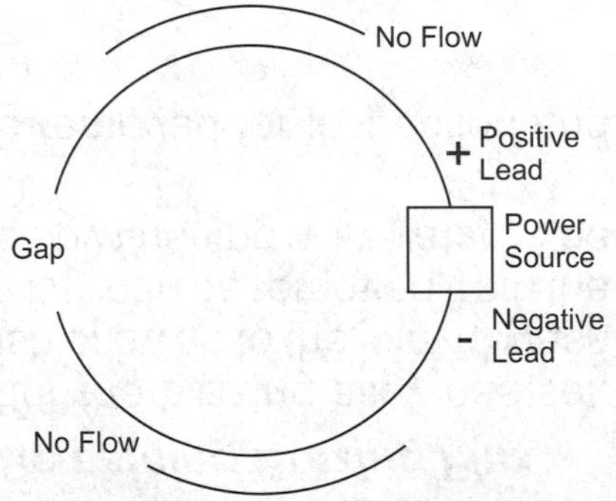
No Flow
+ Positive Lead
Power Source
Gap
- Negative Lead
No Flow

Illustration #392 - Interrupted Circuit

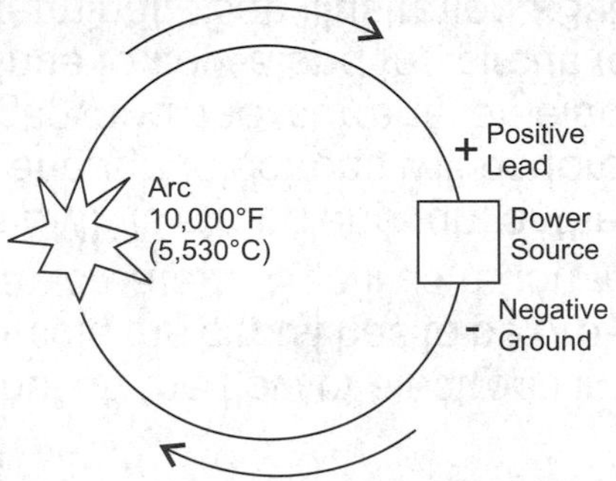
+ Positive Lead
Arc
10,000°F
(5,530°C)
Power Source
- Negative Ground

Illustration #393 - Arcing Circuit

Electric arc welding or resistance welding is a way of putting these two electrical principles to work. The welding machine delivers the current, which is responsible for creating the necessary heat for fusion welding. The operator, or welder, dials in the proper current setting to achieve the desired result.

The welding machine also delivers the voltage required to keep the circuit complete and ensures that the current continues to flow, and avoid having the arc snuff out.

With some welding processes the welder has no control over the voltage as it is pre-set by the manufacturer of the welding machine, or by the power source. With other welding processes it is critical that the welder choose the appropriate welding voltage.

When the welder attaches the ground clamp, and the electrode is brought into intimate contact with the work piece, and then pulled away, the arc is stuck. The arc voltage jumps the gap creating an electric arc, which allows current to flow. This electric arc can develop about 10,000°F (5500°C) which is sufficient to melt any metal it contacts.

The heat generated by the arc melts the metal in the work piece, and the end of the electrode creating a puddle. Molten electrode metal falls through the arc into the puddle of molten base metal and fuses with it.

When the arc is moved away, the molten mixture cools and solidifies into a nugget of new metal.

When the arc is moved slowly along the work piece, a continuous strip of new metal is left behind to form the weld bead, or nugget. If the weld is properly done the base metal and the material deposited by the melting electrode are fused together permanently. See illustration #394.

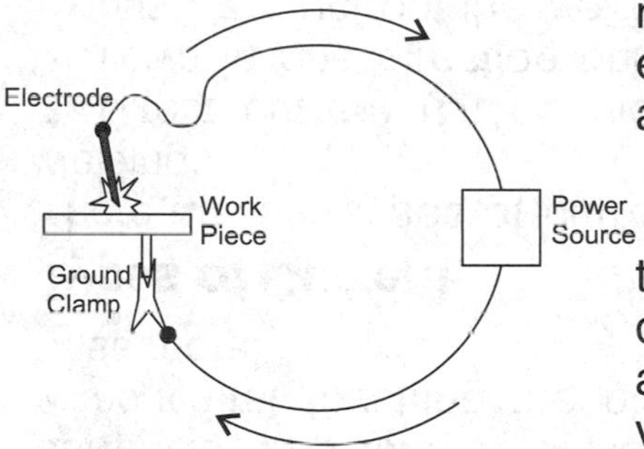
Electrode
Work Piece
Ground Clamp
Power Source
Illustration #394 - Welding Circuit

In a welding circuit, the two main ingredients are voltage and current.

It is important that the required amounts of voltage and current be present if a proper weld is to be produced.

The following is a break-down of the roles of voltage and current in a welding circuit:

Voltage:

- Controls the ease of striking the arc.
- Is directly related to the fluidity of the puddle, as the higher the voltage the more fluid the puddle.

Amperage:

- Controls the burn off rate, as the higher the amps the faster the electrode will be consumed.
- Controls penetration as the higher the amps the more penetration achieved.

Non-touch Starts

In some cases the welder needs to initiate the arc without touching the base metal. This is done in order to prevent contamination of the base metal, such as in the case of aluminium welding with the GTAW process.

Some welding machines have a separate high voltage circuit of about 15,000 volts. This is enough voltage, or EMF, to allow the current to jump across a ¼ inch to ½ inch gap without first touching the electrode to the base metal.

Types of Current

There are two types of current used in arc welding:

- Direct current (DC) - electrical current flows in one direction only and continuously throughout the welding circuit.
- Alternating current (AC) - electrical current has positive and negative values flowing alternately. The most common AC current is 60 cycles, which means the current reverses direction of flow 120 times per second.

Arc welding can be accomplished by using either direct current (DC) or alternating current (AC).

ARC Welding Polarities

There are two DC polarities:

- Electrode negative (straight polarity). This is accomplished by connecting the ground clamp to the positive terminal, and the electrode to the negative terminal.
- Electrode positive (reverse polarity). This is accomplished by connecting the ground clamp to the negative terminal, and the electrode to the positive terminal.

Welding Machine Types

The selection of welding current, either AC or DC, will depend on the availability of welding equipment/machines and the type of electrodes to be used.

An arc-welding machine is designed to deliver voltage and amperage at a sufficient rate or capacity for welding. The welding machines may be broadly classified into either rotating or stationary types:

Rotating Power Sources: a generator/alternator driven by an internal combustion engine (gasoline or diesel) or an electric motor.

Stationary Power Sources: these are plugged into a receptacle, and use a transformer to step down the voltage and step up the current.

Welding machines are sometimes called power sources. There are three basic types of power source:

- AC power sources where AC current is available.
- DC constant current (CC) machines, used for GTAW, SMAW, and sometimes SAW, and FCAW.
- DC constant voltage (CV) machines, used for GMAW, FCAW, and SAW.

The welding processes may require a wide range of currents from a few amps to currents exceeding 1,000 amps. The requirements for voltage and amperage levels determine to a great extent the design of power sources for welding.

Duty Cycle: welding machines are assigned a duty cycle by the manufacturer. A duty cycle is a rating system that determines how long a machine can operate continuously at full capacity in a 10 minute period. If a machine is given a 20% duty cycle that means it can only operate at full capacity continuously for 2 minutes out of a 10 minute cycle.

This also means that the same welding machine can operate at 20% capacity continuously for the entire 10-minute period.

Hobby machines usually have a duty cycle of 20% to 40%, while production machines in industry have a 100% duty cycle.

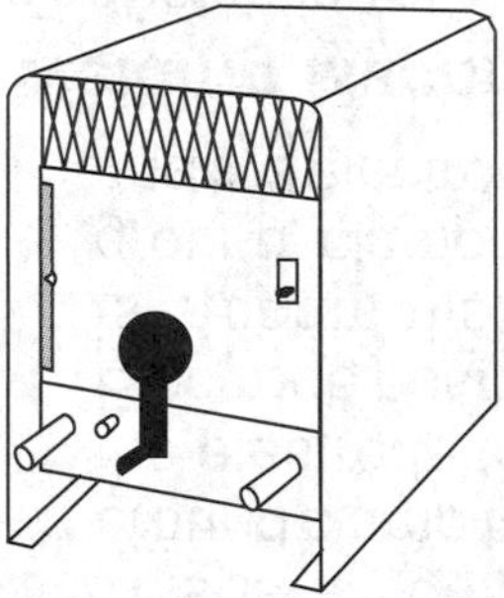

Illustration #395 - AC Transformer

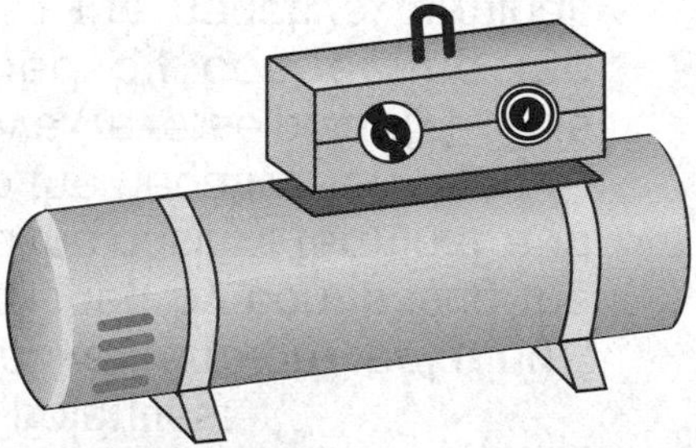

Illustration #396 - Motor Driven DC Generator

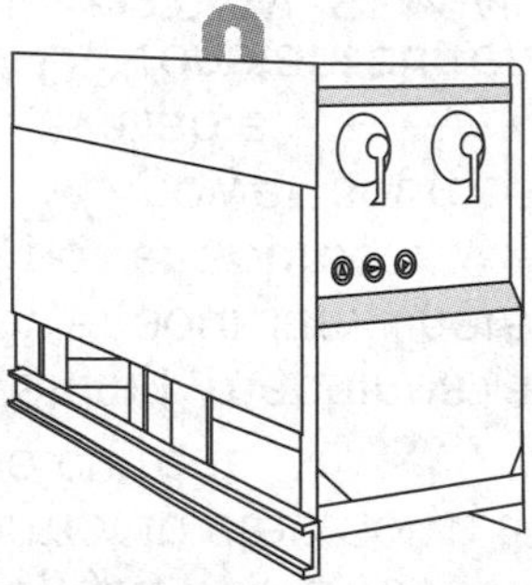

Illustration #397 - Motor Driven AC/DC Rectifier

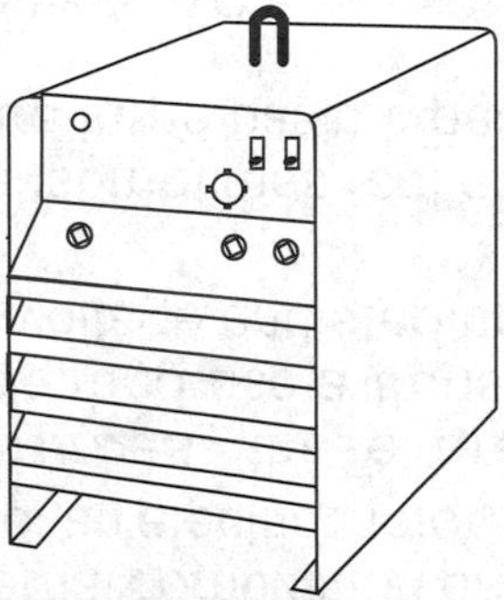

Illustration #398 - AC/DC Rectifier

AC Transformer

AC transformers are the simplest welding machines for supplying current suitable for arc welding. The AC transformer, commonly called a buzz box, has two main components:

A primary transformer connected directly to the wall plug and supplied with household voltage, and current which is typically 220 volts on a 50-amp breaker, and

A secondary transformer which steps the voltage down to about 30 to 40 volts from 220 volts, and steps the current up from 40 amps to about 225 amps.

This type is shown in illustration #395.

Table #69 breaks down the advantages and disadvantages of an AC transformer.

AC transformer, or Buzz Box welder	
Initial cost	Low
Maintenance cost	Very low
Selection of polarities	Poor, only AC
Selection of electrodes	Poor, only AC
Portability	Low, needs 220 volt power supplied
Duty cycle	Poor, only about 20%
Options	No options just AC power

Table #69 - AC Transformer

Motor Driven AC/DC Rectifier or DC Generator

The generator can be powered by an electric motor for shop use, or by an internal combustion engine (gasoline or diesel) for field use. Engine driven welders can have either water or air cooled engines and many of them provide auxiliary power for emergency lighting, power tools, etc.

Another version of the motor driven power source is the AC alternator. The main difference is that only AC welding voltage is available. Since only AC current is available, the welder will be restricted to AC electrodes.

A motor driven DC generator is shown in illustration #396, and a motor driven AC/DC rectifier in illustration #397.

Motor Driven Welding Machines,	
Initial cost	High
Maintenance cost	High
Selection of polarities	Good, DCRP, DCSP, and AC (not with a motor driven AC alternator)
Selection of electrodes	Good, All available electrodes (not with a motor driven AC alternator)
Portability	High, and provides 110 volts and 220 volts
Duty cycle	Good from 60% to 100%
Options	110 Volts, 220 Volts, DCRP, DCSP, AC, arc control may permit use of wire feeders

Table #70 - Motor Driven DC Generator

AC to DC Rectifier

AC to DC rectifiers combine some of the major advantages of both the DC motor generator and the AC transformer.

The rectifier is a method of supplying direct current power to the arc without having to use a rotating generator.

These machines are more efficient electrically than the generator type of welding machines, and they provide quieter operation.

An AC to DC rectifier is shown in illustration #398.

AC to DC Rectifier, Pros and Cons	
Initial cost	High
Maintenance cost	Low, must be cleaned regularly
Selection of polarities	Good, DCRP, DCSP, and AC
Selection of electrodes	Good, all available electrodes
Portability	Poor, heavy, and may need 600 volts 3 phase
Duty cycle	Good, from 60% to 100%
Options	110 Volts, 220 Volts, DCRP, DCSP, AC arc control, permits use of wire feeders

Table #71 - AC to DC Rectifier Pros and Cons

Inverter

This type of power source is the latest in technology. Inverters are light, compact, and are available with a whole host of options. When compared to AC to DC rectifiers they are basically similar in that a wall plug is required to power them up. After that the similarity ends; inverters are lighter and are also a true multi-process welding machine.

Inverter Welding Machine,	
Initial cost	High, will be reduced as more machines reach the market
Maintenance cost	High, will be reduced as more new technology reaches the market
Selection of polarities	Good, DCRP, DCSP, and AC
Selection of electrodes	Good, all available electrodes
Portability	Medium, light enough to be easily moved around by hand
Duty cycle	Good, from 60% to 100%
Options	Lots of options - 110 Volts, 220 Volts, DCRP, DCSP, AC, arc control, use wire feeders, and majority have non-touch start, and hot start abilities.

Table #72 - Inverter Welding Machine Pros and Cons

Welding Machine Installation

All welding machines must be properly connected to the power source as indicated on the manufacturers instructions. Machines must be earth grounded to avoid shock. Corners and walls that interfere with a clean flow of air must be avoided. Support the machine firmly and evenly to avoid misalignment.

Installation concerning electrical connection must comply with electrical codes applicable in that area. The grounding of electrical equipment is a code requirement.

Welding Cables

The welding cables, electrode holder and ground clamp must be large enough in diameter to carry the intended current without undue voltage drop.

There is more resistance with smaller diameter cables and less resistance with larger diameter cables. Therefore when connecting cables of different sizes, connect the larger diameter cable to the welding machine, and the smaller diameter to the electrode holder. Welding cable size numbers are indicated in table #73.

Welding Cable Size Numbers							
smallest <<==============>> LARGEST							
4	3	2	1	1/0	2/0	3/0	4/0

Table #73 - Welding Cable Size Numbers

Recommended Sizes of Welding Cables (Electrode Holder and Ground)												
	Distance from Welding Machine in feet											
AMPS	50	75	100	125	150	175	200	225	250	300	350	400
100	2	2	2	2	1	1/0	1/0	2/0	2/0	3/0	4/0	4/0
150	2	2	1	1/0	2/0	3/0	4/0	4/0				
200	2	1	1/0	2/0	3/0	4/0	4/0					
250	2	1/0	2/0	3/0	4/0							
300	1	2/0	3/0	4/0								
350	1/0	2/0	4/0									
400	1/0	3/0	4/0									
450	2/0	3/0										
500	2/0	4/0										
550	3/0											
600	3/0											

Table #74 Recommended Sizes of Welding Cables

Polarity Check

If unable to verify the polarity configuration of a welding machine due to unmarked terminals it might be necessary to use the following method of identification. (Use only an E-6010 or E-7010 electrode in the recommended heat range to determine the polarity of a welding machine.)

- If the arc blows wildly, and there is a hissing sound, the electrode is fastened to the negative terminal and the polarity would be DCSP, or straight polarity.
- If the arc reacts as expected, the electrode is fastened to the positive terminal and the polarity would be DCRP or reverse polarity.

Welding Electrodes

A consumable electrode is the filler metal for welding. When using the SMAW process the electrode is being melted and used to form the puddle. The American Welding Society (AWS) and the Canadian Standards Association (CSA) have developed specifications for filler metals.

For the common E-60XX and E-70XX series of SMAW electrodes the core wire is generally made from the same wire stock. It is S.A.E. 1010 carbon steel, having a carbon range of 0.05% to 0.15%.

Identification of Electrodes for SMAW

For identification, each class of electrode used for SMAW is designated by the letter E, followed by a four digit (AWS), or five digit (CSA) numbering system;

- The first two digits represent the minimum tensile strength of the deposited weld metal expressed in thousands of pounds per square inch. For example E-60xx indicates 60,000-PSI minimum tensile strength.
- For the metric designation there are three numbers for minimum tensile strength E410XX where the 410 is in Megapascals.

- The second last digit refers to the welding position in which the electrode can be used: E-XX1X all positions, E-XX2X flat and horizontal, E-XX3X flat position only, E-XX4X vertical down, flat, horizontal, and overhead.
- The last digit indicates the chemical composition of the coating, which also dictates the polarity to be used. See table #75.

Identification of Electrodes for SMAW				
Electrode	**Coating**	**Polarity**	**AWS designation**	**F-number**
E-XXX0	Cellulose/sodium	DCRP	E-6010, E-7010	F3
E-XXX1	Cellulose/potassium	DCRP, DCSP, AC	E-6011, E-7011	F3
E-XXX2	Rutile	DCSP, AC	E-6012	F2
E-XXX3	Rutile/potassium	DCRP, DCSP, AC	E-6013	F2
E-XXX4	Rutile/iron powder	DCRP, DCSP, AC	E-7014, E-7024	F2
E-XXX5	Lime/calcium carbonate	DCRP	E-7015	F4
E-XXX6	Lime/calcium carbonate	DCRP, AC	E-7016	F4
E-XXX7	Iron oxide/iron powder	DCRP, DCSP, AC	E-6027, E7027	F1
E-XXX8	Lime/iron oxide	DCRP, AC	E-7018, E-8018	F4

Table #75 - Identification of Electrodes for SMAW

Correct Electrode Selection

Selecting the correct electrode is a matter of analyzing the conditions applying to a particular application, then determining the type and the diameter of electrode best suited to those conditions. The analysis is made easier if the following factors are considered:

- What is the type of base metal to be welded? Is it ferrous, non-ferrous, carbon steel, or stainless steel?
- What are the dimensions of the section to be welded? Is it thick plate, thin sheeting, or long structural shapes?
- What type of current is available, or what type of welding machine is available?
- What welding position or positions will be used? Is all the welding to be done in the flat, or in other positions?
- What type of fit-up does the work permit? Will there be a wide gap, or a tight fit-up requiring penetration through the land?
- What are the specific chemical properties and mechanical properties required of the weld metal? Corrosion resistance, high tensile strength, ductility or others?
- What codes, standards or specifications must be met? Must the weld meet the requirements of the ASME Boiler Code, government specification, or company quality control requirements?
- The skill level of the welder must also be taken into consideration. Not only hand skills but also knowledge of the machine, and the consumables.
- What type of tools are available? Is spatter easily removed, or does the welder have the proper tools to remove the slag so the next pass will have proper fusion?

Once the above factors have been carefully and fully analyzed, there should be no difficulty in selecting an electrode which will provide the arc stability, smoothness of weld bead, easy slag removal and minimum spatter, which are so essential to productive arc welding of the highest quality.

Use table #75 for electrode selection.

Stainless Steel Electrodes

Stainless steel is an alloy that is made from carbon steel, nickel, and a minimum of 10% to 11.5% chromium in order to make it resistant to corrosion.

Stainless steels are manufactured in order to perform in some of the harshest of environments, such as high temperatures, cryogenic service, low temperatures and corrosive atmospheres.

For additional information about stainless steel see Section Thirteen - Weld Metallurgy.

Because of the many different services of stainless steels there have been several types developed, including:

- Austenitic.
- Ferritic.
- Martensitic.
- Duplex.
- Precipitation-hardening.

Austenitic Stainless Steel

Austenitic stainless steels are by far the most widely used. Some of their qualities are:

- 16% to 26% chromium.
- 6% to 22% nickel.
- 0.03% to 0.25% carbon
- Up to 1200°F (649°C) they exhibit good corrosion resistance.
- Austenitic stainless steels are subject to carbide precipitation in the HAZ (heat affected zone) after welding, between 800 to 1500°F (427 to 816°C)
- They are very good for cryogenic and low temperature service.
- Their ductility, and toughness are better than carbon steels.
- Austenitic steels cannot be hardened by heat treatment, however they can be work hardened.

- The protective chromium oxide layer can be rendered useless by small bits of carbon steel, thus allowing the stainless steel to rust.
- Austenitic stainless steels are used in pulp and paper mills, oil refineries, gas plants, and air separation plants.

Carbide Precipitation

Carbide precipitation takes place only in the heat-affected zone (HAZ) after the welding process has been completed. Chromium carbides are formed when chrome is taken out of solution as the stainless steel passes through the temperature of 800 to 1500°F (427 to 816°C), after the weld bead is applied to the base metal.

When chromium carbides are formed in the HAZ this seriously inhibits the ability of steel to resist corrosion. When the steel is put into service, corrosion rapidly happens in the HAZ, and only in the HAZ.

Austenitic stainless steels, and electrodes, must be stabilized with titanium or niobium to prevent the formation of chromium carbides.

Ferritic Stainless Steels

Ferritic stainless steels are sometimes called straight chrome steel because they contain very little, if any, nickel.

These types of stainless steel are less expensive to manufacture. Some of their other qualities are:

- 10.5% to 30% chromium.
- Little or no amounts of nickel.
- 0.07% to 0.25% carbon, and 0.15% to 2.5% nitrogen.
- Non-hardenable by heat treatment, however some types may respond to work hardening.
- Generally this group is more corrosion resistant than the Martensitic group.
- The Ferritic group is hard to weld.
- Uses include automotive exhaust, automotive trim, and cooking utensils.

Martensitic Stainless Steels

Martensitic stainless steels may also be called straight chrome steel as they also contain very little nickel. This group contains more carbon than the Ferritic group. Some of their other qualities include;

- 12% to 18% chromium.
- 0.15% to 1.20% carbon.
- All Martensitic stainless steels are hardenable by heat treatment.
- They have moderate corrosion resistance.
- This group is weldable, but they must be heat-treated after welding to establish their mechanical properties.
- The Martensitic group is highly magnetic.
- Martensitic grades are good at resisting abrasion. Their uses include turbine blades and cutlery.

Duplex Stainless Steels

Duplex stainless steels are a combination of Ferritic and Austenitic stainless steels. One disadvantage is embrittlement after welding. If proper welding procedures and post weld heat treatment (PWHT) procedures are used there should not be any problems. Some of their advantages are:

- Better at resisting stress corrosion, cracking and pitting than Austenitic stainless steels.
- They also have about twice the yield strength of Austenitic stainless steels
- This group has a high strength to weight ratio, therefore they are used in thin sections.

Precipitation-hardening Stainless Steels

Precipitation-hardening stainless steels are easily heat treated, and through simple heat treatment procedures their tensile strength can be greatly increased.

Precipitation-hardening stainless steels have good corrosion resistance without the loss of ductility or notch toughness which is the case with other stainless steels with comparable tensile strengths.

Precipitation hardening is a heat treatment process that relies on the use of heat and one or more elements. These elements may include copper, titanium, niobium, or aluminium. Steels are heated to a pre-determined temperature and the elements are allowed to precipitate throughout the structure of the steel. Thus the mechanical properties of the steel are changed.

Precipitation hardening is performed with stainless steels and aluminium.

Stainless Steel Filler Metals

Stainless steel can be successfully welded by using the SMAW, GTAW, PAW, GMAW, SAW and FCAW processes. When using the PAW, GTAW, and GMAW process the electrode is a bare wire and an inert shielding gas provides shielding for the weld puddle. The FCAW, and SMAW processes require a flux to provide shielding for the weld puddle. In the SAW process a granular flux is used to cover the weld metal to protect it from contamination.

Stainless Steel Filler Metals for SMAW

All SMAW stainless steel electrodes are furnished with an extruded type coating. These electrodes are available with a lime type coating for use with DCRP or with a titania type coating for use with either AC or DCRP. See table #76

AWS Classification of Stainless Steel Filler Metals for SMAW				
AWS classification of EXXXL-XX				
E	**XXX**	**L**	**-**	**XX**
Electrode	Denotes classification - Austenitic 200 and 300 series - Ferritic 400 series - Martensitic 400 series - Chrome steels 500 series	Denotes carbon content - ELC or L limits the carbon to 0.04% - Otherwise the carbon is 0.08%		Designates the usability suffixes which are 15, 16, 17, 25, 26

Table #76 - AWS Classification of Stainless Steel Filler Metals for SMAW

SMAW Usability Suffixes

The type of electrode coating used on SMAW electrodes determines the usability of that electrode. AWS uses five separate digits for this classification. They are 15, 16, 17, 25, and 26. Their characteristics are as listed:

Suffix, -15	- Lime type coating
	- DCRP only
	- 4.0mm (5/32inch) or smaller can be used in all position.

Suffix, -16	- Titania type coating
	- DCRP or AC current maybe used

Suffix, -17	- Silica replaces most of the Titania in the coating of -16 electrodes.
	- DCRP or AC current maybe used.
	- The positions are limited with the -17 electrodes.

Suffix, -25	- Similar to -15 electrodes.
	- Core wire maybe mild steel.
	- Limited to flat and horizontal welding.

Suffix, -26	- Similar to -17 electrodes, and some -16 electrodes.
	- Core wire maybe mild steel..
	- Limited to flat and horizontal welding.

Example:
AWS classification of E308L-15

E = Electrode

308 = 300 series Austenitic

L - indicates the that the carbon content is restricted to 0.04% max

-15 = DCRP only
Line type coating
4.0mm (5/32inch) or smaller maybe used in all position

Table #77 outlines some of the typical filler metals used for Austenitic stainless steels by the GTAW, GMAW, PAW, and SAW processes.

Note: See Section Thirteen - Metallurgy for additional information on stainless steel welding.

Type of Stainless Steel	Recommended Filler Metal
201, 201	ER209, ER219, ER308
301, 302, 304, 305	ER308
304L	ER308L, ER347
309	ER309
316	ER316
316L	ER316L
316H	ER16-8-2, ER316H
321	ER321
347, 348	ER347

Table #77 - Recommended Filler Metal

Basic Weld Joints

There are five basic joints as indicated in illustration #399. These joint configurations are, butt, corner, tee, edge-flange and lap (B - C - T - E - L). However there are many variations of these resulting from the manner of preparation and assembly.

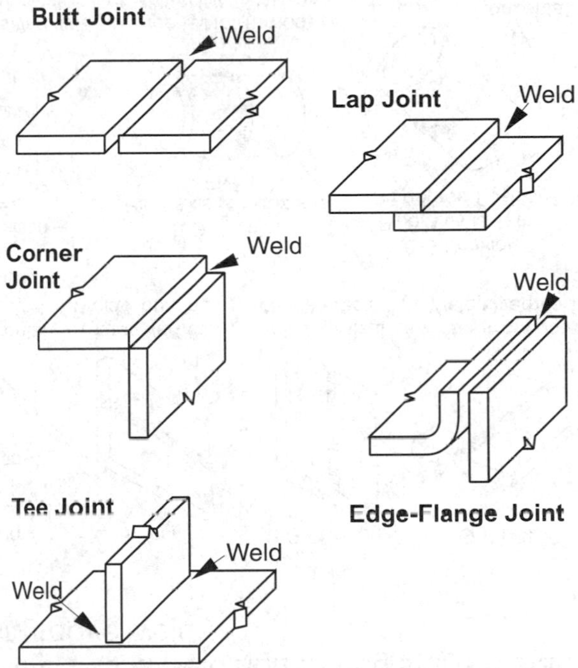
Butt Joint
Weld
Lap Joint
Weld
Corner Joint
Weld
Weld
Edge-Flange Joint
Tee Joint
Weld
Weld

Illustration #399 - Basic Weld Joints

Basic Welds

There are four basic types of welds as indicated in illustration #400. These are groove, fillet, plug, and surface.

Position of Groove Welds

The G in the weld numbering system stands for groove weld.

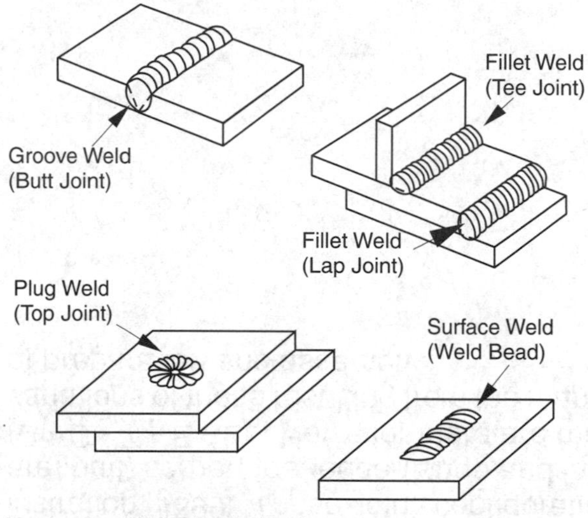

Groove Weld
(Butt Joint)
Fillet Weld
(Tee Joint)
Fillet Weld
(Lap Joint)
Plug Weld
(Top Joint)
Surface Weld
(Weld Bead)

Illustration #400 - Basic Welds

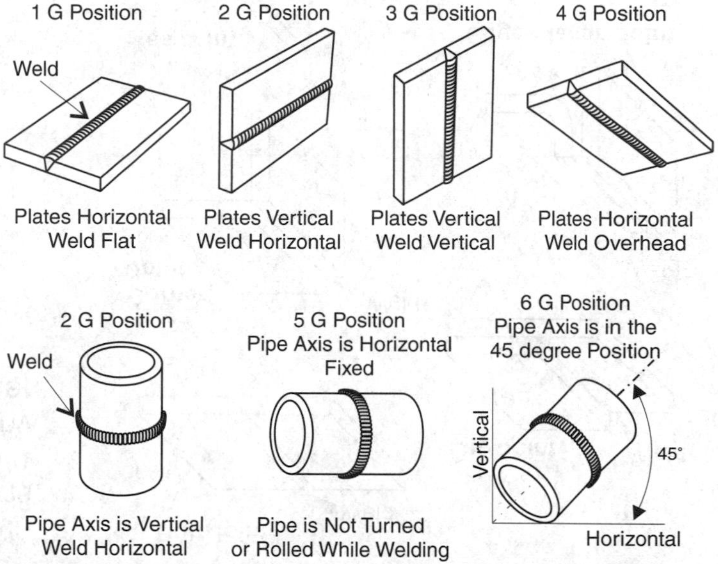

1 G Position
Weld
Plates Horizontal
Weld Flat
2 G Position
Plates Vertical
Weld Horizontal
3 G Position
Plates Vertical
Weld Vertical
4 G Position
Plates Horizontal
Weld Overhead
2 G Position
Weld
Pipe Axis is Vertical
Weld Horizontal
5 G Position
Pipe Axis is Horizontal
Fixed
Pipe is Not Turned
or Rolled While Welding
6 G Position
Pipe Axis is in the
45 degree Position
Vertical
45°
Horizontal

Illustration #401 - Position of Groove Welds

Position of Fillet Welds

The F in the numbering system stands for fillet weld.

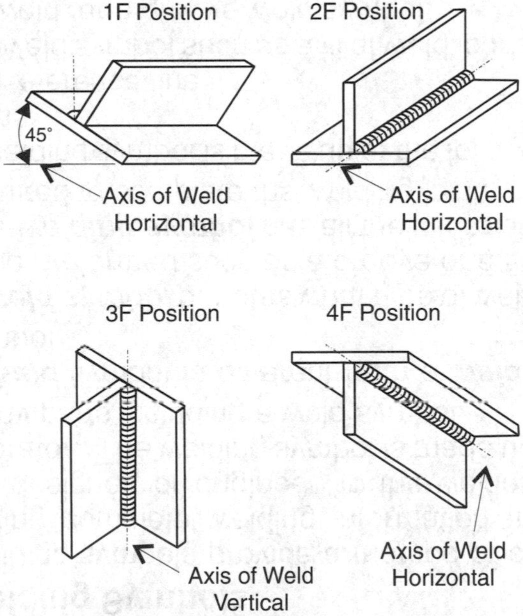
1F Position
2F Position
45°
Axis of Weld Horizontal
Axis of Weld Horizontal
3F Position
4F Position
Axis of Weld Vertical
Axis of Weld Horizontal

Illustration #402 - Position of Fillet Welds

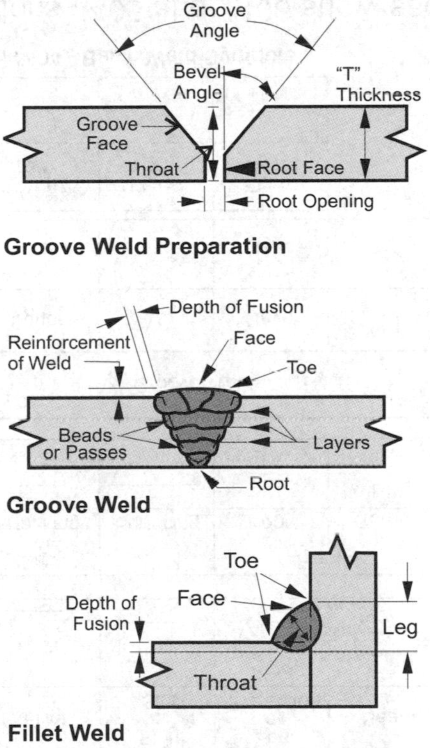
Groove Angle
Bevel Angle
"T" Thickness
Groove Face
Throat
Root Face
Root Opening
Groove Weld Preparation
Depth of Fusion
Reinforcement of Weld
Face
Toe
Beads or Passes
Layers
Root
Groove Weld
Toe
Face
Depth of Fusion
Leg
Throat
Fillet Weld

Illustration #403 - Groove and Fillet Weld Terms

Welding Symbols

Welding symbols provide a method of conveying complete welding information from the designer, or engineer, to the welder or operator. The welding symbol is made up of many parts including a weld symbol.

A ***weld*** symbol is different from a ***welding*** symbol.

A ***weld symbol*** denotes what type of weld is to be preformed such as a groove or a fillet. The ***welding symbol*** has all the information required to complete the welding joint.

A welding symbol is made up of the following items:

- Reference line.
- Weld symbol such as a fillet weld, surface weld, or a groove weld symbol.
- Arrow.
- Supplementary symbols.

Basic Weld Symbols

Arc and gas weld symbols are indicated in illustration #404.

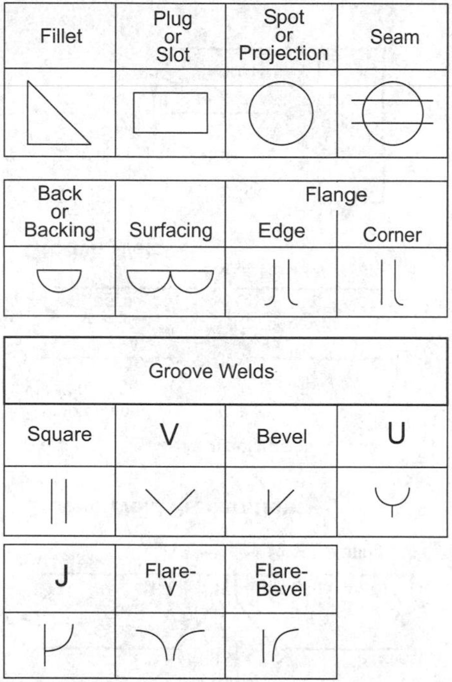
Fillet
Plug or Slot
Spot or Projection
Seam
Back or Backing
Surfacing
Flange
Edge
Corner
Groove Welds
Square
V
Bevel
U
J
Flare-V
Flare-Bevel

Illustration #404 - Basic Weld Symbols

Illustrations #405 and #406 show each type of weld and the corresponding symbol used with the basic welding symbol

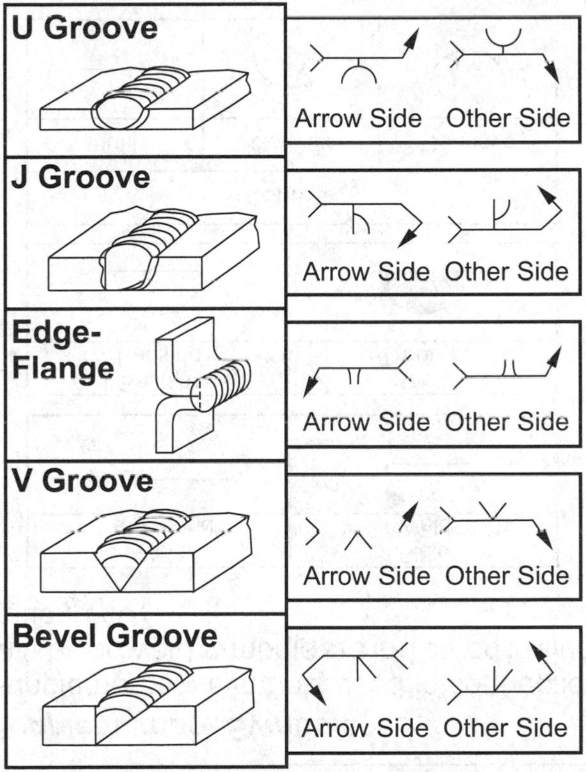
U Groove
Arrow Side
Other Side
J Groove
Arrow Side
Other Side
Edge-Flange
Arrow Side
Other Side
V Groove
Arrow Side
Other Side
Bevel Groove
Arrow Side
Other Side

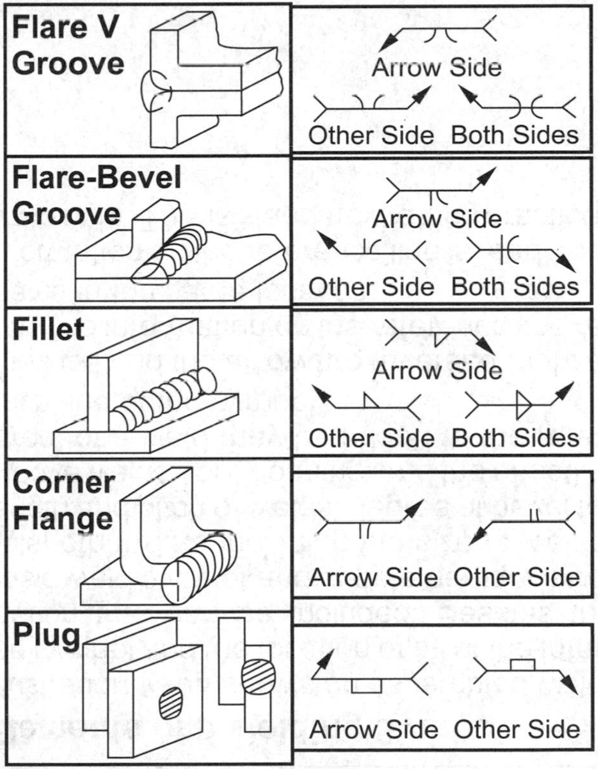
Flare V Groove
Arrow Side
Other Side
Both Sides
Flare-Bevel Groove
Arrow Side
Other Side
Both Sides
Fillet
Arrow Side
Other Side
Both Sides
Corner Flange
Arrow Side
Other Side
Plug
Arrow Side
Other Side

Illustrations #405, 406 - Types of Weld Symbol

Supplementary Symbols

Supplementary symbols used in connection with basic weld symbols are indicated in illustration #407.

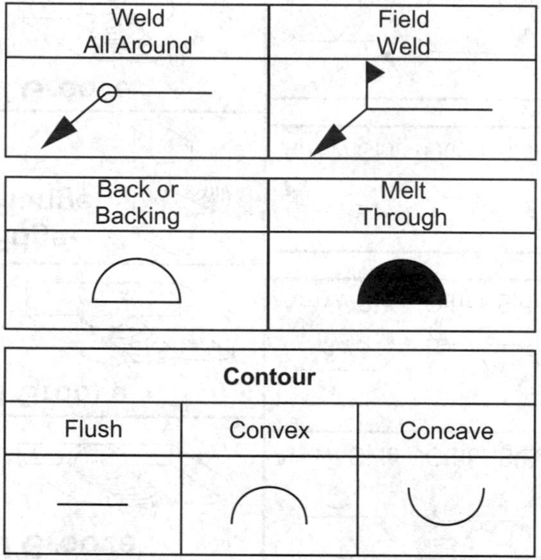
Weld All Around
Field Weld
Back or Backing
Melt Through
Contour
Flush
Convex
Concave

Illustration #407 - Supplementary Symbols

Elements of a welding Symbol

Illustration #408 shows an assembled welding symbol and the location of all of the information that can be included. Besides the basic weld symbol and supplementary symbols, other data including the size of welds, length and pitch of welds, degree of bevel for groove welds, root opening, and the effective throat of a weld may be added to the reference line of the symbol.

If the tail and the arrow are reversed (right to left), the information on the reference line remains in the same location.

Information on the reference line is read from left to right. This is standard drafting practice.

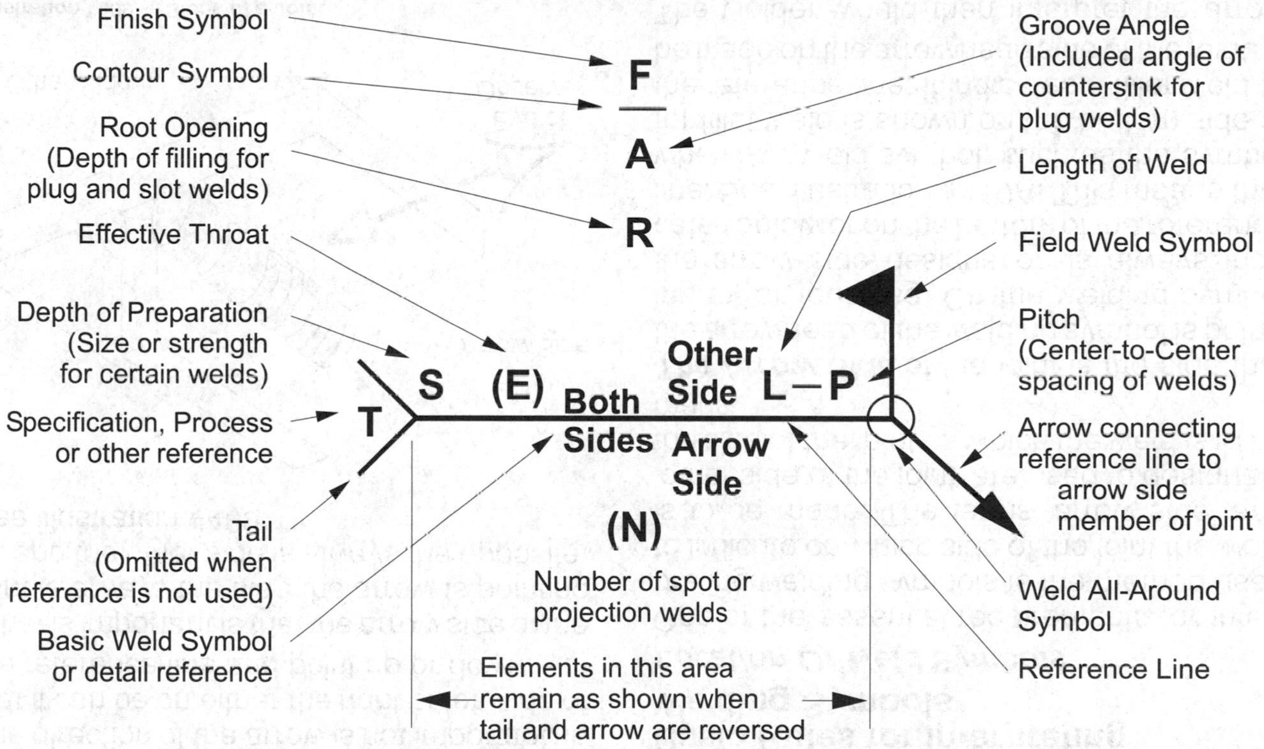
Finish Symbol
Contour Symbol
Root Opening
(Depth of filling for
plug and slot welds)
Effective Throat
Depth of Preparation
(Size or strength
for certain welds)
Specification, Process
or other reference
Tail
(Omitted when
reference is not used)
Basic Weld Symbol
or detail reference
F
A
R
S
(E)
T
Both
Sides
Other
Side
Arrow
Side
L — P
(N)
Number of spot or
projection welds
Elements in this area
remain as shown when
tail and arrow are reversed
Groove Angle
(Included angle of
countersink for
plug welds)
Length of Weld
Field Weld Symbol
Pitch
(Center-to-Center
spacing of welds)
Arrow connecting
reference line to
arrow side
member of joint
Weld All-Around
Symbol
Reference Line

Illustration #408 - Elements of a Welding Symbol

The direction of the arrow is not important, in that it can be on either the right or left side of the reference line and point up or down.

What is important is that the arrow side of the joint is always the side the arrow is pointing to, and the other side is always the opposite. See illustration #409.

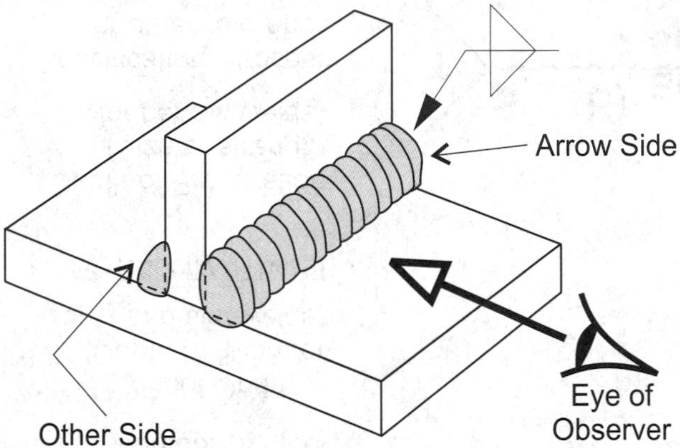
Arrow Side
Other Side
Eye of
Observer

Illustration #409 — Sides of a Joint

Basic Rules for Interpreting Welding Symbols

Location Of Weld Symbols

One of the essential requirements for interpreting welding symbols is the method used to indicate on which side of the joint the weld is to be made. The terms 'arrow side' and 'other side of the joint' are used to designate the side of the joint on which the weld is to be made.

The Arrow Side of the joint is the side that the arrowhead of the welding symbol is pointing to, or touching. On the welding symbol the arrow side designation is always indicated below or on the bottom of the reference line. See illustration #410A. This means that when any weld symbol, such as the symbol for fillet weld is shown on the bottom side of the reference line, it indicates a fillet weld to be made on the arrow head side of the joint.

The welder would then interpret the arrow side of the joint to be the side that the arrowhead of the welding symbol is pointing to.

The Other Side of the joint is the side opposite to which the arrowhead is pointing. Other side of the joint is indicated on the welding symbol by placing the weld symbol on the top side of the reference line. See illustration #410B.

When both sides of the joint are to be welded, as in the case of a fillet weld, then the fillet weld symbol would be placed on both sides of the reference line. The welder would interpret this to mean that both sides of the joint would require a fillet weld. See illustration #410C

Illustration #410D indicates the welding symbol when welding is required on both sides of a solid member. However the drawing may be simplified by using only one welding symbol and another arrow from the reference line to the other joint, or the word *'typical'* may be included in the tail of the welding symbol.

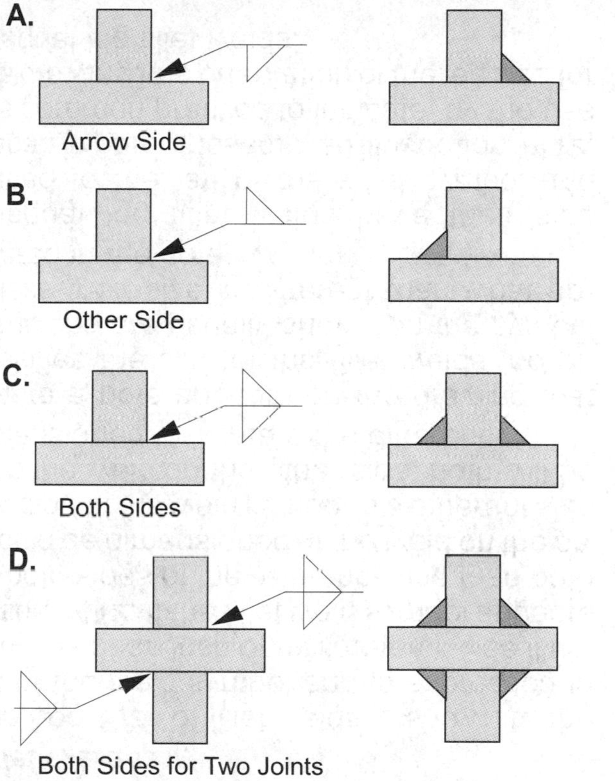
A.
Arrow Side
B.
Other Side
C.
Both Sides
D.
Both Sides for Two Joints

Illustration #410 — Weld Locations

Perpendicular Leg

For standardization, the fillet, bevel, J-groove, flare-bevel and corner-flange weld symbols are drawn with the perpendicular leg on the left side, regardless of whether the arrow points left or right. See illustration #411.

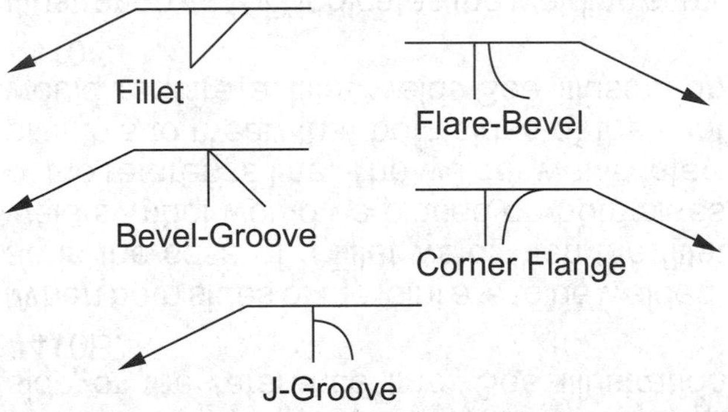
Fillet
Flare-Bevel
Bevel-Groove
Corner Flange
J-Groove

Illustration #411 — Perpendicular Leg on the Left

Fillet Welds

The Leg Size of fillet welds is shown to the left of the weld symbol and is expressed in fractions of an inch or millimeters. See illustration #412. If the fillet weld symbol appears on both sides of the reference line then both should be dimensioned. If the weld on the arrow side of the weld symbol is a different size than the weld on the other side, both will be dimensioned to indicate the difference.

Where a note appears on the drawing that specifies the size of the fillet welds, no dimensions are usually shown on the symbol unless their size is different than what appeared in the note.

Unequal leg fillet welds have their size placed to the left of the weld symbol and placed in parentheses. See illustration #412. It is common practice to indicate, by the use of a drawing, the orientation of the leg size for unequal leg fillet welds.

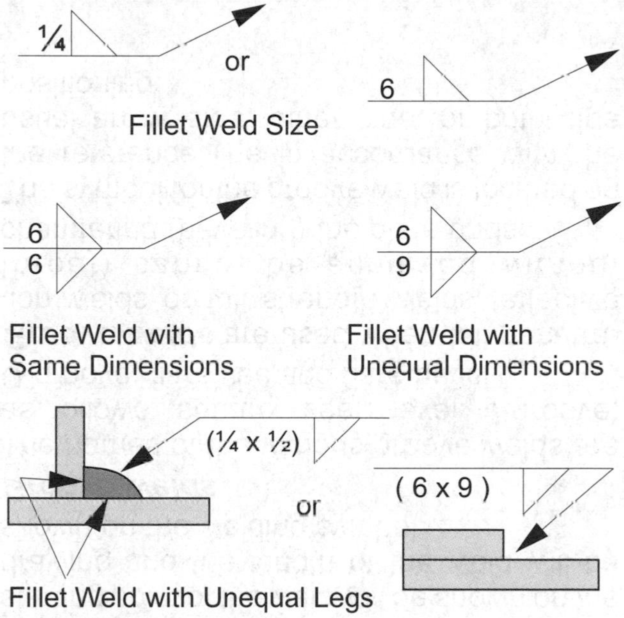
¼
or
6
Fillet Weld Size
6
6
6
9
Fillet Weld with
Same Dimensions
Fillet Weld with
Unequal Dimensions
(¼ x ½)
or
(6 x 9)
Fillet Weld with Unequal Legs

Illustration #412 — Size of Fillet Welds

The Length of the fillet weld increment is shown to the right of the weld symbol, except when the weld is to extend the full length of the joint. See illustration #413.

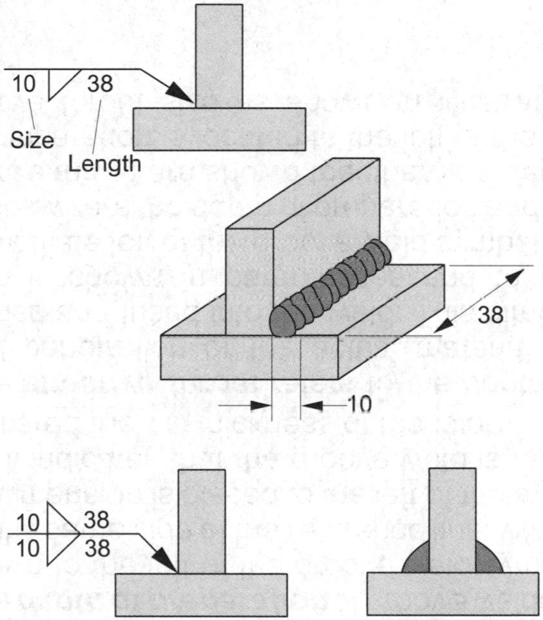
10
38
Size
Length
38
10
10
38
10
38

Illustration #413 — Length of Fillet Welds

For a full length weld, the length measurement is omitted. If the fillet weld does not extend the full length of the joint, then the starting point of the weld will be shown on the drawing and the length of the weld will be shown on the welding symbol.

Groove Welds

The names of the various groove welds are as follows: square, vee, bevel, J-groove, U-groove, flare vee and flare bevel.

Groove welds are used when full penetration welds or full strength welds (effective throat) cannot be achieved without chamfering (beveling) the plate ends.

The symbol for the groove weld is located on the reference line in accordance with the usual arrow side, other side, or both side positioning.

The depth of preparation of groove welds is shown to the left of the groove weld symbol on the same side of the reference line. When no dimension is placed to the left of the symbol it indicates that the groove weld is to be prepared the full thickness of the joint.

The effective throat refers to the depth of root penetration or the actual material included and fused into the weld. This dimension is shown in parentheses and to the immediate left of the groove weld symbol. In cases where the depth of preparation and effective throat are shown together, the depth of preparation is located to the left of the effective throat size as shown in illustration #414.

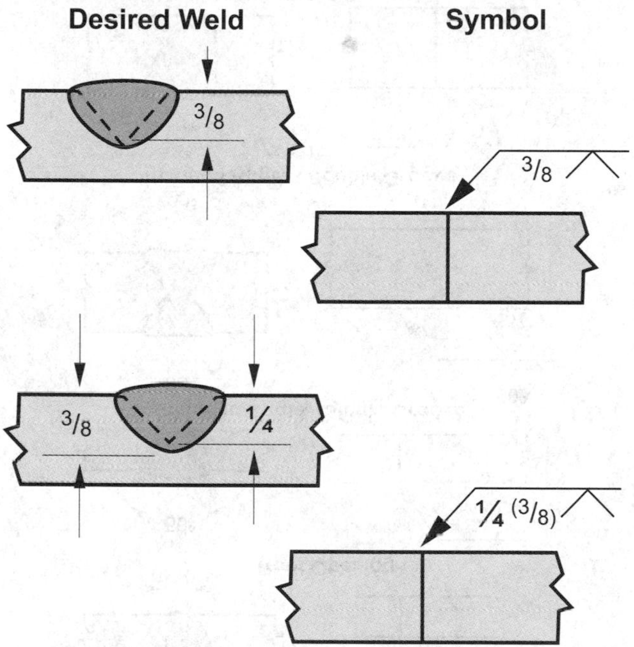
Desired Weld
Symbol
3/8
3/8
3/8
¼
¼ (3/8)

Illustration #414 — Dimensions Showing Groove Bevel Depth

The root face or land size is determined by subtracting the depth of preparation for the required groove weld from the actual thickness of the metal being prepared. For instance, if a $^1/_4$ inch (6 mm) bevel weld is indicated on the welding symbol and the metal thickness is $^3/_8$ inch (9 mm), then the land will be $^1/_8$ inch (3 mm) thick after the bevel is prepared.

The root opening or gap refers to the distance between the pieces to be welded, and is shown by placing the dimension inside the groove weld symbol. See illustration #415.

The bevel or groove angle is the angle formed by the members to be welded. This dimension is given in degrees and is placed just outside of the groove weld symbol. See illustration #415.

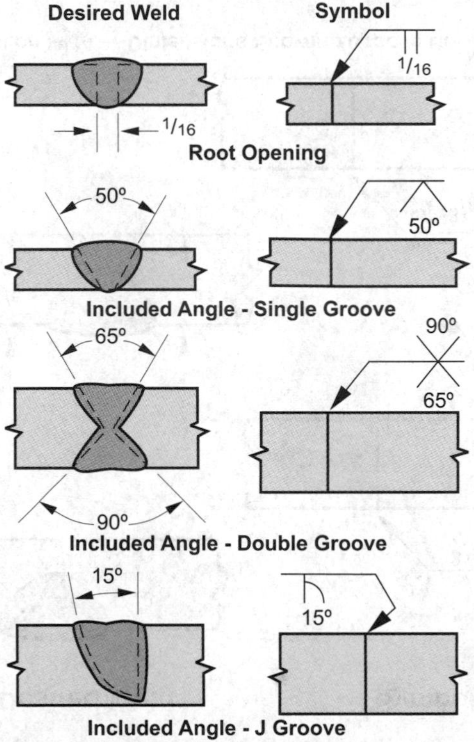
Desired Weld
Symbol
1/16
1/16
Root Opening
50º
50º
Included Angle - Single Groove
65º
90º
65º
90º
Included Angle - Double Groove
15º
15º
Included Angle - J Groove

Illustration #415 — Root Opening and Included Angle for Groove Welds

Broken Arrow Line

When using the bevel or J-groove weld symbol, the arrow line must have a definite break and point towards the member of the joint that is to be prepared, as shown in illustration #416. When it is obvious which member is to be prepared, the broken arrow line may be omitted.

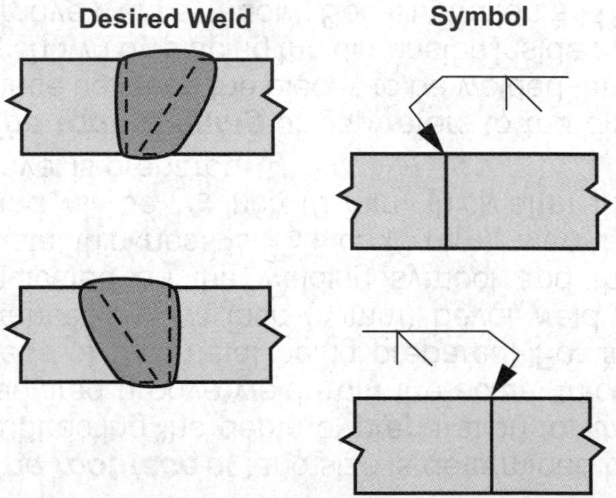
Desired Weld
Symbol

Illustration #416 — Break in Arrow Showing Member to be Beveled

Combined Weld Symbols

Combined weld symbols are used for joints that require more than one type of weld. An example would be a groove weld covered by a fillet weld for extra reinforcement. When this happens a symbol is used for each weld. See illustration #417. Standard dimensioning practices remain the same for each weld symbol.

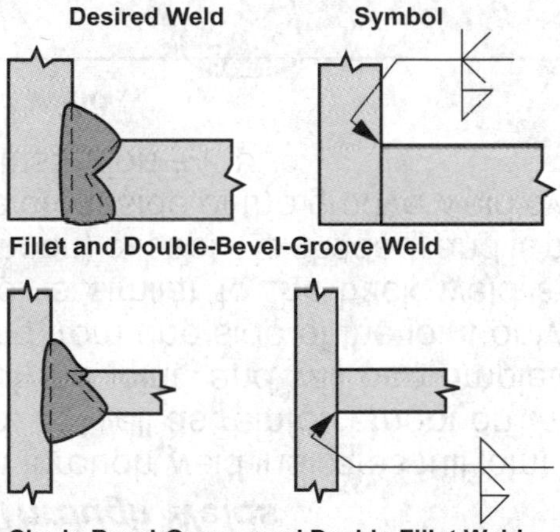
Desired Weld
Symbol
Fillet and Double-Bevel-Groove Weld
Single-Bevel-Groove and Double-Fillet Weld

Illustration #417 — Combined Weld Symbols

Back or Backing Welds

A back or backing weld refers to a weld made on the opposite side of a single groove weld. A half moon symbol is placed on the other side of the groove weld symbol. The height of reinforcement is the only dimension shown on the welding symbol for back welds. See illustration #418.

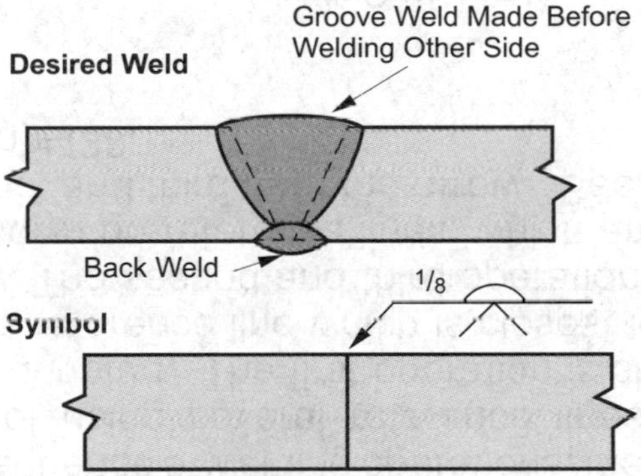
Groove Weld Made Before Welding Other Side
Desired Weld
Back Weld
1/8
Symbol

Illustration #418 — Back Weld Symbol

Melt Through Welds

A melt through weld indicates full joint penetration, as well as reinforcement on the root side of the joint, and will be completed by welding from one side of the joint only. This symbol is similar to the back weld symbol (half moon) except it is shaded, and is placed on the other side of the groove weld symbol. See illustration #419.

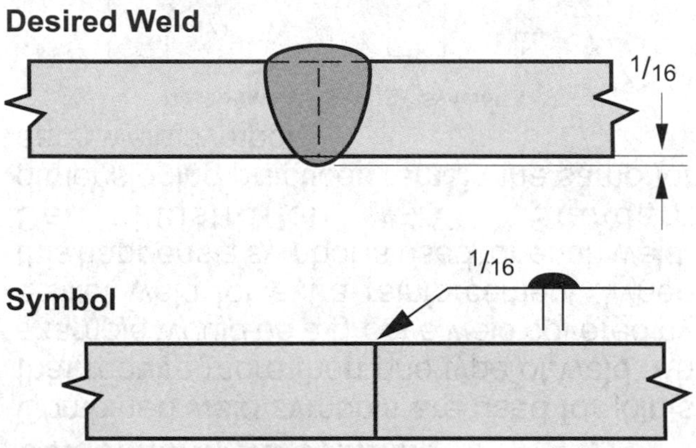
Desired Weld
1/16
Symbol
1/16

Illustration #419 — Melt-Thru Symbol

Multiple Reference Lines

In order to show in a more definitive manner the sequence of welding operations, the concept of using several reference lines has been adopted. The first operation is shown on the reference line which is closest to the arrow. The second and third operations will be shown on reference lines, which are the second, and third from the arrow. See illustration #420.

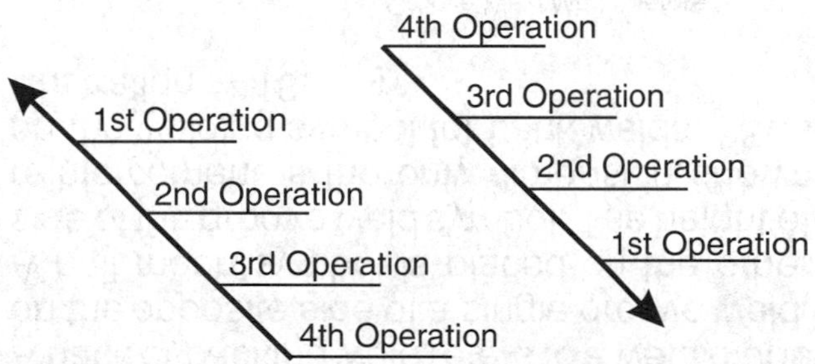
4th Operation
3rd Operation
1st Operation
2nd Operation
2nd Operation
1st Operation
3rd Operation
4th Operation

Illustration #420 - Multiple Reference Lines

Welding Technique

There are many methods of applying the varied welding processes, and welders or welding operators will develop slightly different welding techniques to complete a task. It is the finished product that is important, not the technique.

The American Welding Society has established four specific methods to describe the many welding processes;

Manual MA: The entire welding operation is completed by hand, such as SMAW and manual GTAW.

Semi-Automatic SA: Equipment controls only the filler metal feed. The advance of welding is manually controlled. These processes include GMAW and FCAW where the machine only controls the wire feed

Machine ME: Equipment, performs the welding operation under the constant observation and control of an operator, such as SAW.

Automatic AU: Equipment, which performs the entire welding operation without continued observation and adjustment. These systems are fully automated. An example is the robot welding on assembly lines in manufacturing plants.

Welding Processes

Shielded Metal Arc Welding (SMAW)

Shielded metal arc welding is a welding process where the arc is drawn between the base metal, and a coated electrode. Filler metal is supplied by the coated electrode, as indicated in illustration #421.

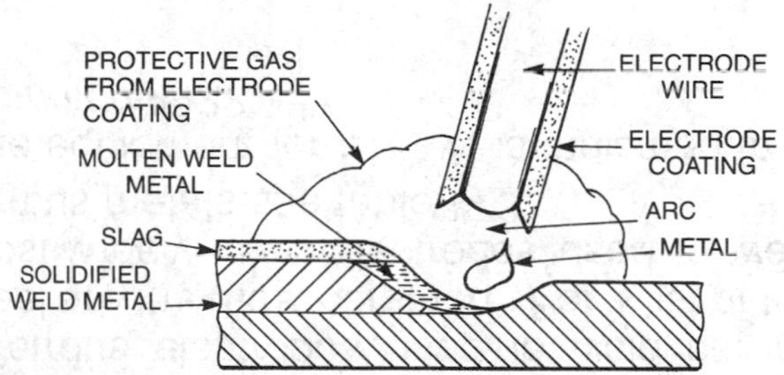
PROTECTIVE GAS
FROM ELECTRODE
COATING
ELECTRODE
WIRE
ELECTRODE
COATING
MOLTEN WELD
METAL
ARC
SLAG
METAL
SOLIDIFIED
WELD METAL

Illustration #421 - Shielded Metal Arc Welding

SMAW or stick welding is still the most common and cost effective welding process. SMAW allows freedom of control and can be used indoors or outdoors to weld carbon steel, stainless steel, nickel, and their alloys. SMAW power supplies can be portable engine driven, DC/CC (constant current), or AC. SMAW is a low technology welding process but does require a high level of welder skill to produce quality welds.

Shielding Gas

The shielding gas is created when the coating on the electrode burns off. CO_2 is commonly produced from the coating of SMAW electrodes.

Filler Metals

There are many SMAW coated electrodes available for ferrous and non-ferrous materials. As manufacturers are continually updating and manufacturing new electrodes, the best policy is to consult with a supplier if not sure of the best electrode for an application.

Ferrous electrodes used to weld carbon steel are the most common. For a list of the most widely used electrodes used to weld ferrous metals see table #78.

The equipment for SMAW is indicated in illustration #422.

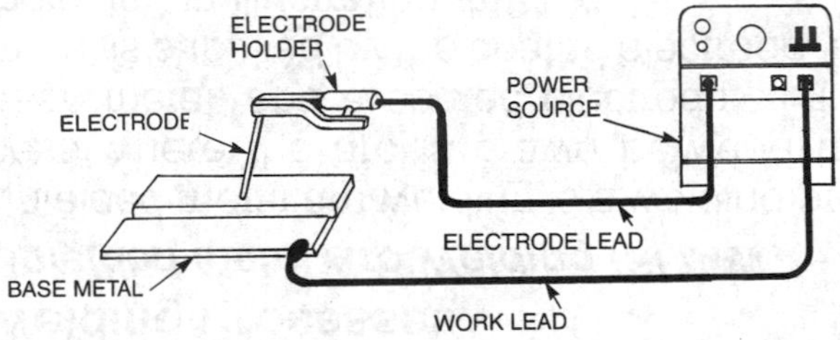
ELECTRODE HOLDER
ELECTRODE
POWER SOURCE
ELECTRODE LEAD
BASE METAL
WORK LEAD

Illustration #422 - Equipment for Shielded Metal Arc Welding

WELDING ELECTRODE SELECTION (MILD STEEL)								
	Electrode Classification							
	E-6010	E-6011	E-6012	E-6013	E-7014	E-7018	E-7024	E-6027
Groove butt welds, flat (> ¼")	4	5	3	8	9	9	9	10
Groove butt welds, all positions (> ¼")	10	9	5	8	6	6	(b)	(b)
Fillet welds, flat or horizontal	2	3	8	7	9	9	10	9
Fillet welds, all positions	10	9	6	7	7	10	(b)	(b)
Current ©)	DCR	AC	DCS	AC	DC	DCR	DC	DC
		DCR	AC	DC	AC	AC	AC	AC
Thin material (< ¼ in.)	5	7	8	9	8	2	7	(b)
Heavy plate or highly restrained joint	8	8	6	8	8	10	7	8
High-sulphur or off-analysis steel	(b)	(b)	5	3	3	10	5	(b)
Deposition rate	4	4	5	5	6	6	10	10
Depth of penetration	10	9	6	5	6	7	4	8
Appearance, undercutting	6	6	8	9	9	10	10	10
Soundness	6	6	3	5	7	10	8	9
Ductility	6	7	4	5	6	10	5	10
Low spatter loss	1	2	6	7	9	8	10	10
Poor fit-up	6	7	10	8	9	4	8	(b)
Welder appeal	7	6	8	9	10	10	10	10
Stag removal	9	8	6	8	8	7	9	9

(a) Rating is on a comparative basis of same size electrodes with 10 as the highest value. Ratings may change with size.
(b) Not recommended.
©) DCR - direct current reverse, electrode positive DCS - direct current straight, electrode negative;
AC - Alternating current; DC - direct current, either polarity

Table #78 - Welding Electrode Selection

Shielded Metal Arc Welding (SMAW) SMAW Power Sources Must be Constant Current (CC)		
Material	**Polarity**	**Filler metal**
Carbon Steel	AC, DCRP or DCSP	F1,F2,F3,F4
Cast Iron	DCRP	Coated electrode for cast iron F4 or NI Rod (nickel electrode for cast iron)
Stainless Steel	AC, DCRP	ER308, ER308L, ER310, ER316, ER321, ER347
Nickel And Nickel Alloys	AC, DCRP	Coated electrode for nickel alloys.
Aluminium	DCRP	Coated electrode with a core wire of either 1100 series, or 4043 series aluminium.
Hard Surfacing /Overlay	DCSP	Suitable overlay material, cladding material.
For more information on filler metals consult a filler metals hand book from a supplier		

Table #79 - Shielded Metal Arc Welding

Gas Tungsten Arc Welding (GTAW)

GTAW is often referred to as "Tig" or "Heliarc" welding. It is a process where the heat for joining metal is produced by an arc drawn between a non-consumable tungsten electrode and the base metal. A copper coated solid bare wire supplies the filler metal. This filler wire can be manually fed. The tungsten electrode and the weld puddle are protected from the atmosphere by inert shielding gas. See illustration #423.

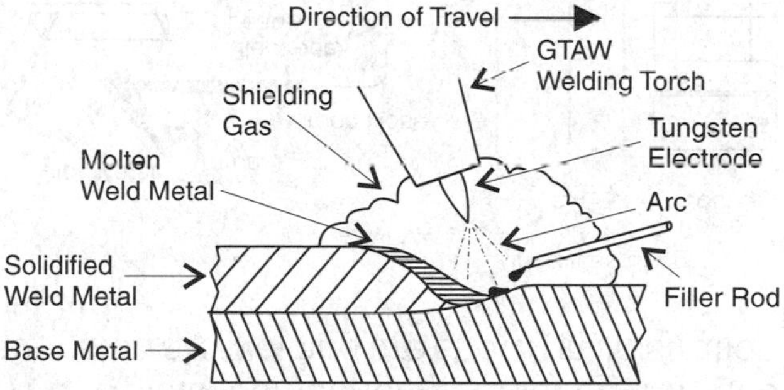
Direction of Travel
GTAW Welding Torch
Shielding Gas
Tungsten Electrode
Molten Weld Metal
Arc
Solidified Weld Metal
Filler Rod
Base Metal

Illustration #423 Gas Tungsten Arc Welding

The GTAW welding process is used in a variety of applications, particularly where the utmost in weld quality is desired.

There are specific advantages compared to other welding processes, such as: the elimination of flux, less distortion, welding of thin material in all positions, very little smoke and sparks. Some of the disadvantages are the potential for large weld grain structure, or grain growth, slow welding speeds, and the need for a high level of welding skill.

GTAW welding equipment can be connected to almost any type of DC constant current, or AC power source that is used for the SMAW process. The selection of power supply and equipment depends upon the material to be welded. A specifically designed welding machine can be used for GTAW welding. These types of machines usually contain a high frequency generator, which is used to aid arc starting when welding with alternating current. Alternating current is used for welding aluminium and magnesium.

The typical components required for gas tungsten arc welding are shown in illustration #424.

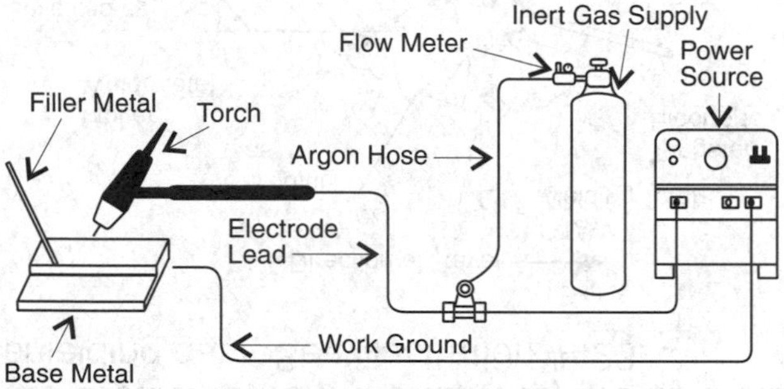
Inert Gas Supply
Flow Meter
Power Source
Filler Metal
Torch
Argon Hose
Electrode Lead
Work Ground
Base Metal

Illustration #424 Equipment for GTAW Welding

GTAW Torches

GTAW torches direct the shielding gas and hold the tungsten electrode. They are sized by current capacities. Some torches are water cooled and are used to handle higher current capacities.

Tungsten Electrodes

Tungsten electrodes come in a variety of diameters and lengths. They may be either pure tungsten or tungsten alloyed with thorium oxide, zirconium oxide, cerium oxide, or lanthanum oxide. They are manufactured to AWS standards or specifications. Tungsten electrodes have a color identification band at one end, as indicated in table #80.

Tungsten Identification	
AWS Listing (Type)	
EWP, (Pure Tungsten)	Green
EWCe-2, (+/- 2% Cerium oxide)	Orange
EWLa-1, (1% Lanthanum oxide)	Black
EWLa-2, (2% Lanthanum oxide)	Black
EWTh-1, (1% Thorium oxide)	Yellow
EWTh-2, (2% Thorium oxide)	Red
EWZr-1, (+/- 2% Zirconium oxide)	Brown
EWG, (unspecified alloys)	Grey

Table #80 - Tungsten Electrode Identification

When preparing an electrode for use with direct current straight polarity (DCSP), the end of the tungsten is ground to a sharp point, as indicated in illustration #425A.

When preparing an electrode for use with alternating current (AC), to weld aluminium or magnesium, use a hemispherical balled end, 1.5 times the diameter of the electrode.

The balled end on the zirconium tungsten is created when striking an arc with DCRP. The size of the ball is in direct correlation to the length of time the arc is maintained. To do this, ensure that the tungsten is completely vertical, or the ball will be off-center. See illustration #425B.

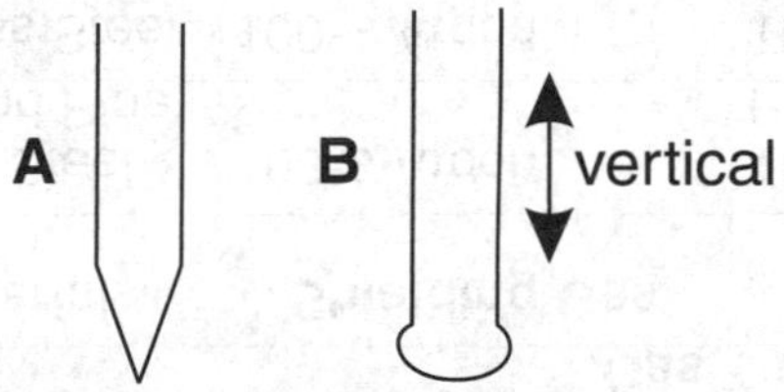
A
B
vertical

Illustration #425 Tungsten Preparation

Shielding Gas

Shielding gas is directed at the weld area by the gas cup on the GTAW torch. The most commonly used shielding gases is argon.

Helium is another inert gas used for the purpose of shielding. However it is a non-renewable resource derived from natural gas, and is more expensive to produce than argon gas. Helium does have an advantage over argon as it will transfer more heat into the base metal using the same welding current. This greater heat transfer may make it an option when welding thick sections, or metals with a high thermal conductivity, such as aluminium and magnesium.

Gas Tungsten Arc Welding (GTAW)					
Material	**Shielding Gas**	**Tungsten Type**	**Flow Rate**	**Type of Current**	**Filler Material**
Carbon Steel Plate and Pipe	100% Argon	Thoriated Pointed End	15/20 CFH	DCSP	E70S-6
Stainless Steel Plate and Pipe	100% Argon	Thoriated Pointed End	15/20 CFH	DCSP	ER308 ER308L ER310 ER316 ER321 ER347
Nickel and Nickel Alloys	100% Argon or Argon and Helium	Thoriated Pointed End	15/20 CFH	DCSP	ERNi ERNiCu-7 ERNiCuFe-5
Aluminium	100% Argon or Argon and Helium	Zirconium Balled End	15/25 CFH	ACHF	ER1100 ER4043 ER5356 ER5556
Magnesium	100% Argon	Zirconium Balled End	15/25 CFH	ACHF	EREZ33A ERAZ61A ERAZ92A
Copper and Copper Alloys	100% Argon or Argon and Helium	Thoriated Pointed End	15/20 CFH	DCSP	ERXXS-X
DCSP - Direct Current Straight Polarity ACHF - Alternating Current with High Frequency					

Table #81 - GTAW Gas Tungsten Arc Welding

Some of the advantages of using argon as a shielding gas when compared to helium are as follows:

- Smoother quieter arc.
- Reduced penetration.
- Good cleaning action when used with aluminium.
- Cheaper to manufacture.
- Easier arc starting.
- Better in drafty areas, because it is heavier than helium
- Lower flow rates than helium because it is heavier.

Filler Metals

The selection of the type of filler metal primarily depends on the type of base metal being joined. The range of base metal can vary from carbon steel to exotic non-ferrous alloys. The filler wire used to weld carbon steel is copper coated, multi-deoxidized and is not the same composition as oxygen acetylene welding (OAW) filler wire. Do not use OAW filler wire when welding with the GTAW process.

Classification of GTAW Filler Metals Mild Steel					
AWS Classification of ERXXS-X					
E	R	XX	S	-	X
Electrode	Rod	Minimum Tensile Strength of deposited Weld Material	Solid	-	Designates the chemical composition of the filler material
AWS Classification of ER70S-6					
E	R	70	S	-	6
Electrode	Rod	70,000 PSI	Solid	-	Designates the chemical composition of the filler material

Table #82 - GTAW Filler Metals

Gas Metal Arc Welding (GMAW)

GMAW or metal inert gas (Mig) is a process whereby heat for welding is generated by an arc drawn between the work and the consumable electrode, which is fed continuously by the equipment. The electrode is a bare, copper coated solid wire. Shielding gas used for mild steel welding is usually CO_2. An example of this process is indicated in illustration #426.

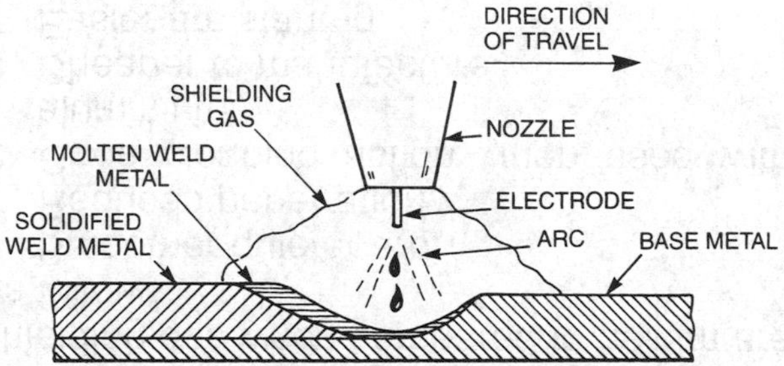
DIRECTION
OF TRAVEL
SHIELDING
GAS
NOZZLE
MOLTEN WELD
METAL
ELECTRODE
SOLIDIFIED
WELD METAL
ARC
BASE METAL

Illustration #426 Gas Metal Arc Welding

The power source normally used is direct current reverse polarity (DCRP) constant voltage, constant arc voltage, or constant potential (CV, CAV or CP). A typical arrangement is indicated in illustration #427. The DC power source, usually of 200-500 amperes, and 100 percent duty cycle is preferred. It may be a transformer, rectifier or generator type. The welding current is determined by the electrode wire-feed speed. The wire feeder houses all the electrical controls and the wire feed motor. The wire feeder also contains solenoids for operating the shielding gas flow valve and water coolant flow valve, when used. The most popular way of using this process is semi-automatically where the machine controls the electrical variables, and the operator manipulates the GMAW gun. The GMAW process can also be used in a fully automatic process.

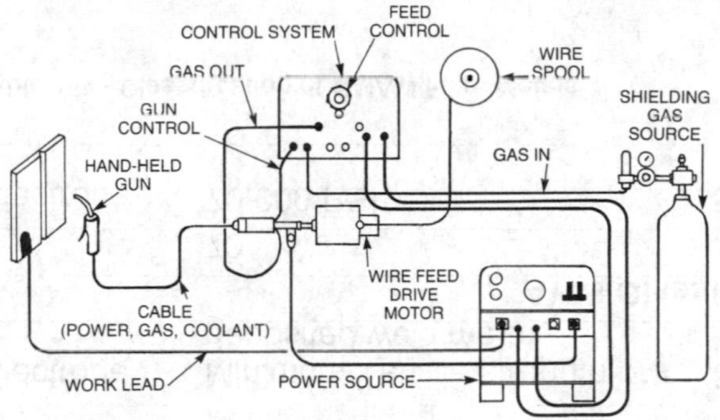
FEED
CONTROL
CONTROL SYSTEM
WIRE
SPOOL
GAS OUT
SHIELDING
GAS
SOURCE
GUN
CONTROL
GAS IN
HAND-HELD
GUN
WIRE FEED
DRIVE
MOTOR
CABLE
(POWER, GAS, COOLANT)
WORK LEAD
POWER SOURCE

Illustration #427 Typical Gas Metal Arc Welding Arrangement

Shielding Gas

The shielding gas is directed to the welding area by the GMAW gun. Shielding gas used for mild steel welding is usually CO_2. Applications of shielding gas are listed in table #83.

Shielding Gas	Chemical Reaction	Application
Argon	Inert	Nonferrous metals (least expensive inert gas)
Argon 50% Helium 50%	Inert	Al, Mg, Copper & their alloys
Carbon Dioxide CO_2	Oxidizing	Plain carbon and low alloy steel
Argon Oxygen 1-2%	Oxidizing	Stainless and alloyed steels
Argon 75% Carbon Dioxide 25%	Slightly Oxidizing	Plain carbon and low alloy steels
Nitrogen	Slightly Inert	For copper and purging stainless steel pipe

Table #83 - Applications of Shielding Gases for Gas Metal Arc Welding

GMAW Filler Metals

The type of filler metal used depends on the base metal composition. GMAW can be used to join carbon steel, stainless steel, nickel alloys, aluminium, and magnesium.

The composition of GMAW filler metals is identical to the composition of comparable GTAW filler metal.

Classification of GMAW Filler Metals				
AWS Classification of EXXS-X				
E	xx	S	-	X
Electrode	Minimum Tensile strength of deposited weld metal	Solid	-	Designates the chemical composition of the filler metal
AWS Classification of ER70S-6				
E	70	S	-	6
Electrode	70,000 PSI	Solid		Designates the chemical composition of the filler metal

Table #84 - Classification of GMAW Filler Metals

Gas Metal Arc Welding (GMAW) Short Circuit Metal Transfer				
Material	**Shielding Gas**	**Flow Rate**	**Polarity**	**Filler Metal**
Carbon Steel	75%Ar-25%CO_2	15/20 CFH	DCRP	E70S-6
Stainless Steel	90%He-7.5%Ar-2.5%CO_2	15/20 CFH	DCRP	ER308 ER308L ER310 ER316 ER321 ER347
Nickel and Nickel Alloys	1 00%Ar or Argon with a small percentage of helium	15/20 CFH	DCRP	ERNi ERNiCu-7 ERNiCrFe-5
Aluminium	1 00%Ar or Argon with a small percentage of helium	15/25 CFH	DCRP	ER1100 ER4043 ER5356 ER5556
Magnesium	1 00%Ar or Argon with a small percentage of helium	15/25 CFH	DCRP	EREZ33A ERAZ61A ERAZ92A
Low alloy steels	60-70%He+25-35%Ar+4.5%CO_2	15/20 CFH	DCRP	ERXXS-X

Table #85 - Gas Metal Arc Welding (GMAW) Short Circuit Metal Transfer

Flux Cored Arc Welding (FCAW)

When using the FCAW welding process the heat for welding is generated by an arc drawn between a continuously fed hollow filler wire and the base metal. FCAW filler wires are hollow and contain a flux material that tends to serve the same purpose as the coating on shielded metal arc welding (SMAW) electrodes.

Additional shielding gas may or may not be supplied from an external source. FCAW is a high heat, high production process that is very cost effective when compared to GMAW, SMAW, and GTAW.

The power source used in the FCAW process can either be DC/CV (constant voltage), or DC/CC (constant current), however DC/CV (constant voltage) is more commonly used.

When using a DC/CC (constant current) power source such as a portable, a suit case welder is hooked up to the welding machine. A suit case welder is a voltage sensing wire feeder that the operator uses in place of a SMAW electrode holder.

The remaining equipment required for FCAW is basically the same as for GMAW. The FCAW process is indicated in illustration #428.

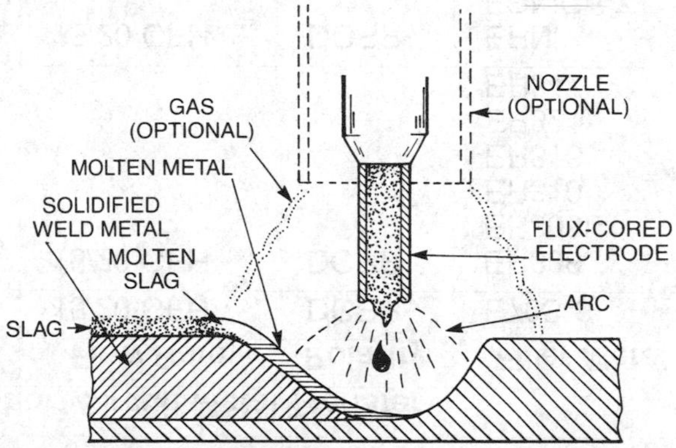
NOZZLE
(OPTIONAL)
GAS
(OPTIONAL)
MOLTEN METAL
SOLIDIFIED
WELD METAL
MOLTEN
SLAG
FLUX-CORED
ELECTRODE
ARC
SLAG

Illustration #428 - Flux Cored Arc Welding Process

Shielding Gas

The shielding gas used in the FCAW process is similar to the gas used in the GMAW process. CO_2 is used extensively with carbon steel because it is inexpensive, and produces good results. However 75% Argon and 25% CO_2 will produce a weld with less spatter which results in quicker clean up time.

Typical flow rates for shielding gases used in the FCAW process are about 30 up to 50 cubic feet/hour.

FCAW Filler Metals

The majority of filler metals in the FCAW process are used to weld carbon steel in the structural steel, and pressure vessel industries. FCAW is used in the heavy equipment industry to apply hard facing or hard surfacing.

Classification of FCAW Filler Metals						
AWS Classification of EXXTX-X						
E	X	X	T	X	-	X
Electrode	Minimum Tensile strength of deposited weld material	Position 0 = Flat and horizontal 1 = All position	Tubular filler electrode, flux cored	Usability character -istics	-	Designates the chemical composition of the filler metal
AWS Classification of E80T5-Ni3						
E	8	0	T	5		Ni3
Electrode	80,000 PSI	Flat and horizontal position only	Tubular filler electrode, flux cored	Usability character -istics		Designates the chemical composition of the filler metal

Table #86 - Classification of FCAW Filler Metals

Mild Steel FCAW Electrodes		
AWS Classification	**Shielding gas**	**Polarity**
EXXT-1	CO_2	DCRP
EXXT-2	CO_2	DCRP
EXXT-3	None	DCRP
EXXT-4	None	DCRP
EXXT-5	CO_2	DCRP
EXXT-6	None	DCRP
EXXT-7	None	DCSP
EXXT-8	None	DCSP
EXXT-9	None	DCSP
EXXT-10	None	DCSP
EXXT-1 1	None	DCSP
EXXT-G	*	*
EXXT-GS	**	**

Note:
*- G designation is for multi pass welding
**- GS designation is for single pass welding neither is covered under any of the presently defined classifications

Table #87 - Mild Steel FCAW Electrodes

Submerged Arc Welding (SAW)

SAW is a welding process that uses heat generated by the arc drawn between the solid bare filler wire and the work piece to fuse the metal. The end of the bare wire, arc, and weld puddle is submerged in a granulated flux deposited ahead of the wire. The entire process takes place under a blanket of flux. Only a portion of the flux is required to protect the weld area, the rest is recycled into the flux hopper to be used again.

When the weld cools, the fused layer of granulated flux hardens and peels away, revealing a smooth weld. There is no visible arc, flash, sparks, spatter or smoke. This process is normally limited to the flat and horizontal fillet positions due to the flux used. With special flux dams, the process can be used in the horizontal groove weld position, such as storage tanks wall plates, and pressure vessels. The SAW process is indicated in illustration #429.

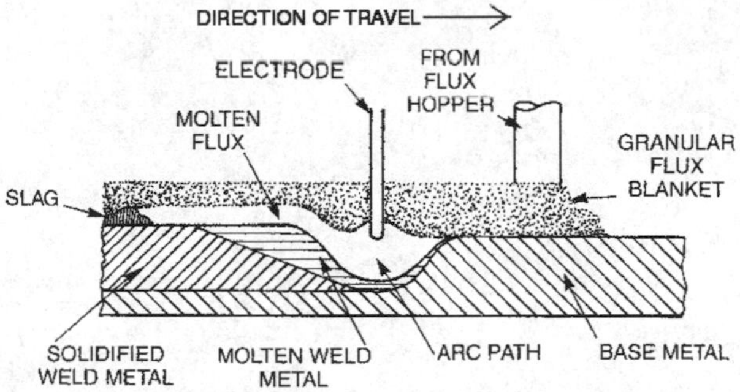
DIRECTION OF TRAVEL
ELECTRODE
FROM FLUX HOPPER
MOLTEN FLUX
GRANULAR FLUX BLANKET
SLAG
SOLIDIFIED WELD METAL
MOLTEN WELD METAL
ARC PATH
BASE METAL

Illustration #429 Submerged Arc Weld

The welding machine can be either an AC or DC power source. It must be rated at a 100% duty cycle. In some cases two or more electrode wires are employed in the same weld and occasionally one electrode may be on DC and the other on AC. Welding currents as high as 4,000 amperes on a single filler wire electrode can be used.

Recommended current settings for SAW Filler Wire		
Wire Diameter		Welding Current
inches	mm	amps
5/64	2.3	200 to 500
3/32	2.4	300 to 600
1/8	3.2	300 to 800
5/32	4.0	400 to 900
3/16	4.8	500 to 1200
7/32	5.6	600 to 1300
¼	6.4	600 to 1600

Table #88 - SAW Filler Wire

A single pass up to a 3 inch (76 mm) thickness, and multi-pass welding to any thickness can be done. Up to 200 inches (5,080 mm) per minute with a single welding wire may be attained. The equipment used in submerged arc welding is indicated in illustration #430.

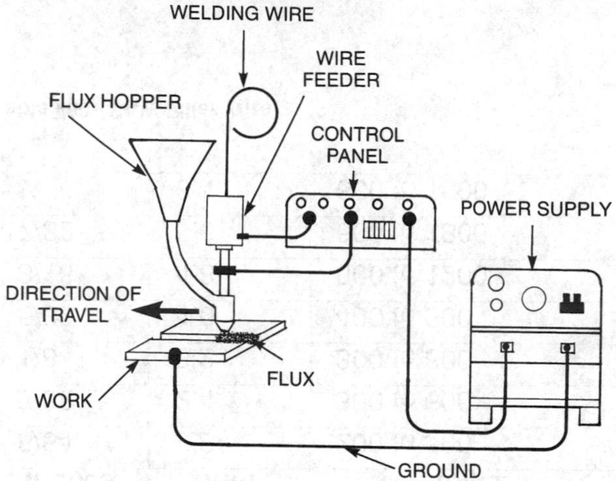
WELDING WIRE
WIRE FEEDER
FLUX HOPPER
CONTROL PANEL
POWER SUPPLY
DIRECTION OF TRAVEL
FLUX
WORK
GROUND

Illustration #430 Submerged Arc Welding Equipment

Electrode and Flux Classification System for Sub Arc Welding (SAW)								
AWS Classification for Combination of FXXX-EXXX								
F	X	X	X	-	E	X	X	X
Flux	Minimum tensile strength of the weld bead using this flux in the process	Indicates heat treatment A = as welded P = PWHT	Lowest temp at which the impact strength of the weld meets or exceeds 20ft-lbs or 27J		Electrode	Manganese content L =Low M=Medium H=High	Percent carbon	Killed steel
AWS Classification for Combination of F7A6-EM12K								
F	7	A	6	-	E	M	12	K
Flux	70,000 PSI tensile strength	Weld left in the as welded state	Impact tested at -60°F		Electrode	Medium Manganese content	0.12% carbon	Killed steel

Table #89 - Electrode and Flux Classification System for Sub Arc Welding (SAW)

Plasma Arc Welding (PAW)

Plasma arc welding, in its basic form, is really an extension of the GTAW process. Instead of the arc being used as a heat source for the purpose of melting the filler metal as in GTAW, PAW uses a column of plasma gas as a heat source.

Plasma gas is considered to be the fourth state of matter, as it is neither a solid, liquid, or gas. Plasma gas is formed when gas, such as Argon, is subjected to the intense heat of an electric arc, and becomes ionized by losing one of its electrons.

The orifice gas, or plasma gas, is directed through the torch to surround the electrode. It becomes ionized in the arc to form the plasma, and then discharges from the orifice in the torch nozzle as the plasma jet.

For most operations an auxiliary gas, or shielding gas, is provided through a gas cup similar to GTAW. For the majority of PAW operations the auxiliary gas is the same as the orifice, or plasma, gas. Typical gases used in various welding operations for widely used metals are in table #90

Gas-Selection for PAW (The following list is not complete and will vary between gas suppliers)					
Metal		**Thickness**		**Welding technique**	
		Inches	**mm**	**Keyhole**	**Melt in**
Carbon Steel	Under	1/8	3.2	Argon	Ar
	Over	1/8	3.2	Argon	75%He-25%Ar
Low Alloy Steel	Under	1/8	3.2	Argon	Ar
	Over	1/8	3.2	Argon	75%He-25%Ar
Stainless Steel	Under	1/8	3.2	Ar or 92.5% Ar-7.5% H_2	Ar
	Over	1/8	3.2	Ar or 95% Ar-5%H_2	75%He-25%Ar
1 Nickel Alloys	Under	1/8	3.2	Ar or 92.5% Ar-7.5%H_2	Ar
	Over	1/8	3.2	Ar or 95% Ar-5%H_2	75%He-25%Ar

Table #90 - Gas-Selection for PAW

In the PAW process, certain ranges of metal thicknesses along with gas selection, welding current, and travel speed will produce a small puddle with a hole penetrating completely through the parent metal. This type of welding technique is called keyhole welding. This technique is generally used with the downhand progression on plates between 1/16 to 3/8 in. (1.6 to 9.5 mm).

When using the PAW process, filler metal may or may not be required to complete the weld nugget to achieve good quality welds.

Plasma arc welding uses straight polarity, direct current from a constant current power supply, with a GTAW power source almost exclusively. The non-consumable electrode in the plasma torch is recessed within the constricting nozzle and must have a means for arc initiation. This can be done either by a pilot arc or the use of a high frequency current.

The plasma weld is indicated in illustration #431.

The PAW process can be used to join all metals welded by the GTAW process. The

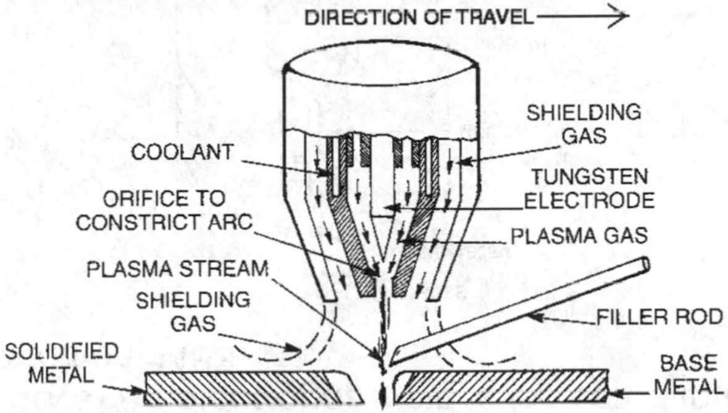
DIRECTION OF TRAVEL
SHIELDING GAS
COOLANT
TUNGSTEN ELECTRODE
ORIFICE TO CONSTRICT ARC
PLASMA GAS
PLASMA STREAM
SHIELDING GAS
FILLER ROD
SOLIDIFIED METAL
BASE METAL

Illustration #431 Plasma Arc Weld (PAW)

equipment used in the plasma arc welding process is indicated in illustration #432.

The two types of nozzle used are single-port and multi-port. The multi-port has an advantage in that greater welding speeds can be used with a narrower heat affected zone while using the same amperage.

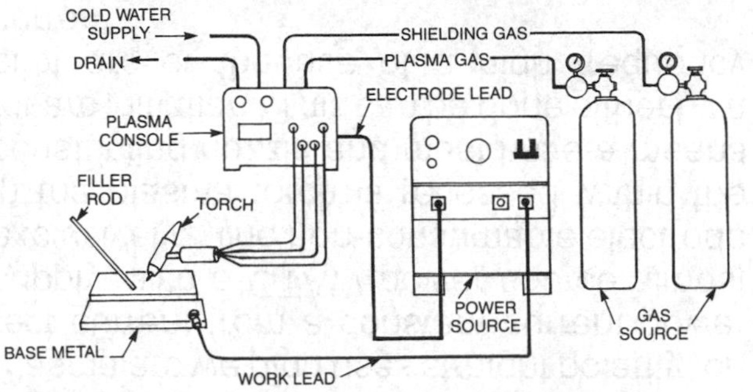
COLD WATER SUPPLY
DRAIN
SHIELDING GAS
PLASMA GAS
ELECTRODE LEAD
PLASMA CONSOLE
FILLER ROD
TORCH
POWER SOURCE
GAS SOURCE
BASE METAL
WORK LEAD

Illustration #432 Plasma Arc Welding Equipment (PAW)

Electrogas Welding

Electrogas welding is a process that joins metals with electrically conductive slag that melts the filler metal and the surfaces of the work pieces to be joined. The slag in this process is electrically conductive and when a current is applied an intense heat is produced which melts the electrode and joins it to the parent metal.

The electrogas process is used to make full thickness, single pass welds on joints positioned in the vertical or near vertical plane.

The passage of welding current through the flux generates the heat required to melt the flux and the filler metal. The filler metal is fed into the groove continuously and consistently, by a wire feed motor and comes into contact with the bottom of the weld through a layer of slag formed by the melted flux. It is necessary to keep the weld pool within the confines of the welding groove by means of a water-cooled dam on each side of the groove. An electrogas weld is indicated in illustration #433.

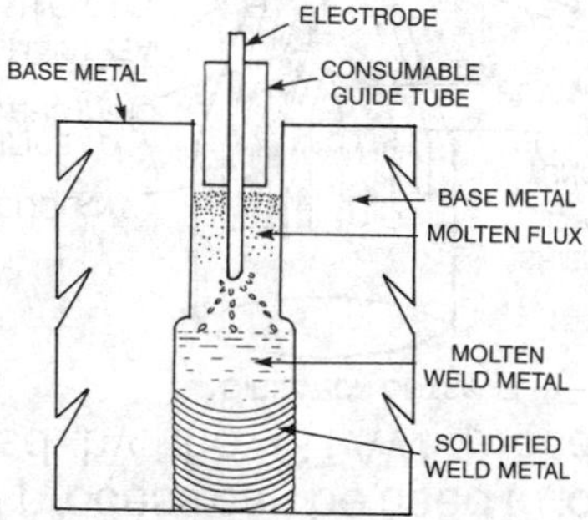
ELECTRODE
BASE METAL
CONSUMABLE GUIDE TUBE
BASE METAL
MOLTEN FLUX
MOLTEN WELD METAL
SOLIDIFIED WELD METAL

Illustration #433 Electrogas Weld

Electrogas welding has the advantage of speed over other processes with deposit rates of 36 to 45 kg per hour (80 to 100 pounds). The disadvantage of this type of welding is that the weld nugget develops a coarse grained structure. Therefore it is usually necessary to use an approved post weld heat treatment (PWHT) procedure before the weld can be put into service. This generally involves heating the entire component to approximately 1600°F (871°C), and cooling in still air.

Other heat treatments may be necessary depending on the mechanical properties desired for the weld nugget, and the heat affected zone (HAZ). The cost of heat treatment usually outweighs the advantages of this type of welding. The equipment used in Electrogas welding is indicated in illustration #434.

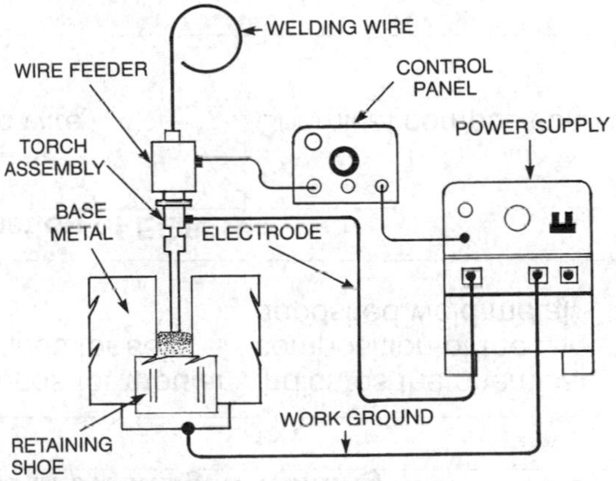
WELDING WIRE
WIRE FEEDER
CONTROL PANEL
POWER SUPPLY
TORCH ASSEMBLY
BASE METAL
ELECTRODE
WORK GROUND
RETAINING SHOE

Illustration #434 Electrogas Welding Equipment

AWS Classification of Electrodes Used in Electrogas Welding				
EG	x	x	T or S	xxx
Electrogas	Minimum tensile strength of the weld bead	Indicates the minimum impact strength of the weld metal.	T stands for tubular S stands for solid	Indicates the chemical composition of the deposited weld metal.
AWS Classification for Combination of EG62S-1				
EG	6	2	S	1
Electrogas	60,000 PSI tensile strength	20 foot pounds impact strength at -40°F	Solid wire	Chemical composition

Table #91- AWS Classification of Electrodes

Stud Welding

Stud welding is a process of arc welding used to attach specially designed studs to a metal work piece. In stud welding the heat from the arc heats the end of the stud, which will come in contact with the base metal. When the stud and the base metal are at the proper temperature they are brought into intimate contact, and the process is complete.

The stud gun holds the stud, and a ferrule is fitted over the end of the stud. The operator presses the stud against the work plate until the ferrule is flat against the plate. The trigger is pressed and the stud is automatically pulled away from the plate. This creates an arc between the stud and the plate. A portion of the plate and the end of the stud are melted.

After completion of the arcing period, as preset and controlled by the timer unit, the stud is plunged into the molten pool on the plate to complete the weld. The stud gun is then pulled away from the stud, and the ferrule is chipped off. This process is indicated in illustration #435.

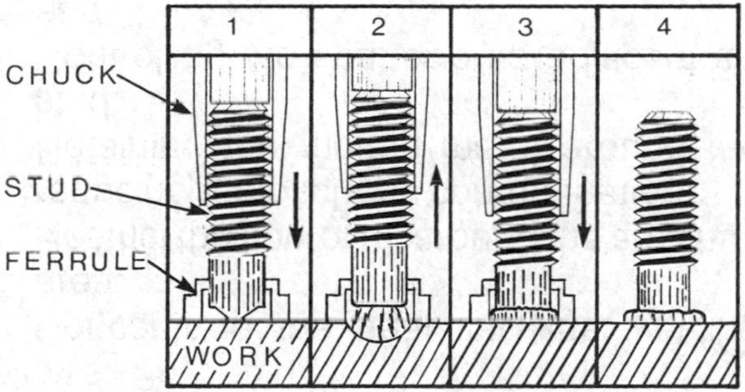
1
2
3
4
CHUCK
STUD
FERRULE
WORK

Illustration #435 Stud Welding Process

The most basic stud welding equipment consists of a stud gun, timing unit, studs, ferrules, and a power source. A DC welding machine, either a transformer rectifier or generator/alternator, set on straight polarity (DCSP) is used for stud welding of mild steel. For the stud welding of aluminium and magnesium a DC power source set on reverse polarity (DCRP) is recommended.

Initially standard power sources were used in stud welding, but the demand for higher capacities resulted in special units for stud welding being developed. These special units have very high output capacities for short periods, and are rated at 20 percent duty cycle or less.

A ferrule is required for the stud welding process. Ferrules are a single use item and are usually made out of a ceramic material. Some of the functions of the ferrule are as follows:

- Concentrate the heat into the welding area.
- Restrict the flow of air around the arc, thus reducing atmospheric contamination.
- Retaining the molten metal around the stud.
- Controlling the spatter onto adjacent areas.

A typical stud welding system is indicated in illustration #436.

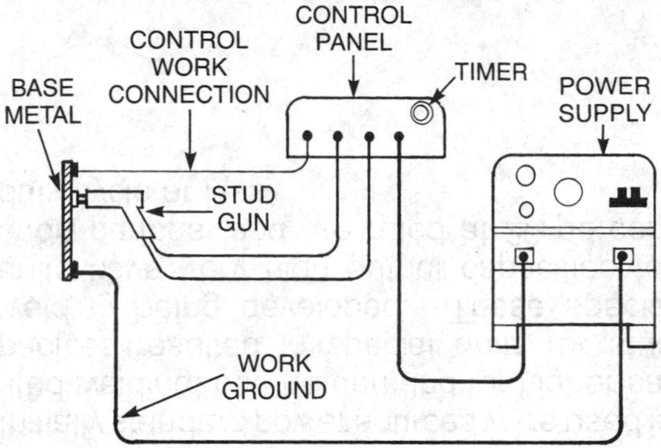
CONTROL PANEL
CONTROL WORK CONNECTION
TIMER
BASE METAL
POWER SUPPLY
STUD GUN
WORK GROUND

Illustration #436 Stud Welding System

Welding Pre-heat

One of the most troublesome features of the welding process is the danger of cracks developing in the weld metal or in the adjacent base metal zone, commonly referred to as the heat affected zone (HAZ). This is due to rapid heating and cooling during the welding operation, which in turn can change the way iron and carbon interact. This interaction between iron and carbon will ultimately change the mechanical properties of steel.

There are two areas in a welded joint which may crack as a result of the welding operation.

The first is the HAZ, where the weld nugget ends and the base metal starts. The second area which may crack under certain conditions is the weld metal, or the weld bead. The root bead is the most common location of cracking in the weld metal. The filler metal used in most applications has so low a carbon content that there is no marked change in mechanical properties as compared to the base metal, even during quenching after welding.

The base metal closest to the weld will pull heat away from the weld nugget during and after welding.

This quenching effect of the base metal causes the heat affected zone (HAZ), and the weld nugget to undergo important changes in the microstructure of iron. This changes the mechanical properties, which in turn may lead to cracking.

Welding Pre-heat

Welders, engineers, and end users are always concerned about cracks. Cracks are a serious weld fault and the majority of them can be easily avoided by following simple pre-heating procedures.

Pre-heating before welding is a well recognized preventive measure against cracking. It was used for many years before scientific reasons were advanced to explain its function in preventing cracks.

The importance of pre-heating is advanced by the fact that recommendations for pre-heating are written into many welding specifications whenever there is the slightest risk of a weld defect being present.

If a welder is working under a construction code such as API, ASME Section 1, Section 8, or ASME B31.1 piping code, there are pre-heat tables that must be followed before any welding starts.

For the hobby welder it is a good idea to warm up the base metals before welding.

Pre-heating can be loosely defined as raising the temperature of the base metal to a specified level before welding, and maintaining the temperature during welding. General pre-heat is when the entire component is pre-heated before welding starts. Local pre-heat is when only the base metal in the vicinity of the weld is heated. Some of the desired effects of pre-heating are as follows:

- Eliminates or lessens the danger of crack formation.
- Minimizes hard zones adjacent to welds.
- Minimizes shrinkage stresses.
- Lessens distortion.
- Enhances diffusion of hydrogen from steel.

Heavy fabrication and manufacturing of large pressure vessels require continuous application of pre-heat. One popular method utilizes electrical strip heaters. Another widely employed method utilizes low frequency induction heating. This is used mainly in pre-heating of alloy steel piping prior to welding. While pre-heating methods and temperatures will depend on many factors there is agreement that pre-heating before welding is the best possible insurance against cracks.

NOTE: Pre-heat should not be used on some steels due to their intended uses. Always consult the referencing code.

NOTE: See Section Thirteen - Weld Metallurgy for additional information on HAZ (heat affected zone) and welding pre-heat and post-heat.

PRE-HEAT FOR WELDING

Metal Group	Metal Designation	Recommended pre-heat
Plain Carbon Steels	Plain Carbon Steel	Up to 200°F
Carbon Moly Steels	Carbon Moly Steel	400°F - 600°F
Manganese Steels	Silicon Structural Steel	300°F - 500°F
	Medium Manganese Steel	300°F - 500°F
	SAE T 1330 Steel	400°F - 600°F
	SAE T 1340 Steel	500°F - 800°F
	SAE T 1350 Steel	600°F - 900°F
	12% Manganese Steel	Usually Not Required
High Tensile Steels	Manganese Moly Steel	300°F - 500°F
	Jalten Steel	400°F - 600°F
	Manten Steel	400°F - 600°F
	Armco High Tensile Steel	Up to 200°F
	Double Strength #1 Steel	300°F - 600°F
	Double Strength #1A Steel	400°F - 700°F
	Otiscoloy Steel	200°F 400°F
	Nax High Tensile Steel	Up to 300°F
	Cromansil Steel	300°F - 400°F
	A.W. DYN-EL	Up to 300°F
	Corten Steel	200°F - 400°F
	Chrome Copper Nickel Steel	200°F - 400°F
	Chrome Manganese Steel	400°F - 600°F
	Yoloy Steel	200°F - 600°F
	Hi-Steel	200°F - 500°F

Table #92A - Pre-heat for Welding

PRE-HEAT FOR WELDING

Metal Group	Metal Designation	Recommended pre-heat
Nickel Steels	SAE 2015 Steel	Up to 300°F
	SAE 2115 Steel	200°F - 300°F
	2 ½% Nickel Steel	200°F - 400°F
	SAE 2315 Steel	200°F - 500°F
	SAE 2320 Steel	200°F - 500°F
	SAE 2330 Steel	300°F - 600°F
	SAE 2340 Steel	400°F - 700°F
Medium Chrome Moly Steels	5% Cr. - ½% Mo. Steel	600°F - 900°F
	8% Cr. - 1% Mo. Steel	600°F - 900°F
Plain High Chromium Steels	12 - 14% Cr. Type 410	300°F - 500°F
	16 - 18% Cr. Type 430	300°F - 500°F
	23 - 30% Cr. Type 446	300°F - 500°F
High Chrome Nickel Stainless Steels	18% Cr. 8% Ni. Type 304 25 - 12 Type 309 25 - 20 Type 310 18 - 8 Cb. Type 347 18 - 8 Mo. Type 316 18 - 8 Mo. Type 317	Usually do not require pre-heat but it may be desirable to remove chill

Table #92B - Pre-heat for Welding (cont'd)

PRE-HEAT FOR WELDING

Metal Group	Metal Designation	Recommended pre-heat
Medium Nickel Chromium Steels	SAE 3115 Steel	200°F - 400°F
	SAE 3125 Steel	300°F - 500°F
	SAE 3130 Steel	400°F - 700°F
	SAE 3140 Steel	500°F - 800°F
	SAE 3150 Steel	600°F - 900°F
	SAE 3215 Steel	300°F - 500°F
	SAE 3230 Steel	500°F - 700°F
	SAE 3240 Steel	700°F - 1000°F
	SAE 3250 Steel	900°F - 1100°F
	SAE 3315 Steel	500°F - 700°F
	SAE 3325 Steel	900°F - 1100°F
	SAE 3435 Steel	900°F - 1100°F
	SAE 3450 Steel	900°F - 1100°F
Moly Bearing Chromium and Chromium Nickel Steels	SAE 4140 Steel	600°F - 800°F
	SAE 4340 Steel	700°F - 900°F
	SAE 4615 Steel	400°F - 600°F
	SAE 4630 Steel	500°F - 700°F
	SAE 4640 Steel	600°F - 800°F
	SAE 4820 Steel	600°F - 800°F
Low Chrome Moly Steels	2% Cr. - 1% Mo. Steel	4600°F - 800°F

Table #92C - Pre-heat for Welding (cont'd)

Distortion

Distortion is the natural result of stresses in the work piece through heating and cooling, coupled with factors such as expansion and contraction.

Due to the intense heat from welding, distortion will always exist to some degree, however the following may be used to alleviate or minimize distortion:

- Use as few weld passes as the weld design will allow, as the more passes the more distortion.
- Weld as fast as the weld design will allow, keeping the heat affected zone (HAZ) narrow, or smaller. The slower the speed, the more heat and the higher the distortion.
- Prepare joint edges accurately. This keeps the weld travel from slowing for wide sections or speeding up for narrow sections.
- Use correct joint preparation. This will reduce excessive weld metal deposit.
- Use local pre-heat to counteract the approximate size of the affected area caused by welding, as in illustration #437. Apply a local pear shaped pre-heat about the expected width of the affected area caused by welding. Each heat spot should be applied immediately prior to the welding of each coupling.

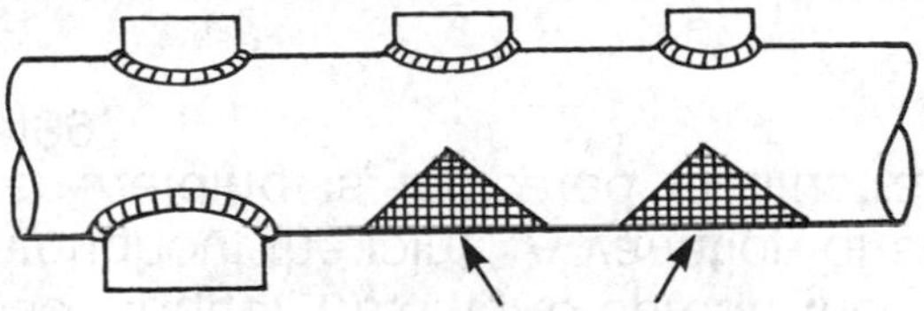
HEAT BEFORE
WELDING

Illustration #437 - Local pre-heat

- A heavy strong-back can be placed beneath the parts to be welded. The parts are then clamped directly to the strong back to maintain alignment. A strong-back can also be curved to offset weld pull.

- Determine the amount of distortion before making a weld and pre-set the parts to compensate for the distortion, as in illustration #438.

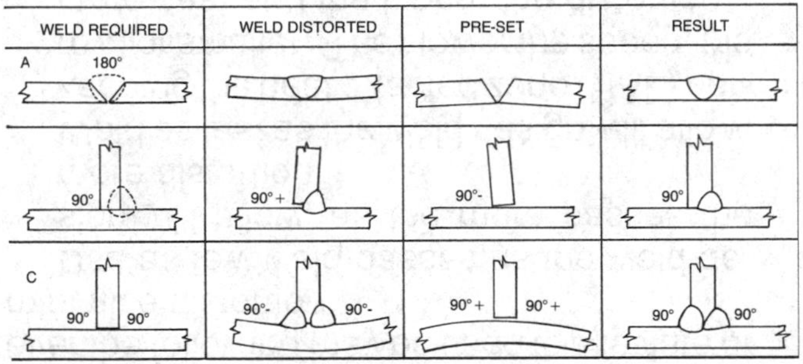
WELD REQUIRED
WELD DISTORTED
PRE-SET
RESULT
A
180°
90°
90° +
90°-
90°
C
90°
90°
90°-
90°-
90° +
90° +
90°
90°

Illustration #438 - Preset Distortion

- Plan a welding sequence so that one weld counteracts another by pulling in the opposite direction. This is working around a neutral axis.
- To reduce distortion it is advisable to divide the job into a number of component parts and weld these parts first, before attaching them to the main assembly. Much of the stress created in welding the components will not be transferred to the main assembly
- Use stagger welding to spread the heat throughout the joint. A variation of stagger welding is indicated in illustration #439.

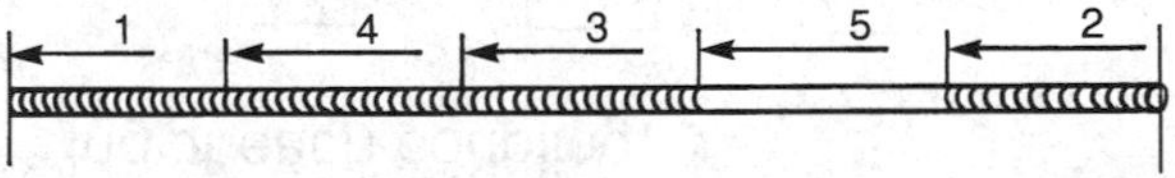
1
4
3
5
2

Illustration #439 - Stagger Welding

- A considerable amount of residual stress will be left in the welds after any welding. If maximum joint efficiency is required, the welded fabrication should be stress relieved using an approved post weld heat treatment (PWHT) process.

Window Welds

A window weld is used as a last resort to join pipe or tube sections when every other welding procedure is unsuitable. The window weld preparation is time consuming and the welder must be very experienced to complete the weld successfully. This method is primarily used to repair boiler wall tubes or pipe joints located in the corner of walls with restricted access to the backside. The window segment of the procedure allows the welder to complete the entire joint from one side. The following is a description of the procedure:

- The window opening is cut after marking the outline on the tube or pipe using a round template with a diameter approximately one-third the size of the circumference of the tube.
- The same template is used to mark out the replacement window on a piece of tubing. See illustrations #440 and #441.

Note: Allow a weld gap of 1/8" (3.175 mm) before marking the window on the weld joint.

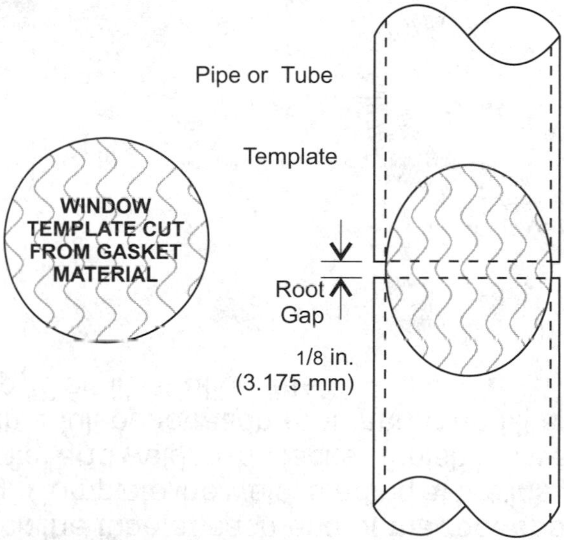
Pipe or Tube
Template
WINDOW TEMPLATE CUT FROM GASKET MATERIAL
Root Gap
1/8 in. (3.175 mm)

Illustration #440 - Window Template

A pencil grinder is used to bevel the tube and the window. The tube is beveled from the inside to the outside, the window and window openings are beveled from the outside to the inside. See illustration #442.

Tack the tube at each end of the root opening. Complete the weld, starting at the inside center and weld to the tacks. Finish the weld with a full penetration root, and then fill and cap. See illustration #443.

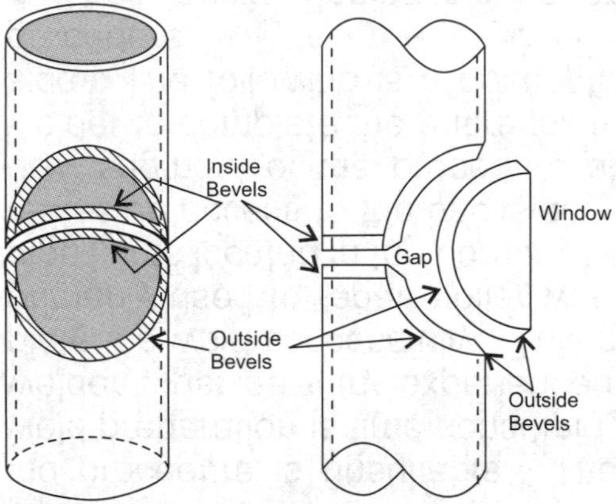
Inside
Bevels
Window
Gap
Outside
Bevels
Outside
Bevels

Illustration #441 - Window Weld Beveling

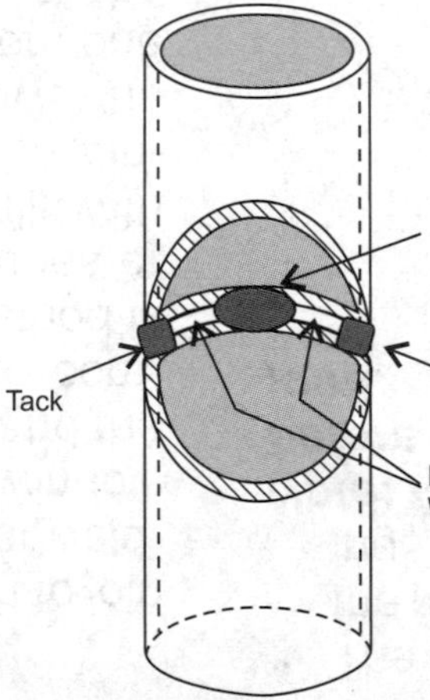
Start
Weld
Tack
Tack
Finish
Weld

Illustration #442 - Tacking and Welding the Pipe or Tube

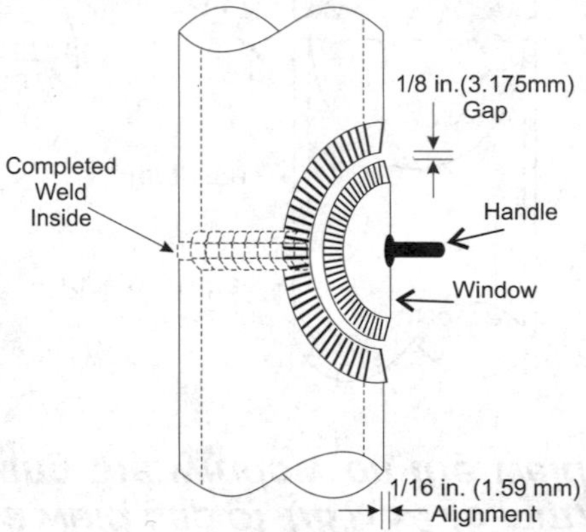
1/8 in.(3.175mm)
Gap
Completed
Weld
Inside
Handle
Window
1/16 in. (1.59 mm)
Alignment

Illustration #443 - Window Alignment

Bevel the weld at the T's, making sure that the weld is free of porosity. Tack a welding rod to the window to use as a handle. Before tacking, align the window approximately 1/16 in. (1.60 mm) to the outside of the tube to allow for weld shrinkage. After the window is tacked, complete the weld from the bottom to the top, see illustration #443.

Mirror Welding

Mirror welding is a method used when a welder is unable to see the back side of the item to be joined. The welder's hands must have access to the restricted side of the joint.

The location of the mirror and the direction of welding are the most important factors when completing a mirror weld.

The mirror should be located to the side of the welding area and turned slightly to give a clear view of the welding area, as indicated in illustration #444.

The direction of travel can be either left or right, but always work toward the mirror. If the weld progresses from right to left, the mirror should be positioned on the left, if the weld progresses from left to right, the mirror should be on the right. See illustration #444.

Gas tungsten arc welding (GTAW) is the welding process that gives the most satisfactory results when mirror welding, but if this is not available, shielded metal arc welding (SMAW) is acceptable.

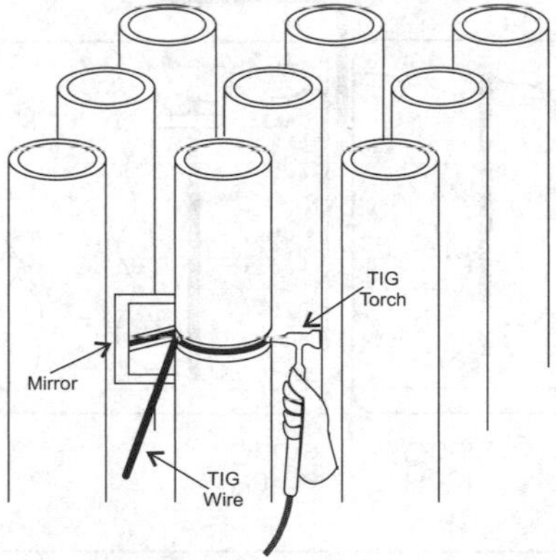
TIG
Torch
Mirror
TIG
Wire

Illustration #444 Mirror Welding Process

Pipe or Tube Purging

The welding of mild steel pipe can be done with the GTAW process without the use of a purging gas to protect the root side.

Stainless steel, carbon steel alloys containing chrome higher than $2^1/_2$ %, nickel, and nickel alloys must have extra protection at the root side of the joint. This is accomplished by filling the inside of the pipe or tube with an inert gas.

Several methods can be employed to contain the inert gas in the pipe. These include:

- Rubber pistons.
- Plastic balloons.
- Water-soluble paper or bread.

The purge gas can be supplied either through the purge dams or through the joint. See illustration #445.

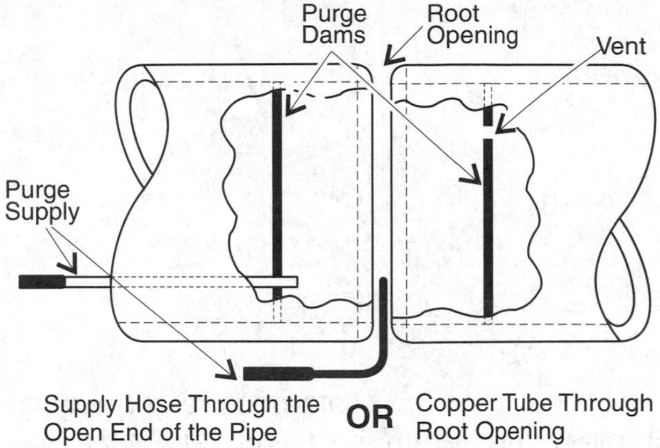
Purge Dams
Root Opening
Vent
Purge Supply
Supply Hose Through the Open End of the Pipe
OR
Copper Tube Through Root Opening

Illustration #445 - Pipe or Tube Purging

The purge tube can be a copper tube or a hose with a football air filler needle fitted to the end. As argon is heavier than air, a vent must be provided to allow the air to escape from the top. The pipe joint is taped shut and this tape is removed in sections ahead of the welding direction.

Preparation of Pipe Test Coupons

The proper preparation of test coupons is vital to the successful completion of a welder performance test. Such things as land, or root face, and gap must be closely monitored. Also the welder must ensure that the two surfaces are parallel in order to achieve a consistent root gap. The following procedure should be followed as a guideline:

- Grind a land onto the test coupons, and use an electrode stub as a guide to ensure that the land is consistent.
- It may be necessary to true up the land with a file in order to eliminate any uneven surfaces. Again use an electrode stub as a guide to check the consistency of the land.
- After satisfied with the preparation, put the two coupons together with no gap in order to check that the surfaces are parallel.
- Whenever performing a weld test on pipe it is a good idea to match up the inside of the two coupons by turning one to avoid out-of-round misalignment. After getting the best match, mark with a soap stone.
- Most pipe test coupons should be tacked in the 2G position with the pipe in the vertical axis. Bend an electrode, having a diameter equal to the width of the required root opening, into a V shape.
- Place the gap rod between the two coupons to act as a spacer. Align the coupons on the inside to the soap stone marks.
- With the pipe coupons properly aligned, one tack is made in the root of the joint. See illustration #446A.

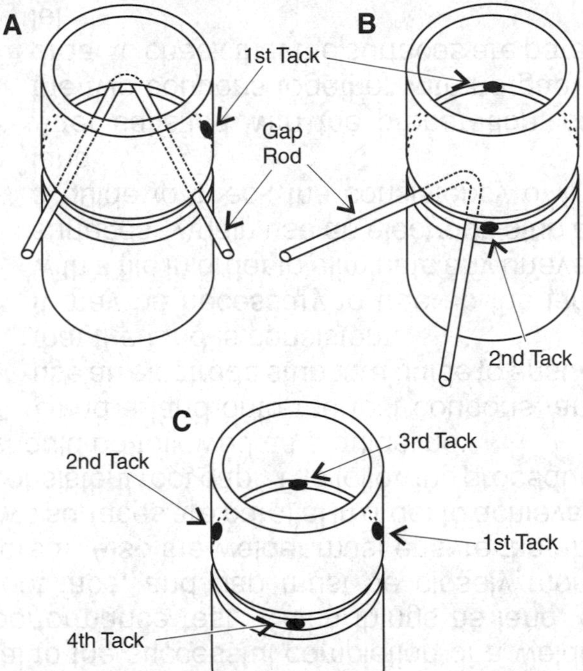
A
B
1st Tack
Gap
Rod
2nd Tack
C
3rd Tack
2nd Tack
1st Tack
4th Tack

Illustration #446 Pipe Test Coupons

- The gap rod is then moved so that only the end is between the coupons.
- When the gap is correct, make the second tack 180° from the first tack. See illustration #446B.
- Remove the gap rod and adjust the gap until the openings are as equal as possible. If unable to equalize the gaps then place the third tack into the section with the largest opening.
- The fourth tack is made in the last location. When finished there should be four equal spaces separated by four tack. See illustration #446C.

Recommended Root Pass Variables								
Weld Type	**Pipe & Tube Diameter**	**Wall Thickness**	**Root Face Land**	**Gap Space**	**Polarity**	**Length of Tack**	**Number of Tacks**	**Shielding Gas Pressure**
SMAW 1/8" (3.2 mm) E-6010, E-7010	all diameters	ALL	1/8" (3.2 mm)	3/32" - 1/8" (2.5 - 3.2 mm)	reverse	½" - 1" (13-25.4 mm)	4	
SMAW 3/32" (2.5 mm) E-6010, E-7010	all diameters	ALL	3/32" (2.5 mm)	3/32" (2.5 mm)	reverse	½" - 1" (13-25.4 mm)	4	
SMAW 3/32" (2.5 mm) E-7018, E-8018	all diameters	ALL	3/32" (2.5 mm)	3/32" (2.5 mm)	reverse	½" - 1" (13-25.4 mm)	4	
SMAW 3/32" (2.5 mm) stainless steel	all diameters	ALL	3/32" (2.5 mm)	3/32" (2.5 mm)	reverse	½" - 1" (13-25.4 mm)	4	
GTAW finger rest process, 2% thoriated tungsten 3/32" (2.5 mm) filler wire	all diameters	ALL	no land	5/32" (4.0 mm)	straight	½" - 1" (13-25.4 mm)	4	15 cu. ft.
GTAW gas cup rest process, 2% thoriated tungsten 3/32" (2.5 mm) filler wire	all diameters	ALL	no land	3/32" (2.5 mm)	straight	½" - 1" (13-25.4 mm)	4	15 cu. ft.

Table #93 - Recommended Root Pass Variables

Plasma Arc Cutting (PAC)

The development of plasma arc cutting has mainly been focused on the cutting of nonferrous metals. Plasma arc cutting, or PAC, operates under a different principle from that of oxy-fuel cutting. Instead of relying on a chemical reaction for the cutting process, it relies on extremely high temperatures to achieve the cutting. The PAC process uses a high velocity jet of ionized gas to melt and expel the metal.

Plasma gas or ionized gas is considered to be the fourth state of matter. It is created when the electron in the outer valence is stripped off by the application of electricity. Atmospheric air is a poor conductor of electricity. However when air becomes ionized it readily conducts electricity, such as an electrical storm. This can also be said about argon, helium, and carbon dioxide. These shielding gases are commonly used with PAC of ferrous and non-ferrous materials.

Compressed air is the recommended choice when cutting thin sections of mild steel. It is cheap and readily available, but it must be free from oil and contaminants.

There are two basic modes of operation. One mode is the transferred arc, and the other mode is the non-transferred arc.

Transferred arc mode relies on a ground clamp to complete the electrical circuit for the power supply, or welding machine. Transferred arc PAC can only cut materials that conduct electricity, such as carbon steel, stainless steel, aluminium or copper.

Non-transferred arc mode does not require a ground clamp to complete the circuit as the circuit is completed inside the PAC torch. Non-transferred arc PAC can be used to cut anything, such as steel, glass, fiberglass, wood, plastics and rubber.

The basic operating principle of a PAC process is as follows:

- High frequency is used to initiate a pilot arc inside the PAC torch. This step is the same for both the transferred arc mode and non-transferred arc mode.
- At about 18,000°F to 25,000°F (11,000°C to 15,000°C) the gas will ionize and turn into plasma gas. The plasma gas, commonly referred to as orifice gas, may be a choice of many gases including compressed air, argon, nitrogen or hydrogen.
- The plasma gas expands inside the torch from the tremendous heat of ionization.
- The plasma gas is then fed through a restrictive nozzle which in turn accelerates the gas as it leaves the restrictive orifice.
- As the plasma gas strikes the material it transfers its energy to the material. This process raises the temperature of the base material enough to vaporize and expel it.

The power supply for PAC is direct current, either AC to DC rectified, or DC generated. The PAC process uses DCSP which cuts down on the amount of heat build up in the non-consumable electrode inside the torch.

Along with DCSP, PAC machines use a high frequency generator to initiate the pilot arc because the non-consumable electrode is well inside the PAC torch, and the operator is unable to strike the arc the same way as with the GTAW process.

PAC power supplies also have high open circuit voltages ranging from 120 volts to 400 volts, and the amperage range is between 70 amps to 1000 amps.

The following is a list of some of the other equipment required to cut with PAC:

- A source of compressed air, such as an air compressor. This can be used for the cutting of carbon steel.

- A source of compressed gas, such as a compressed gas cylinder, either for the shielding gas or the plasma gas.
- A filter and water trap for compressed air.
- A power source.
- A torch for manual use, or for use in a multi-head-burning table.
- A supply of different restrictive orifices. Some suppliers include gap guides on their orifices to regulate the stand off distance between the orifices and the work.
- A supply of non-consumable electrodes. When using compressed air the air quality can affect the life of the electrode.

Most non-ferrous metals can be successfully cut by using nitrogen or argon. Argon is best for aluminium because there are fewer fumes.

The cutting of stainless steel can be accomplished by using pure nitrogen or a combination of nitrogen and hydrogen or a combination of nitrogen and oxygen.

The PAC process has many advantages over mechanical cutting or oxy-fuel cutting. Some of the advantages are as follows:

- Slag free cuts.
- Minimal heat affected zone.
- Very little distortion.
- High cutting speeds.

Tables can be used as a guide when selecting various plasma orifice gases. In some cases the thickness of material being cut increases greatly with the addition of auxiliary gas.

Table #94 has information on plasma gases, and table #95 has information on the addition of auxiliary gas.

Plasma or orifice gases - Flow Rates Are Usually 20 CFH to 30 CFH (The following list is not complete and will vary between gas suppliers)			
Plasma/ Orifice Gas	**Carbon Steel**	**Stainless and Nickel Alloys**	**Aluminium**
Compressed Air	Up to 1 inch thick	Up to 1 inch thick	Up to ½ inch thick
Nitrogen	Up to 5.5 inches thick	Up to 4.5 inches thick	Up to 4.5 inch thick
Oxygen	Up to 2 inches thick	Not applicable	Not applicable

Table #94 - Plasma or Orifice Gases

Auxiliary Gases - Flow Rates Are Usually 160 CFH to 220 CFH (The following list is not complete and will vary between gas suppliers)			
Auxiliary Gas	**Carbon Steel**	**Stainless Steel and Nickel Alloys**	**Aluminium**
Compressed Air	Up to 5 inches thick	Up to 5 inches thick	Up to 4 inches
Nitrogen	Up to 2.5 inches thick	Up to 2.5 inches thick	Up to 4 inches
Oxygen	Up to 2.5 inches thick	Up to 2.5 inches thick	Up to 1.5 inch

Table #95 - Auxiliary Gases

Typically the auxiliary gas is the same as the plasma gas.

If planning to do a substantial amount of cutting on any type of steel it is recommended that more research be done on the amount, and type of gas being used.

Gas suppliers are a good source of reference when gathering information about shielding, and cutting gases.

Air Carbon Arc Cutting or Gouging (CAC-A)

In this process an arc is established between a carbon electrode and the metal. The arc melts the base metal while an air jet is directed at the arc, blowing away the molten metal. This is indicated in illustration #447.

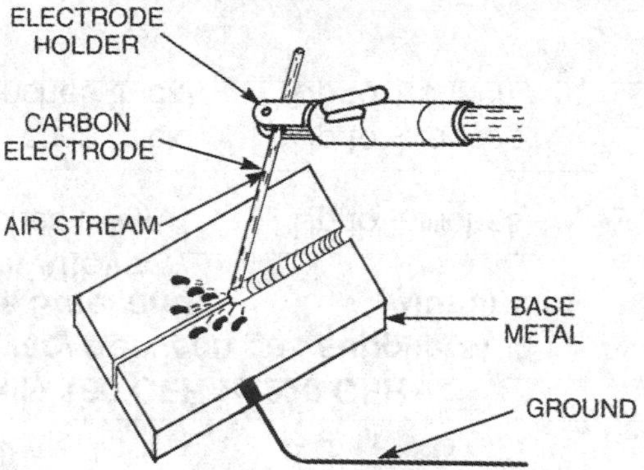
ELECTRODE
HOLDER
CARBON
ELECTRODE
AIR STREAM
BASE
METAL
GROUND

Illustration #447 Carbon Arc Cutting or Gouging

The carbon arc process is effective on all ferrous, stainless steels and most non-ferrous metals.

Operating techniques for various metals are indicated in table #96.

Metals	Techniques
Carbon steel & low alloys	DC electrode with DCRP
Stainless steel	DC electrode with DCRP
Cast iron	AC electrode with DCRP
Copper alloys up to 60%	DC electrodes with DCRP
Copper alloys over 60%	AC electrodes with AC
Nickel alloys	AC electrodes with AC
Aluminum Alloys	DC electrodes with DCRP
Welding Current Terms DC - Direct Current DCRP - Direct Current Reverse Polarity AC - Alternating Current	

Table #96 - Carbon Arc cutting or Gouging Operating Techniques

Direct current constant current DC/CC welding machines used for SMAW can also be used for air carbon arc cutting, or gouging.

If large electrodes are to be used, a specially designed machine with 100% duty cycle is recommended. The equipment needed in carbon arc gouging is indicated in illustration #448.

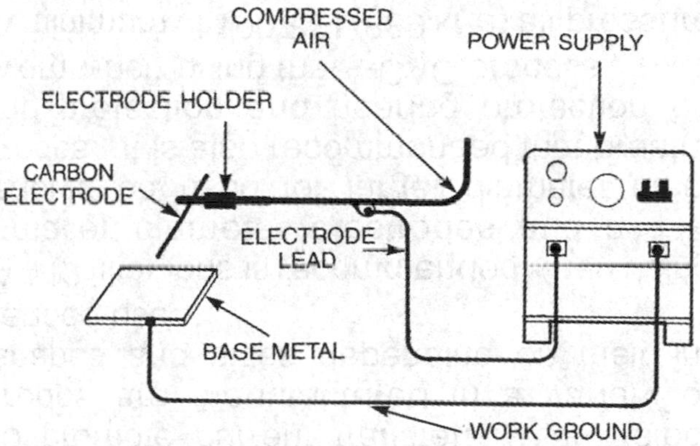
COMPRESSED AIR
POWER SUPPLY
ELECTRODE HOLDER
CARBON ELECTRODE
ELECTRODE LEAD
BASE METAL
WORK GROUND

Illustration #448 Carbon Arc cutting or Gouging Equipment

The carbon electrode should protrude from the end of the holder a maximum of 7 inches (168 mm) to a minimum of 2 inches (51 mm). The air stream should be turned on before touching the electrode to the base metal. After the arc is established the arc length must be maintained in order to provide enough clearance to allow the base metal to be blown clear of the joint.

Air Carbon Arc Cutting (CAC-A) can be used on DCRP, DCSP, or AC current. The consumable electrode must be compatible with the type of current being used.

DCRP electrodes are usually copper coated to promote current transfer. A-CAC electrodes are manufactured in a variety of shapes and sizes depending on their intended use.

A #12 filter lens is recommended when using smaller diameter electrodes and a #14 should be used for larger diameter electrodes. It is also recommended that breathing protection and hearing protection be worn when using the A-CAC process.

A minimum of 100 PSI (689 kPa) air pressure should be used when carbon arc gouging.

SECTION TWELVE QUESTIONS

Welding

1. *What section of the American Society of Mechanical Engineers (ASME) code must be referenced when taking or administering a welding test?*
   - ❒ Section I
   - ❒ Section IV
   - ❒ Section IX
   - ❒ none of above

2. *Determine if the following statement is true or false. A welder certified to one construction code is qualified to weld under all construction codes.*
   ❒ true ❒ false

3. *What does AWS stand for?*
   - ❒ all welding sides
   - ❒ always weld standing
   - ❒ American Welding Society
   - ❒ at weld side

4. *What does PWHT stand for?*
   - ❒ post weld heat treatment
   - ❒ put weld heavy throughout
   - ❒ plasma weld heat treatment
   - ❒ pacific weld heat treatment

5. *What is the most popular clothing used by welders?*
   - ❒ leather
   - ❒ cotton denims
   - ❒ rayon
   - ❒ nylon

6. *Which of the following welding filter lenses would give the most eye protection?*
   - ❒ #4
   - ❒ #6
   - ❒ #8
   - ❒ #10

7. *Determine if the following statement is true or false. Argon gas is heavier than air.*
   ❒ true ❒ false

8. *Metal fume fever or zinc chills are caused from welding on:*
   - ❒ mild steel
   - ❒ stainless steel
   - ❒ galvanized steel
   - ❒ rusty steel

9. *Determine if the following statement is true or false. Oxygen should be considered dangerous.*
   - ❒ true ❒ false

10. *What do acetylene regulators have to ensure that they are not connected to oxygen cylinders?*
    - ❒ right hand threads
    - ❒ left hand threads
    - ❒ snap connections
    - ❒ slip-on connections

11. *What should never be used to fabricate an acetylene manifold system?*
    - ❒ steel pipe
    - ❒ stainless steel tubing
    - ❒ yellow brass fittings
    - ❒ copper or red brass

12. *What valve is closed first when shutting down oxy-acetylene equipment?*
    - ❒ oxygen torch valve
    - ❒ acetylene torch valve
    - ❒ oxygen cylinder valve
    - ❒ acetylene cylinder valve

13. *What oxy-acetylene welding flame is rich in acetylene?*
    - ❒ neutral flame
    - ❒ carbonizing/reducing flame
    - ❒ oxidizing flame
    - ❒ red flame

14. *At what temperature does iron or carbon steel progressively burn?*
    - ❒ 10,000 °F (5,500 °C)
    - ❒ 7,000 °F (4,200 °C)
    - ❒ 5,800 °F (3,200 °C)
    - ❒ 1,742 °F (950 °C)

15. *What type of oxy-acetylene torch is better to use when only cutting is required?*
- ❒ combination oxy-acetylene torch
- ❒ right hand oxy-acetylene torch
- ❒ left hand oxy-acetylene torch
- ❒ heavy-duty hand cutting torch

16. *What type of flame should be used when cutting with oxy-acetylene?*
- ❒ neutral flame
- ❒ carbonizing/reducing flame
- ❒ oxidizing flame
- ❒ red flame

17. *Determine if the following statement is true or false. On thicker material, the oxy-acetylene torch is held perpendicular to the work.*
- ❒ true ❒ false

18. *Determine if the following statement is true or false. An oxy-acetylene tip can be used with propane gas.*
- ❒ true ❒ false

19. *What type of fuel gas has the hottest flame?*
- ❒ propylene
- ❒ propane
- ❒ acetylene
- ❒ natural gas

20. *What type of filler metal is used to weld carbon steel when using the oxy-acetylene welding process?*
- ❒ everdur 1010
- ❒ L.A. superweld
- ❒ strips of base metal
- ❒ AA 4043 Aluminum

21. *What is low temperature brazing or soldering usually used to do?*
- ❒ joining heavy steel
- ❒ joining aluminum pipe
- ❒ joining stainless steel pipe
- ❒ joining copper tubing

22. *What is used on a low temperature brazing or soldering application to indicate the correct time to add solder?*
- ❒ a temperature stick
- ❒ flux
- ❒ the color of the material
- ❒ a reamer

23. *Determine if the following statement is true or false. The electron theory states that electrons flow from the negative terminal to the positive terminal in the electrical circuit.*
- ❒ true ❒ false

24. *What are the two main ingredients in an arc welding circuit?*
- ❒ voltage and current
- ❒ electricity and power
- ❒ electrode and welding machine
- ❒ arc and voltage jump

25. *Determine if the following statement is true or false. With alternating current (AC), the electrical current flows in one direction only and continuously throughout the welding circuit.*
- ❒ true ❒ false

26. *Determine if the following statement is true or false. A duty cycle is a rating system which determines how long a welding machine can operate continuously in a 10 minute period.*
- ❒ true ❒ false

27. *Which of these welding machines is the simplest unit for supplying current suitable for arc welding?*
- ❒ AC rectifier
- ❒ DC generator
- ❒ AC generator
- ❒ AC transformer

28. *What welding cable size would produce the least resistance to the flow of current?*

❒ 4/0
❒ 3/0
❒ 1
❒ 4

29. *Which one of the following electrodes can be used in all welding positions?*

❒ electrode E-6010
❒ electrode E-6024
❒ electrode E-7028
❒ electrode E-7027

30. *Determine if the following statement is true or false. Austenitic stainless steels are not good for cryogenic and low temperature service.*

❒ true ❒ false

31. *Why are ferritic stainless steels sometimes called straight chrome steel?*

❒ ferritic stainless steels contain a high level of nickel
❒ ferritic stainless steels contain very little, if any, nickel
❒ ferritic stainless steels contain a high level of aluminum
❒ ferritic stainless steels contain a high level of lime

32. *What determines the usability of stainless steel welding electrodes?*

❒ the type of electrode coating
❒ the type of steel used to make the electrodes
❒ the type of welding machine
❒ the type of base metal to be welded

33. *Determine if the following statement is true or false. The five basic weld joints are: butt, lap, corner, tee, and edge-flange.*

❒ true ❒ false

34. *The G in the weld numbering system stands for:*
- ❒ grind weld
- ❒ groove weld
- ❒ gouging
- ❒ good weld

35. *Determine if the following statement is true or false. A weld symbol denotes what type of weld is to be performed.*
- ❒ true ❒ false

36. *When using a bevel or J-groove weld symbol, the plate to be prepared is indicated by a:*
- ❒ straight arrow line
- ❒ broken arrow line
- ❒ pointed arrow line
- ❒ a line with the arrow on the right side

37. *What is used in a welding symbol to show more definitive manner of the sequence of welding operations?*
- ❒ broken arrow lines
- ❒ included angle
- ❒ multiple reference lines
- ❒ bill of welding operations

38. *Determine if the following statement is true or false. (SMAW) stands for shielded metal arc welding.*
- ❒ true ❒ false

39. *What type of current is used when welding with an E-6010 electrode?*
- ❒ alternating current (AC)
- ❒ direct current straight polarity (DCS)
- ❒ direct current reverse polarity (DCR)
- ❒ direct current (DC)

40. *What is the non-consumable electrode made from when using the Gas Tungsten Arc Welding (GTAW) process?*
- ❒ copper
- ❒ steel
- ❒ stainless steel
- ❒ tungsten

41. *What is the most commonly used shielding gas used in the Tungsten Arc Welding (GTAW) process?*
- ❒ helium
- ❒ argon
- ❒ carbon dioxide
- ❒ nitrogen

42. *What type of coating is used on filler wire used in the Tungsten Arc Welding (GTAW) process when welding carbon steel?*
- ❒ copper
- ❒ lime
- ❒ no coating
- ❒ iron powder

43. *What type of current is normally used when welding with the Gas Metal Arc Welding process?*
- ❒ alternating current (AC)
- ❒ direct current straight polarity (DCS)
- ❒ direct current reverse polarity (DCR)
- ❒ direct current (DC)

44. *Determine if the following statement is true or false. Additional shielding gas may be used with the flux cored arc welding (FCCAW) process.*
❒ true ❒ false

45. *Determine if the following statement is true or false. Submerged arc welding (SAW) is a welding process done under water.*
❒ true ❒ false

46. *What duty cycle does the welding machine have to be when using the submerged arc welding process?*
- ❒ 50 %
- ❒ 30 %
- ❒ 100 %
- ❒ 70 %

47. *Determine if the following statement is true or false. Plasma gas in the plasma arc welding process is considered to be the fourth state of matter.*
❒ true ❒ false

48. *What type of shielding gas is used when welding carbon steel with the plasma arc welding process?*
- ❒ helium
- ❒ argon
- ❒ carbon dioxide
- ❒ nitrogen

49. *Determine if the following statement is true or false. The electrogas welding process is used to make full thickness, single pass welds on joints positioned in the vertical or near vertical plane.*
❒ true ❒ false

50. *In the stud welding process, what is a ferrule made out?*

- ❐ steel
- ❐ plastic
- ❐ copper
- ❐ ceramic

51. *What is the most common location of cracking in the weld metal?*

- ❐ root bead
- ❐ the cap
- ❐ the heat affected zone (HAZ)
- ❐ the base metal

52. *What procedure can be used to reduce cracks when welding?*

- ❐ cooling the weld with water
- ❐ pre-heating the base metal before welding
- ❐ grinding the root bead
- ❐ filing the cap

53. *Determine if the following statement is true or false. Due to the intense heat from welding, distortion will always exist.*

❐ true ❐ false

54. *When is a window weld used as a welding procedure?*

- ❐ when a weld has to be completed inside a house
- ❐ when a repair has to be completed on a double walled ship
- ❐ when a weld has to be completed on a boiler water wall
- ❐ when a weld has to be completed on a steel window frame

55. *What is the best welding method used when mirror welding?*

- ❐ gas tungsten arc welding (GTAW)
- ❐ shielded metal arc welding (SMAW)
- ❐ gas metal arc welding
- ❐ oxy-acetylene welding (OAW)

56. *Where should the vent be located when purging a pipe for extra root side protection?*

- ❐ side of the weld joint
- ❐ bottom of the weld joint
- ❐ top of the weld joint
- ❐ front of the weld joint

57. *What position should most pipe weld test coupons be tacked in?*

- ❒ 3 G
- ❒ 4 G
- ❒ 2 G
- ❒ 6 G

58. *What should be the root face (land) measurement using a 1/8" (3.2mm) electrode on a weld test coupon?*

- ❒ no root face (land)
- ❒ 3/23 inch (2.5 mm)
- ❒ 1/8 inch (3.2 mm)
- ❒ 1/4 inch (6.4 mm)

59. *Determine if the following statement is true or false. A high velocity jet of ionized gas is used to melt and expel the metal when cutting nonferrous material using the plasma arc cutting (PAC) process.*

❒ true ❒ false

60. *What is used to initiate a pilot arc inside the plasma arc torch?*

- ❒ high frequency
- ❒ low frequency
- ❒ shielding gas
- ❒ tunsten electrode

61. *What thickness of carbon steel can be cut using the plasma arc cutting (PAC) process with compressed air as the orifice gas?*

- ❒ 5 1/2 inches thick
- ❒ 2 inches thick
- ❒ 1 inch thick
- ❒ not applicable

62. *Determine if the following statement is true or false. Air carbon cutting or gouging (A-CRC) uses argon as the shielding gas.*

❒ true ❒ false

63. *What number helmet filter lens should be used when cutting with the air carbon arc cutting (A-CRC) process using large diameter electrodes?*
- ❒ #5
- ❒ #7
- ❒ #8
- ❒ #14

SECTION THIRTEEN

WELD METALLURGY

Steel Classification System

Some of the organizations that write specifications for steels used in the welding industries are:

- CSA - Canadian Standards Association
- AISI - American Iron & Steel Institute
- SAE -Society of Automotive Engineers
- ASTM - American Society for Testing Materials
- ASME - American Society of Mechanical Engineers

Specifications covered by each organization are:

- CSA - Structural Steel Plates and Shapes
- AISI - Sheet and Bar Steel
- SAE - Bar Steel
- ASTM - Steel Plate
- ASME - Structural Steel Plates and Shapes

CSA System

The CSA issues a wide variety of standards including CAN/CSA-G40.21M-98 that covers structural quality steel plate, shapes, hollow sections, and steel bars for general construction.

The types of steels covered by this standard are:

- Type G, general construction.
- Type W, weldable.
- Type WT, weldable notch tough steel.
- Type R, atmospheric corrosion resistant steel.
- Type A, atmospheric corrosion resistant weldable steel.
- Type AT, atmospheric corrosion resistant weldable notch tough steel.
- Type Q, Quenched and tempered low alloy steel plate.
- Type QT, Quenched and tempered low alloy notch tough steel plate.

SAE and AISI System

Both SAE and AISI use identical numbers for the same steel, the only difference is that the AISI use a letter prefix to indicate how the steel was made. The numbers indicate the composition of the steel.

The SAE or AISI numbers are four digits, the first indicates the class of steel. The second is used to indicate subclasses. See tables #97 and #98 for an example of SAE 1020

Classes of Steel	
1	Plain Carbon Steels
2	Nickel Steels
3	Nickel Chromium Steels
4	Chromium Molybdenum Steels
5	Chrome Steels
6	Chrome Vanadium Steels
7	Not Used
8	Nickel Chrome Molybdenum
9	Nickel Chrome Molybdenum with Manganese and Silicon

Table #97 - Classes of Steel

Sub-Classes of Steel (this is not a complete listing)	
10XX,	Plain Carbon Steel - nothing added
11XX,	Plain Carbon Steel - sulphur added
12XX,	Plain Carbon Steel - sulphur and phosphorus added
13XX,	Plain Carbon Steel - extra manganese added
21XX,	Nickel Steel - 1 % nickel
23XX,	Nickel Steel - 3% nickel
25XX,	Nickel Steel - 5% nickel
30XX,	Nickel Chromium Steel - 0.70% nickel &.07% chromium
31XX,	Nickel Chromium Steel - 1.25% nickel & 0.6% chromium
32XX,	Nickel Chromium Steel - 1.75% nickel & 1.0% chromium
35XX,	Nickel Chromium Steel - 3.50% nickel & 1.5% chromium
41XX,	Chromium Molybdenum Steel
43XX,	Chromium Molybdenum Nickel Steels
46XX,	Nickel Molybdenum with 1.65% Nickel
48XX,	Nickel Molybdenum with 3.25% Nickel
50XX,	Low Chromium Steel
51XX,	Chromium Steel with 1 % Chromium
52XX,	Chromium Steel with 2% Chromium
61XX,	Chromium Vanadium Steel
86XX,	Nickel 0.55%, Chromium 0.50%, Molybdenum 0.20%
87XX,	Nickel 0.55%, Chromium 0.50%, Molybdenum 0.25%
92XX,	Manganese 0.80%, Silicon 2.00%
94XX,	Manganese 0.95% to 1.15%, Silicon 0.50%, Nickel 0.35%, Chromium 0.30%,
95XX,	Manganese 1.35%, Silicon 0.50%, Nickel 0.55%, Chromium 0.50%, Molybdenum 0.20% Molybdenum 0.12%

Table #98 - Sub-Classes of Steel

Carbon Content

The last two numbers in the SAE numbers indicate the carbon content of the steel in hundredths of one per cent. This would mean that SAE 1020 has twenty points of carbon, or 0.20% while SAE 1040 has 0.40% carbon.

Note: The last two points are very important to the welder as they indicate weldability. The higher the percentage of carbon, the greater the difficulty in welding.

In every case the last two digits are carbon content, except in the 52100 steel which has 1.00% carbon.

ASTM and ASME System

Steel plate designations have been reduced to simple numbers because material designers, and code users, insist on knowing mechanical, physical, and chemical properties. These two groups use identical numbers for the same steel whether it is carbon steel plate or stainless steel backing rings.

The only real difference is that ASTM will put an A in front of all listings, and ASME will use an SA, such as ASTM A36 or ASME SA36. Table #99 indicates the uses of some of the more popular specifications.

Popular ASTM Plate Uses	
ASTM Spec. No.	**Uses**
A242-49T	Low Alloy Structural Steel
A245-48T	Light Gauge Structural Quality Flat
A246-48T	Hot Rolled Carbon Steel
A283-49T	Carbon Steel Plates of Structural Quality up to 2" thick
A284-49T	Carbon-silicon Steel Plates
A285-49T	Carbon Steel Plate FLANGE Up to 2" thick
A285-49T	Carbon Steel Plate Firebox up to 2"

Table #99 - Popular A.S.T.M. Plate Uses

<table>
<tr><th colspan="6">Comparison Chart of Common Weldable Metals (Using Mild Steel as the Medium of Comparison)</th></tr>
<tr><th>Metal</th><th>Melting Point</th><th>Thermal Conductivity</th><th>Expansion Rate</th><th>Tensile Strength</th><th>Ductility</th></tr>
<tr><td>Wrought Iron</td><td>2800°F</td><td>Medium</td><td>Medium</td><td>45,000 psi (Avg.)</td><td>Contains layers of slag to give mild corrosion resistance.
Medium (Apt to separate)</td></tr>
<tr><td>Low Carbon Steels</td><td>2750°F</td><td>Medium</td><td>Medium</td><td>50,000 psi (Avg.)</td><td>Medium</td></tr>
<tr><td>Low Alloy High Strength Steels</td><td>2700°-2750°F</td><td>Medium</td><td>Medium</td><td>60,000 -85,000 psi</td><td>Medium (Stiffer and Tougher)</td></tr>
<tr><td>Medium and High Carbon Steels</td><td>2400°-2700°F (Caused by Carbon)</td><td>Low to Medium</td><td>Medium</td><td>60,000 - 120,000 psi</td><td>As carbon content is increased (within limits), tensile strength is increased but ductility is lowered.
Low to Medium</td></tr>
<tr><td>Stainless Steels</td><td>2400°-2700°F (Caused by Alloys)</td><td>Low</td><td>Very High (1 1/2 times Mild Steel)</td><td>Up to 150,000 psi</td><td>Martensitic types (hardenable) are not highly weldable and must be preheated.
Low to Medium (Very Tough)</td></tr>
<tr><td>Copper</td><td>1900°F</td><td>High</td><td>High</td><td rowspan="2">Up to 60,000 psi (Hard). Work hardens under cold working, causing rise in tensile rapidly strength and drop in ductility</td><td rowspan="3">High when annealed</td></tr>
<tr><td>Brasses and Bronzes</td><td>1600°-1800°F</td><td>High</td><td>High</td></tr>
<tr><td>Aluminum and Alloys</td><td>1200'-1400' F</td><td>High</td><td>High</td><td>13,000 to 17,000 psi for pure aluminum. Some aluminum alloys will range as high as 50,000 psi. Many higher tensile strength aluminum alloys are not highly weldable.</td></tr>
</table>

Table #100 - Comparison Chart of Common Weldable Materials

Mechanical Properties of Metal

Strength is one of the most important mechanical properties concerning a welder. Other various mechanical properties such as hardness, ductility, and toughness must also be known in order to design or replace a welded structure.

Some of the mechanical properties of steel are as follows:

- Tensile strength is the ultimate load required to pull the metal apart.
- Elastic limit is the load that a metal can withstand without becoming permanently deformed.
- Elasticity is the ability of metal to stretch and return to its original dimensions without deforming.
- Yield strength is the stress or load at which permanent deformation occurs.
- Ductility is the ability of metal to stretch beyond the elastic limits without breaking or cracking.
- Toughness or impact strength is the ability of a metal to withstand repeated sharp blows.
- Hardness is the ability of a metal to resist penetration.

Rule of Thumb Conversion Chart Plain Carbon Steel	Tensile Strength (psi)
File bites into surface very easily	50,000
File removes metal with slightly more pressure	111,000
Metal exhibits its first real resistance to the file	146,000
It is very difficult for the file to remove metal	195,000
File just barely removes metal	245,000
File will not remove metal and file teeth are dulled	300,000

Table #101 - Tensile Strength Chart

Identification of Metals

Generally a close visual examination will distinguish between cast iron, malleable cast iron, steel, brass, aluminium, copper, etc. A magnet is a useful tool for the identification of ferrous materials. Another way to identify metals is by their weight, and how they feel in your hand.

A spark test is based on the fact that the carbon content of steel affects the appearance of sparks that fly from a grinding wheel. Take some sample pieces of known grades of steel and use them to compare spark streams.

Low carbon steels:

- Sparks are bright, long, straight, and yellow in color.
- Very little branching.
- Few carbon bursts.

High carbon steels:

- Sparks tend to bursts and branch off more than low carbon steels.
- Their color is more to a yellow-orange, and they burst closer to the grinding wheel.
- The sparks tend to follow around the wheel more than low carbon steel.

Cast iron:

- Sparks are a red color near the grinding wheel, and a yellow color further out.
- The stream is not as long as with carbon steels.
- More pressure is required when grinding cast iron than with carbon steel.

High speed steels, or tool steels:

- Sparks maybe orange in color, and tend to ball up.
- Tool steels contain alloys that may affect the spark stream. Therefore, a spark stream may not be a satisfactory method to identify the carbon content of tool steels.

Scratching the surface with a new file is another way to determine the approximate hardness of a metal. Rockwell and Brinell hardness tests are the most common for precise and accurate measurements of hardness.

A Brinell 100 is a soft steel, and a Brinell 600 is very hard to penetrate. Rockwell hardness tests are split into two categories "B" and "C".

The "B" category relates to softer steels, and the "C" category is more associated with harder steels.

Table #102 lists the reaction of a file to certain steels, and an approximate Brinell and Rockwell comparison.

Hardness Judged by the Use of a Hand File				
Reaction of the file	Steel type	Brinell	Rockwell	
			B	C
File easily scratches the surface	Low carbon	100	57	
Some pressure is required on the file	Medium carbon	200	93	
More pressure is required to scratch the surface	High alloy	300		32
Steel can be filed but with great difficulty	High carbon	400		43
The steel is almost as hard as the file	Tool steel	500		52
Steel is harder than the file	Hardened tool steel	600		59

Table #102 - Using a Hand File to Judge Hardness

Uses for Steel by Carbon Content in percent		
Low	0.05-0.15	Chain, nails, and screws
	0.15-0.30	Structural steel, and plate
Medium	0.30-0.45	Axelshafts
High	0.45-0.60	Crankshafts
	0.60-0.75	Springs, and wood saws
Very High	0.75-0.90	Chisels
	0.90-1.00	Shear blades
	1.00-1.10	Taps and dies
	1.10-1.20	Lathe tools
	1.20-1.30	Files and reamers
	1.40-1.50	Metal saws
Cast Iron	2.5-6.5	Anvils, engine blocks, and vices.

Note; When the carbon content is higher than 0.30%, or medium carbon steel, a proper welding procedure should be used, along with preheat, and post weld heat treatment.

Table #103 Steel Carbon Content

Melting Temperatures of Metals	
Non-Ferrous	**Temperature**
Bronze	1655°F - (902°C)
Copper	1980°F - (1082°C)
Aluminum	1260°F - (682°C)
White metal	700°F - (371°C)
Lead	620°F - (327°C)
Silver brazing alloys	1140 - 1300°F (615 to 704°C)
Ferrous	**Temperature**
Wrought iron	2800°F - (1538°C)
0.15 carbon steel	2750°F - (1151°C)
0.60 carbon steel	2600°F - (1427°C)
Iron oxide	2460°F - (1348°C)
Cast iron	2400°F - (1316°C)
Stainless steel	2640°F - (1449°C)

Table #104 Melting Temperatures of Metals

Welding Heat Affected Zone

When a weld is made, the joining is accomplished by a flowing together of the deposited weld metal and the base metal. Both are liquefied by the heat of the arc. Between the liquid metal and the base metal away from the weld, there is a sharp temperature drop from the molten metal to room (or outside) temperature. The heat is conducted away from the weld to the base metal. This creates a zone of heat-affected material adjacent to the weld.

The properties and size of this heat affected zone (HAZ) are dependent on the rate at which the temperature changed. The rapid heat removal may be seen by watching the disappearance of red heat from the weld metal. This usually occurs within about 6 seconds. The temperature of the adjacent base metal may change from 2400°F to 1200°F (1315°C to 649°C) in three seconds.

The initial heating melts the grains and iron carbide particles. The carbon dissolves into the iron. Oxygen from the air is excluded from the weld puddle by slag formed from the melting of the welding rod coating, or by the use of a shielding gas. The rapid heat removal freezes this puddle of iron and dissolved carbon.

Current, electrode size, and welding speed of travel affect the amount of heat entering the steel. Generally the greater the amount of heat input, the wider the HAZ and the slower the rate of cooling. Thus large heat input tends to increase the width of the HAZ and reduce its hardness. Larger heat input results from use of large diameter rods, high current, and a slow rate of travel. It is possible to put too little heat into a weld by using a combination of small diameter welding rod, low current, and fast welding speed. This increases the rate of heat transfer to the point where the HAZ becomes hardened and underbead cracking occurs.

This hardened HAZ and cracking effect can be reduced or eliminated by preheating the weld area, thus reducing the rate of heat transfer. Energy input is measured in joules per inch, and is calculated by multiplying the amperage, times the voltage drop across the arc times seconds per inch of travel:

amps x volts x seconds per inch
= joules per inch

Illustration #449 illustrates how the cooling rate varies with energy input and plate thickness.

With multiple pass welds, the heat from the new bead radically changes the structure of the beads below. The heat causes the grains to become small and uniform resulting in increased toughness and ductility.

Welds made at very low temperatures (outside in winter) have a tendency to be harder and have more tendency to crack due to the higher heat transfer rate.

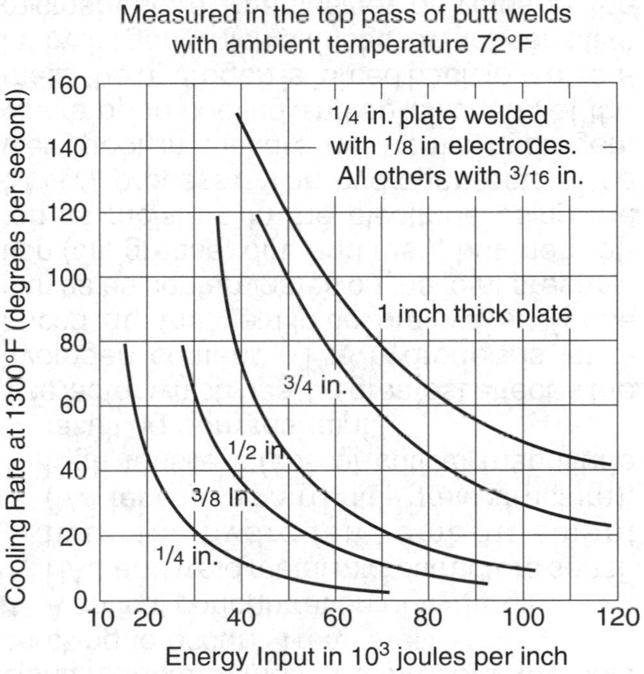
Measured in the top pass of butt welds with ambient temperature 72°F
1/4 in. plate welded with 1/8 in electrodes. All others with 3/16 in.
1 inch thick plate
3/4 in.
1/2 in.
3/8 in.
1/4 in.
Cooling Rate at 1300°F (degrees per second)
Energy Input in 10³ joules per inch
0
20
40
60
80
100
120
140
160
10
20
40
60
80
100
120

Illustration #449 - Varied Cooling Rate

Carbon and Low Alloy Steels

Plain carbon steels with less than 0.2% carbon present few problems in achieving a sound microstructure in the weld and heat affected zone (HAZ). As the carbon and alloy content in steel increases, there is a greater tendency to form harder and more crack sensitive regions in the HAZ which may be detrimental to the serviceability of the product.

High Strength Low Alloy (HSLA) steels which have a higher carbon and alloy content require special considerations in order to achieve a satisfactory weld and HAZ microstructure.

By far the most common type of weld failure in hardenable carbon and low alloy steels is Hydrogen Induced Cold Cracking. These cracks occur after the weld has cooled below 150°F (65°C), and they usually form in the HAZ or at points of stress or restraint.

Certain factors must be present for cold cracking to occur. They are:

- A critical concentration of hydrogen.
- HAZ and weld metal microstructure sensitive to hydrogen embrittlement (Martensite : a hard brittle grain structure).
- High tensile stress of critical magnitude resulting from restraint.

The factor which has the greatest effect is the hydrogen content. The hydrogen is introduced into the weld in several ways. These can be as contaminates on the joint preparation (oil, grease, dirt, and rust), but more often as moisture in the electrode using the SMAW process. The hydrogen enters the weld pool in the arc as atomic hydrogen, where upon cooling and solidification of the metal the hydrogen is forced back to molecular hydrogen which diffuses toward sensitive microstructure (martinsite), or voids in the steel. The pressure can become tremendous resulting in a crack or complete failure of the weld.

Weld Preheat

Controlling one or more of the above factors will reduce the possibility of cold cracking. Hydrogen input into the weld can be minimized by:

- Using a low-hydrogen (basic) electrode which has been properly stored and conditioned in an electrode oven. ***Low hydrogen electrodes can absorb a detrimental amount of hydrogen from the atmosphere in only 2 to 4 hours.***
- Cleaning the base metal thoroughly of grease, oil, and dirt.
- Strict use of preheat.

Preheat is essential for reduction of hydrogen content and hardness in the weld and HAZ. It allows more time for the atomic hydrogen to diffuse out of the weld before it can form as molecular hydrogen. Preheating also reduces the amount of martinsite formed which is susceptible to cracking. A slower cooling rate also improves the notch toughness and increases a materials resistance to fatigue.

Preheat is maintained by using non oxy-acetelylene torches, electrical heating elements, or placing the workpiece in a furnace. The temperature must be accurately controlled by temperature sensitive crayons, or the use of a surface contact pyrometer.

Interpass Temperature

The interpass temperature is the temperature of the weldment between weld passes or beads. It is crucial that the interpass temperature not fall below the preheat temperature or cold cracking may occur in HSLA steels. It is also critical that the interpass temperature not exceed the upper critical temperature (above approximately 1200°F (649°C) for most HSLA steels) to prevent excessive grain growth resulting in a severe loss in the materials mechanical properties.

Note: Preheat and interpass temperatures are calculated based on the percentage of carbon and material thickness.

Weld Postheat

Post heating reduces hardness in the HAZ and reduces some or all stress that may exist. Post heat temperatures may range from 400°F (204°C) to 1200°F (649°C). Post heat will increase the toughness of metal in the HAZ.

Thermal stress relieving tends to slightly reduce the ultimate tensile strength and yield strength of the weld and base metal and increase toughness while removing residual stress.

Arc Strike

Arc strikes are a hidden hazard in the pressure welding industry. They occur, and are then ground and buffed out of existence. However, without exception, arc strikes always return in the form of corrosion, cracks, or complete material failure.

When a live electrode or tungsten is briefly struck across any type of steel, the high open circuit voltage imparted by the machine is sufficient to produce a localized heat affected zone (HAZ). This creates martinsite, a hard brittle grain structure, and a high hydrogen content due to the sharp cooling curve. It is only a matter of time before this combination, with the added strain of pressure and service, contributes to the partial or complete failure of the unit.

Arc strikes can happen to the best of welders. To help avoid future problems it is essential that an open dialogue exist that allows the welder to report the occurrence of all arc strikes so they may be repaired in accordance with the applicable code.

Stainless Steel Welding

There are two main classifications of stainless steels:

- 400 series - straight chrome stainless steels.
- 300 series - chrome-nickel stainless steels

400 Series Stainless Steels: These are composed of iron and chromium with small amounts of other elements to provide properties such as toughness or machineability. The percentage of chromium may vary from 11.5% to 29% depending on the alloy.

Note: Straight chrome stainless steels are easily identified because they are highly magnetic while 300 series stainless steels are non magnetic.

Straight chrome steels may be hardened by heat treatment while chrome-nickel steels will not. This ability to be hardened by heat treatment results in hard and brittle welds requiring the use of preheat and post heat to reduce the heat transfer rate.

400 series stainless steels can be further divided into two groups:

- ***Martensitic*** stainless steels with 1.5 to 17% chromium. These steels are air hardening and are hard and brittle. They are identified by numbers such as 410, 414, 416, 420.
- ***Ferric*** stainless steels with 17% to 29% chromium. These steels are usually soft and ductile. They are identified by numbers such as 430, 442, 446.

400 Series Grain Growth: These steels are subject to grain growth which occurs quickly at temperatures above 1650°F (900°C). As the grains grow larger, brittleness increases. This brittleness is most damaging to ferric stainless steels.

Grain growth, which has occurred in low chromium (14% Cr. and less) 400 series stainless steels because of exposure to high temperatures, can be reduced by heating several times through a transformation temperature of 1600°F (870°C).

Grain growth that has occurred in higher (18% and up) chromium steels cannot be corrected.

To minimize grain growth and the resultant brittleness, unnecessary heat build up must be avoided. This can be done by using small diameter electrodes, low currents, and by allowing the weld zone to cool to the preheat temperature after each bead is applied.

Note: Both martensitic and ferric types of 400 series require preheat and post heat when welding. These steels should be preheated to 400°F (204°C) and interpass temperature (80% of preheat temperature) maintained during welding. The weld should be post heated or annealed and slowly cooled.

300 Series Stainless Steels: They are composed of iron, chromium, and nickel, and are referred to as austenitic stainless steels.

The effect of the addition of nickel is to reduce heat transferability and increase the ductility.

The percentages of chromium in 300 Series stainless steels are 16% to 21%. Nickel is added at between 6% and 12%.

Note: These steels can be identified by the fact that they are non-magnetic.

300 Series stainless steels contain small amounts of carbon. Welding heat allows some of this carbon to form chromium carbides (carbide precipitation), which have no corrosion resistance. Chromium carbides are formed when the steel is held at temperatures of 800°F to 1600°F (427°C to 870°C) for prolonged periods, such as during welding and slow cooling. This robs the base metal of the corrosion resisting chromium in the heat affected zone.

This effect can be prevented by:

- Using extra low carbon (ELC) stainless steels. These typically have .03% or less carbon content.
- Using steels stabilized by the addition of columbium or titanium. These two elements combine with carbon to form harmless columbium carbide or titanium carbide. Examples are types 347 and 321 steels.
- When welding 300 Series stainless steels, the carbide precipitation can be remedied by post heat treatment. This involves heating the entire structure to between 1900°F to 2100°F (1038°C to 1150°C) followed by rapid cooling.

Note: 300 Series stainless should never be preheated, and interpass temperatures should not be allowed to go above 600°F (316°C).

Use small diameter electrodes and low amperage to keep heat to a minimum. Hold a short arc as a long arc overheats the base metal, which burns out chromium and reduces its corrosion resistance.

Austenetic stainless steel derives much of its corrosion resistance from a thin self-healing layer of chrome oxide on it's surface. It is the oxide layer which prevents stainless steel from being cut using an oxy-acetylene torch due to the fact that the oxide layer melts at a considerably higher temperature than the interior metal.

The oxide layer is self-healing to a degree, but it can become contaminated leaving the metal below open to corrosion and rust attack. Contamination occurs when particles of carbon steel or rust are introduced abrasively to the surface of the stainless.

Chemical Analysis of AISI Stainless Steels (per cent)						
AISI Type Number	% Carbon	% Manganese	%Silicon	%Chromium	%Nickel	% Other Elements
201	max 0.15	5.5-7.5	1	16-18	3.5-5.5	N_2 0.25max
202	max 0.15	7.5-10	1	17-19	4-6	N_2 0.25max
301	max 0.15	2	1	16-18	6-8	
302	max 0.15	2	1	17-19	8-10	
302B	max 0.15	2	2.0-3.0	17-19	8-10	
303*	max 0.15	2	1	17-19	8-10	S 0.15 min
303SE*	max 0.15	2	1	17-19	8-10	Se 0.15 min
304	max 0.08	2	1	18-20	8-12	
304L	max 0.03	2	1	18-20	8-12	
305	max 0.12	2	1	17-19	10-13	
308	max 0.08	2	1	19-12	10-12	
309	max 0.20	2	1	22-24	12-15	
309S	max 0.08	2	1	22-24	12-15	
310	max 0.25	2	1	24-26	19-22	
310S	max 0.08	2	1	24-26	19-22	
314	max 0.25	2	1.5-3.0	23-26	19-22	
316	max 0.08	2	1	16-18	10-14	Mo 2-3
316L	max 0.03	2	1	16-18	10-14	Mo 2-3
317	max 0.08	2	1	18-20	11-15	Mo 3-4
321	max 0.08	2	1	17-19	9-12	Ti 5xC min
347	max 0.08	2	1	17-19	9-13	Cb+Ta 10xC min
348	max 0.08	2	1	17-19	9-13	Cb+Ta 10xC min Ta 0.01 max

Table #105 - Chemical Analysis of AISI Stainless Steels

Contamination may be avoided by implementing the following procedures:

- Use of a low carbon stainless steel and low carbon electrode.
- Use of Aluminum Oxide (Al_2O_3) grinding disks which have not been in contact with carbon steel.
- Use of a stainless steel brush when interpass cleaning during welding.

Table #105 shows a comparison of the chrome and nickel content of various stainless steel types

Stainless Steel Welding Hints

- All dirt, grease or oxide films must be removed before welding.
- For flat welding, the electrode is held at 15 degrees with the top of the electrode leading in the direction of travel. Use as short an arc as possible.
- For vertical welding, the electrode should be held perpendicular to the plate using a slight oscillation for the root bead.
- For overhead welds the deposit should be made in stringer beads with a short arc. Do not use oscillation.
- For best corrosion resistance use minimum amperage and stringer beads to minimize heat input and reduce cracking tendency. If weave beads are necessary, limit weave to 2.5 times electrode diameter. Always fill craters before breaking the arc.

- Too low amperage results in an unstable arc and electrode sticking, excessive spatter and poor bead shape.
- Too high amperage and/or too long an arc can cause severe spatter, cracks in the weld, undercut, poor bead control, difficult slag removal, and loss of corrosion resistance.
- Difficult slag removal can be caused by contaminants on the plate, poorly formed welds, and joints too tight to allow slag to expand when struck. Allow welds to cool before removing slag.
- Cracking in stainless welds can be caused by unfilled craters, too long an arc, overheating of the workpiece, too fast a travel speed, poor joint design, and use of incorrect electrodes. Most cracking problems are caused by excessive heat or unfilled craters.
- Before breaking the arc when welding, fill all craters at the end of beads, particularly on types 310, 330, and 347. Unfilled craters can cause cracks. Select electrodes that match the base metal.
- Electrodes should be kept in a warming oven until immediately before use.

SECTION THIRTEEN QUESTIONS
Metallurgy

1. *Which of the following is not an organization that writes specifications for steel in the welding industries?*
   - ❒ ASME
   - ❒ SAE
   - ❒ AISI
   - ❒ API

2. *Determine if this statement is true or false. The SAE and AISI systems use the same two digit numbers to indicate the class of steel.*
   ❒ true ❒ false

3. *Determine if the following statement is true or false. The last two numbers in the SAE system indicate carbon content.*
   ❒ true ❒ false

4. *Determine if the following statement is true or false. The last two SAE numbers indicate the "weldability" of the steel.*
   ❒ true ❒ false

5. *Which of the following is not a mechanical property of steel plate?*
   - ❒ radiography difficulty
   - ❒ toughness
   - ❒ ductility
   - ❒ yield strength

6. *When using a basic grinding wheel spark test, the sparks from low carbon steel would be:*
   - ❒ orange
   - ❒ red
   - ❒ yellow-orange
   - ❒ yellow

7. *The area between the molten welding metal and the surrounding room temperature metal is called the "heat affected zone".*
   ❒ true ❒ false

8. *Which of the following does not affect the amount of heat entering steel during the welding process?*
   - ☐ current
   - ☐ electrode size
   - ☐ type of welding machine
   - ☐ welding speed

9. *What could be the affect of not having enough heat input in the welded joint?*
   - ☐ hardening & cracking
   - ☐ annealing
   - ☐ porosity
   - ☐ none of above

10. *Referring to question 9, how can this problem be reduced or eliminated?*
    - ☐ preheat
    - ☐ postheat
    - ☐ more welding amperage
    - ☐ bigger welding rod

11. *What is the most common type of weld failure in hardenable carbon and low alloy steels?*
    - ☐ undercut
    - ☐ porosity
    - ☐ hydrogen induced cold cracking
    - ☐ annealing of steel around welded joint

12. *Which of the following will not reduce the condition known as "cold cracking"?*
    - ☐ strict preheat
    - ☐ high hydrogen content welding rod
    - ☐ use of electrode oven
    - ☐ thorough cleaning of base metal

13. *Post heating a welded joint will have what affect on the HAZ?*
    - ☐ increase toughness
    - ☐ decrease toughness
    - ☐ decrease ductility
    - ☐ increase tensile strength

14. *Determine if the following statement is true or false. An accidental arc strike on a pipe or pressure vessel shell will not cause any future problems if it is ground out to a smooth finish.*

❒ true ❒ false

15. *Determine if the following statement is true or false. Chromium and nickel are the two primary alloys in 400 Series stainless steel.*

❒ true ❒ false

16. *Which stainless steel series is magnetic?*

❒ 400 series
❒ 300 Series
❒ both a and b
❒ neither a or b

17. *Determine if the following statement is true or false. To avoid hard and brittle welds in straight-chrome steel, both preheating and postheating should be done.*

❒ true ❒ false

18. *What are the normal characteristics of 410, 414, 416, and 420 stainless steel?*

❒ soft and ductile
❒ hard and brittle
❒ elastic
❒ all of the above

19. *What is the affect of grain growth in 400 Series stainless steel?*

❒ steel becomes softer
❒ steel becomes more ductile
❒ steel becomes more brittle
❒ grain growth reduces need for heat treatment

20. *Determine if the following statement is true or false. Grain growth which has occurred in 18% and higher chromium steels cannot be corrected.*

❒ true ❒ false

21. *400 Series stainless steel should be preheated to what temperature?*
- ☐ 250 degrees F
- ☐ 400 degrees F
- ☐ 600 degrees F
- ☐ 800 degrees F

22. *Determine if the following statement is true or false. Adding nickel alloy to steel will increase the heat transfer and decrease ductility.*
- ☐ true ☐ false

23. *Determine if the following statement is true or false. Carbide precipitation is caused by welding heat allowing some carbon to form chromium carbides.*
- ☐ true ☐ false

24. *Determine if the following statement is true or false. The problem in question 23 can be remedied by preheat and slow cooling.*
- ☐ true ☐ false

25. *300 Series stainless should be preheated before welding.*
- ☐ always
- ☐ never
- ☐ depends on thickness
- ☐ depends on type of machine used

26. *Which situation applies to flat stainless steel welding?*
- ☐ electrode at 5 degrees with top leading
- ☐ electrode at 5 degrees with arc leading
- ☐ electrode at 15 degrees with top leading
- ☐ electrode at 15 degrees with arc leading

27. *What can result from an unfilled crater at the end of a bead when welding 300 Series stainless steel?*
- ☐ porosity
- ☐ slag
- ☐ decreased ductility
- ☐ cracks

28. *Which of the following will cause cracks in a welded stainless steel joint?*
- ☐ unfilled craters
- ☐ arc too long
- ☐ travel too fast
- ☐ all of above

SECTION FOURTEEN

NON-DESTRUCTIVE TESTING

NDT Benefits

Non Destructive Testing (NDT) is a general term for all test methods that permit inspection of material without impairing its future usefulness. These tests can determine if a part will perform its intended function. Since 100% perfect industrial material does not exist, these tests tell us if the specimen is within specified tolerances.

The benefits of using NDT tests are:

a. Increased productivity and profits
b. Increased serviceability
c. Safety
d. Material identification

Detection of Material Defects

There are numerous types of defects that can effect the integrity of modern industry. Some of the components affected are building steel, refining and process equipment including pressure vessels, pumps, motors, turbines and piping systems.

Some of the types of defects that can be detected by NDT are listed below:

- Surface and subsurface cracks
- Porosity
- Tears
- Machining, rolling & plating defects
- Laminations
- Lack of fusion
- Inclusions
- Segregation
- Lack of weld penetration
- Fatigue defects
- Seams
- Blowholes
- Flakes
- Pitting
- Laps
- Undercut
- Dimensional tolerance (e.g. thickness)

Types of NDT Testing

Various methods of NDT are commonly used. These include:

- Visual Testing
- Pressure and Leak Testing
- Liquid Penetrant Testing
- Magnetic Particle Testing
- Ultrasonic Testing
- Radiography
- Eddy Currents

Visual Testing

Visual inspection is simple, quick and usually low in cost and therefore should not be ignored, even if other NDT tests are to be done. The most important criteria for visual inspection are adequate illumination, thorough cleaning of the surfaces and a knowledgeable inspector.

Aids to visual examination include microscopes, borescopes, and optical comparators.

Pressure and Leak Testing

The most common pressure test is a hydrostatic (liquid) test where the internal pressure is gradually raised above the outside pressure. Leakage can be detected by seepage of the internal fluid, a drop in the applied pressure or by the formation of bubbles. Bubbles can be formed by applying a soap film to the outside, or immersing the object in water or alcohol (see illustration #450).

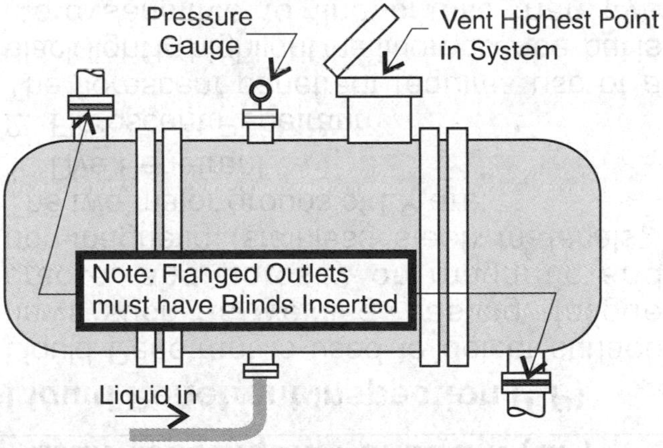
Pressure Gauge
Vent Highest Point in System
Note: Flanged Outlets must have Blinds Inserted
Liquid in

Illustration #450 - Pressure and Leak Test

Always vent the uppermost point in the container while filling with water or other liquid. Air trapped in the container could make it very difficult to obtain the necessary test pressure.

Note: Caution must be exercised during this type of test to avoid structural damage to the vessel or container by over pressurizing. Most cylindrical or spherical pressure vessels or containers are designed to be tested at 1.5 times the normal working pressure. Check the manufacturers name plate for design and test pressures prior to pressurizing.

A similar type of test can be performed with internal air pressure. Again, use extreme caution to guard against overpressure. A container not designed as a pressure vessel can be easily damaged by any pressure exceeding atmospheric pressure (approximately 15 psia).

Liquid Penetrant Inspection (LP)

Liquid Penetrant is used to detect surface flaws such as welding, casting, fatigue cracks, and porosity on magnetic and non-magnetic (stainless steel) materials.

The two major groups of LP are:

1. Dye Penetrant
2. Florescent Penetrant

The florescent penetrant requires use of a black light to highlight the fluorescence, but is more sensitive to fine cracks than dye penetrant.

The technique of liquid penetrant involves a thorough cleaning of the surface to remove wax, paint, grease, or scale followed by the application of a low viscosity fluid such as a commercial dye, or fluorescent penetrant by immersion, brushing, or spraying.

Time is allowed for the penetrant to seep into any flaws that may exist. All traces of excess penetrant are then removed from the surface using water or an approved solvent. The surface is then allowed to dry.

The developer is applied to the dried surface to draw the penetrant from the defect, thereby leaving a stain on the powdered surface. The bleeding action of the penetrant into the developer causes the stain to be larger than the defect making it easy to see.

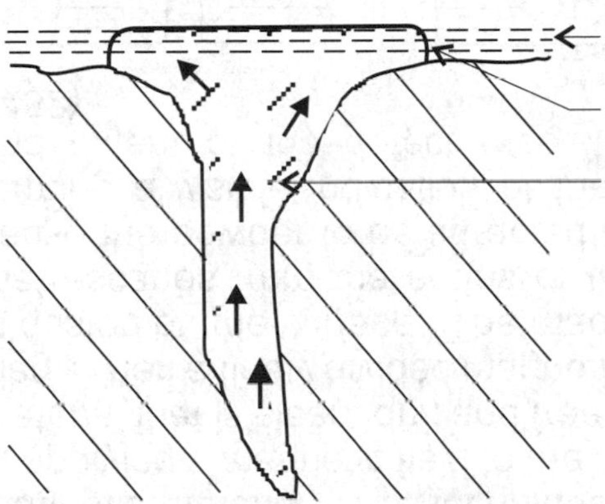
Developer
Powder
Indication
Penetrant

Action of developer. When the developer dries, it draws the penetrant out of the crack onto the surface of each side of it, increasing the size of the indication.

Illustration #451 - Liquid Penetrant Action

The developer should be applied so that all surfaces are covered, however only a thin layer should be applied as a thick coating may hide small defects. See illustration #451 for the action of the developer.

Developers fall into two main categories, that are:

1. Dry
2. Wet

The Wet developer is further divided into two groups:

a. Water Based:
   Powder suspended in water, that requires the use of tanks for dipping the object being tested. This process is limited to a large factory setting.

b. Solvent Based:
   Powder suspended in a rapid drying solvent applied using an aerosol container. This method is most frequently used due to its portability.

Magnetic Particle Testing (MP)

Magnetic particle testing is used to detect surface and shallow subsurface cracks in magnetic material. The technique consists of applying a magnetic field to the surface of material that is clean, dry, and free of rust or slag. Then a finely divided magnetic powder is dusted on the surface. The magnetic flux that escapes from the edges of the defect cause the powder to be attracted and held, forming a visible indication of the location and extent of the defect (see illustration #452).

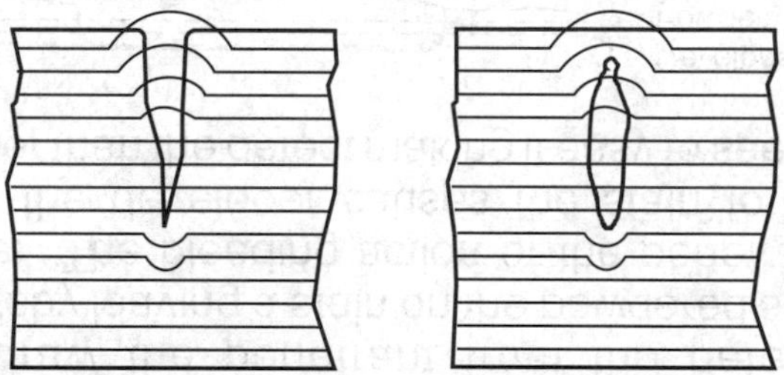
Leakage Field
Due to Surface Flaw
Leakage Field
Due to Subsurface Flaw

Illustration #452 - Magnetic Particle Testing

Setting Up Magnetic Field

The magnetic field can be set up in a magnetic material by:

1. Passing an electric current through the test piece.
2. Subjecting the test piece to an electromagnetic field.
   a. prod method
   b. yoke method
3. Subjecting the test piece to the field surrounding permanent magnets.

Note: If the current is applied directly to the test piece, the surface must be clean to avoid arcing or burning under the contacts. The contacts must be securely attached to the test piece when the magnetizing current is turned on and off.

Note: Transverse (across face) or longitudinal (lengthwise) cracks will or will not be indicated depending on the method used to apply the current to the test piece (see illustrations #453 and #454).

Transverse Cracks

If a magnetic field is induced by placing the test piece in the center of a conductor arranged in the shape of a coil it will cause the lines of force to flow the length of the sample (see illustration #453). Cracks that occur across the lines of force (transverse) will be indicated by the powder. Cracks that line up with the lines of force (longitudinal) will not be revealed.

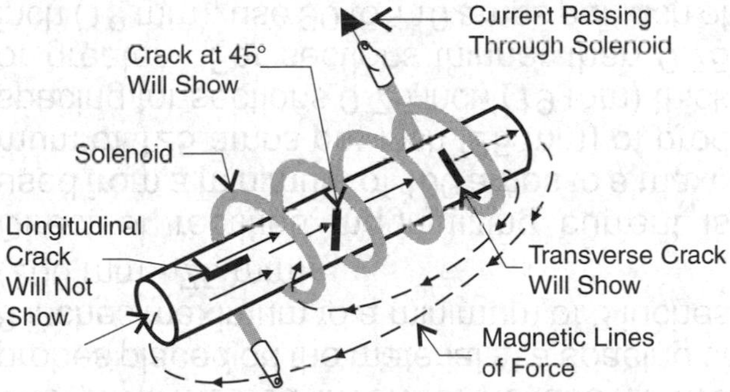
Current Passing Through Solenoid
Crack at 45° Will Show
Solenoid
Longitudinal Crack Will Not Show
Transverse Crack Will Show
Magnetic Lines of Force

Illustration #453 - Longitudinal Magnetization

Longitudinal Cracks

Longitudinal cracks can be detected by passing current through the length of the object, or along a central conductor if the test piece is hollow.

The resulting circular lines of magnetic force will allow the powder to indicate longitudinal cracks (see illustration #454).

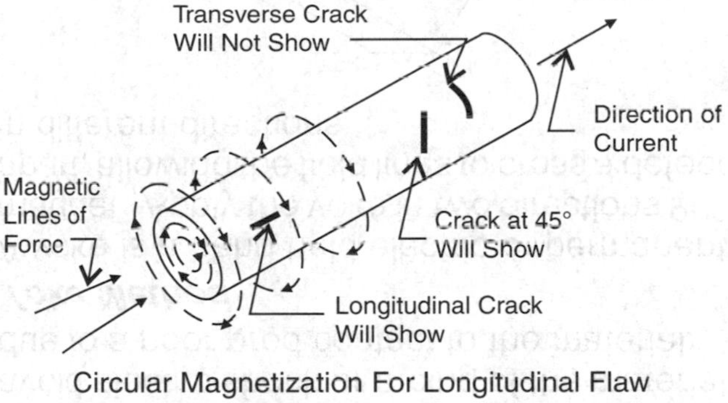
Transverse Crack Will Not Show
Direction of Current
Magnetic Lines of Force
Crack at 45° Will Show
Longitudinal Crack Will Show
Circular Magnetization For Longitudinal Flaw

Illustration #454 - Circular Magnetization

Prod Method

The prod method involves the use of two probes placed on the material at a spacing of 8 inches maximum to a minimum of 3 inches (200 mm - 75 mm).

Direct or rectified magnetizing current is used from a minimum of 100 amps to a maximum of 125 amps per inch (25 mm) of prod spacing for sections 0.75 inch (19 mm) thick or greater. For sections thinner than 0.75 inch (19 mm), use 90 to 110 amps per inch of prod spacing.

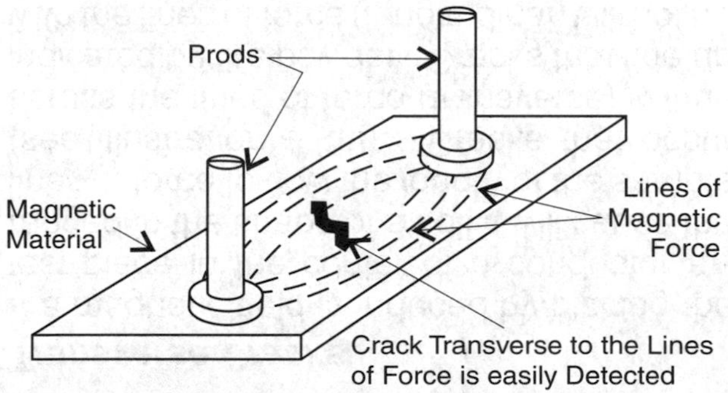
Prods
Magnetic Material
Lines of Magnetic Force
Crack Transverse to the Lines of Force is easily Detected

Illustration #455 - Prod Method

Prods are most effective on larger and thicker components. Care must be taken to avoid electric shock or arcing of the material due to a poor prod contact to the material.

Yoke Method

A yoke is a hand held electric or permanent magnet. Apply the yoke in two directions 90° apart, allowing the field lines to cross a defect in different directions.

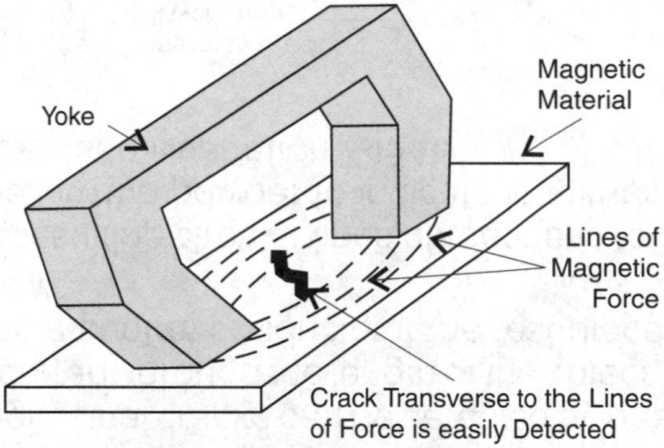
Yoke
Magnetic Material
Lines of Magnetic Force
Crack Transverse to the Lines of Force is easily Detected

Illustration #456 - Yoke Method

There are two types of yokes available.

1. Direct current or permanent electromagnetic yoke may be used, provided it has a lifting power of at least 40 pounds (18 kg) with a pole spacing of at least 3 to 6 inches (75 - 150 mm).
2. Alternating current electromagnetic yoke may be used, provided it has a lifting power of at least 10 pounds (4.5 kg) with a pole spacing of 3 to 6 inches (75 - 150 mm).

Magnetic Particle (Powder)

The magnetic particle (or powder) is available in two forms :

1. Dry - Various colors of iron oxide powder
2. Wet - Florescent coated iron oxide powder in a liquid suspension. When viewed under a black light it makes finer indications more visible.

The magnetic particles can be applied either while the magnetizing current is flowing, or after, using the residual magnetism left after the electric current is removed. The residual magnetism is weaker, therefore the test is less sensitive.

Field Intensity and Defect Visibility

The intensity of the magnetic field and hence the visibility of the defect, depends on the magnitude of the current. Since high currents are used, the applied voltage should be low to avoid danger to the operator or damage to the object.

Direct Currents (DC) produce magnetic fields that penetrate deep into the metal. These are best at locating subsurface flaws. Alternating Currents (AC) produce fields on the surface of the metal and are best at locating surface flaws.

The current used to magnetize the test piece is not important; however if too weak a current is used, no pattern will develop. Also if too strong a current is used, a dense accumulation of powder will occur making the pattern difficult or impossible to see.

If the induced magnetism from the electric current is very strong it could cause leakage that might be falsely interpreted as a defect. Since the disruption of the magnetic field must leak through the surface to affect the magnetic particles, defects no deeper than 0.5 inch (13 mm) from the surface can be detected.

For welds, the magnetizing current varies from 600 to 2000 amps, depending on plate thickness and prod spacing.

Ultrasonic Testing

Sound is created by a vibration of the medium through which it travels. Audible sound is created when the air vibrates at between 20 and 20,000 cycles per second, or hertz (Hz). If these sound frequencies are used to try to detect defects in an object the long wave length would merely go around the defect.

Therefore to locate a defect a sound is needed that has a wavelength approximately equal to the size of the defect. Sound waves with wavelengths of this size have a frequency above the ability of the human ear to detect. They are called ultrasonic waves. Ultrasonic waves are created and detected by a transducer.

Several techniques can be used in ultrasonic testing. These are:

a. Pulse Echo

b. Transmission

c. Resonance

d. Frequency Modulation

Pulse Echo: In the pulse echo technique an ultrasonic beam is sent through the specimen. If a defect is present, some of the beam is reflected. The remainder of the beam is reflected from the back surface. The time difference between the two echoes determines the depth of the defect. See illustration #457.

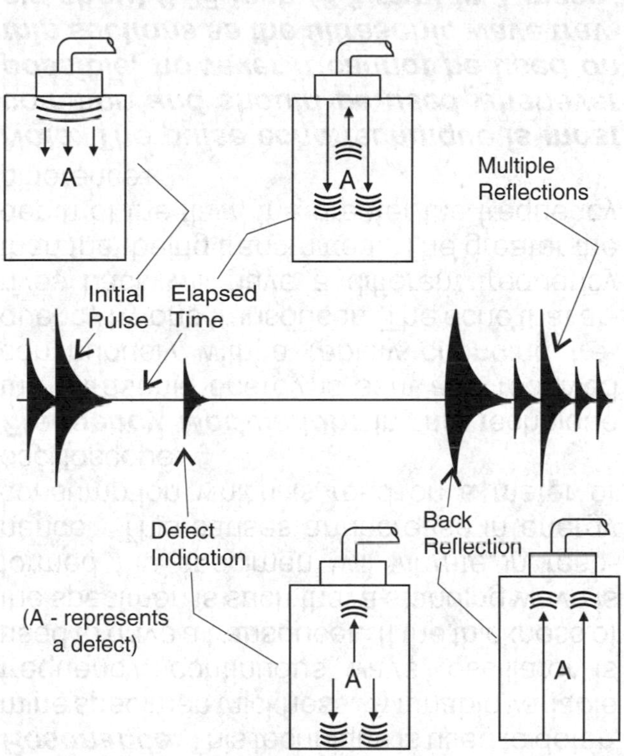
A
A
Multiple
Reflections
Initial
Pulse
Elapsed
Time
Defect
Indication
Back
Reflection
(A - represents
a defect)
A
A

Illustration #457 - Pulse Echo Technique

Transmission: The transmission technique requires a separate sending and receiving transducer. Defects cause the amplitude of the beam to be decreased due to reflection and scattering. See illustration #458.

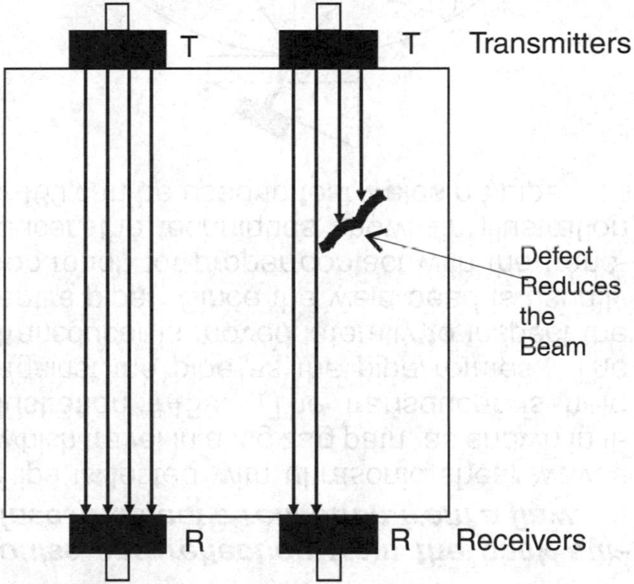
T
T
Transmitters
Defect
Reduces
the
Beam
R
R
Receivers

Illustration #458 - Transmission Technique

Resonance: This technique is used to determine specimen thickness. A tunable variable frequency, continuous wave, oscillator is used to drive a transducer. If the thickness of the specimen is such that a standing wave is formed the specimen will vibrate in resonance. This causes an increase in energy consumption which is read on a meter or oscilloscope.

Frequency Modulation: In this technique the ultrasonic energy is sent and received continuously with a rapidly changing frequency by one transducer. The echo that arrives back will have a different frequency than that being transmitted. The greater the depth of the flaw, the greater the frequency difference.

Note: The pulse echo technique is most common and should be used whenever possible, however it cannot be used on thin sections as the ultrasonic wave travels about 0.25 inch (6.3 mm) in 1 msec. There is not enough time between initial pulse and reflection from the back surface to detect a reflection from a flaw.

Pipe is tested with ultrasonic shear waves which travel in a zig zag path, as shown in illustration #459. The transducer is held against the pipe as the pipe rotates. The transducer is moved laterally to inspect the entire pipe. Since the weld bead is usually too rough for proper contact with the transducer, the techniques shown in illustration #460 can be used to test welds on pipe.

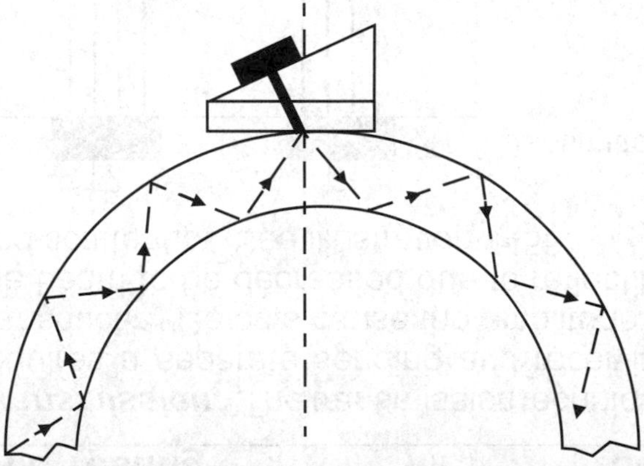

Illustration #459 - Pipe Ultrasonic Shear Waves

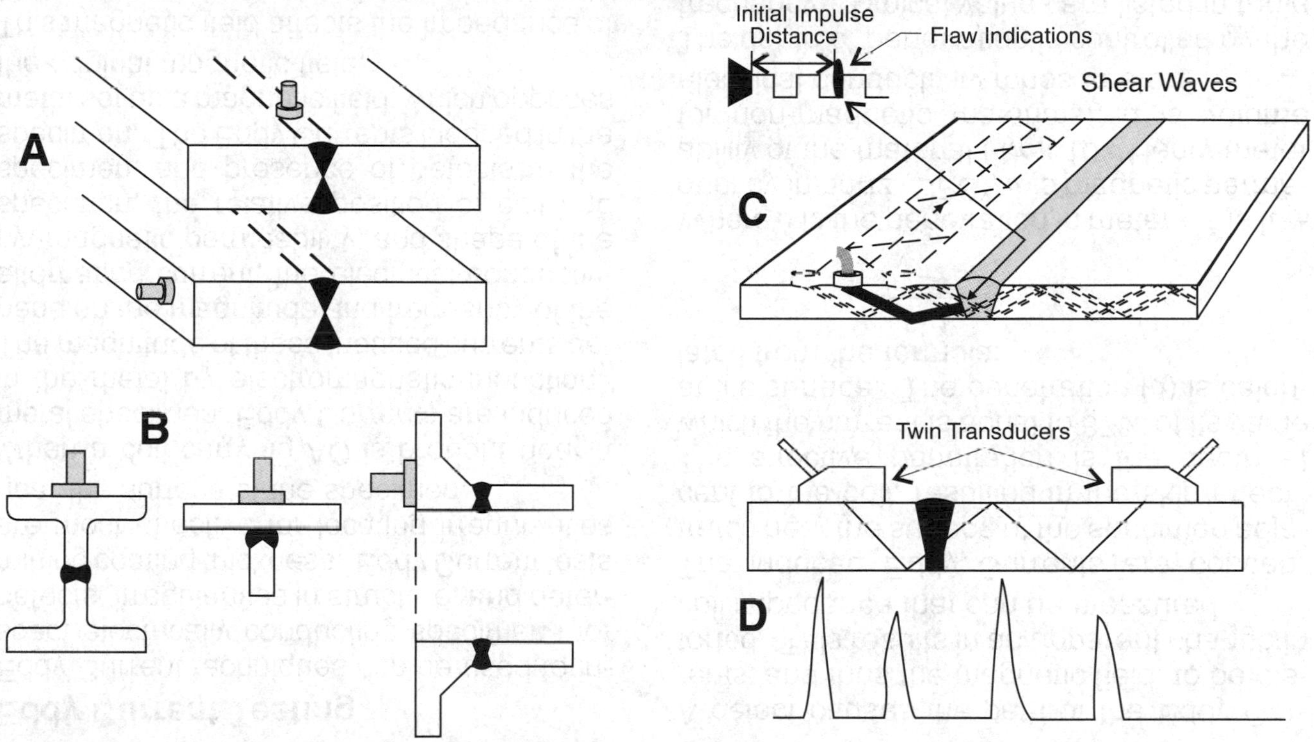
A
B
Initial Impulse
Distance
Flaw Indications
Shear Waves
C
Twin Transducers
D

Illustration #460A,B,C,D - Methods to Test Welds

Eddy Current Testing

Eddy Current techniques can be used to inspect electrically conducting specimens for defects, irregularities in structure, and determining coating thickness. Eddy Current tests are most effective for locating irregularities near the surface of the specimen.

When a coil carrying AC is brought near a metal specimen, Eddy Currents are induced in the metal by electromagnetic induction. The magnitude of these induced currents depend on the magnitude and frequency of the alternating current, the electrical conductivity, magnetic permeability, and shape of the specimen, the relative position of coil and specimen, and presence of defects in the specimen. The Eddy Currents induced in the metal set up a magnetic field, which opposes the original magnetic field.

This magnetic field affects the impedance of the exciting coil, or any pickup coil close to the specimen.

A defect causes the path of the Eddy Currents, and thus the magnetic field, to be distorted. This results in an apparent change in coil impedance that can be measured.

The induced Eddy Currents are concentrated near the surface of the specimen adjacent to the coil, resulting in the skin effect. The effective penetration is the depth at which the current is equal to 37% of its value at the surface. The penetration (δ) is calculated from the formula:

$$\delta = \frac{1}{\sqrt{\pi f \sigma \mu}}$$

Where δ is the penetration in meters, f is frequency in hertz (CPS), μ is magnetic permeability of the material ($4\pi \times 10^{-7}$ Henry/meter for non-magnetic materials), σ is volume electrical conductivity mhos /meter.

The depth of penetration is controlled by the frequency. Typical values are listed in table #106.

Depth of Penetration (mm)			
Material	**Frequency (kHz)**		
	1.0	**10**	**50**
Copper	2.00	0.64	0.28
Aluminum	2.65	0.84	0.04
70:30 Copper:Nickel	10.00	3.15	1.41
Titanium	12.00	3.80	1.67
Cast Steel	0.50	0.15	0.07
Graphite	45.00	13.00	6.20
Zirconium	12.00	3.50	1.90
Note: Low frequencies give deeper penetration but this is achieved at thc expense of sensitivity. Multifrequency systems have been developed to give acceptable penetration and sensitivity			

Table #106 - Eddy Current Penetration Depth

Most Eddy Current equipment is dedicated to specific problems such as coating thickness measurement, crack detection, tube inspection and metal sorting. For these applications the Eddy Current testing equipment needs to be custom designed for each application.

Note: Eddy Current testing is most widely applied to non-magnetic materials because the magnetic permeability (μ) is equal to one. For magnetic materials, the relative magnetic permeability can vary widely. These variations produce a high background noise which makes applications such as crack detection more difficult than on non-magnetic applications.

Eddy Current Test Coils

Test coils and probes vary greatly in size and construction. Coils may be of an air core type, or a magnetic core for increased sensitivity. Coils may also be shielded with magnetic material or copper to increase sensitivity.

Note: As a general rule, low frequency currents give deeper eddy current penetration, and high frequency currents in the test coil detect surface defects.

For a coil of a given diameter, the sensitivity to a defect decreases rapidly as the defect size becomes less than that of the coil diameter.

Three types of test coils are commonly used:

a. Concentric coil

b. Inside or bobbin coil

c. Point probe

The concentric coil completely surrounds the specimen and tests a width equal to the effective width of the coil.

The inside or bobbin coil is made to be moved through a tube or pipe.

The point probe is a small coil placed near the surface of the specimen and tests an area equal to the cross sectional area of the probe. See illustration #461 for examples.

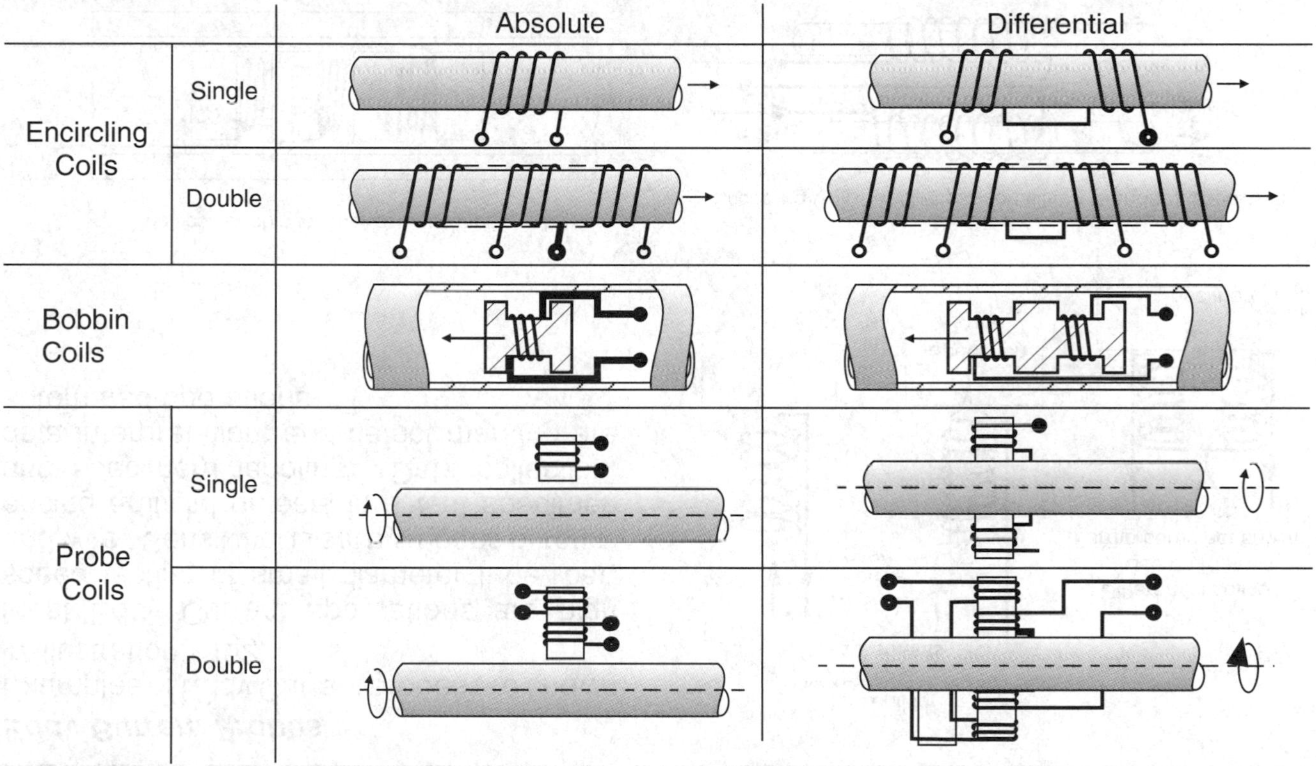
Absolute
Differential
Encircling Coils
Single
Double
Bobbin Coils
Probe Coils
Single
Double

Illustration #461 - Eddy Current Testing

Eddy Current Probes

Examples of Eddy Current probes are shown in illustration #462.

Most Eddy Current applications are high speed testing of small diameter tube, bar, and wire. Sensitivity is set by means of referencing artificial defects in a test specimen and specimen handling. Data collection, data interpretation, and defect marking are automated operations.

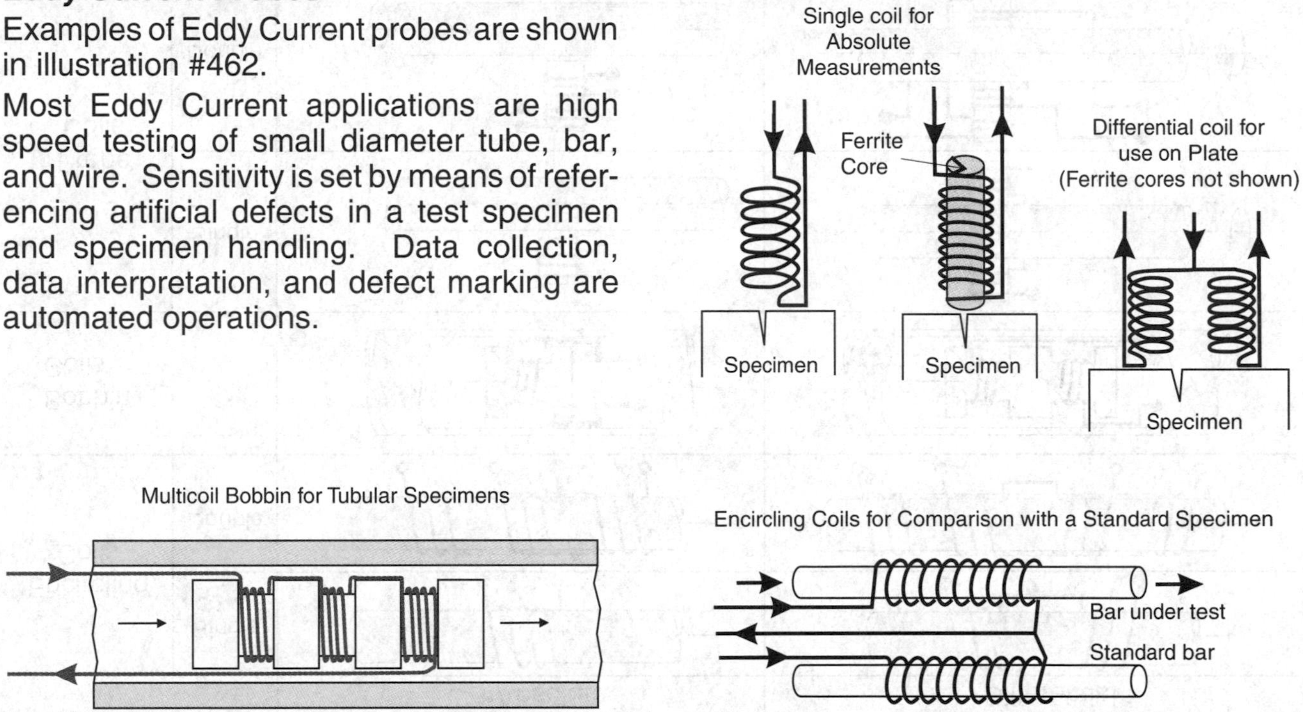
Single coil for Absolute Measurements
Ferrite Core
Differential coil for use on Plate (Ferrite cores not shown)
Specimen
Specimen
Specimen
Multicoil Bobbin for Tubular Specimens
Encircling Coils for Comparison with a Standard Specimen
Bar under test
Standard bar

Illustration # 462 - Types of Eddy Current Probe

Radiography

Radiography is one of the most popular and widely used processes of non-destructive testing to detect sub-surface defects and faults. A permanent record is produced in the form of an image created on a film that was exposed to a source of radiant energy.

Radiation has a very short wave length that allows it to pass through solid and opaque material. The radiation intensity is reduced in relation to the absorption rate of the structure it passes through.

Example: When radiation passes through a material that has an internal void such as porosity or slag the amount of absorption is reduced in that area, allowing a greater amount of radiation to reach the film directly behind the void. Unexposed film will darken when exposed to radiation and the degree of darkening is dependent upon the amount of radiation that reaches the film in a given area. (see illustration #463)

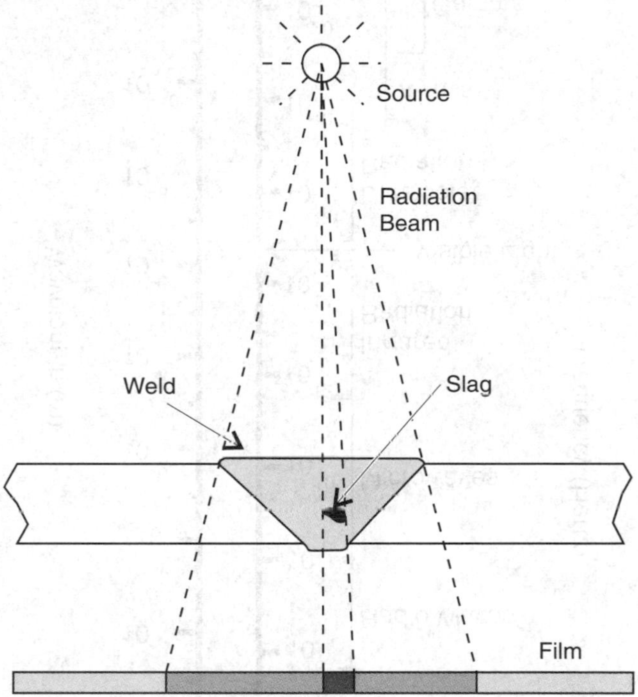
Source
Radiation
Beam
Weld
Slag
Film

Illustration #463 - Differential Absorption Recorded on Film

Radiography Sources

There are two sources of penetrating waves suitable for radiography:

1. X-ray
2. Gamma Ray

X-rays have a wavelength ranging from about 10^{-9}m to about 10^{-12}m. Gamma Rays are the most energetic form of electromagnetic radiation with a very short wavelength of less than 10-10m, as shown in illustration #464.

X-rays

X-rays are generated in a near vacuum tube by propelling at high speeds a stream of electrons against a target constructed of a very dense material with a high melting point, such as tungsten. The electron stream impacts onto the target with tremendous force that temporarily dislodges electrons from the tungsten material.

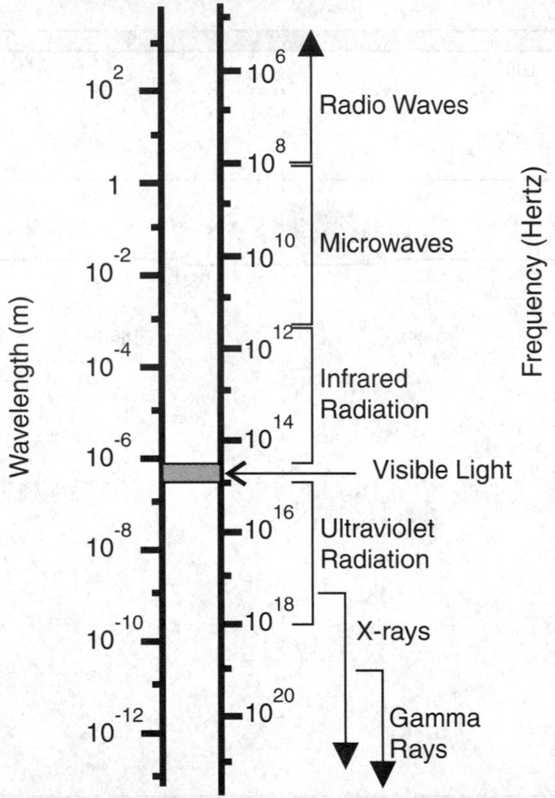
Wavelength (m)
10^{2}
1
10^{-2}
10^{-4}
10^{-6}
10^{-8}
10^{-10}
10^{-12}
10^{6}
10^{8}
10^{10}
10^{12}
10^{14}
10^{16}
10^{18}
10^{20}
Radio Waves
Microwaves
Infrared Radiation
Visible Light
Ultraviolet Radiation
X-rays
Gamma Rays
Frequency (Hertz)

Illustration #464 - Wavelengths

The by-products of this reaction are 1% X-rays and 99% heat, thus the importance of the target material having a high melting point.

The electron stream density is controlled by the current input (m\a), and the wavelength (that determines the rays penetrating power) is controlled by the high voltage input (kV) across the tube from anode to cathode.

Only a small amount of the 1% of X-rays produced is usable as the majority of the waves are shielded by the X-ray tubes shell.

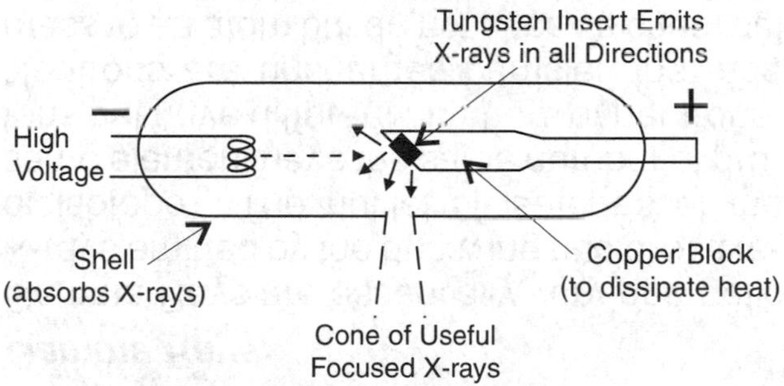
Tungsten Insert Emits X-rays in all Directions
−
+
High Voltage
Shell (absorbs X-rays)
Copper Block (to dissipate heat)
Cone of Useful Focused X-rays

Illustration #465 - Diagram of an X-ray tube

Only the rays that are emitted through the small opening in the camera are usable for radiography, as shown in illustration #465.

Advantages of X-rays

- No residual radiation is generated or retained when the power is switched off
- Penetrating power is adjustable through varying the high voltage (kV) input
- Can be used on all materials (including aluminum)
- Provides radiographs with good contrast and sensitivity
- Sufficient size machines exist to radiograph through 20 inches (500 mm) of steel

Disadvantages

- High initial cost
- Requires source of electrical power
- Equipment not very portable, also relatively fragile
- Tube head usually large in size, unusable in tight locations
- Electrical hazard from high voltage

Gamma Rays

Gamma Rays are essentially very energetic X-rays emitted by the decaying nuclei of a radioisotope. The nuclei of isotopes of the same element have the same number of protons but have different numbers of neutrons. Neutrons are uncharged particles that add mass to an atom but do not alter it's chemical behavior. This means the nucleus is either stable or unstable. A radioactive isotope is created by placing a stable isotope in the particle stream of a nuclear reactor where it's atoms pick up an extra neutron making the nucleus unbalanced or unstable.

Examples: - Cobalt 59 (stable) is changed in the reactor to Cobalt 60 (unstable); and Iridium 191 (stable) is changed in the reactor to Iridium 192 (unstable).

Upon removal from the reactor the unstable isotope proceeds to disintegrate by emitting the extra neutron from the nucleus. This reaction produces gamma rays and is often accompanied by alpha and beta particles.

This decay continues at a specific rate until the isotope reaches stability.

The rate of disintegration of a given isotope is based on the amount of time it takes for the isotope to reach half its strength from any given time.

This standard is known as a material's half-life.

Half-Life of X-ray Materials		
Source	**Half-Life**	**Useful thickness (Steel)**
Cobalt 60	5.3 years	2 - 6 inches
Iridium 192	72 days	0.5 - 2 in.
Cesium 137	33 years	0.5 - 1.5 in.

Table #107 - Half-Life of Isotope Materials

As the isotope disintegrates, the length of time to expose a film and create a clear radiograph increases until eventually the source must be replaced with a fresh source.

The Gamma source is stored and transported in a lead or tungsten shielded container referred to as a camera or "Pig". The source is remotely pushed by a flex cable to a safe distance where it can be focused toward an object and the film (see illustration #466).

Advantages of Gamma Rays

- Small initial and low maintenance costs
- Rugged construction, more suited to industrial locations
- No electric power required or concern of electrical hazard
- High penetrating power
- Portable with access into small areas with source tube

Disadvantages

- Radiation hazard and radiation emitted continuously
- Penetrating power cannot be adjusted
- Radioisotope decays in strength requiring recalibration and replacement
- Radiographic contrast generally less than X-ray
- Cannot be used on all materials (e.g. aluminum)

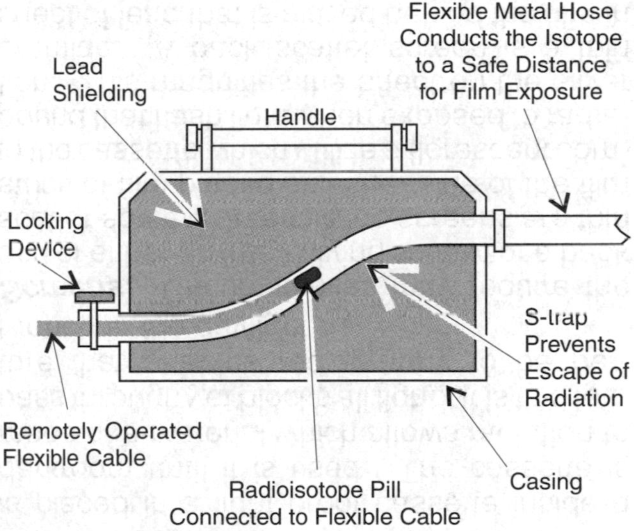
Flexible Metal Hose Conducts the Isotope to a Safe Distance for Film Exposure
Lead Shielding
Handle
Locking Device
S-trap Prevents Escape of Radiation
Remotely Operated Flexible Cable
Casing
Radioisotope Pill Connected to Flexible Cable

Illustration #466 - Typical Isotope Camera

Radiographic Film

Radiographic film is similar to photographic film in that it is a plastic strip of cellulose acetate that has been coated in an emulsion suspension that contains very fine crystals of silver bromide. When light or radiation is exposed to the film it sensitizes the silver bromide, whereupon developing it precipitates from the emulsion as metallic silver. It is this silver that darkens the film and produces the image to interpret.

Film Types: Films are graded and classed by the grain size of the silver bromide ranging from very fine to large grain. A large grain film is more sensitive to radiation and requires less exposure time, but the image is lacking in sharpness. A very fine grain requires a considerably longer exposure time although the image is excellent. Normal radiography standards allow for the use of a fine to medium grain.

Film Cassette: Because light can affect or destroy a film, undeveloped radiography film is placed in a light proof cassette inside a darkroom until it is used. The cassette is made of a material which allows radiation to pass through yet blocks all light. It is this feature that enables radiography to be performed in the daylight.

Screens: Circumstances may require the use of either an intensifying screen or a back scatter screen. Intensifying screens are thin strips of film placed on either side of the film in the cassette which utilize a florescent compound that flash light when exposed to radiation. This magnifies the effect on the silver bromide. A back scatter screen is a thin sheet of lead that is placed behind the film in the cassette to prevent radiation reflecting off of surrounding objects and back into the film thereby clouding the image.

Film Image Acceptance Criteria

Radiographs are considered acceptable provided they meet specified requirements depending on the code or standard the work is being performed to.

Radiograph images are measured by density, contrast, and sensitivity. Several factors must be considered and calculated in order to achieve a properly exposed radiograph image such as:

- Type and thickness of material being radiographed
- X-ray tube current in milliampere, or Gamma Ray source strength in curies
- Size of focal spot
- Source to film distance
- Type of film used
- Type of screen used if any

Density: The density of a radiograph is the degree of blackness the image possesses. To measure this variable, an instrument called a densitometer is used, or it is compared against a calibrated film strip. The value achieved must fall within the range specified by the applicable code. In general the larger the density number the darker the image.

Contrast: The contrast of an image is defined as the density difference between two adjacent areas in the image and the ease by which they can be distinguished from each other. Contrast is also the degree of difference between the image and the background. The two main factors that affect contrast are the exposure time (which depends on the strength of the source) and the film type (grain size).

Sensitivity: The sensitivity of a radiograph is determined by the ability to detect small details in the film image. This ability is determined by placing a known defect in the area of interest on the source side of the material being radiographed. This defect is called a penetrameter or (IQI) image quality indicator. A penetrameter is usually a thin plate of the same material being radiographed which has a specified percentage of thickness of the material under inspection. Holes of a specific diameter are drilled into the penetrameter to gage the visibility with which defects may be revealed.

The thickness of the penetrameter is usually 2% of the material thickness being radiographed. This means that when the outline of the penetrameter is visible in the radiograph that it is at least sensitive to a 2% thickness change. Also there shall be at least 3 holes of diameter equal to one, two and four times the penetrameters thickness. The specific code will define which hole must be visible.

The ASME Boiler and Pressure Vessel Code requires that at least one penetrameter shall be used for each exposure, to be placed at one end of the exposed length, parallel and adjacent to the weld seam. Where the source is positioned to radiograph a circumferential seam with one 360 degree exposure, three penetrameters located at 120 degree intervals shall be used.

As it may not be possible to place the penetrameter on the source side, there are provisions in some codes that allow the penetrameter to be on the film side. Circumstances may require the use of a shim under the penetrameter to compensate for the height of the cap and the root reinforcement. This is necessary to get an accurate sensitivity assessment of the complete thickness of the weld in the area of most interest.

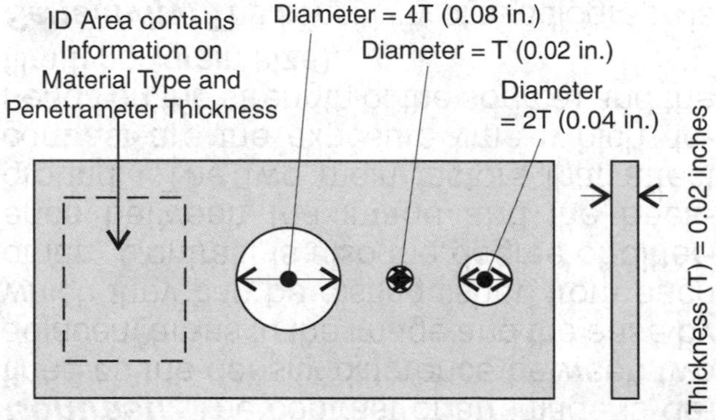
ID Area contains Information on Material Type and Penetrameter Thickness
Diameter = 4T (0.08 in.)
Diameter = T (0.02 in.)
Diameter = 2T (0.04 in.)
Thickness (T) = 0.02 inches

Illustration #467 - Standard Penetrameter for I inch Material

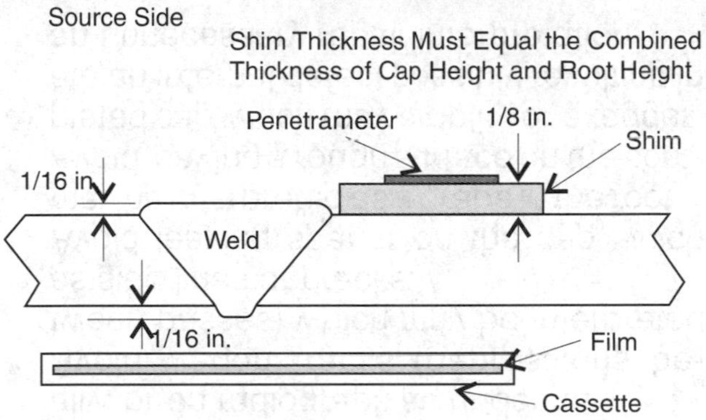
Source Side
Shim Thickness Must Equal the Combined Thickness of Cap Height and Root Height
Penetrameter
1/8 in.
Shim
1/16 in.
Weld
1/16 in.
Film
Cassette

Illustration #468 - Penetrameter with Shim

Weld Radiography

Flaws found in welds by radiography include porosity, slag inclusions, inadequate penetration, incomplete fusion, undercutting, cracking, pinholes and misalignment.

Porosity results when bubbles of gas are trapped as the weld metal freezes. It can be scattered throughout the weld or may occur in groups or clusters.

Slag consists of non metallic inclusions that are trapped below the surface of the weld.

Undercutting is the term used to describe the reduction in base metal thickness as the last bead is fused to the surface. This appears as a dark line on the radiograph.

Inadequate penetration is the term used to describe the condition when the first or root pass does not penetrate through to the back of the joint.

Incomplete fusion indicates a lack of bond between weld beads or between the beads and the parent metal.

Cracking of welded joints occurs when localized stresses exceed the ultimate strength of the material. Three types of cracks can occur in the weld metal. These are transverse, longitudinal, and crater cracks. Cracking can occur in the base metal if it is hard or brittle.

Misalignment means the edges of the material being welded do not match up properly.

Tips to Welders

There are several things a welder can do to prevent a misinterpretation of the radiographic image resulting in an unnecessary exploratory repair.

- Avoid the placement of stray or forceful chipping hammer marks which may be interpreted as a window (hole in the root) or a porosity pocket.
- Avoid excessive filing marks on the edge of the cap. This may be picked up visually, or on radiograph as undercut.
- Avoid wagon tracks (depressions between passes) which may be interpreted as slag lines or cracks.
- Avoid leaving spatter on the cap which may be interpreted as a grape in the root.
- Avoid leaving a rough surface on the completed cap which may amplify or exaggerate an internal defect possibly resulting in an unnecessary repair interpretation.

Casting Radiography

Casting defects come from two sources: improper foundry technique, and defects caused by natural shrinkage that takes place when molten metal cools and solidifies.

The first category includes gas holes, cold laps, inclusions, and misruns. The second category includes hot and cold cracks and shrinkage cavities. Generalized gas porosity is caused by the precipitation of gases dissolved in the molten metal when it cools. Gas holes can be caused by moisture in the mold or air trapped in the mold cavity. Misruns result from low pouring temperature that causes solidification before the cavity is filled.

A cold crack is a distinct separation which will always start at the surface, and usually exists as a single crack. It will show on a radiograph as a relatively straight dark line, continuous through its length. Hot cracks appear as irregular dark lines of varying width and density with numerous branches.

Pipe Radiography

Pipe radiography can be done in three ways (see illustration #469):

a. The first technique involves inserting the source into the pipe, with the film on the outside. A practical source to film distance is 7t, (t = wall thickness).

b. The second technique involves the source placed outside the pipe, and the film inside. The weld is radiographed in stages. New film is used for each area of interest.

c. The third technique has the source outside the pipe and the film on the opposite side. The image of both walls is developed on the film.

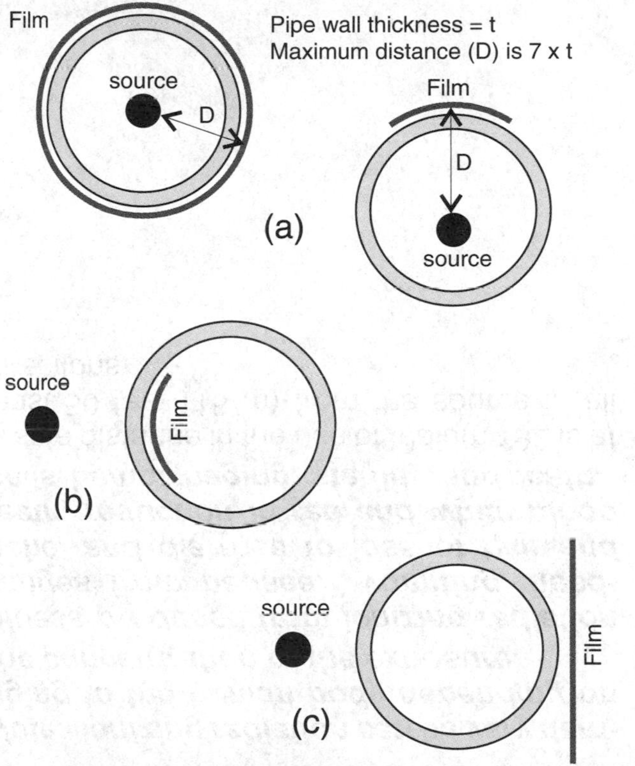
Film
Pipe wall thickness = t
Maximum distance (D) is 7 x t
source
D
Film
D
(a)
source
source
Film
(b)
source
Film
(c)

Illustration #469A,B,C - Pipe Radiography

Radiography Safety

The process of radiography can be performed safely and without risk to the operator and personnel in the surrounding areas provided safety precautions are strictly followed.

It is the responsibility of the licensed operator to assure that all persons are kept a safe distance from the exposure area by the use of rope barricades and warning signs placed at all access points to the area.

Upon completion of the radiograph exposure and safe storage of the source, the barricades and signs should be removed immediately to avoid the development of a complacent attitude toward the warnings.

Note: Ionizing radiation can be very damaging to the human body depending on the concentration of the exposure.

Illness produced from ionizing radiation ranges from nausea, vomiting, headache, and diarrhea to loss of hair and teeth, reduction in red and white blood cells, hemorrhaging, sterility, and death.

A safe distance in the use of Iridium 192 is at least 50 feet (15 m) from the source in all directions.

SECTION FOURTEEN QUESTIONS

Non-Destructive Testing

1. *Determine if the following statement is true or false. Non Destructive Testing is a form of inspection that cuts through or alters the physical shape or condition of a material to check for flaws.*

   ❒ true ❒ false

2. *Determine if the following statement is true or false. Welding coupon bend tests are a form of NDT testing.*

   ❒ true ❒ false

3. *Which of the following defects would require some type of NDT testing other than visual?*

   ❒ corrosion pitting
   ❒ weld undercut
   ❒ porosity
   ❒ surface cracks

4. *Which of the following is a type of NDT?*

   ❒ liquid penetrant
   ❒ ultrasonic
   ❒ eddy current
   ❒ all of above

5. *Determine if the following statement is true or false. Adequate illumination, thorough cleaning, and a knowledgeable inspector are the main requirements for visual inspection.*

   ❒ true ❒ false

6. *How is a hydrostatic pressure test achieved?*

   ❒ external pressure higher than internal
   ❒ internal pressure higher than external
   ❒ equal internal and external pressure
   ❒ will vary with size of unit being tested

7. *Determine if the following statement is true or false. Air trapped inside a pressure vessel will make it easier to obtain the required test pressure while performing a hydrostatic test?*

   ❒ true ❒ false

8. *The common hydrostatic test pressure used on pressure vessels is:*
   - ❐ 1.5 times atmospheric pressure
   - ❐ normal working pressure
   - ❐ 1.5 times normal working pressure
   - ❐ 5 times atmospheric pressure

9. *What type of testing uses a black light?*
   - ❐ magnetic particle
   - ❐ radiography
   - ❐ ultrasonic
   - ❐ liquid penetrant

10. *Determine if the following statement is true or false. Several thick coats of developer are required when applying the developer on a liquid penetrant test.*
    ❐ true ❐ false

11. *What type of product is used for magnetic particle testing?*
    - ❐ air pressure
    - ❐ dry developer
    - ❐ resonance transducer
    - ❐ magnetic powder

12. *Circular magnetic lines of force used in particle testing will detect which type (direction) of crack in a pipe?*
    - ❐ longitudinal
    - ❐ transverse
    - ❐ both a and b
    - ❐ neither a or b

13. *Referring to question #12, how are these circular lines of magnetic force obtained?*
    - ❐ place pipe in a coil shaped conductor
    - ❐ pass current lengthways through the pipe
    - ❐ either a or b depending on pipe size

14. *Determine if the following statement is true or false. The yoke method type of portable magnetic particle testing is hand held and easy to use.*
    ❐ true ❐ false

15. *Which type of current used in particle testing is best to detect subsurface or deeper cracks?*
- ❒ direct current
- ❒ alternating current
- ❒ either a or b
- ❒ neither a or b

16. *Which type of current used in particle testing is best to detect surface flaws?*
- ❒ direct current
- ❒ alternating current
- ❒ either a or b
- ❒ neither a or b

17. *The most common method used for ultrasonic testing is:*
- ❒ frequency modulation
- ❒ resonance
- ❒ transmission
- ❒ pulse echo

18. *Determine if the following statement is true or false. Eddy current testing is not a good method of testing for irregularities near the surface.*
- ❒ true ❒ false

19. *Eddy Current testing works best on:*
- ❒ magnetic material
- ❒ non-magnetic material
- ❒ either a or b
- ❒ neither a or b

20. *Determine if the following statement is true or false. Welding flaws such as slag or porosity allow more radiation to reach the film, thereby being being visible on the film.*
- ❒ true ❒ false

21. *Determine if the following statement is true or false. The two types of waves suitable for radiography are X-Ray and Gamma Ray.*
- ❒ true ❒ false

22. *Which of the following is not an advantage of using gamma ray inspection on a construction site.*
- ❒ cannot be used on all materials
- ❒ radiation emitted continuously
- ❒ no penetrating power adjustment
- ❒ all of above

23. *Which of the following is NOT a disadvantage of Gamma Ray radiography?*
- ❒ penetrating power can not be adjusted
- ❒ radiation hazard emitted continuously
- ❒ radioisotope decays, thereby requiring re-calibration
- ❒ electrical power required

24. *A thin sheet of lead behind the film cassette to stop reflecting radiation from clouding the film is called a:*
- ❒ back scatter screen
- ❒ deflector
- ❒ stop screen
- ❒ film screen

25. *A device positioned in the area to be radiographed that is used to gauge the visibility of material flaws is known as a:*
- ❒ penetrameter
- ❒ camera
- ❒ film cassette
- ❒ shim

26. *What does the ASME code require per weld exposure?*
- ❒ one camera
- ❒ at least one penetrameter
- ❒ the use of a densitometer
- ❒ one yoke

27. *Which flaw cannot be detected by radiography?*
- ❒ inadequate penetration
- ❒ incomplete fusion
- ❒ misalignment
- ❒ none of above

28. *A welder can cause misinterpretation on a radiography film by which of the following:*
- ❒ chipping hammer marks
- ❒ leaving weld spatter
- ❒ excessive filing marks
- ❒ all of above

29. *Casting defects can be caused by:*
- ❒ improper foundry techniques
- ❒ natural shrinkage
- ❒ both a and b
- ❒ neither a or b

30. *Select all the correct methods for pipe radiography.*

- ❐ source inside, film outside
- ❐ source outside, film inside
- ❐ source outside, film outside
- ❐ all of above

31. *Radiography is a non-destructive testing method which does not require any additional safety precautions beyond those required for hydrostatic, magnetic particle, or dye penetrant.*

❐ true ❐ false

SECTION FIFTEEN

CHARTS AND DATA

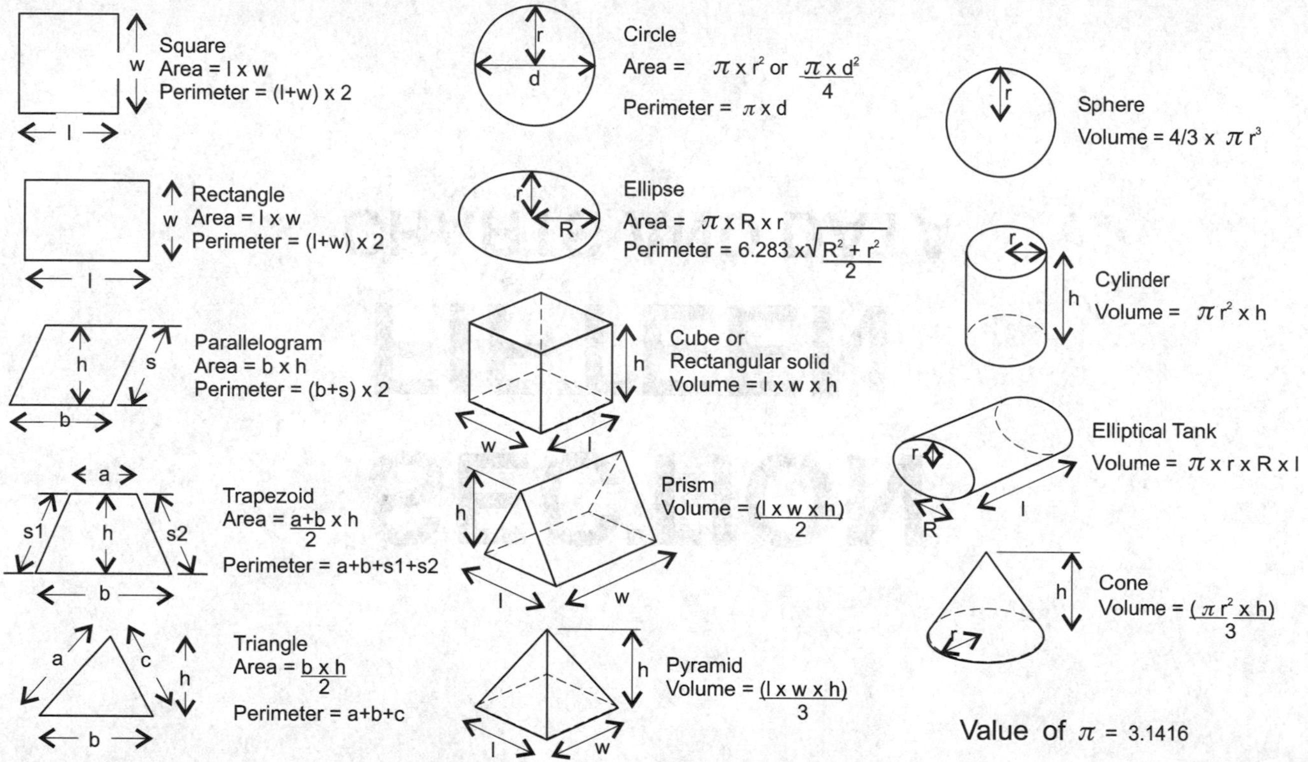
Square
Area = l x w
Perimeter = (l+w) x 2
Rectangle
Area = l x w
Perimeter = (l+w) x 2
Parallelogram
Area = b x h
Perimeter = (b+s) x 2
Trapezoid
Area = a+b/2 x h
Perimeter = a+b+s1+s2
Triangle
Area = b x h/2
Perimeter = a+b+c
Circle
Area = π x r² or π x d²/4
Perimeter = π x d
Ellipse
Area = π x R x r
Perimeter = 6.283 x √((R² + r²)/2)
Cube or
Rectangular solid
Volume = l x w x h
Prism
Volume = (l x w x h)/2
Pyramid
Volume = (l x w x h)/3
Sphere
Volume = 4/3 x π r³
Cylinder
Volume = π r² x h
Elliptical Tank
Volume = π x r x R x l
Cone
Volume = (π r² x h)/3
Value of π = 3.1416

Illustration #470 - Useful Mathematical Formulas

Weights of Seamless and Welded Pipe (in pounds)

Nom. Pipe Size	Schedule Number											
	STD	X.S.	X.X.S.	10	20	30	40	50	60	100	120	140	160
2	3.65	5.02	9.03				3.65		5.02				7.46
$2^1/_2$	5.79	7.66	13.70				5.79		7.66				10.01
3	7.58	10.25	18.58				7.58		10.25				14.31
$3^1/_2$	9.11	12.51					9.11		12.51				
4	10.79	14.98	27.54				10.79		14.98		18.98		22.52
5	14.62	20.78	38.55				14.62		20.78		27.04		32.96
6	18.97	28.57	53.16				18.97		28.57		36.42		45.34
8	28.55	43.39	72.42		22.36	24.70	28.55	35.66	43.39	50.93	60.69	67.79	74.71
10	40.48	54.74	104.13		28.04	34.24	40.48	54.74	64.40	77.00	89.27	104.13	115.65
12	49.56	65.42	125.49		33.38	43.77	53.56	73.22	88.57	107.29	125.49	139.68	160.33
14	54.57	72.09		36.71	45.68	54.57	63.37	85.01	106.13	130.79	150.76	170.22	189.15
16	62.58	82.77		42.05	52.36	62.58	82.77	107.54	136.58	164.86	192.40	223.57	245.22
18	70.59	93.45		47.39	59.03	82.06	104.76	138.17	170.84	208.00	244.14	274.30	308.55
20	78.60	104.13		52.73	78.60	104.13	123.06	166.50	208.92	256.15	296.37	341.10	379.14
22	86.61	114.81		58.07	86.61	114.81		197.42	250.82	302.88	353.61	403.01	451.07
24	94.62	125.49		63.41	94.62	140.80	171.17	238.29	296.53	367.45	429.50	483.24	542.09
26	102.63	136.17		85.73	136.17								
28	110.64	146.85		92.41	146.85	182.73							
30	118.65	157.53		99.08	157.53	196.08							
32	126.66	168.21		105.76	168.21	209.43	229.92						
34	134.67	178.89		112.43	178.89	222.78	244.60						
36	142.68	189.57		119.11	189.57	236.13	282.36						
42	166.71	221.61			221.61	276.17	330.41						

Pipe weights shown above are given in pounds per lineal foot of plain end pipe. To convert lbs/ft to metric: 1lb/ft = 1.49 kg/m

Table #108 - Weights of Steel Pipe

Weight of Steel Plate

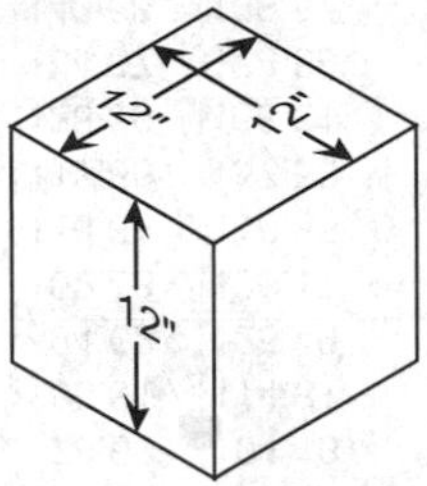
12"
12"
12"
One Cubic Foot of Steel
weighs 490 lbs

Illustration #471 - Cubic Foot of Steel

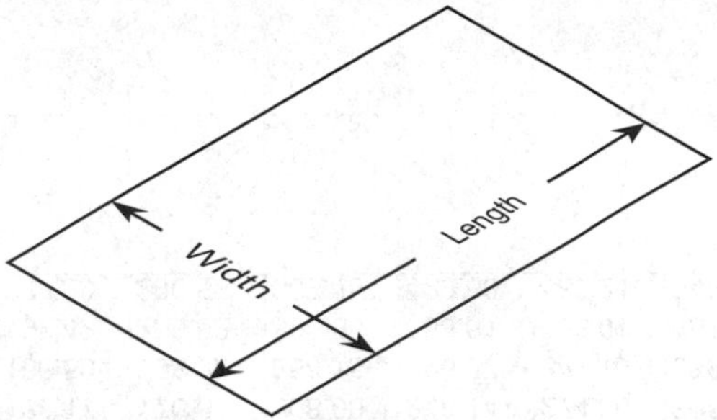
Width
Length

Illustration #472 - Area of Steel Plate

One cubic foot of steel plate = 490 pounds.
490 /12 = 40.8 lbs/sq.ft. per inch thickness
This 40.8 lb./sq.ft. per inch of thickness is rounded off to 40 for convenience.
Therefore every $^1/_8$ inch of plate one foot square = 5 lbs.

- $^1/_8$" = 5 lbs. ¼" = 10 lbs.
- $^3/_8$" = 15 lbs. ½" = 20 lbs.
- $^5/_8$" = 25 lbs. ¾" = 30 lbs.
- $^7/_8$" = 35 lbs. 1" = 40 lbs.

Area = Length x Width A = L x W
Weight = Area (in sq. ft.) x Weight/sq. ft.

Example:
4 ft. x 12 ft. x $^7/_8$" steelplate.
A = L x W
A = 4 x 12 = 48sq. ft.
Weight = Area x Wt. sq. ft.
Weight = 48 sq. ft. x 35 lbs./sq. ft.
= 1680 pounds.
Rectangular Container
Weight = Area of All Sides (in sq. ft.) x Weight/sq. ft.
Volume = Area of Base x Height
Weight of Contents = Cu. ft. x Weight/ cu. ft.

Weight of Cylindrical Objects

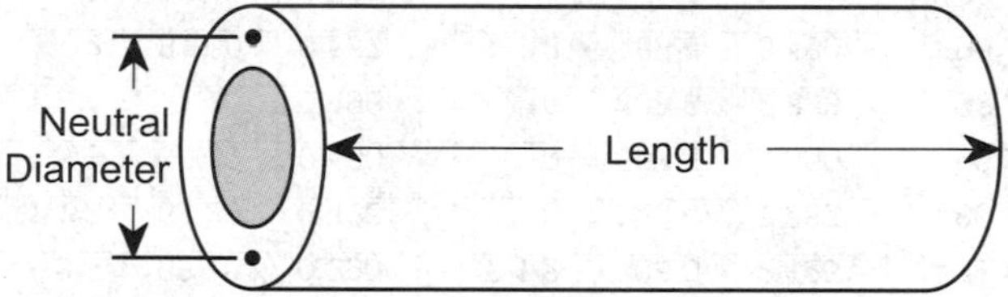
Neutral
Diameter
Length

Illustration #473 - Neutral diameter of a Pipe

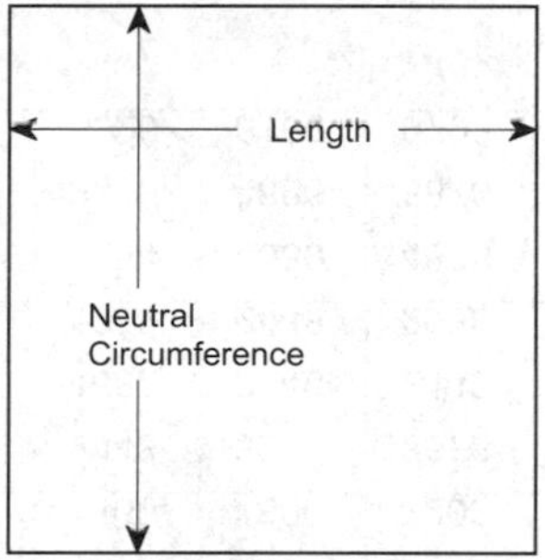
Length
Neutral
Circumference

Illustration #474 - Surface Area of a Pipe

1. Measure thickness to get wt./sq.ft.
2. Measure neutral diameter
3. Circumference =neutral diameter x 3.14.
4. Convert circumference to feet
5. Area = Circumference (ft.) x Length (ft.)
6. Weight = Area in sq.ft. x Wt./sq.ft

Weight Example
18 inch pipe, $^3/_8$" wall, 20' - 9" long

1. Wt./sq.ft. ($^3/_8$") = 15 pounds
2. Neutral diameter = 17 $^5/_8$" (1'- 5 $^5/_8$")
   1.4688 ft.
3. Circumference = Diameter x 3.14
   1.4688 x 3.14 = 4.61 ft.
4. Length = 20' - 9" = 20.75 ft.
5. Area = Circumference x Length
   = 4.61 ft. x 20.75 ft.
   = 95.66 sq.ft.
6. Weight = Area x Wt./sq.ft.
   = 95.66 sq.ft. x 15 lbs./sq.ft.
   = 1435 pounds

Weight of Steel Plate Based on 40.8 lbs/sq.ft.					
Thickness in Inches	lbs/ sq.ft	lbs/ sq.in.	Thickness in Inches	lbs/ sq.ft.	lbs/ sq.in.
1/4	10.20	0.071	3	122.4	0.850
3/8	15.30	0.106	3 1/2	142.8	0.992
1/2	20.40	0.142	4	163.2	1.133
5/8	25.50	0.177	4 1/2	183.6	1.275
3/4	30.60	0.213	5	204.0	1.417
7/8	35.70	0.248	5 1/2	224.2	1.560
1	40.80	0.284	6	244.8	1.700
1 1/8	45.90	0.319	6 1/2	265.2	1.842
1 1/4	51.00	0.354	7	285.6	1.983
1 3/8	56.10	0.390	7 1/2	306.0	2.125
1 1/2	61.20	0.426	8	326.4	2.267
1 5/8	66.30	0.460	9	367.2	2.550
1 3/4	71.40	0.496	10	408.0	2.833
2	81.60	0.567	12	489.6	3.400
2 1/2	102.0	0.708			

Plate Size (in.)	Weight in Pounds						
	1/4 in	3/8 in	1/2 in	5/8 in	3/4 in	7/8 in	1 in
48 x 96	326	490	653	816	979	1142	1306
48 x 120	408	612	816	1020	1224	1428	1632
48 x 144	490	734	979	1224	1469	1714	1958
48 x 240	816	1224	1632	2040	2448	2856	3264
60 x 120	510	765	1020	1275	1530	1785	2040
60 x 144	612	918	1224	1530	1836	2142	2448
60 x 240	1020	1530	2040	2550	3060	3570	4080
72 x 120	612	918	1224	1530	1836	2142	2448
72 x 144	734	1102	1469	1836	2203	2570	2938
72 x 240	1224	1836	2448	3060	3672	4284	4896
96 x 120	816	1224	1632	2040	2448	2856	3264
96 x 144	980	1468	1958	2448	2938	3428	3916
96 x 240	1632	2448	3264	4080	4896	5712	6528
96 x 288	1960	2936	3916	4896	5876	6856	7832
120 x 384	3264	4896	6528	8160	9792	11424	13056

Table #109 - Weight of Steel Plate

Weights of Structural Shapes

Calculate the weight of each part and add them together, or refer to a steel data book for weight per linear foot of various structural shapes.

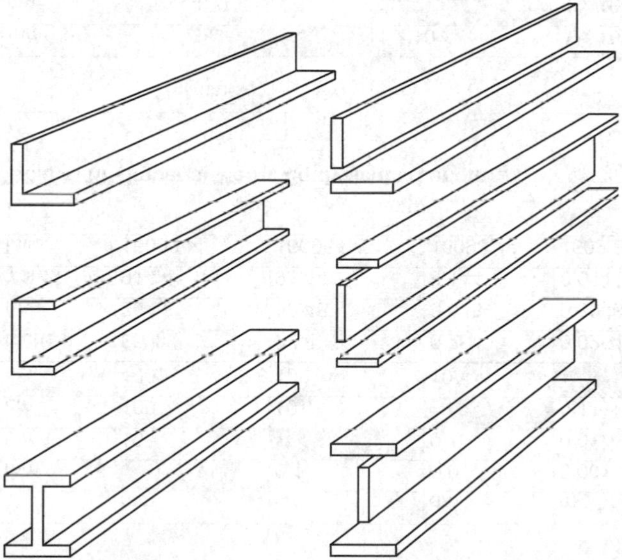

Illustration #475 - Weight of Structural Shapes

Use of Equivalent Tables

For tables #110 to #113, units in the left hand column are equivalent to the number under each unit across the top.

For example in the length table, one m (metre) in the first column of the length table is equivalent to 39.37 inches under the inches column.

In the tables, "scientific notation" is used to express large numbers with several zeros. To interpret these numbers, move the decimal to the left or right as dictated by the exponent.

For example, $9.53 \times 10^{4} = 95300$ (4 decimal places to right).

A negative moves the decimal left.

Therefore $9.53 \times 10^{-4} = 0.000953$ (4 decimal places to the left).

	mm	cm	dm	m	Inches	Feet	Yards	Miles
mm	1	0.1	0.01	0.001	39.37×10^{-3}	3.2808×10^{-3}	1.0936×10^{-3}	6.214×10^{-7}
cm	10	1	0.1	0.01	39.37×10^{-2}	3.2808×10^{-2}	1.0936×10^{-2}	6.214×10^{-6}
dm	100	10	1	0.1	3.937	0.3281	0.1094	6.214×10^{-5}
m	1000	100	10	1	39.37	3.2808	1.0936	6.214×10^{-4}
Inches	25.4	2.54	0.254	0.0254	1	8.33×10^{-2}	2.778×10^{-2}	1.578×10^{-5}
Feet	304.8	30.48	3.048	0.3048	12	1	0.3333	1.894×10^{-4}
Yards	914.4	91.44	9.144	0.9144	36	3	1	5.682×10^{-4}
Miles	1609344	160934.4	16093.44	1609.344	63,360	5280	1760	1

Table #110 - Imperial-Metric Equivalents (Length)

	mm^2	cm^2	dm^2	m^2	Square Inches	Square Feet
mm^2	1	1×10^{-2}	1×10^{-4}	1×10^{-6}	1550×10^{-6}	10.76×10^{-6}
cm^2	100	1	1×10^{-2}	1×10^{-4}	1550×10^{-4}	10.76×10^{-4}
dm^2	1×10^{4}	100	1	0.01	1550×10^{-2}	10.76×10^{-2}
m^2	1×10^{6}	1×10^{4}	100	1	1550	10.76
Square Inches	6.452×10^{2}	6.452	6.452×10^{-2}	6.452×10^{-4}	1	6.944×10^{-3}
Square Feet	9.2903×10^{4}	9.2903×10^{2}	9.29	9.29×10^{-2}	144	1

Table #111 - Imperial-Metric Equivalents (Area)

	Cubic cm	litres	Cubic m	Cubic Inches	Cubic Feet	US Gallon	Can. Gallon	US Barrels
Cubic cm	1	1×10^{-3}	1×10^{-6}	61.024×10^{-3}	0.035315×10^{-3}	0.2642×10^{-3}	0.21997×10^{-3}	0.00629×10^{-3}
litres	1000	1	1×10^{-3}	61.024	0.0353	0.2642	0.22	0.00629
Cubic m	1×10^{6}	1000	1	61023.744	35.3147	264.2	219.9694	6.29
Cubic Inches	1.63871	0.0164	1.638706×10^{-5}	1	5.787×10^{-4}	4.329×10^{-3}	3.606×10^{-3}	1.03×10^{-4}
Cubic Feet	2.8317×10^{4}	2.8317×10	2.8317×10^{-2}	1728	1	7.48055	6.22888	0.1781
US Gallon	3.785×10^{3}	3.78541	3.785×10^{-3}	231	0.1337	1	0.833	2.38×10^{-2}
Can. Gallon	4.5461×10^{3}	4.54609	4.5461×10^{-3}	277.4193	0.1605	1.20095	1	2.877×10^{-2}
US Barrels	158.98×10^{3}	158.98	0.15898	9701.856	5.6145	42	34.973	1

Table #112 - Imperial-Metric Equivalents (Volume)

	Ounce	Pound	milligram	gram	kilogram	Short Ton	Metric Tonne
Ounce	1	0.0625	28344.67	28.3447	0.02835	3.125×10^{-5}	2.835×10^{-5}
Pound	16	1	453257.8	453.2578	0.4536	0.0005	4.536×10^{-4}
milligram	35.28×10^{-6}	2.205×10^{-6}	1	0.001	0.001×10^{-3}	1.102×10^{-9}	1×10^{-9}
gram	35.28×10^{-3}	2.205×10^{-3}	1000	1	0.001	1.102×10^{-6}	1×10^{-6}
kilogram	35.28	2.205	1×10^{6}	1000	1	1.102×10^{-3}	0.001
Short Ton	32000	2000	907.2×10^{6}	907.2×10^{3}	907.2	1	0.907
Metric Tonne	35280	2205	1×10^{9}	1×10^{6}	1000	1.103	1

Table #113 - Imperial-Metric Equivalents (Mass)

Fractions	Decimal Inches	mm	Fractions	Decimal Inches	mm	Fractions	Decimal Inches	mm
	0.00394	0.1	$^{5}/_{64}$	0.078125	1.9844	$^{3}/_{16}$	0.1875	4.7625
	0.00787	0.2		0.07874	2.0		0.19	4.826
	0.01	0.254		0.08	2.032		0.19685	5.0
	0.01181	0.3		0.09	2.286	$^{13}/_{64}$	0.2	5.08
$^{1}/_{64}$	0.015625	0.3969	$^{3}/_{32}$	0.09375	2.3812		0.203125	5.1594
	0.01575	0.4		0.1	2.54		0.21	5.334
	0.01969	0.5	$^{7}/_{64}$	0.109375	2.7781	$^{7}/_{32}$	0.21875	5.5562
	0.02	0.508		0.11	2.794		0.22	5.588
	0.02362	0.6		0.11811	3.0		0.23	5.842
	0.02756	0.7		0.12	3.048	$^{15}/_{64}$	0.234375	5.9531
	0.03	0.762	$^{1}/_{8}$	0.125	3.175		0.23622	6.0
$^{1}/_{32}$	0.03125	0.7938		0.13	3.302		0.24	6.096
	0.0315	0.8		0.14	3.556	$^{1}/_{4}$	0.25	6.35
	0.03543	0.9	$^{9}/_{64}$	0.140625	3.5719		0.26	6.604
	0.03937	1.0		0.15	3.810	$^{17}/_{64}$	0.265625	6.7469
	0.04	1.016	$^{5}/_{32}$	0.15625	3.9688		0.27	6.858
$^{3}/_{64}$	0.046875	1.1906		0.15748	4.0		0.27559	7.0
	0.05	1.27		0.16	4.064		0.28	7.112
	0.06	1.524		0.17	4.318	$^{9}/_{32}$	0.28125	7.1438
$^{1}/_{16}$	0.0625	1.5875	$^{11}/_{64}$	0.171875	4.3656		0.29	7.366
	0.07	1.778		0.18	4.572	$^{19}/_{64}$	0.296875	7.5406

Table #114 - Millimetres, Fractions, Decimal Inch Equivalents

Fractions	Decimal Inches	mm
	0.30	7.62
	0.31	7.874
5/16	0.3125	7.9375
	0.31496	8.0
	0.32	8.128
21/64	0.32815	8.3344
	0.33	8.382
	0.34	8.636
11/32	0.34375	8.7312
	0.35	8.89
	0.35433	9.0
23/64	0.359375	9.1281
	0.36	9.144
	0.37	9.398
3/8	0.375	9.525
	0.38	9.652
	0.39	9.906
25/64	0.390625	9.9219
	0.39370	10.0
	0.40	10.16
13/32	0.40625	10.3188

Fractions	Decimal Inches	mm
	0.41	10.414
	0.42	10.668
27/64	0.421875	10.7156
	0.43	10.922
	0.43307	11.0
7/16	0.4375	11.1125
	0.44	11.176
	0.45	11.430
29/64	0.453125	11.5094
	0.46	11.684
15/32	0.46875	11.9062
	0.47	11.938
	0.47244	12.0
	0.48	12.192
31/64	0.484375	12.3031
	0.49	12.446
1/2	0.50	12.7
	0.51	12.954
	0.51181	13.0
33/64	0.515625	13.0969
	0.55	13.970

Fractions	Decimal Inches	mm
	0.55118	14.0
	0.56	14.224
9/16	0.5625	14.2875
	0.57	14.478
37/64	0.578125	14.6844
	0.58	14.732
	0.59	14.986
	0.59055	15.0
19/32	0.59375	15.0812
	0.60	15.24
39/64	0.609375	15.4781
	0.61	15.494
	0.62	15.748
5/8	0.625	15.875
	0.62992	16.0
	0.63	16.002
	0.64	16.256
41/64	0.640625	16.2719
	0.65	16.510
21/32	0.65625	16.6688
	0.66	16.764

Table #114 (cont'd) - Millimetres, Fractions, Decimal Inch Equivalents

Fractions	Decimal Inches	mm	Fractions	Decimal Inches	mm	Fractions	Decimal Inches	mm
	0.66929	17.0	25/32	0.78125	19.8438	57/64	0.890625	22.6219
	0.67	17.018		0.78740	20.0		0.90	22.860
43/64	0.671875	17.0656		0.79	20.066		0.90551	23.0
	0.68	17.272	51/64	0.796875	20.2406	29/32	0.90625	23.0188
11/16	0.6875	17.4625		0.80	20.320		0.91	23.114
	0.69	17.526		0.81	20.574		0.92	23.368
	0.70	17.78	13/16	0.8125	20.6375	59/64	0.921875	23.4156
45/64	0.703125	17.8594		0.82	20.828		0.93	23.622
	0.70866	18.0		0.82677	21.0	15/16	0.9375	23.8125
	0.71	18.034	53/64	0.828125	21.0344		0.94	23.876
23/32	0.71875	18.2562		0.83	21.082		0.94488	24.0
	0.72	18.288		0.84	21.336		0.95	24.130
	0.73	18.542	27/32	0.84375	21.4312	61/64	0.953125	24.2094
47/64	0.734375	18.6531		0.85	21.590		0.96	24.384
	0.74	18.796	55/64	0.859375	21.8281	31/32	0.96875	24.6062
	0.74803	19.0		0.86	21.844		0.97	24.638
3/4	0.75	19.050		0.86614	22.0		0.98	24.892
	0.76	19.304		0.87	22.098		0.984375	25.0031
49/64	0.765625	19.4469	7/8	0.875	22.225		0.99	25.146
	0.77	19.558		0.88	22.352	1	1.00000	25.4000
	0.78	19.812		0.89	22.606			

Table #114 (cont'd) - Millimetres, Fractions, Decimal Inch Equivalents

Fractional Diameter inches	Circumference Decimal inches
1/64	0.049
1/32	0.098
1/16	0.196
1/8	0.393
3/16	0.589
1/4	0.785
5/16	0.982
3/8	1.178
7/16	1.374
1/2	1.571
9/16	1.767
5/8	1.963
11/16	2.160
3/4	2.356
13/16	2.553
7/8	2.749

Diameter inches	Circumference Decimal inches
1	3.142
2	6.283
3	9.425
4	12.566
5	15.708
6	18.850
7	21.991
8	25.133
9	28.274
10	31.416
11	34.558

Diameter ft.	Circumference Decimal inches
1	37.699
2	75.398
3	113.097
4	150.796
5	188.496
6	226.195
7	263.894
8	301.593
9	339.292
10	376.992

Table Example:

Diameter = 16 feet 7 $^5/_8$ inches

10 feet = 376.992

6 feet = 226.195

7 inches = 21.991

$^5/_8$ inch = 1.963

Total = 627.141 inches

= 627 $^1/_8$ inches

Table #115 - Calculating the Circumference of a Circle

Chord Chart

The following chord chart can be used to find the center-to-center distance of bolt holes when laying out a flange. The distances are based on a diameter of any measurement of one (1 in., 1 ft., 1 cm, etc.).

For any diameter, multiply the diameter by the applicable number of bolt holes.

Example: For an 18 inch bolt circle diameter with 16 bolt holes the chord length would be 0.195090 x 18 = 3.51 inches (3 ½ inches).

No. of spaces	Length of chord
3	0.866025
4	0.707106
5	0.587785
6	0.500000
8	0.382683
10	0.309017
12	0.258819
14	0.222520
16	0.195090
18	0.173648
20	0.156434
24	0.130526
28	0.111964
32	0.098017
36	0.087155

No. of spaces	Length of chord
40	0.078459
44	0.071339
48	0.065403
52	0.060378
56	0.056070
60	0.052336
64	0.049067
68	0.046183
72	0.043619
76	0.041324
80	0.039259
84	0.037391
88	0.035692
92	0.034141
96	0.032719

No. of spaces	Length of chord
100	0.031410
104	0.030202
108	0.029084
112	0.028046
116	0.027079
120	0.026176
124	0.025332
128	0.024541
132	0.023797
136	0.023097
140	0.022438
144	0.021814
148	0.021225
152	0.020666
156	0.020137

No. of spaces	Length of chord
160	0.019663
164	0.019154
168	0.018698

Table #116 - Chord Chart

Conversion of Feet in Decimals

To change feet in decimal form to inches, multiply the number of feet by 12, then change the decimal part of the answer to a fraction of an inch.

Example: 0.482 feet to inches

0.482 feet x 12 (inches in a foot)
= 5.784 inches

The next step will be to convert the decimal portion of 0.784 inches to a fraction.

Most construction tradesmen, other than millwrights, using a measuring tape do not usually require fractions more exact than 32nds of an inch. 32 will then be the base number. Therefore 0.784 inches x 32
= 25.088 or 2 5/3 2 inches.
0.482 feet is equal to 5 $^{25}/_{32}$ inches.

Example: 0.639 feet to inches

0.639 ft. x 12 = 7.668 in.
= 7 in. + 0.668 in.
0.668 in. x 32 = 21.376 or $^{21}/_{32}$ in.
therefore
0.639 feet = 7 $^{21}/_{32}$ inches

Convert Inches to Feet

To change inches to a decimal of a foot, change the fractions to a decimal and divide by 12.

Example: 33 $^{7}/_{8}$ inches to feet:

33 $^{7}/_{8}$ in. = 2 ft. 97/8 in.
$^{7}/_{8}$ in. = 7 ÷ 8 = 0.875 in.
now divide 9.875 inches by 12
= 0.823 inches
therefore 33 $^{7}/_{8}$ inches = 2.823 feet.

NOTE: For further conversions of inches to feet, see Table #117.

Inches to Decimals of a Foot												
	0	1	2	3	4	5	6	7	8	9	10	11
0	0.0000	0.0833	0.1667	0.2500	0.3333	0.4167	0.5000	0.5833	0.6667	0.7500	0.8333	0.9167
1/16	0.0052	0.0885	0.1719	0.2552	0.3385	0.4219	0.5052	0.5885	0.6719	0.7552	0.8385	0.9219
1/8	0.0104	0.0938	0.1771	0.2604	0.3438	0.4271	0.5104	0.5938	0.6771	0.7604	0.8438	0.9271
3/16	0.0156	0.0990	0.1823	0.2656	0.3490	0.4323	0.5156	0.5990	0.6823	0.7656	0.8490	0.9323
1/4	0.0208	0.1042	0.1875	0.2708	0.3542	0.4375	0.5208	0.6042	0.6875	0.7708	0.8542	0.9375
5/16	0.0260	0.1094	0.1927	0.2760	0.3594	0.4427	0.5260	0.6094	0.6927	0.7760	0.8594	0.9427
3/8	0.0313	0.1146	0.1979	0.2813	0.3646	0.4479	0.5313	0.6146	0.6979	0.7813	0.8646	0.9479
7/16	0.0365	0.1198	0.2031	0.2865	0.3698	0.4531	0.5365	0.6198	0.7031	0.7865	0.8698	0.9531
1/2	0.0417	0.1250	0.2083	0.2917	0.3750	0.4583	0.5417	0.6250	0.7083	0.7917	0.8750	0.9583
9/16	0.0469	0.1302	0.2135	0.2969	0.3802	0.4635	0.5469	0.6302	0.7135	0.7969	0.8802	0.9635
5/8	0.0521	0.1354	0.2188	0.3021	0.3854	0.4688	0.5521	0.6354	0.7188	0.8021	0.8854	0.9688
11/16	0.0573	0.1406	0.2240	0.3073	0.3906	0.4740	0.5573	0.6406	0.7240	0.8073	0.8906	0.9740
3/4	0.0625	0.1458	0.2292	0.3125	0.3958	0.4792	0.5625	0.6458	0.7292	0.8125	0.8958	0.9792
13/16	0.0677	0.1510	0.2344	0.3177	0.4010	0.4844	0.5677	0.6510	0.7344	0.8177	0.9010	0.9844
7/8	0.0729	0.1563	0.2396	0.3229	0.4063	0.4896	0.5729	0.6563	0.7396	0.8229	0.9063	0.9896
15/16	0.0781	0.1615	0.2448	0.3281	0.4115	0.4948	0.5781	0.6615	0.7448	0.8281	0.9115	0.9948

Table #117 - Inches to Decimals of a Foot

BEVELS TO SLOPE DEGREE RELATIONSHIP					
Bevel		**Slope**	**Bevel**		**Slope**
1"	in 12"	= 4 ¾°	7 ¼"	in 12"	= 31 ¼°
1 ½"	in 12"	= 7 ¼°	7 ½"	in 12"	= 32°
2"	in 12"	= 9 ½°	7 ¾"	in 12"	= 32 ¾°
2 ½"	in 12"	= 11 ¾°	8"	in 12"	= 33 ¾°
3"	in 12"	= 14°	8 ¼"	in 12"	= 34 ½°
3 ¼"	in 12"	= 15°	8 ½"	in 12"	= 35 ¼°
3 ½"	in 12"	= 16 ¼°	8 ¾"	in 12"	= 36°
3 ¾"	in 12"	= 17 ½°	9"	in 12"	= 37°
4"	in 12"	= 18 ½°	9 ¼"	in 12"	= 37 ¾°
4 ¼"	in 12"	= 19 ½°	9 ½"	in 12"	= 38 ½
4 ¾"	in 12"	= 21 ½°	9 ¾"	in 12"	= 39°
5"	in 12"	= 22 ¾°	10"	in 12"	= 39 ¾°
5 ¼"	in 12"	= 23 ¾°	10 ¼"	in 12"	= 40 ½°
5 ½"	in 12"	= 24 ¾°	10 ½"	in 12"	= 41 ¼°
5 ¾"	in 12"	= 25 ¾°	10 ¾"	in 12"	= 41 ¾°
6"	in 12"	= 26 ½°	11"	in 12"	= 42 ½°
6 ¼"	in 12"	= 27 ½°	11 ¼"	in 12"	= 43 ¼°
6 ½"	in 12"	= 28 ½°	11 ½"	in 12"	= 43 ¾°
6 ¾"	in 12"	= 29 ¼°	11 ¾"	in 12"	= 44 ½°
7"	in 12"	= 30 ¼°	12"	in 12"	= 45°

Table #118 - Bevels and Slope Degrees

TAP AND DRILL TABLE		
Threads Per Inch	**Tap Size**	**Drill Size**
40 N.C.	1/8"	5/64"
24 N.C.	3/16"	9/64"
20 N.C.	1/4"	13/64"
18 N.C.	5/16"	1/4"
16 N.C.	3/8"	5/16"
13 N.C.	1/2"	13/32
11 N.C	5/8"	17/32"
10 N.C.	3/4"	21/32"
9 N.C.	7/8"	3/4"
8 N.C.	1"	7/8"
N.C. = National course thread		

Table #119 - Threads, Taps and Drill Sizes

Proper Angles for Sharpening Drills	
30°	for drilling wood, hard rubbor. Also for countersinks.
49°	for copper and other soft materials.
59°	for general shop use.
68°	for ¼" and smaller drills for high production
88°	For drilling thin sheets and very hard material.

Table #120 - Drill Sharpening Angles

Notes: